ANALYTICAL CHEMISTRY OF PCBs

ANALYTICAL CHEMISTRY OF PCBs

Mitchell D. Erickson

BUTTERWORTH PUBLISHERS
Boston • London
Sydney • Wellington • Durban • Toronto
An Ann Arbor Science Book

Ann Arbor Science is an imprint of Butterworth Publishers.

Library of Congress Cataloging in Publication Data

Erickson, Mitchell D.
  Analytical chemistry of PCBs.

  "An Ann Arbor science book."
  Bibliography: p.
  Includes index.
  1. Polychlorinated biphenyls—Analysis.   I. Title.
QD412.C5E75 1985   628.5   85–15130
ISBN 0–250–40647–0

Butterworth Publishers
80 Montvale Avenue
Stoneham, MA 02180

10 9 8 7 6 5 4 3 2 1

Printed in the United States of America

To my sister, Beverly J. Erickson, who was most interested in my progress with this book, but did not live to see it completed.

ABOUT THE AUTHOR

Mitchell D. Erickson is a Principal Chemist with Midwest Research Institute in Kansas City, Missouri. He has conducted research in all major areas of trace organic analysis in air, water, soil, sediment, biota, tissue, sludge, and hazardous waste; has developed methods for determination of PCBs in a variety of matrices; provided technical assistance to the U.S. EPA in permitting PCB destruction processess; has investigated the formation of chlorinated dibenzofurans and other toxic products from PCBs and other transformer fluids under fire conditions. He has also studied halogenated hydrocarbon levels in the environment and human tissues and fluids, and developed methods for the analysis of organic materials in diesel exhaust. He has worked extensively in developing analytical techniques using GC, FTIR and GC/FTIR.

Dr. Erickson has published 40 government reports, 36 papers in peer review journals and presented 36 papers at scientific meetings. He is a member of the American Chemical Society, the American Society for Mass Spectrometry, the Society for Applied Spectroscopy, Sigma Xi (Scientific Research Society of North America), and the Coblentz Society. He received the A.B. in Chemistry (1972) from Grinnell College and the Ph.D. in Analytical Chemistry (1976) from the University of Iowa.

CONTENTS

LIST OF FIGURES

PREFACE

This book is a comprehensive review of the analytical chemistry of polychlorinated biphenyls (PCBs). It is part history, part annotated bibliography, part comparison and part guidance. It is *not*, however, a cookbook for the neophyte. There are no written step-by-step procedures for the analysis of given matrices for PCBs; the field is much too complex to recommend a finite set of analytical procedures. Chemists with no experience in PCB analysis should benefit greatly from this book by gaining an appreciation for the analytical complexity and reviewing possible approaches to analytical problem. Experienced analysts may find some guidance on possible improvements to their current practices.

This project grew out of a literature review that I conducted along with a colleague, John Stanley, in 1982 for the Office of Toxic Substances of the U.S. Environmental Protection Agency (Erickson and Stanley, 1982). All of the material from that review has been substantially revised, updated, and augmented. In addition the size of the bibliography has more than doubled.

The references in the bibliography were obtained by multiple computer and manual searches of the published literature and from personal contacts. Every effort has been made to be comprehensive and current in the coverage of articles pertaining to analysis. Nevertheless, I am quite sure that there are some omissions. I apologize in advance to those authors whose work may have been slighted and request that they send a reprint so that any subsequent editions can be properly updated. No attempt was made to be comprehensive on the ancillary subjects (environmental occurrence, toxicology, etc.) presented in Chapter 2.

The book contains ten chapters. Following an introductory chapter, Chapter 2 reviews the physical, chemical, commercial, environmental, and biological properties of PCBs. While these areas are not all central to analytical concerns, they provide relevant data and a perspective on the properties of PCBs which make them of such great interest to analysts. Chapter 3 discusses the available written procedures (standard methods, etc.) which may be used directly by analysts. For those desiring more detail or where no written procedure exists, the next six chapters discuss the discrete steps of analysis: sampling, extraction, cleanup, determination, data reduction, and quality assurance. Chapter 10 discusses collaborative testing, which is the ultimate step in a method validation.

A bibliography is presented. All references in the text are in the bibliography; however, not all entries in the bibliography are discussed in the text. The sheer volume of data overwhelms any attempt to adequately discuss all of the references. In addition, many references are redundant or outdated. The additional references in the bibliography may help those who need details in a specific area. Where appropriate, secondary citations to *Chemical Abstract* have been included to assist those interested in obtaining the reference. The reference callouts in the text use the date of the original citation, not that of the secondary citation. Five appendices present ancillary material on PCB nomenclature and physical properties, composition of commercial mixtures, mass spectra characteristics, and PGC/ECD chromatograms. The final appendix (E) is a glossary of the specialized terms and abbreviations used throughout this book.

As noted repeatedly throughout this book, the analytical chemistry of PCBs is an evolving science or, in some cases, an evolving art. Much research still needs to be done to supply methods for the routine analysis of all of the sample matrices in which PCBs may occur. Many of the current methods suffer from lack of precision or accuracy, or they do not provide the proper qualitative information. This book should bring the discipline into better focus and permit analysts to move forward with development of need methods.

Mitchell D. Erickson
Midwest Research Institute
Kansas City, Missouri

ACKNOWLEDGMENTS

I wish to thank many colleagues who provided encouragement and reviewed the book during its gestation. They devoted a great deal of time and thought to their reviews and supplied several references to augment certain sections and tables. I also received reviews of individual chapters from John Craddock, John Going, Daniel Heggem, John Hosenfeld, and John Stanley.

I have received encouragement on this project from Midwest Research Institute's management, particularly John Going. The editorial staff at Butterworths, has been most helpful in providing assistance and encouragement. Some of the data were tabulated and proofread by Leslie Moody, Jon Onstot, Audrey Sanford, Steve Turner, and P. J. Boone. Technical assistance was provided by the Midwest Research Institute Office Services Department, notably the Word Processing Center consisting of Kathy Funk, Cindy Melenson, Lanora Moore, Susie Powell, Carol Shaw, and especially Gloria Sultanik.

I would like to thank my family and friends, especially my wife Colleen and my son Adam, for their forbearance over the past two years. They lost many weekends to this project.

To all of you who helped me make this book a reality, thanks!

1

INTRODUCTION

Polychlorinated biphenyls (PCBs) are a class of 209 discrete chemical compounds, called congeners, in which one to ten chlorine atoms are attached to biphenyl.

m + n = 1 to 10

Polychlorinated biphenyls (PCBs) were commercially produced as complex mixtures for a variety of uses, including dielectric fluids in capacitors and transformers. The major producer, Monsanto Corporation, marketed PCBs under the trade name Aroclor® from 1930 to 1977. Aroclors® were marketed for use in transformers, capacitors, printing inks, paints, dedusting agents, pesticides, and many other applications (Durfee et al., 1976). Their chemical and physical stability and their electrical insulating properites led to the commercial utility of PCBs. The production and use of PCBs is discussed in detail in Chapter 2.

Their chemical and physical stability has also been responsible for the PCB environmental contamination problem. Since PCBs do not readily degrade in the environment after disposal or dissemination and are lipophilic, they are persistent and tend to bioaccumulate. In 1966, Jensen (Anon., 1966; Jensen et al., 1969; Jensen, 1972; Hutzinger et al., 1974a) reported PCBs in eagles, herring, and other Swedish environmental samples. Since then, PCBs have been shown to be nearly ubiquitous environmental pollutants, occurring in most human and animal adipose samples, milk, sediment, and numerous other matrices.

As early as 1936, occupational exposure was reported to cause toxic effects and workplace threshold limit values were subsequently set. Animal studies with both commercial mixtures and individual congeners have shown a variety of chronic toxic effects (National Research Council, 1979). PCB-contaminated cooking oil caused a total of 1,291 "Yusho" patients in 1968 in western Japan. The clinical manifestations include various somatic complaints, low birth weights, chloracne, and pigmentation (Kuratsune, 1972; Higuchi, 1976). The animal toxicological data have tended to indicate that PCBs are toxic. However, contamination of the commercial PCB mixtures with more toxic compounds such as polychlorinated dibenzofurans (PCDFs) confounds the toxicological data. For example, it is unclear whether the PCBs or other contaminants in the Yusho oil are responsible for the observed health effects. In addition, it has been shown that the toxicity of PCBs varies with both homolog and isomer (Safe et al., 1983e). Thus, the toxicology of PCBs remains an area of controversy and continued research.

The discovery of the widespread environmental occurrence, the increased general environmental concern, and the apparent link to carcinogenesis prompted a public outcry which culminated in the United States in 1976 with the regulation of PCBs by the Toxic Substances Control Act (TSCA), PL 94-469 (U.S. Congress, 1976). Section 6(e) of TSCA specifically regulates manufacture, processing, distribution in commerce, or use of PCBs. The U.S. Environmental Protection Agency (EPA) was charged with rule promulgation and enforcement. The EPA was also given latitude to grant exemptions to the ban if the manufacture, processing, distribution in commerce, or use is totally enclosed or will not present an unreasonable risk of injury to health or the environment. The EPA subsequently promulgated a series of rules on the various aspects of the law.

Several EPA rules are of concern to analytical chemists, since they require determination of PCBs in various matrices. A rule promulgated on May 31, 1979 (EPA, 1979d; Velie and Kuntz, 1982; EPA, 1983d) categorized the use, concentration, and type (liquid or nonliquid) of PCBs. Portions of this rule were declared invalid by a U.S. Court of Appeals and several rules have since been issued to satisfy the court-ordered changes. Certain totally enclosed electrical uses of PCBs are allowed for the remainder of the useful life of existing equipment (EPA, 1982f; Department of Transportation, 1984). In 1982, a rule on use in closed and controlled manufacturing processes was promulgated (EPA, 1982c; Velie and Kuntz, 1982; EPA, 1983d). The rule excludes PCBs in products or wastes below the practical limit of quantitation

(LOQ) from the TSCA ban on manufacture, processing, distribution in commerce, and use; i.e., PCBs below the LOQ are not regulated. The practical LOQ was defined as 10 µg/m³ per resolvable gas chromatographic peak for air, 100 µg/L per resolvable gas chromatographic peak for water, and 2 µg/g per resolvable gas chromatographic peak for any product or waste. It should be noted that these defined LOQs are much higher than those obtainable with state-of-the-art instrumentation and with low levels of interferences. In this rule, the EPA recommended high resolution (capillary) gas chromatography/ electron impact mass spectrometry (HRGC/ EIMS) as the analytical technique and supplied suggested methods for the three matrices (Erickson et al., 1982). The EPA also recognized that the PCB composition as by-products would not resemble that of commercial products such as Aroclors and cautioned against the use of classic Aroclor-based analyses methods. TSCA and the PCB rules promulgated under it were reviewed recently (Dyer, 1981; Trench, 1981; Cairns and Siegmund, 1981b; Velie and Kuntz, 1982; Department of Transportation, 1984).

Disposal has been a major area of concern since the restriction of PCB use in the United States and other countries. Large quantities of PCB-containing products such as transformer oils and capacitors are being removed from service and must be disposed of properly. In the United States (EPA, 1979d), the allowed methods of disposal are keyed both to concentration and to the matrix. If the PCB concentration is 500 ppm or greater, disposal in a high efficiency incinerator is stipulated. If the concentration is 50 to 500 ppm and the PCBs are in a liquid matrix such as a mineral oil dielectric fluid, then incinerators, landfills, or high efficiency boilers can be used. In addition, alternate methods of disposal are allowed if they can be shown to be equivalent. To demonstrate compliance, incinerators must pass an initial test which, among other things, requires that air emissions be ≤ 1 mg PCB/kg PCB introduced for nonliquid PCBs. A full listing of current U.S. EPA rules on PCBs may be obtained in the current annual edition of the Code of Federal Regulations, 40 CFR 761 (EPA 1983d or current update).

While PCB regulations and disposal requirements differ from country to country, there is a common analytical interest in determining their presence in the environment and in potential sources to the environment. Regardless of the laws and rules, the analytical needs are similar: reliable, practical, sensitive methods which can determine PCBs--commercial mixtures, by-products, and destruction residues--in a variety of matrices.

This book reviews the publications related to PCB analysis. Some of the older methods may be merely of historical interest, but are included for completeness and to provide the reader with a record of what techniques have been used for specific applications. In addition and more importantly, state-of-the-art methods are discussed and their relevance to various applications presented. The analyst moving into PCB analysis for the first time or encountering a new PCB-related problem will find the discussions helpful in choosing or designing appropriate methods.

2

PHYSICAL, CHEMICAL, COMMERCIAL, ENVIRONMENTAL, AND BIOLOGICAL PROPERTIES

I. INTRODUCTION

This chapter presents brief overviews of PCB nomenclature, physical and chemical properties, synthesis, commercial production and use, toxicology, metabolism, degradation
and destruction, environmental occurrence, environmental fate
and transport, and occupational exposure of PCBs. The treatment of these subjects is not intended to be comprehensive
but rather to provide sufficient information to give the
reader a perspective of the PCB problems which have lead to
the analysis of various samples. Where possible, monographs
and review articles have been cited to guide the reader with
more than a casual interest in a topical area.

II. PCB NOMENCLATURE

For the purposes of this book, a PCB is one of 209
compounds having the formula $C_{12}H_{10-n}Cl_n$, where n = 1-10;
i.e., monochlorobiphenyl through decachlorobiphenyl (Table
A-I, see Appendix A), with the general structure:

The term "PCB" is used to refer to the entire class or any
subset of one or more compounds. I recognize that, strictly
speaking, "mono" is not "poly;" however, the three monochlorobiphenyls have been included in this book since they are
members of the chemical class, colloquial usage usually includes them, and U.S. court rulings (Perlman, 1980; McCallum,
1982) have declared them to be PCBs for EPA enforcement purposes. Biphenyl is not counted as a PCB, although some investigators have used it as a degenerate member of the set

for chromatographic retention behavior and other studies (see, for example, Albro et al., 1977). Biphenyl is included in some physical and chemical property tables in this work for completeness.

PCBs are listed in Chemical Abstracts under "1,1'-biphenyl, chloro derivs." with a generic CAS registry number of 1336-36-3. However, this CAS number does not yield many citations in a computerized literature search. Apparently it is not widely used. CAS No. 12767-79-2 is assigned to "Aroclor" and may be useful in generic PCB literature searches. The synonyms listed by Chemical Abstracts are biphenyl, chlorinated; chlorinated diphenyl; and diphenyl, chlorinated.

The entire set of 209 PCBs forms a set of congeners (Table 2-I). When PCBs are subdivided by degree of chlorination, the term homolog is used; e.g., the trichlorobiphenyl homolog. PCBs of a given homolog with different chlorine substitution position are called isomers (Table 2-II, Figure 2-1). 2,3,4-Trichlorobiphenyl and 3,3',5-trichlorobiphenyl are two of the twelve trichlorobiphenyl isomers.

Many researchers have found the full chemical names unwieldy and have adopted various shorthand nomenclatures. For instance, 3,3',4,4',5,5'-hexachlorobiphenyl has been referred to as 3,3',4,4',5,5'-hexa or simply 3,3'4,4',5,5'. Recently Ballschmiter and Zell (1980) arranged the 209 congeners in ascending numeric order and assigned what are commonly termed "Ballschmiter" or "IUPAC" numbers from 1 to 209, as shown in Table A-I. A minor discrepancy was corrected by Schulte and Malisch (1983) and has been incorporated into Table A-1. This shorthand nomenclature has become increasingly popular and is convenient for many uses such as labeling chromatograms. An alternate shorthand numbering system, using base 16, can designate each PCB congener by a three digit number (Zitko, 1983).

Table 2-I. PCB Nomenclature Categories

Category	Number of Individual Compounds[a]
Congener	209
Homolog	10
Isomers/Homolog	1-46

a Natural isotopic abundance only.

Table 2-II.   Composition of Chlorinated Biphenyls by Homolog

Empirical Formula Chloro-biphenyls	Molecular Weight[a]	Average Molecular Weight[b]	Percent Chlorine	No. of Isomers
$C_{12}H_{10}$	154.1	154.2	0	1
$C_{12}H_9Cl$	188.0	188.7	19	3
$C_{12}H_8Cl_2$	222.0	223.1	32	12
$C_{12}H_7Cl_3$	256.0	257.6	41	24
$C_{12}H_6Cl_4$	289.9	292.0	49	42
$C_{12}H_5Cl_5$	323.9	326.4	54	46
$C_{12}H_4Cl_6$	357.8	360.9	59	42
$C_{12}H_3Cl_7$	391.8	395.3	63	24
$C_{12}H_2Cl_8$	425.8	429.8	66	12
$C_{12}HCl_9$	459.7	464.2	69	3
$C_{12}Cl_{10}$	493.7	498.7	71	1

a   Based on ^{35}Cl (atomic weight 34.969) and ^{12}C (atomic weight 12.000) and ^1H (atomic weight 1.0079). Corresponds to the lowest mass in the molecular cluster of the mass spectrum.
b   "Average" molecular weight; based on natural abundance chlorine (atomic weight 35.453), carbon (atomic weight 12.011) and hydrogen (atomic weight 1.0088).

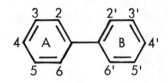

		0	1	2	3	4	5
			Chlorine Atoms on Ring A				
Chlorine Atoms on Ring B	0	1	3	6	6	3	1
	1		6	18	18	9	3
	2			21	36	18	6
	3				21	18	6
	4					6	3
	5						1

Figure 2-1.   Distribution of Chlorine Atoms in the
Two Rings of Biphenyl

As with any complex, symmetric molecule, several nomenclatures may be employed for the same structure. The molecule shown here would be correctly identified as the

2,2',4,5' congener, with alternate but less correct designations of 2,4,2',5'; 2,2',4',5; 2,3',4,6'; 2',3,4',6; etc. Another example is Ballschmiter congener No. 98, designated 2,2',3',4,6; which is listed by <u>Chemical Abstracts</u> as 2,2',3,4',6'. The reader should convince himself that these are in fact the same compound and be wary of these types of redundancies.

The complex commercial mixtures marketed as PCBs (see "Commercial Production," below) have often been treated as a single chemical entity. Repeatedly, authors have used the term "PCB" to refer specifically to the commercial mixtures (e.g., Aroclors) rather than the entire compound class. The reader must develop an awareness of the difference and an appreciation of the significance. For instance, many PCB analytical methods focus on only one or more of the commercial PCB mixtures and could neither detect nor quantitate all PCBs.

III. PHYSICAL PROPERTIES

The physical properties of PCBs are important to an understanding their analytical properties as well as their physiological and environmental properties. The interactions of the various physical properties and their relevance to specific applications can be extremely complex and are not well defined. Many of the references cited in the sections below use physical properties to derive bioconcentration factors (Mackay, 1982b), environmental transport and data (Mackay, 1982a), aqueous movement (Yalkowsky et al., 1980), and environmental persistence (Neely, 1983).

A. Molecular Weights

Table 2-II lists the molecular weight, and percent chlorine for the PCB homologs. Two values of the molecular

weight are presented based on the atomic weight of the most
common isotopes (^{12}C, ^{35}Cl, and ^{1}H) and on the average atomic
weight of the natural abundance ratios of the different isotopes. The former corresponds to the lowest mass in the molecular cluster of the mass spectrum. The latter is the average molecular weight. The exact masses and relative abun-
dances of the major components of the molecular cluster are
listed in Table C-1.

   B.   Physical Constants

        Table A-I in Appendix A presents the CAS registry
number for all 209 PCB congeners, and the available melting
point, and aqueous solubility data. The physical and electrical properties of the commercial mixtures are discussed in
the "Production and Use" section below. There is growing evidence that the subcooled liquid properties of organic chemicals control some environmental partitioning processes
(Mackay, 1982b; Mackay et al., 1982). Thus, melting point
data are important in calculating various environmental properties of PCBs. Table 2-III presents the boiling points,
vapor pressures and octanol-water partition coefficients (log
K_{ow}) for several PCBs. The boiling point and vapor pressure
data from Neely (1983), Weast and Selby (1967), Cook (1972),
Leifer et al. (1983), Bidleman et al. (1983), and Bidleman
(1984) may not be comparable since different experimental
techniques were used in the determinations. Bidleman et al
(1983), for example, compared vapor pressures determined by
gas saturation, gas chromatography, and from the literature.
While most values were in reasonable agreement, some of their
determinations differ by more than a factor of two. As can
be seen in Table 2-III, the boiling points and vapor pressures vary not only with the degree of chlorination, but also
with the position of substitution. This is manifested in the
gas chromatographic elution orders, as discussed in Chapter
7. The vapor pressures of Aroclor 1232, 1242, 1248, and 1254
were discussed by Bopp (1983). Additional data on vapor
pressures (Westcott and Bidleman, 1981) and boiling points
(Augood et al., 1953) of individual PCB congeners has been
published.

        The log K_{ow} and water solubility data (Table A-I)
are useful in estimating transport and fate through the environment (Mackay, 1982b), as well as analytical properties.
Mackay (1982b) has published the octanol-water partition coefficients for Aroclor 1016, 1248, 1254, and 1260. Additional work on aqueous solubility (Mackay et al., 1980,
Stolzenburg and Andren, 1983; Leifer et al., 1983; Yalkowsky
et al., 1983) and partitioning (Voice et al., 1983; Shaw and

Table 2-III. Boiling Points, Vapor Pressures, and
Octanol-Water Partition Coefficients (K_{ow}),
of Selected PCB Congeners

IUPAC No.	Compound	Boiling Point (°C) (mm Hg)[a,b]	Vapor Pressure (mm Hg, 25°C)[a]	Log K_{ow}[c]
–	Biphenyl	255	9.5×10^{-3}	4.10
1	2	274	8.4×10^{-3}	4.56
2	3	284-5[d]	1.5×10^{-3}[e]	4.72
3	4	291	4.6×10^{-3}	4.69
4	2,2'		1×10^{-3}	5.02
5	2,3	172 (30)[f]		
7	2,4		1.8×10^{-3}[e]	5.15
8	2,4'			< 5.32[g]
9	2,5	171 (15)[f]	1.4×10^{-3}[e]	5.18
11	3,3'	322-4[f]	6.8×10^{-4}[e]	5.34
12	3,4	195-200 (15)[f]		
14	3,5	166 (10)[f]		
15	4,4'	315-9[d]	1.9×10^{-5}	5.28
18	2,2',5		9×10^{-5}	5.64
33	2',3,4		7.7×10^{-5}[h]	6.1[a]
28	2,4,4'			5.74
29	2,4,5		3.3×10^{-4}[e]	5.77
30	2,4,6		8.8×10^{-4}[e]	
31	2,4',5		3.0×10^{-4}[e]	5.77
37	3,4,4'			5.90
40	2,2',3,3'		7.3×10^{-5}[e]	6.67[g]
44	2,2',3,5'			6.67[g]
47	2,2',4,4'		8.6×10^{-5}	6.44[a]
52	2,2',5,5'		3.7×10^{-5}	6.26
53	2,2',5,6'		2.1×10^{-4}[e]	
54	2,2',6,6'			5.94
61	2,3,4,5			6.39
66	2,3',4,4'		4.6×10^{-5}[e]	6.67[g]
70	2,3',4',5		4.4×10^{-6}[e]	6.39
77	3,3',4,4'		2.3×10^{-6}[i]	6.52
80	3,3',5,5'			6.58
86	2,2',3,4,5		5.8×10^{-7}[i]	6.38[a]
87	2,2',3,4,5'		1.6×10^{-5}[e]	6.85
88	2,2',3,4,6			7.51[g]
99	2,2',4,4',5		2.1×10^{-5}[e]	
101	2,2',4,5,5'		9.0×10^{-6}	6.85
105	2,3,3',4,4'		6.8×10^{-6}[e]	
116	2,3,4,5,6			6.85

Table 2-III (continued)

IUPAC No.	Compound	Boiling Point ($^\circ$C) (mm Hg)[a,b]	Vapor Pressure (mm Hg, 25°C)[a]	Log K_{ow}[c]
118	2,3',4,4',5	195-220 (10)[f]	9.0 x 10^{-6}[e]	
128	2,2',3,3',4,4'		2.6 x 10^{-6}[e]	7.44
129	2,2',3,3',4,5			8.26[g]
134	2,2',3,3',5,6			8.18[g]
138	2,2',3,4,4',5'		4.0 x 10^{-6}[e]	
149	2,2',3,4',5',6		1.1 x 10^{-5}[e]	
153	2,2',4,4',5,5'		5.2 x 10^{-6}[e]	7.44
155	2,2',4,4',6,6'		1.3 x 10^{-5}	7.12
156	2,3,3',4,4',5		1.6 x 10^{-6}[e]	
170	2,2',3,3',4,4',5		6.3 x 10^{-7}[e]	
171	2,2',3,3',4,4',6		1.8 x 10^{-6}[e]	
180	2,2',3,4,4',5,5'	240-280 (20)[f]	9.7 x 10^{-7}	
185	2,2',3,4,5,5',6			7.93
187	2,2',3,4',5,5',6		2.3 x 10^{-6}[e]	
194	2,2',3,3',4,4',5,5'			8.68
202	2,2',3,3',5,5',6,6'			8.42
206	2,2',3,3',4,4',5,5',6			9.14
209	Decachlorobiphenyl			9.60

a Neely (1983), unless otherwise noted.
b Values in parentheses indicate pressure of measurement if dif-
      ferent from 760 mm Hg.
c All log K_{ow} values from Bruggenman et al. (1982), unless other-
      wise noted.
d Weast and Selby, 1967.
e Bidleman, 1984. Values presented here are averages of two ex-
      perimental values in original publication.
f Cook, 1972.
g Yalkowsky et al., 1983.
h Bidleman et al., 1983.
i Calculated by Neely (1983).

Connell, 1984; Rapaport and Eisenreich, 1984; Leifer et al., 1983; Yalkowsky et al., 1983; NTIS, 1984a) has been reported.

Considerable work has been done on measuring and calculating the gas-phase physical constants, especially the Henry's Law constants and fugacities (Mackay et al., 1980, 1983; Mackay, 1982a, 1982b; Murphy et al., 1983; Leifer et al., 1983; Bapp, 1983; Mackay and Hughes, 1984). The Henry's Law constant is a measure of the equilibrium distribution coefficient between air and water (or other gas and liquid). Fugacity is a quantitative measure of the escaping tendency of a substance and is the driving force that causes diffusion and partitioning between phases (environmental compartments). The fugacity in the gas phase is simply the vapor pressure. In the liquid phase, fugacity is the product of the Henry's Law constant and the concentration in solution.

C. Electrochemical Properties

The electrochemical properties of PCBs have not been well studied. Since PCBs are very stable molecules, determining their oxidation/reduction potential is difficult. However, many of the commercial destruction methods, some metabolic pathways and other routes of degradation, occur via free radical mechanisms. Thus, their electrochemical properties can be important. A limited study gave the standard potentials and electron transfer routes of four PCB congeners (Conners et al., 1985).

D. Ultraviolet and Fluorescence Spectra

The UV spectral properties of PCBs are of use not only for HPLC analysis with UV detection, but also for identification of synthetic products. The UV spectral properties of PCBs were reviewed by Hutzinger et al. (1974a). More recently, additional data on individual congeners (IARC, 1978; Appleby, 1976; Brinkman et al., 1976b) and Aroclor mixtures (Brinkman et al., 1976a) have been published.

The excitaton, fluorescence, and room temperature phosphorescence maxima for six congeners have been reported (Weinberger et al., 1983). The fluorescence spectra of seven congeners in cyclodextrin have been reported (Femia et al., 1985).

E. Infrared Spectra

The IR spectral properties of PCBs were reviewed (Hutzinger et al., 1974a). A major component of that review was based on the work of Webb and McCall (1972). Recently,

the diffuse reflectance IR spectra of 16 PCB congeners were
published (Nyquist et al., 1983). In addition to the spectra, the group frequencies were assigned and correlations
presented which should be of use in the identification of
other PCB congeners.

F. Nuclear Magnetic Resonance (NMR) Spectra

Hutzinger et al. (1974a) presented an extensive review with 22 references of the proton NMR data on PCBs. Data
on 17 synthetic congeners, the major components of Aroclor
1254, and other data were tabulated. Both the ^{13}C and ^{1}H NMR
spectra of 10 symmetric PCB congeners were investigated by
Wilson and Anderson (1973). The relationship of structure to
shielding and coupling constants were discussed. As part of
a program to synthesize all 209 congeners, the proton NMR
spectral features were reported for all tetra-, penta-,
hexa-, and heptachlorobiphenyls (Mullin et al., 1984) and for
all octa- and nonachlorobiphenyls (Mullin et al., 1981).

IV. SYNTHESIS AND STANDARDS

The commercial PCB mixtures were synthesized by
chlorination of biphenyl with chlorine gas (NRC, 1979; Durfee
et al., 1976). Commercial production is discussed in the
following section. Small quantities (10 to 1,000 mg or dilute solutions) of Aroclors are available for use in scientific studies from Analabs, North Haven, Connecticut; Ultra
Scientific, Hope, Rhode Island; and other suppliers.

Routes for synthesis of specific congeners have
been reviewed (Hutzinger et al., 1974a; Roth et al., 1982;
Mullin et al., 1981, 1984). Recently, 3,3',4,4'-tetrachloro-
biphenyl was synthesized in gram quantities (Nakatsu et al.,
1982). Although all 209 congeners have been synthesized recently (Mullin et al., 1984), only about 80 are commercially
available from Ultra Scientific, Hope, Rhode Island, and
Analabs, North Haven, Connecticut, in small quantities (5 to
50 mg or 100-ppm solutions).

Various isotopically labeled PCBs have been synthesized. ^{36}Cl-Labeled (β-emitter) Aroclors 1248 and 1254 were
prepared by neutron irradiation of the natural abundance materials (Stalling and Huckins, 1971). A universally-^{14}C-
labeled PCB mixture with 54% chlorine (i.e., Aroclor 1254)
has been available from New England Nuclear (Kohli et al.,
1979a). Chlorination of ^{14}C-labeled biphenyl to 54% chlorine
content was reported by Albro et al. (1984). Tritiation of
Aroclor 1254 to yield an Aroclor 1248-like mixture was also

reported by Albro et al. (1984). Several ^{14}C-labeled individual congeners have been used in PCB studies. For instance,   ^{14}C-2,2',5,5'-tetrachlorobiphenyl   and
[14]C-2,2',4,4',5,5'-hexachlorobiphenyl were used in determining the tissue distribution in trout and mice (Vodicnik,
1983). ^{14}C-2,2',4,4',5,5'-hexachlorobiphenyl has also been
used to study sorption from water to glass surfaces (Pepe and
Byrne, 1980; Muldrew et al., 1981) and was obtained from
California Bionuclear Corp. d_6-3,3',4,4'-Tetrachlorobiphenyl
has been available from ICN-KOR Isotopes, Cambridge,
Massachusetts, and MSD Isotopes, Pointe Claire-Dorval, Quebec,
Canada. $^{13}C_6$-4-Chlorobiphenyl, $^{13}C_{12}$-3,3',4,4'-tetrachloro-
biphenyl, $^{13}C_{12}$-2,2',3,3',5,5',6,6'-octachlorobiphenyl, and
$^{13}C_{12}$-decachlorobiphenyl were synthesized by Roth et al.
(1982) and are available as a mixed solution from Quality Assurance Branch, Environmental Monitoring and Support Laboratory, U.S. Environmental Protection Agency, Cincinnati, Ohio,
and also from Chemsyn Science Laboratories, Lenexa, Kansas.

Standard reference materials, usually a solution of
an Aroclor, are available. These SRMs are discussed in
Chapter 9 (see Table 9-III).

V.   PRODUCTION AND USE

A.   Aroclor and Related Mixtures

PCBs were commercially produced as complex mixtures
beginning in 1929. They are not known to occur naturally.
Most producers throughout the world reduced or stopped production in the 1970s (Brinkman and DeKok, 1980), although
some production continued through at least 1983 (personal
communication, G. Kuntz, USEPA, Washington, DC, December
1983). Production by Monsanto, the major world manufacturer,
ceased in 1977. All of the commercial mixtures were synthesized by direct chlorination of biphenyl with chlorine gas.
The average degree of chlorination was controlled by the reaction conditions to yield the desired physical and chemical
properties. The total worldwide production through 1976 is
estimated at about 6.1×10^{11} g (1.3 billion pounds; Durfee
et al., 1976), of which about 5.7×10^{11} g (93%, 1.25 billion
pounds) were produced by Monsanto in the United States. The
total production of PCBs through 1980 is estimated to be
about 1.1×10^{12} g (2.4 billion lb; unpublished OECD estimate, J. D. Bletchly, PCB Seminar, The Hague, Netherlands,
September 1983). The Monsanto PCB mixtures were sold under
the registered trade-mark of Aroclor®. The Aroclor (the
trademark designation is not used throughout this book)
trade-name designated a variety of polychlorinated aromatic

mixtures, not just PCBs. For instance, Aroclor 5460 is a complex mixture of polychlorinated terphenyls. Additional information has been presented in a review by Brinkman and deKok (1980).

Commercial PCB mixtures were used in a wide variety of applications, including dielectric fluids in capacitors and transformers, heat transfer fluids, hydraulic fluids, lubricating and cutting oils, and as additives in pesticides, paints, copying paper, carbonless copy ("NCR") paper, adhesives, sealants, and plastics. In 1974, capacitor manufacture (10×10^9 g) and transformer manufacture (5×10^9 g) accounted for all of the PCBs sold by Monsanto. An additional 1.8×10^8 g used in investment casting and 2.2×10^7 g used in specialized heat transfer systems (totaling 1% of U.S. sales) were imported. The PCB used in investment casting, unlike the other commercial PCBs, was decachlorobiphenyl (Durfee et al., 1976).

As reviewed by WHO (1976), an Organization for Economic Cooperation and Development report (1973) divided PCB use into three categories:

Controllable closed systems. PCBs used as dielectrics in transformers and large capacitors have a life equal to that of the equipment, and with proper design leakage does not occur. When the equipment is scrapped the quantity of dielectric is sufficiently large to justify regeneration.

Uncontrollable closed systems. PCBs are used in heat transfer and hydraulic systems which, although technically closed, permit leakage. The need for frequent replacement of small quantities makes recovery impractical. PCBs are very widely dispersed in small capacitors, and there are great difficulties in collecting these items for disposal.

Dissipative uses. PCBs have been used in the formulation of lubricating and cutting oils, in pesticides, and as plasticizers in paints, copying paper, adhesives, sealants, and plastics. In these applications, the PCBs are in direct contact with the environment, and there is no way of recovering them when the product is scrapped. (OECD, 1973; WHO, 1976)

It should be noted that one uncontrollable closed system, old fluorescent light ballasts, continues to put PCBs in close contact with humans. When they fail, high indoor air concentration have been observed (MacLeod, 1979).

Since the vast majority of PCBs of concern to analytical chemists are derived from the commercial sources, the general composition and characteristics of these mixtures are relevant. Table 2-IV presents a comparison of the commercial PCBs. The approximate compositions of Aroclors by homolog are presented in Table 2-V. The composition has been shown to vary from batch to batch and according to the analytical procedure. As can be seen in Table 2-IV, with the exception of 1016, the last two digits of the Aroclor series number correspond to the percent chlorine. A more detailed list of physicochemical properties of the Aroclor mixtures is presented in Table 2-VI (Brinkman and DeKok, 1980). Similar tables are in the literature (Hubbard, 1964; Hutzinger et al., 1974a; Durfee et al., 1976; NIOSH, 1977c; NRC, 1979; Hutzinger and Roof, 1980a). Some of these contain other properties of the commercial mixtures.

A common PCB-containing product class used in transformers and capacitors is askarel. The capacitor askarels include neat Aroclor 1242, 1254, and 1016 and a mixture of 75% Aroclor 1254 and 25% trichlorobenzene. The most common transformer askarels were 60% Aroclor 1260/40% trichlorobenzene (Type A) and 70% Aroclor 1254/30% trichlorobenzene (Type D). The transformer askarels contain other minor components used as free radical scavengers. The ASTM (1978a,b) published standard specifications for askarels.

PCB production and use has been thoroughly reviewed by several authors (Sarofim, 1972; OECD, 1973; Hutzinger et al., 1974a; Durfee et al., 1976; WHO, 1976; IARC, 1978; NRC, 1979; OECD, 1979; Brinkman and DeKok, 1980; Miller, 1982).

B. Impurities in Commercial Mixtures

The impurities in the commercial PCBs are reportedly < 0.01% (NRC, 1979), although Table 2-V indicates that, in some cases, biphenyl can be present at well over 1% levels. The presence of polychlorodibenzofurans (PCDFs) has been documented (Table 2-VII) at the microgram per gram level and may account for some of the toxicological properties attributed to the commercial PCB mixtures (NRC, 1979). PCDFs, polymeric adducts such as polychloroquaterphenyls (PCQs), and other impurities may form during use and handling. The presence and levels of impurities are thought to vary widely from batch to batch. The subject of impurities in the commercial PCBs is presented in more detail (Zitko and Choi, 1971; Anon., 1972; Nagayama et al., 1975; Bowes et al., 1975a, 1975b; Miyata and Kashimoto, 1976; NIOSH, 1977c; Morita et al., 1977; Buser, 1978; Kamps et al., 1978; Buser et al., 1978a; IARC, 1978; OECD, 1979; NRC, 1979; Brinkman and DeKok, 1980; Vuceta et al., 1983; Cull and Dobbs, 1984).

Table 2-IV. Comparison of Commercial PCB Mixtures

Trade Names						Av. No. Cl/ Molecule	Approx. Wt.% Cl	Approx. "Mol. Wt."
Aroclor[a]	Clophen[b]	Phenoclor[c]	Pyralene[c]	Kanechlor[d]	Fenclor[e]			
1221						1.15	21	193.7
1232			2,000			2	32–33	223.0
			1,500	200		2.5	38	240.3
1242, 1016	A30	DP3	3,000	300	42	3	40–42	257.5
1248	A40	DP4		400		4	48	291.9
1254	A50	DP5		500	54[f]	5	52–54	326.4
1260	A60	DP6		600	64	6–6.3	60	366.0
1262					70[f]	6.8	62	388.4
						7.7	65	419.4
1268						8.7	68	453.8
1270					DK	9.5	70	481.4
						10	71	498.6

a Monsanto Industrial Chemicals Company, USA.
b Bayer, GFR.
c Caffaro, Italy.
d Kanegafuchi Chemical Company, Japan.
e Prodelec, France.
f The two-digit number should indicate the wt.% Cl; however, this does not fit in with the manufacturer's specifications.
Source: Brinkman and DeKok, 1980. Reproduced with permission, copyright 1980, Elsevier Biomedical Press BV.

Table 2-V. Average Molecular Composition
(wt.%) of Some Aroclors

Homolog	Aroclor						
(Chlorines)	1221	1232[a]	1016	1242	1248	1254	1260
0	10						
1	50	26	2	1			
2	35	29	19	13	1		
3	4	24	57	45	2	1	
4	1	15	22	31	49	15	
5				10	27	53	12
6					2	26	42
7						4	38
8							7
9							1

a Five percent unidentified (biphenyl?).
Source: Brinkman and DeKok, 1980. Reproduced with permission, copyright 1980, Elsevier Biomedical Press BV.

Table 2-VI. Characteristics of Aroclor Mixtures

Aroclor	Density (at 20°C)	Viscosity (Saybolt Univ. sec) at 98.9°C	n_D^{20}	Flash Point (°C)	Fire Point (°C)	Pour Point (°C)	Distillation Range (°C)	Vaporization Rate (g/cm²/h) x 10⁶, at 250°C	Dielectric Const. At 20°C	Dielectric Const. At 100°C	Solubility in Water at 25°C (µg/L)	CAS Registry No. [b]
1221	1.18	30-31	1.618	141-150	176	1	275-320	1,740				11104-28-2
1232	1.26	31-32	1.621	152-154	238	-35	270-325	874	5.7	4.6		11141-16-5
1016	1.37		1.623	170	ntb		323-356					12674-11-2
1242	1.38	34-35	1.628	176-180	ntb	-19	325-366	338	5.8	4.9	240	53469-21-9
1248	1.44	36-36	1.631	193-196	ntb	-7	340-375	152	5.6	4.6	52	12672-29-6
1254	1.54	44-58	1.640	ntb[a]	ntb	10	365-390	53	5.0	4.3	12	11097-69-1
1260	1.62	72-78	1.648	ntb	ntb	31	385-420	13	4.3	3.7	3	11096-82-5
1262	1.64	86-100	1.651	ntb	ntb	35-38	390-425	9				37324-23-5
1268	1.81			ntb	ntb		435-450		2.5			11100-14-4
1270	1.95			ntb	ntb		450-460					

a ntb = none to boiling.
b The registry number for "Aroclor" (number unspecified) is 12767-79-2.
Source: Brinkman and DeKok, 1980. Reproduced with permission, copyright 1980, Elsevier Biomedical Press BV.

Table 2-VII.   Levels (µg/g) of PCDFs in Commercial PCBs

Mixture	Tri-	Tetra-	Penta-	Hexa-	Hepta-	Total
Aroclor 1248 (1969)	-	0.5	1.2	0.3	-	2.0
Aroclor 1242	-	0.07	0.03	0.003	-	0.15
Aroclor 1242	-	2.3	2.2	N.D.[a]	-	4.5
Aroclor 1243	0.1	0.25	0.7	0.81	-	1.9
Aroclor 1254 (1969)	-	0.1	0.2	1.4	-	1.7
Aroclor 1254 (1970)	-	0.2	0.4	0.9	-	1.5
Aroclor 1254	-	0.02	0.2	0.4-0.6	-	0.8
Aroclor 1254 (KK 602)	-	0.05	0.1	0.02	-	0.2
Aroclor 1254	-	0.1	3.6	1.9	-	5.6
Aroclor 1260	0.06	0.3	1.0	1.10	1.35	3.8
Aroclor 1260 (1969)	-	0.1	0.4	0.5	-	1.0
Aroclor 1260	-	0.8	0.9	0.5	-	2.2
Aroclor 1260 (AK 3)	-	0.2	0.3	0.3	-	0.8
Aroclor 1016 (972)	-	N.D.	N.D.	N.D.	-	-
Clophen A60	-	1.4	5.0	2.2	-	8.4
Clophen T64	0.1	0.3	1.73	2.45	0.82	5.4
Phenoclor DP-6	-	0.7	10.0	2.9	-	13.6
Prodelec 3010	0.41	1.08[b]	0.35	0.07	-	2.0
Kanechlor 400	-	-	-	-	- ca.	20.0
Mitsubishi (used)	2.13	4.00	3.30	0.53	-	10.0

a   N.D. = None detected.
b   Major isomer 2,3,7,8-tetra-CDF.
Source: Vuceta et al., 1983.   Reproduced with permission, copyright
    1983, Electric Power Research Institute.

C. Monochlorobiphenyls

Monochlorobiphenyl (isomer unspecified) was a low concentration component of several products manufactured by Dow Chemical Company. Dowtherm G, a heat transfer fluid designed to replace the Aroclor-type fluids, is primarily biphenyl phenyl ether but contains up to 1,000 ppm monochlorobiphenyl. Manufacture of Dowtherm G was estimated to produce up to 1.8×10^6 g (4,000 lb) of monochlorobiphenyl (Copeland, 1979; Perlman, 1980; McCallum, 1982). Current production levels are assumed to be negligible. No other instances of monochlorobiphenyl manufacture in commerce are known.

D. Decachlorobiphenyl

As can be seen in Table 2-IV, Fenclor DK is technical grade decachlorobiphenyl. It was imported to the United States and used in investment casting waxes in the middle 1970's (Durfee et al., 1976; Brinkman and DeKok, 1980). Presumably applications in other countries were similar.

E. PCBs as By-products

PCBs can be unintentionally produced as by-products in a wide variety of chemical processes. These by-product PCBs are also referred to as incidental PCBs, inadvertently generated PCBs, or unintentionally generated PCBs. Primary concern about these contaminants came about in the United States when the EPA published a rule to implement the TSCA ban on these PCBs (EPA, 1979d; Velie and Kuntz, 1982). A rule amendment for PCB processes which are not closed or controlled set an annual average upper limit of 25 ppm for products (EPA, 1984b). Closed manufacturing processes and controlled waste manufacturing processes are excluded from the TSCA ban if the PCBs are not quantifiable; with practical limits of quantitation defined as 10 $\mu g/m^3$/resolvable chromatographic peak for air; 100 $\mu g/L$/resolvable chromatographic peak for water; and 2 $\mu g/g$/resolvable chromatographic peak for products and wastes (EPA, 1982c).

Thus, current U.S. rules not only control the use of dilute commercial mixtures such as "contaminated" transformer oils, but also impinge on any manufacturing process which could manufacture PCBs as a by-product. These processes include, but are not limited to, manufacture of chlorinated benzenes, chlorinated solvents (e.g., chloroform), chlorinated alkanes, chlorophenylsiloxane adhesives, organosilicone drugs, organic intermediates (e.g., 3,3'-dichlorobenzidine salts), and pigments (e.g., phthalocyanine green). The PCB composition in these products or their wastes has been shown to range from a single congener (e.g., 3,3'-di-chlorobiphenyl in a pigment; DCMA, 1982) to complex mixtures (e.g., over 80 congeners representing all 10 homologs in a chlorinated aromatic production waste; Hanneman, 1982; Hodges et al., 1983).

Since by-product PCBs are not generally looked for in routine production QC analyses, and no organized production records are kept or reported, estimates of by-product PCB production are crude at best. The (U.S.) Chemical Manufacturers Association (CMA) surveyed its members on the subject of by-product PCB manufacture, processing, distribution, and use (Pittaway et al., 1981; Zoll et al., 1982). The production of by-product PCBs has also been estimated by EPA (1982b) and Versar, 1982). Based on these surveys, along with data from the Dry Color Manufacturers Association, the total annual by-product PCB production in the United States is estimated at about 4.5×10^7 g (100,000 lb), of which $< 5 \times 10^6$ g (11,000 lb) is found in products and $< 4.5 \times 10^5$ g (1,000 lb) enters the free environment [personal communication, R. J. Fensterheim, E. Warren, and T. Hardy, Kirkland and Ellis, Washington, D.C., February 15, 1983].

F.   PCB Formation During Water Chlorination

A laboratory study (Gaffney, 1977) demonstrated the formation of mono- and dichlorobiphenyls under municipal water chlorination conditions. The lack of other studies in this area and the paucity of data on PCB formation in municipal water systems would indicate that the incidence of PCBs from this source is small, relative to the commercial mixtures already in the environment.

G.   PCB Formation from Thermal Degradation of Other Chlorinated Organics

Mono- through tetrachlorobiphenyls have been found in the pyrolysis (helium atmosphere) and combustion (air atmosphere) products of chloroalkanes (Bergman et al., 1984b). Polychlorododecanes (59% chlorine and 70% chlorine) were combusted for 10 to 1,200 sec at temperatures from 300 to 700°C. Several hundred micrograms of the PCB isomers were found under most conditions. Many other compounds were detected, including other chlorinated organics, and many nonchlorinated organics. It may be speculated that combustion of other chlorinated organics may lead to formation of PCBs.

VI. ENVIRONMENTAL OCCURRENCE

A. General Levels and Distribution

        PCBs may be considered ubiquitous pollutants. They
have been found in nearly all marine plant and animal speci-
mens, fish, mammals, birds (especially fish-eating birds),
bird eggs, and, of course, humans. All U.S. residents have
measurable PCBs in their adipose tissue (Lucas et al., 1983).
The occurrence in animals was thoroughly reviewed by
Wassermann et al. (1979) and is summarized in Table 2-VIII.
Generally, the PCB levels increase through the food chain, as
depicted in Figure 2-2 and reviewed by EPA (1980d).

        Selected levels in air, water, soil, sediment, and
food are summarized in Tables 2-IX through 2-XII. Note that
the units are not the same for all matrices. This is a re-
flection of the general levels of parts per billion in soil,
sediment and food, and sub-parts per trillion in water. The
concentrations in all matrices generally span a large range
since everything from highly polluted to pristine environ-
ments has been monitored. Differences in analytical methodology and elimination of interferences make direct comparison
of the data difficult. In addition, some matrices are poorly
defined in the literature. For example, the high value reported for birds (14,000 ppm) may in fact be selected tissue
since the value was reported for an eagle, which is not easily analyzed in toto.

        Dietary exposure to PCBs was reviewed by Cordle et
al. (1978). The environmental occurrence of PCBs has been
reviewed in numerous articles and monographs (Yobs, 1972;
Finklea et al., 1972; Nisbet, 1972a; Holden, 1973; Harvey et
al., 1974; Kutz and Strassman, 1975; Fuller et al., 1976;
Risebrough et al., 1976; DeNardi and Desmarais, 1976; Finlay
et al., 1976; WHO, 1976; NIOSH, 1977c; Cordle et al., 1978;
IARC, 1978; Wasserman et al., 1979; National Research Council, 1979; EPA, 1980d; Landrigan, 1980b; Kimbrough, 1980b;
Pavlou, 1980; Hutzinger and Roof, 1980b; Baker et al., 1980;
Eisenreich et al., 1981a; Murphy et al., 1981; Miller, 1982;
Mackay, 1982; Vodicnik, 1983; Hunter, 1983; Eisenreich et
al., 1983a, 1983b; Kauss et al., 1983; Cone et al., 1983;
Farrington et al., 1983; Leifer et al., 1983; Tanabe et al.,
1983; NTIS, 1982, 1983a, 1983b, 1984a, 1984b).

B. Major Environmental Contamination

        Two major contaminations by localized discharge are
of note since they have received so much attention and have
stimulated analytical research: Yusho and the Hudson River.

Table 2-VIII. Occurrence of PCBs in Animals

Organism	Concentration Range (μg/g)
Marine Organisms	
Zooplankton	< 0.003 - 1.055
Shellfish	< 0.003 - 7
Seals	3 - 212
Whales and Dolphins	0.012 - 147
Fish	
Fresh Water (USA)	0.1 - 15
Marine	0.03 - 190
Birds	
North America	0.1 - 14,000
Europe	0.5 - 9,570
Eggs	0.1 - 434
Terrestrial Animals	0.01 - 45
Humans	
Adipose (general population)	0.3 - 10.0
Plasma (general population)	0.001 - 0.029
Plasma (occupational exposure)	0.036 - 1.9
Adipose (Yusho)	0.7 - 75.5
Plasma (Yusho)	0.002 - 0.015
Milk	0.01 - 0.39
Milk-extracted Lipids	0.01 - 18.6

Adapted from Wassermann et al., 1979. Reproduced with permission, copyright 1979, New York Academy of Sciences.

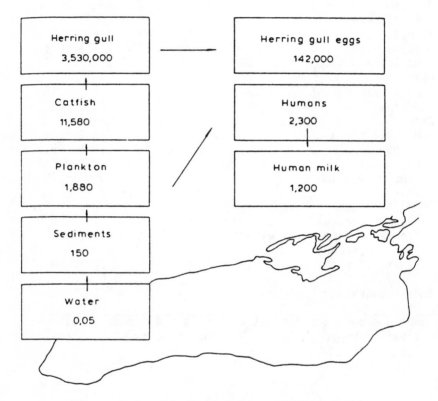

Figure 2-2.   Bioaccumulation of PCBs in the
              Lake Ontario Ecosystem

All values are in parts per billion (ng/g).

Reprinted, with permission, from Safe (1980); copyright 1980
by Elsevier Biomedical Press B.V.

Table 2-IX. Occurrence of PCBs in Air

Matrix	Location	Concentration (ng/m^3)	Source
Ambient Air	Antarctic Coast	0.06 - 0.2	Tanabe et al., 1983
	Remote	0.02 - 0.5	Eisenreich et al., 1983b
	Great Lakes	0.1 - 5	Eisenreich et al., 1983b
	Rural	0.1 - 2	Eisenreich et al., 1983b
	Urban	0.5 - 30	Eisenreich et al., 1983b
	Various USA Locations	0.02 - 36	NRC, 1979
	Marine Air	0.05 - 2.0	NRC, 1979
	Atlantic Ocean	0.05	WHO, 1976
	Gulf of Mexico	0.2 - 0.9	Giam et al., 1976
	North Pacific Ocean	0.54	Atlas and Giam, 1980
	North Atlantic Ocean	1.84	Tanabe et al., 1982
	West Pacific Ocean	0.06 - 1.2	Tanabe et al., 1982
	North Atlantic Ocean	< 0.05 - 0.2	Bidleman et al., 1976
	North Atlantic Ocean	< 0.05 - 1.6	Bidleman et al., 1981b
	Tokyo, Japan	20	Kimbrough, 1980b
	Matsuyama, Japan	2 - 5	Kimbrough, 1980b
	Sweden	< 0.8 - 3.9	WHO, 1976

Table 2-IX (continued)

Matrix	Location	Concentration (ng/m³)	Source
	USA	5	WHO, 1976
	USA, Indoor Contaminated by Light Ballast Burnout	5,860	MacLeod, 1979
	USA, Indoor	39 - 620	MacLeod, 1979
	USA, Indoor Near Spill Site	< 10 - 190	MacLeod, 1979
	USA, Landfills	2 - 18	MacLeod, 1979
	USA, Electrical Substations	1 - 47	MacLeod, 1979
	USA, Transformer Manufacturer	17 - 5,900	MacLeod, 1979
	USA, Spill Site	10 - 10,800	MacLeod, 1979
Stack Gas	ENSCO, El Dorado, Arkansas	12,000 - 58,000	Erickson et al., 1984a
	Rollins, Deer Park, Texas	9.8	Erickson et al., 1984a
Occupational	Massachusetts, PCB User Plants	0.1-5.8×10^6	NIOSH, 1977c
	Capacitor Factory	5-7×10^6	NIOSH, 1977c
	Various Occupational Environments	0.01-10×10^6	Kimbrough, 1980c

Table   2-X.   Occurrence   of   PCBs   in   Water

Matrix	Location	Concentration (ng/L)	Source
Water	Antarctic, Marine	0.03 - 0.07	Tanabe et al., 1983
	Antarctic, Snow	0.3 - 1.0	Tanabe, et al., 1983
	Ocean Water	0.3 - 4,200[a]	Bidleman et al., 1976
	North Pacific Ocean	0.2 - 1.1	Tanabe & Tatsukawa, 1980
	West Pacific Ocean	0.04 - 0.25	Tanabe et al., 1982
	Deep Ocean[b]	0.03 - 0.6	Tanabe et al., 1983
	Atlantic	0.3 - 8	Harvey & Steinhauer, 1976
	Mediterranean Coast	13	Elder, 1976
	Sweden, River	0.5	WHO, 1976
	Sweden, Tap	0.33	WHO, 1976
	USA/Canada, Great Lakes	0.8 - 31	NRC, 1979
	Japan, Tap	1 - 100	WHO, 1976
	USA, Lake Michigan, Spill Site	100 - 450	WHO, 1976
	General Unpolluted Rivers	< 0.5	WHO, 1976
	USA/Canada, Great Lakes	< 5	WHO, 1976
	General, Moderately Polluted Rivers	< 50	WHO, 1976
	General, Highly Polluted Rivers	< 500	WHO, 1976
Rain	Remote	0.1 - 10	Eisenreich et al., 1983b

TABLE   2-X   (continued)

Matrix	Location	Concentration (ng/L)	Source
	Marine	0.5 - 10	Eisenreich et al., 1983b; Atlas & Giam, 1980
	Rural	1 - 50	Eisenreich et al., 1983b
	Great Lakes	10 - 150	Eisenreich et al., 1983b
	Urban	10 - 250	Eisenreich et al., 1983b

a   Review of several studies at coastal and open ocean sites.
b   No significant concentration differences were observed at depths from 0 to 4,500 m.

Table 2-XI.   Occurrence of PCBs in Soil and Sediment

Matrix	Location	Concentration (µg/g)	Source
Soil	Sweden	15	WHO, 1976
	Japan - Agricultural	< 1,000	WHO, 1976
	Japan - Near Electrical Component Factory	510,000	WHO, 1976
	USA - 1972	(99.9% < LOD)	Kimbrough, 1980b
	USA - Urban	(27% < LOD)	Kimbrough, 1980b
	USA - Transformer Manufacturer	17 - 17,800	MacLeod, 1979
Sediment	Spill Site	1,400 - 61,000	WHO, 1976
	16 km Downstream	600	WHO, 1976
	Sweden - Atmospheric Deposition Only	8 - 20	NRC, 1979
	Sweden - Potential Industrial Contamination	4 - 170	NRC, 1979
	USA	20 - 300[a]	NRC, 1979
	USA/Canada - Great Lakes	tr - 250	NRC, 1979
	Japan (1,445 sites)	< 1,000	Kimbrough, 1980b
	Japan - Polluted Site	up to 2,700	Kimbrough, 1980b

a   Median values by state for 10 to 293 samples/state in nine
    states.

Table 2-XII.   Occurrence of PCBs in Food

Matrix	Location	Concentration (μg/kg)
Food		
Fish	USA	1,870
Fish By-products	USA	1,170
Cheese	USA	250
Milk	USA	2,270
Shell Eggs	USA	550

Source: Finlay et al., 1976.

The contamination of other ecosystems, including New Bedford, MA, Waukegan, IL, and Bloomington, IN has been reviewed (Weaver, 1984).

1.   Yusho: "Yusho" was a mass food poisoning caused by the ingestion of a commercial brand of rice oil contaminated with PCBs, polychlorinated dibenzofurans (PCDFs), and polychlorinated quaterphenyls (PCQs). The poisoning occurred in Western Japan in 1968, involving more than 1,600 people. The clinical criteria for the Yusho patient included fatigue, headache, joint swelling and pain, bursitis, inhibition of growth and tooth formation in children, anemia, unusual PCB patterns in the blood, reduced neural conduction velocity, acneform eruptions, increased skin pigmentation, and swelling of the eyes. PCB concentrations in blood averaged about 7 ppb (range 1-32) for Yusho patients (Kuratsune, 1980), while a control population of normal persons had a mean of 3 ppb (range 1-7) and a group of PCB production workers showing only minor clinical signs had a mean of 364 ppb (range 60-920). This, plus other evidence, indicated that the PCBs in the rice oil were not solely responsible for the clinical manifestations. Other, more toxic, chlorinated aromatics have been found in the Yusho oil, including PCDFs and polychlorinated quaterphenyls but not polychlorinated dibenzodioxins (PCDDs). Table 2-XIII summarizes the PCDF concentrations (Kuratsune, 1980). Polychlorinated quaterphenyls, along with minor amounts of polychlorinated terphenyls and polychloroquaterphenyl ethers, were found at concentrations equal to or up to four times that of PCBs in Yusho oil, although saponification during cleanup may have created these compounds as artifacts (Miyata et al., 1977; NRC, 1979). Many of the Yusho patients have died and epidemiological studies continue. Yusho was the subject of a

Table 2-XIII.   Concentrations of PCBs and PCDFs and Their
Ratios in Yusho-Related Materials

Materials	PCBs (ppm[b])	PCDFs (ppm[b])	PCBs/PCDFs
Kanechlor-400 (unused)	1,000,000	ca. 20	50,000
Yusho oils[a]	ca. 1,000	5	200
Yusho patients[c]			
Adipose tissue	1.3	0.009	144
Liver	0.05	0.013	4

a   Produced on February 5 or 6, 1968.
b   On whole base.
c   Two patients who died in 1969 and one patient who died
      in 1972 were included.
Source: Kuratsune, 1980; reproduced with permission, copyright 1980 by Elsevier Biomedical Press BV.

book (Higuchi, 1976) and was more recently reviewed
(Kuratsune, 1980). Other reviews and key articles include
Kuratsune (1972); Kuratsune et al. (1972); Nagayama et al.
(1975); Miyata and Kashimoto (1976); Miyata et al. (1977);
Morita et al. (1977); Bowes et al. (1978); Cordle et al.
(1978); Kamps et al. (1978); Urabe et al. (1979); Rappe et
al. (1979); Kashimoto et al. (1981a, 1981b); and Masuda et
al. (1982).

        A similar outbreak in Taiwan affected about 2,000
people between 1979 and 1981. This so-called Taiwanese Yusho
incident was reported by Chen et al. (1980, 1981, 1982);
Kashimoto et al. (1982); Masuda et al. (1982); and Chen and
Hites (1983).

        2.   Hudson River: General Electric manufactured
PCB-containing capacitors in two plants at Hudson Falls and
Ft. Edward, New York. Both plants are located immediately
adjacent to the Hudson River about 5 km apart and about
320 km (200 miles) from the river mouth. PCB discharges from
these plants have led to massive contamination of the Hudson
basin estimated at a total of 6×10^8 g. The problem has
been reviewed by Horn et al. (1979) and Carcich and Tofflemire
(1982). Average sediment levels ranged as high as 150 µg/g
in some of the river reaches, with occasional samples ex-
ceeding 1,000 µg/g. It has been estimated that 2.6×10^6
g/year of PCBs flow over the dam 67 km (42 miles) downstream
of Ft. Edward and into the estuarian portion of the river.

Thus, not only is the ecosystem contaminated, but the PCBs are not controlled and the contamination is spreading.

The contamination of the Hudson River Basin exceeds, in level and scope, any other area found to date in the United States. River sediment concentrations are at least an order of magnitude higher than other contaminated systems (e.g., Lake Ontario; Lake Michigan; Escambia Bay, Florida; and soils from the Monsanto plant). The PCB levels at a few other sites (e.g., Waukegan River, Illinois and Housatonic River, Connecticut) are comparable, but the size of the areas contaminated do not appear to be as great as the Hudson River. Estimates of the quantity of PCBs in the sediments of the Great Lakes (e.g., Lake Ontario, 9×10^6 g; Lake Erie, 3.6×10^7 g; and Lake Michigan, 7×10^6 g) are considerably lower than those for the Hudson River (6×10^8 g; Horn et al., 1979; Carcich and Tofflemire, 1982). Between 1966 and 1974, General Electric's Ft. Edward and Hudson Falls facilities purchased 3.5×10^{10} g of PCBs or approximately 15% of Monsanto's domestic sales during that time. This suggests that General Electric's discharges to the Hudson River Basin might represent close to 15% of the nationwide total discharges to the environment (Horn et al., 1979).

VII. ENVIRONMENTAL TRANSPORT AND FATE

Of the 5.7×10^{11} g (1.25 billion lb) of PCBs estimated to have been produced in the United States (NRC, 1979; see Section V, above, for more details) about 5.5×10^{11} g are thought to be in service, destroyed, or otherwise unavailable, leaving 0.11×10^{11} g (24 million lb) in the mobile environmental reservoir. Table 2-XIV presents an estimate of the PCB distribution (Mackay, 1982a). In 1979, the NRC estimated that 50-80% of the PCBs in the environment had been deposited in the North Atlantic Ocean and that the major continental sink for PCBs is freshwater sediment.

The environmental transport of PCBs is complex and global. PCBs are transported by air, water, fish, birds, and other routes. They are deposited from air by rain, snow, dry fall-out, and vapor-phase deposition. As noted in Tables 2-IX and 2-X, environmental transport has resulted in fairly uniform global background of PCBs.

By virtue of their high lipid-water partition ratio (see octanol-water partition coefficients in Table 2-III), PCBs tend to accumulate in fatty tissues. The long-term distribution in tissue is adipose > skin > liver > muscle > blood (Safe, 1980). As with the well-publicized case of DDT (Carson, 1962), PCBs biomagnify through the food chain (see

Table 2-XIV.   Estimated Distribution of PCBs in 1981

	Mass of PCB (g $\times$ 10^6)	Concentration (g/m^3)
Atmosphere	18	1.2×10^{-9}
Water	20	1.7×10^{-6}
Fresh water sediments	4,000	9.3×10^{-2}
Fresh water biota	15	3.0
Soil - natural	1,000	1.1×10^{-2}
Soil - sewage sludge	4,800	?
Vegetation	1,000	1.7×10^{-3}
Wildlife	0.3	0.48
Livestock	0.6	9.3×10^{-3}
Humans	5	0.36
TOTAL ACCESSIBLE	10,859	
Oceanic water and biota	6,000	
Oceanic sediments	1,000	
Total near oceanic	7,000	
Landfill and storage	175,000	
Other industry	75,000	
Electric utilities	74,000	
TOTAL INACCESSIBLE	324,000	
TOTAL DEGRADED AND ADVECTED	228,000	
GRAND TOTAL (equals amount produced)	570,000	

Source: Mackay, 1982a. Reproduced with permission from author and Edison Electric Institute.

Table 2-VIII). A concentration factor of nearly 10^8 was reported from Lake Ontario water to herring gulls (International Joint Commission, 1977).

The environmental transport and fate is of great importance since use and disposal practices of existing PCBs must be controlled based on sound predictions of their environmental impact. The subject has been reviewed (Nisbet and Sarofim, 1972a, 1972b; Nisbet, 1972b; Durfee et al., 1976; Bidleman et al., 1976; Risebrough et al., 1976; Fuller et al., 1976; Finlay et al., 1976; WHO, 1976; NIOSH, 1977c; Pomerantz et al., 1978; NRC, 1979; Hutzinger and Roof, 1980b; Pavlou, 1980; Miller, 1982; Mackay, 1982a, 1982b; Neely,

1983; Vodicnik, 1983; Moolenaar, 1983; Eisenreich and Johnson, 1983; Hunter, 1983; James, 1983; Leifer et al., 1983; NTIS, 1984a, 194b; Mackay and Hughes, 1984). A recent monograph, Physical Behavior of PCBs in the Great Lakes (MacKay et al., 1983b), contains 13 chapters which discuss various aspects of environmental transport and fate.

VIII.   DESTRUCTION, DEGRADATION, AND METABOLISM

        PCBs are very stable compounds and do not degrade easily. However, under certain conditions, they may be destroyed by chemical, thermal, and biochemical processes. These may occur intentionally (e.g., incineration), unintentionally, or metabolically. Because of their high thermodynamic stability, all degradation mechanisms are difficult. Intentional degradation generally requires high heat or catalysis. Environmental and metabolic degradation generally proceeds quite slowly relative to most other compounds.

    A. Intentional Destruction

        Destruction has generally been limited to incineration, although some chemical degradation processes (e.g., dechlorination with metallic sodium) are permitted in the United States and other countries. PCB destruction is of particular analytical interest since the determination of destruction efficiency requires the analysis of feed stocks, stack gases, and other effluents.

        In the United States, incinerators are strictly regulated to assure that PCBs are effectively destroyed. The rules specify for nonliquid PCBs (i.e., solids containing PCBs, such as capacitors) that < 0.001 g/kg of the PCB introduced may be emitted to air. This 99.9999% ("six-9's") destruction efficiency has generally been the overall target in the United States for all emissions from all PCB categories. Most incinerators employ a combination of high heat (ca. 1200°C), a long residence time (> 2 sec), an agitation mechanism such as a rotary kiln to mix and move solids through the heated zone, and various pollution control systems (filters, precipitators or scrubbers). PCBs may also be effectively and legally destroyed in the high efficiency boilers used by utilities to generate electricity (EPA, 1983d; Hunt et al., 1984).

        Several nonthermal processes for PCB destruction are being used, investigated, or developed. The chemical techniques include adsorption, chlorinolysis, catalytic dehydrochlorination, microwave plasma, ozonation, photolytic, wet air oxidation, reaction with sodium naphthalide, reaction with molten sodium, and reaction with a sodium salt in an amine solvent. The biological processes include activated sludge, trickling filters, and special bacterial methods. The subject of nonthermal PCB destruction has been reviewed (Ackerman et al., 1981; Ackerman et al., 1983a; Fradkin and Barisas, 1982; Addis and Komai, 1984).

Reviews by Erickson and Shah (1983) and Neulicht et al. (1985) contain annotated bibliographies of major books, articles, rules, and documents on PCB destruction. A book on detoxication of hazardous waste (Exner, 1982a) contains two reviews of PCB destruction technology (Exner, 1982b; Weitzman, 1982), a chapter summarizing the U.S. PCB regulations (Velie and Kuntz, 1982), and four chapters on research into novel destruction technologies (Barton and Arsenault, 1982; Brown et al., 1982; Kitchens et al., 1982; Miller and Fox, 1982).

B. Environmental Degradation

In the environment, photolysis is the only signif-icant chemical degradation process (Hutzinger et al., 1972b; WHO, 1976; NRC, 1979). Several recent publications also dis-cuss photochemical degradation (Kalmaz et al., 1982; Parlar and Mansour, 1982; West et al., 1983; Dilling et al., 1983; Zabik, 1983). The atmospheric half-lives for photodegrada-tion are dependent on the degree of chlorination. Half-lives of the monochlorobiphenyls range from 0.62 to 1.4 days, while pentachlorobiphenyl had a half-life of 67 days (Dilling et al., 1983). Acid- or base-catalyzed reactions are not likely to degrade PCBs under environmental conditions. It should be noted that volatilization and other transport mechanisms can result in significant removal of PCBs from an environmental compartment without any net loss of PCBs from the environ-ment. Once volatilized, however, the chances of photolytic degradation are increased. The environmental degradation of PCBs has been reviewed (Zell and Ballschmiter, 1980; Neely, 1983; Leifer et al., 1983).

C. Microbial Degradation

Microbial degradation of PCBs depends on the degree of chlorination and the position of the chlorine atom on the biphenyl molecule. Lower chlorinated biphenyls are readily transformed by bacteria, but the higher chlorinated compounds are not, as illustrated in Figure 2-3 (Moolenaar, 1983). In addition, the position of chlorine substitution affects bio-degradation; ortho substitution decreases the rate. The major products are conjugated and/or free hydroxychlorobi-phenyls. A further degradation product of 4-chlorobiphenyl is 4-chlorobenzoic acid (Messier et al., 1983).

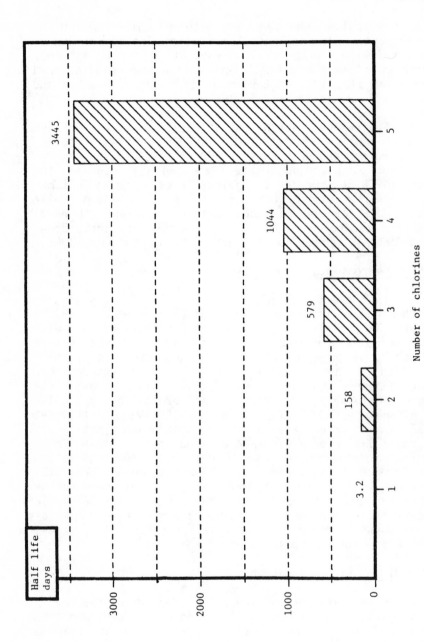

Figure 2-3. Environmental Persistence of Selected Chlorinated Biphenyl Isomers

Reprinted from Moolenaar (1983).

The half-lives of the three monochlorobiphenyls were reported to be 2 to 3 days in river water (Bailey et al., 1983). Wong and Kaiser (1975) showed complete metabolic breakdown of Aroclor 1221 by lake water bacteria after 1 month incubation. The products were identified only as "several low molecular weight compounds." Furukawa et al. (1978) studied the microbial degradation of 31 PCB congeners from mono- through pentachlorodiphenyls. They concluded that degree of chlorination and extent of ortho substitution affected degradability, as discussed in the previous paragraph. In addition, they found that PCBs with a nonchlorinated ring degraded faster, with preferential fission of the unsubstituted benzene rings. Microbial degradation has been reviewed (Menzie, 1978, 1980; NRC, 1979; Leifer et al., 1983; Peyton, 1984).

D. Metabolism by Higher Animals

The major PCB metabolites in higher animals are mono- and dihydroxychlorobiphenyls and their conjugates. These compounds are then excreted in the urine. Figure 2-4 summarizes the in vivo metabolites (Safe, 1980). Methylthio- and methylsulfone PCB derivatives have also been identified in tissues from Yusho victims (Haraguchi et al., 1984) and other environmental matrices, as reviewed by Bergman et al. (1980). Bergman et al (1980) synthesized and characterized 25 of the methylthio- and 28 of the methylsulfone PCB derivatives.

The metabolic rates are both isomer- and homolog-dependent. The higher the homolog, the slower the metabolism (Safe, 1980). Most of the studies reported have used rats, rabbits, and other high level species. It is assumed that hydroxylation is also the major degradation route in other species. Biological degradation does not significantly reduce the total environmental burden, although it does have a marked influence on the relative concentrations of PCBs (i.e., chromtographic patterns) passing through the food chain (WHO, 1976). The metabolism of PCBs has been reviewed (Hammond, 1972; Hutzinger et al., 1974a; NIOSH, 1977; Menzie, 1978, 1980; IARC, 1978; Matthews et al., 1978; Matthews and Kato, 1979; Safe, 1980; Safe et al., 1980; Hutzinger and Roof, 1980b; Safe et al., 1983b; Hutzinger, 1983a, 1983b; Matthews, 1983; NTIS, 1984b).

E. Degradation During Use and Analysis

Some PCB uses generate sufficient heat to degrade commercial PCB mixtures, forming PCDFs (Buser et al., 1978a, 1978b) and polymeric products (Zitko and Choi, 1971; NRC, 1979). These findings are of interest, expecially to the

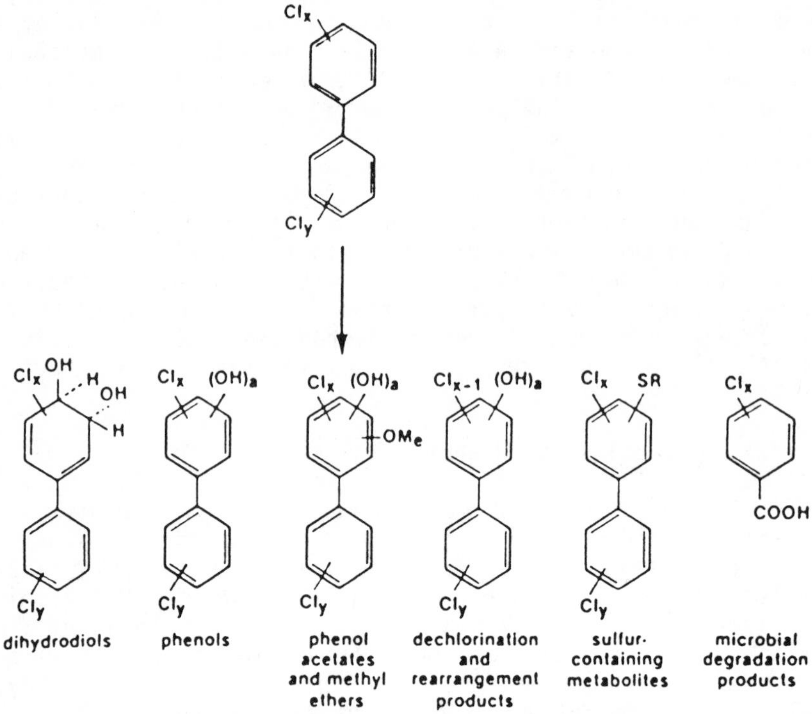

Figure 2-4.   Common In Vivo PCB Metabolites

Reprinted, with permission, from Safe (1980); copyright 1980 by Elsevier Biomedical Press B.V.

---

toxicologists and epidemiologists studying the health effects of PCBs, since toxic contaminants can confound research results. The classic case of toxic effects caused by PCB contaminants is the Yusho incident discussed in Section VI.B.1, above.

A variety of hostile conditions can degrade PCBs by oxidation, hydrolysis, alcoholysis, and photochemistry (Pomerantz et al., 1978). These conditions are of particular interest to those investigating nonthermal PCB destruction methods. In addition, the analyst must be aware that certain harsh cleanup techniques can destroy PCBs, especially the lower chlorinated congeners. This topic is addressed more thoroughly in the acid and base cleanup sections of Chapter 6 (Cleanup).

F.   Degradation in Fires

An extreme case of degradation while in use occurs when PCB-containing electrical equipment is involved in a

fire.   Not only are PCBs degraded but they are also dispersed.   Such an event occurred in 1981 in Binghamton, New
York, where the 18-story State Office Building was damaged by
fire (Vuceta et al., 1983; EPA, 1984a).   Leakage from a PCB
transformer was dispersed throughout the building.   The average PCB concentration on exposed horizontal surfaces was
162 µg Aroclor 1254/m^2.   Samples of the soot were found to
contain PCDDs (20 µg/g), PCDFs (700-2,200 µg/g), and polychlorinated biphenylenes (54 µg/g).   Hilker et al. (1983)
analyzed samples from the same fire and found 200 ppm of
2,3,7,8-TCDF and 2.8 ppm of 2,3,7,8-TCDD.   Similar results at
several other PCB fire sites were reported by Williams et al.
(1983a, 1983b, 1985).   The contaminants from Binghamton and
other "accident" sites were recently reviewed (Vuceta et al.,
1983)   Table 2-XV presents a summary of the compounds found
at these sites.

        Some research has been conducted to identify the
products, expecially the PCDFs, of incomplete PCB combustion
(Buser et al., 1978a,b; Buser and Rappe, 1979; Rappe et al.,
1983; Buser and Rappe, 1984; Rappe, 1984; Erickson et al.,
1984b, 1984c, 1984e, 1985a, 1985b; Swanson et al., 1985).
PCDFs were observed to form on heating in sealed ampules containing PCBs (Aroclors or individual congeners) and oxygen
(Buser and Rappe, 1979).   Even at temperatures as low as
300°C, increased levels of PCDFs were observed after 1 week
(Morita et al., 1978).   Figure 2-5 shows the reaction products of 2,2',4,5,5'-pentachlorobiphenyl.   The trichlorodi-
benzofuran was the major product, with smaller amounts of the
four tetra- and a single pentachloro dibenzofuran (Buser and
Rappe, 1979).

        Using a bench-scale thermal combustion system,
Erickson et al. (1984b, 1984c, 1984e; 1985a, 1985b; Swanson
et al., 1985) found that the optimum conditions for PCDF formation from PCBs are near 675°C for 0.8 sec or longer, with
8% excess oxygen.   Under these conditions, percent levels of
PCDFs are formed from mineral oil or silicone oil contaminated with PCBs at 5 ppm or greater.   The amount of PCDFs
formed from the PCB-containing materials was directly dependent on the amount of PCBs fed into the system.   As illustrated in Figure 2-6, the composition of the PCDF mixtures
formed was independent of the feed concentration or matrix.
PCDFs and PCDDs are formed at much lower levels from a trichlorobenzene dielectric fluid used in askarels which contained no detectable PCBs.   As illustrated in Figure 2-6, the
composition of the PCDF mixture formed from the trichlorobenzene mixture is different from that formed from the PCB
feed.

Table 2-XV. Summary of Chlorinated Aromatic Hydrocarbons
Detected During Different PCB Accidents[a]

Accident	PCDDs	PCDFs	PCQs	PCQEs	PCTs	PCBPs	PCPYs	PCCYs
Toronto		5 ppm						
Norrtalje, Sweden		45-107 µg/g						
Binghamton, NY	2.8-19.9 ppm	124-2,163 ppm			b	b	b	b
Stockholm (1981)		43-104 µg/g			b	b	b	b
Skovde, Sweden		0.01-0.773 µg/m²				b	b	b
Yusho, Japan		1-18 ppm	b	b	b			
Yusho, Taiwan		0.18-1.68 ppm	b		b			

a PCQs = polychlorinated quaterphenyls
   PCQEs = polychlorinated quaterphenyl ethers
   PCTs = polychlorinated terphenyls
   PCBPs = polychlorinated biphenylenes
   PCPYs = polychlorinated pyrenes
   PCCYs = polychlorinated chrysenes.
b Quantification and confirmation not possible due to lack of standards.
Source: Vuceta et al., 1983. Reproduced with permission, copyright 1983, Electric Power
   Research Institute.

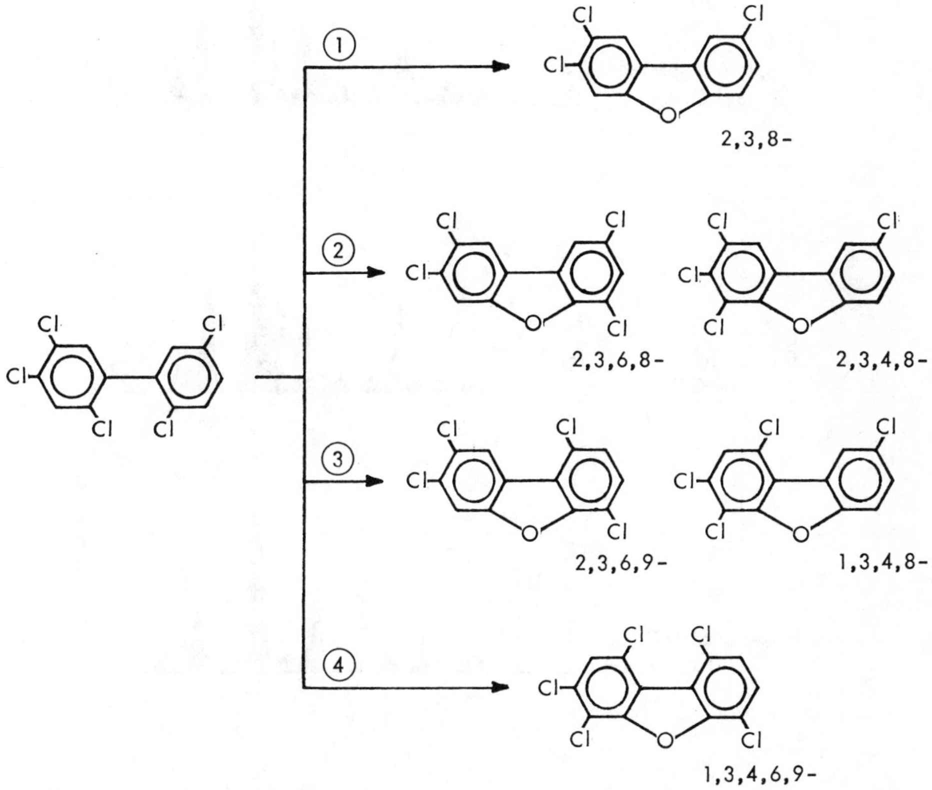

Figure 2-5.   Polychlorinated Dibenzofurans
Formed from Thermal Degradation of
2,2',4,5,5'-Pentachlorobiphenyl

Mechanism 1 involves loss of two ortho chlorines; Mechanism 2 involves loss of HCl and a 2,3 chloride shift; Mechanism 3 involves loss of HCl, and Mechanism 4 involves loss of H_2. The sample (100 µg) was heated in the presence of air in a sealed ampule at 600°C for 60 sec.

Reprinted, with permission, from Buser and Rappe (1979); copyright 1979 by Pergamon Press.

TETRA CDFs

FEED

500 ppm Aroclor 1254
in Mineral Oil

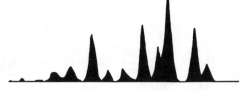

500 ppm Aroclor 1254
in Silicone Oil

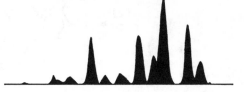

70% Aroclor 1260
30% Trichlorobenzene

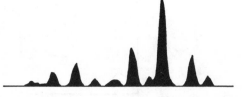

Trichlorobenzene

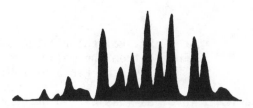

Figure 2-6. Tetrachlorodibenzofurans Formed from Thermal
Combustion of PCBs and a Trichlorobenzene Mixture

All mixtures were combusted at 675°C for 0.8 sec with 8% excess oxygen. The products were trapped on XAD-2, extracted,
cleaned up, and analyzed by HRGC/EIMS. The samples were analyzed under slightly different conditions, accounting for
the minor variations in the chlormatographic patterns.

Reprinted from Erickson et al. (1984b).

The formation of PCDFs and other compounds from thermal degradation of PCBs has been reviewed (Choudhry and Hutzinger, 1983; Addis and Komai, 1984; Rappe, 1984; Erickson et al., 1984b).

IX. TOXICOLOGY

The public, legal, and scientific concerns about PCBs arose from the findings that PCBs were toxic and therefore undesirable as commercial products or environmental contaminants. The evidence for this toxicity was sufficient for special citation by the U.S. Congress in the Toxic Substances Control Act (see Chapter 1) as well as similar actions by other governments. However, the degree of toxicity and the nature of the effects on man and other organisms has been and continues to be highly debatable. The U.S. National Research Council (1979) concluded,

> "An analysis of PCB data...leads to the conclusion that PCBs are persistent, and are likely to accumulate. PCBs do not appear particularly toxic for short-term exposure, but results are subject to interpretation (Roberts et al. 1978)."

Table 2-XVI presents the NRC's survey of the chronic effects of PCBs. Table 2-XVII presents a summary of PCB effects from Reggiani (1982) and Table 2-XVIII presents a summary of the pathologic findings from McConnell (1980). Many studies of both occupational or environmental exposure and laboratory exposure are subject to question because of the type and purity of PCB used. All of the occupational and environmental studies and many other laboratory studies have been conducted with commercial mixtures. Not only are the effects of up to 70 different PCB congeners being studied simultaneously, but the possible presence of contaminants such as polychlorinated terphenyls and quaterphenyls and the much more toxic PCDDs and PCDFs make assignment of the observed effects to PCBs subject to criticism.

Some studies, however, have been conducted on individual pure congeners. These studies indicate that PCB toxicity is dependent not only on the degree of chlorination but also on the isomer. For instance, those PCBs which have no ortho-substitution and are heavily substituted at the meta and para positions are capable of assuming a planar conformation which can interact with the same receptor as TCDD. Examples   include   3,3',4,4'-tetrachlorobiphenyl   (I), 3,3',4,4',5-pentachlorobiphenyl (II), and 3,3',4,4',5,5'-hexachlorobiphenyl (III).

Table 2-XVI.   Summary of Chronic Toxic Effects of PCBs

Test	Effects
Chronic feeding	
Aquatic species	Threshold effects in egg hatchibility of vertebrates and invertebrates at levels of 2-5 µg/L
	Embryo toxicity evident at 50 µg/L
Terrestrial species	Mouse - some liver change with exposure to high chlorine containing products, 300-500 µg/g
	Rat - some liver changes, minimal reproductive effects, 100-500 µg/g
	Monkey - Yusho symptoms, altered reproduction cycles, hyperplastic gastritis and ulceration, 2.5-5 µg/g
	Chicken - some morphologic deformity, reproduction decline, subcutaneous edema, 20-50 µg/g
	Mink - dose response relationship in growth and reprodction, 10 µg/g
	Pelican - some hepatocellular changes, 100 µg
	Dogs - reduced growth, some liver changes, 100 µg
	Wildfowl - some reproduction changes, varies with species, 50-200 µg/g

TABLE 2-XVI (continued)

Test	Effects
Teratogenicity	Effects seen in avian species, 50-200 µg/g
Mutagenicity	Chromosomal abnormalities - negative results
	Dominant lethal mutations - negative results
	Ames test - 1221, 4 chloro-biphenyl significantly muta-genic
Oncogenicity	High chlorinated compounds pro-duced tumors in rats and mice, relationship with PCB not always clear

Source: National Research Council (1979); reprinted with permission from the National Academy of Science.

Table 2-XVII.   Clinical Features Following Exposure to PCBs

Signs and Symptoms	Rat Mice	Monkey	Yusho Cases	Kanechlor Workers Japan (n = 32)	Aroclor Workers USA (n =34)
Blood Levels in ppb			12-34	60-920	105-353
1. Dermatological	-				
Chloracne		+	+	(chloracne) 2 cases	+
Hyperpigmentation		+	+		+
Hair Loss		+	+		
2. Ocular	-			-	+
Cyst Formation of Tarsal Gland		+	+		
Swelling and Pigmentation of Eyelid and Conjunctive		+	+		
3. Stomatological	?	?		?	?
Pigmentation of Oral Mucosa			+		
Anomalies of Teeth Growth and number			+		
4. Liver		-	-	-	
Enlargement	+				-
Serum Enzymes	+		-		-
Enzymes Induction	+		-		+
Parenchymal Lesions	+		-		-
5. Respiratory Tract	-	-			
Chronic Bronchitis			+ +	-	-
Reduction of Vital Capacity			+	-	+
6. Neurological	-	-			
Polyneuropathics	+		- +	-	-
Sensorial Impairment			- +		
Reduced Conduction Velocity			+		
7. Endocrinological					
Irregular Cycles		+	+	?	-
8. Metabolism					
Porphyrin	+	-	-	-	-
Carbohydrates		-	-	-	-
Fat (triglycerides)		+	+		
9. Urology	+	+	+	?	?
10. G.I. Tract					
Gastric Hyperplasia	+	+	+	?	?
Ulcer	+	+	-		

Source: Reggiani (1982); reprinted with permission, copyright 1982, Pergamon Press.

Table 2-XVIII.   Summary of Pathologic Findings Due to
                  the Toxicity of PCBs

Pathologic Finding	Rat	Mouse	Guinea Pig	Chicken	Monkey	Human
Decreased Body Weight	+	+	+	+	+	+
Acne/Alopecia	(-)	(-)	(-)	(-)	+	+
Edema	(-)	+	(-)	+	+	+
Lymphoid Atrophy						
Thymus	+	+	+	+	+	n.r.
Spleen	+	+	+	+	+	n.r.
Hepatomegaly	+	+	+	+	+	+
Hepatomegalo-cytosis	+	+	(-)	(-)	+	+
Multinucleated Giant Cell	+	(-)	(-)	(-)	(-)	(-)
Necrosis, Degeneration	+	+	+	+	+	+
Fat	+	+	+	+	+	+
Bile Duct Hypertrophy	+	(-)	(-)	(-)	(-)	(-)
Porphyria	+	+	(-)	+	(-)	+
Urinary Bladder Hypertrophy	(-)	(-)	+	(-)	(-)	(-)
Gastropathy	(-)	(-)	(-)	+	+	(-)
Tumor Induction	+	+	(-)	(-)	(-)	(-)

Source: McConnell, 1980. Reprinted with permission, copyright 1980, Elsevier Biomedical Press, BV.

These are known as cytochrome P-448 inducers or 3-MC inducers (Goldstein, 1980) or aryl hydrocarbon hydroxylate (AHH) inducers (Safe et al., 1981, 1982). These congeners are not major components (generally much less than 1%) of the Aroclor mixtures (Albro and Parker, 1979; Huckins et al., 1980; Albro et al., 1981; Safe et al., 1981, 1982, 1983d; see Appendix B).

The other active group of congeners is the phenobarbital-type or "PB-type" inducers or cytochrome P-450 inducers, as shown in Figure 2-7 (Goldstein, 1980). Many congeners exhibit mixed responses or no observable response.

Other reviews are available (Hammond, 1972; Kimbrough, 1974; Fishbein, 1974; Calandra, 1976; Durfee et al., 1976; NIOSH, 1977; Matthews et al., 1978; Kimbrough et al., 1978; IARC, 1978; Department of Health, Education and Welfare, 1978a, 1978b, 1978c; Wassermann et al., 1979; EPA, 1980d; Strik et al., 1980; Goldstein, 1980; McConnell, 1980; Baker et al., 1980; Vos et al., 1980; Brown et al., 1981a; Ecology and Environment, 1982; Gaffey, 1983a,b; Friess et al., 1983; Safe et al., 1982, 1983a, 1983b, 1983d, 1983e; and James, 1983; Goodman, 1983; Sleight, 1983; Ringer, 1983; Safe, 1984).

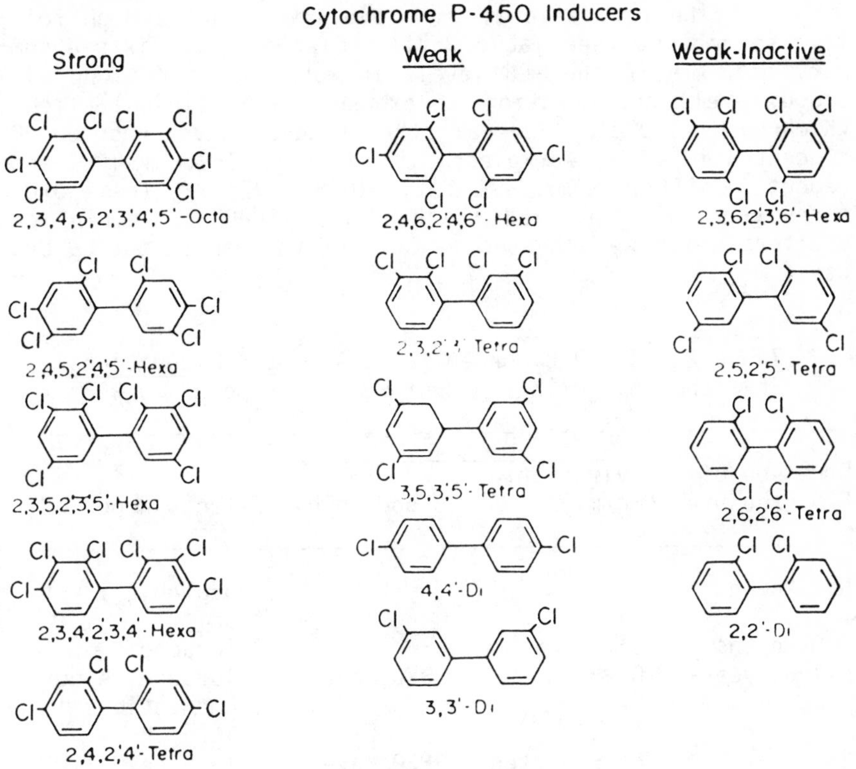

Cytochrome P-450 Inducers

| Strong | Weak | Weak-Inactive |

Figure 2-7.   Summary of PCB Isomers Which Induce
Cytochrome P-450

Reprinted, with permission, from Goldstein (1980); copyright
1980 by Elsevier Biomedical Press B.V.

X.   OCCUPATIONAL EXPOSURE AND ITS EFFECTS

Workers in PCB production and use occupations were
exposed to high levels of commercial mixtures of PCBs through
both dermal contact and inhalation of vapors (Table 2-IX).
Capacitor plants provided the highest reported exposure potential (Kimbrough, 1980c).   The first report of any effects
of occupational exposure was in 1936 (Jones and Alden, 1936),
when chloracne was associated with PCBs.   Symptoms of high
PCB exposure include burning of eyes, face, and skin.   Several clinical symptoms are indicative of PCB-related liver
injury, including elevated serum triglycerides and induction
of mixed function oxidases.   Although there has been some
evidence of increased incidences of cancer, it is inconclusive (Kimbrough, 1980c).

The occupational air levels were quite high relative to ambient (see Table 2-XII). Table 2-XIX lists a summary of some of the PCB levels in workplace air along with
blood levels and duration of exposure and clinical effects
(Kimbrough, 1980c). Several other studies have reported PCB
concentrations in workplace air in the 1-10 mg/m^3 range
(about 1 million times ambient; NIOSH, 1977c). These exposures generally involved the handling of PCB-containing capacitors which were heated as part of the manufacturing process.

Table 2-XIX. PCB Concentrations in the Occupational
Environment and in Blood of Workers Exposed to PCBs

Druation of PCB Exposure	PCB Levels Environmental (mg/m^3)	Blood (ppb)	Effects Reported
Not known	10	-	Unbearable irrita-tion
4-8 months	5-7	-	Chloracne
< 1-20 years	0.2-1.6	370, ave.	Chloracne, hyper-pigmentation, liver injury
2.5 year ave.	Not reported	820, ave.	Chloracne
2.5-18 years	0.013-0.27	36-286	Irritation, liver injury
14 months	0.1	-	Chloracne, liver injury
2-23 years	0.32-1.44	> 200	Chloracne, liver injury
Up to 15 years	Not reported	7-300	Chloracne, elevated triglycerides
	< 1	74-1,900	No effect

Source: Kimbrough (1980c). Reprinted with permission, copyright 1980, Elsevier Biomedical Press, BV.

As noted in the WHO document (1976), occupational
exposure may be widespread among workers handling PCBs in
use: mechanics handling lubricating and hydraulic oils,
office workers handling carbonless copy paper, analytical
laboratory workers, and electrical component handlers.

Occupational exposure was thoroughly reviewed (NIOSH, 1977c; Kimbrough, 1980c). Other reviews include Hubbard (1964), WHO (1976), IARC (1978), and Cordle et al. (1978).

Reviews specifically concentrating on the epidemiological aspects of PCB exposure, both occupational and accidental (Yusho) include WHO (1976), NIOSH (1977), and IARC (1978). The seven epidemiologic and three cohort mortality studies reported since 1978 were reviewed by Gaffey (1983a, 1983b).

3

ANALYTICAL PROCEDURES

ANALYTICAL PROCEDURES

This chapter focuses on the written analytical procedures for the analysis of PCBs in various matrices. These procedures have been written in sufficient detail that the analyst can implement them in the laboratory with little or no modifications or development. Most also contain detailed descriptions of the apparatus, instrumentation, supplies and reagents necessary for use of the procedure. Table 3-I and the sections below describe the techniques and methods which comprise some of the procedures, the applicable matrices, and the limits of detection, where available. Subsequent chapters are devoted to the specific techniques for PCB analysis and present these techniques in more detail.

The methodology definitions of Taylor (1983), given below in increasing heirarchical order, have generally been followed throughout this book.

Technique: Scientific principle or specific operation (e.g., GC/ECD, Florisil column cleanup, or Webb and McCall quantitation).

Method: A distinct adaptation of a technique for a selected measurement purpose (e.g., a specific GC/ECD operating mode for analysis of PCBs, including column specifications and sample preparation.

Procedure: The written directions necessary to use a method or series of methods and techniques.

Protocol: A set of definitive directions that must be followed without deviation to yield acceptable analytical results. A true analytical protocol is rare, possibly nonexistent, in PCB analysis.

Table 3-I lists the analytical procedures available for PCBs. Several are general organic pollutant or chlorinated hydrocarbon procedures which include PCBs along with many other analytes. These include Devenish, EPA (Halocarbon), EPA (Priority Pollutant), EPA (soil and sediment), EPA (304h), EPA (B100), EPA (5,A,[1]), EPA (5,A,[3]), EPA (608), EPA (625), EPA (8080), EPA (8250), EPA (8270), and FDA-PAM. The procedures in Table 3-I address a variety of materials including water, wastewater, soil, sediment, sludge, air, combustion and incinerator emissions, capacitor askarels, transformer fluid, waste oil, mixtures of chlorinated benzenes, pigments, food, milk, blood, and adipose tissue.

Extraction and cleanup techniques are presented in Table 3-I in terms of the materials and reagents required for analysis. Less than half of the procedures comment on the criteria required to make qualitative determinations for the presence of PCBs in sample extracts. The quantitation technique for each of the analysis schemes is presented along with the limit of detection (LOD), if specified. More than half of the procedures mention quality control (QC). The quality control steps presented include analysis of blanks, replicates, control samples, spiked additions, and criteria for accuracy, precision, and instrumental performance.

Not all of the procedures listed are sanctioned by a sponsoring organization at this point. Many have interim status and some have been proposed but never endorsed by an organization.

I.   ANSI AND ASTM PROCEDURES

The ANSI procedures for the isolation and determination of PCBs in air, water, soil, sediment, and biological materials are based on techniques that were used by the Monsanto Industrial Chemical Company. Packed column gas chromatography with electron capture detection (PGC/ECD) is the designated method for quantitation of PCBs as Aroclors in the ANSI procedures. The PCBs are quantitated against an Aroclor standard using the largest peak, or a secondary peak if the largest peak appears to be interfered with. If the PCB profile is altered with respect to the standard, all major peaks are summed. Mass spectrometry is recommended for confirmation. The cleanup techniques are required only if interferences are noted for the PGC/ECD determination. The quality control measure in the ANSI procedures emphasize the number of theoretical plates and tailing factor for the packed gas chromatography column. The LOD for the procedure is 2 ppb in air, based on an instrumental LOD of 0.5 ng. The calculation

Table 3-I. Standard Procedures of Analysis for PCBs

Procedure Designation	Matrix	Extraction	Cleanup[c]	Determination Method	Qual.	Quantitation Method	LOD	QC	Reference
D3534-80	Water	Hexane/CH2Cl2	(Florisil) (Silica Gel)	PGC/ECD[d]	No	Total area or Webb-McCall	0.1 µg/L	No	ASTM, 1981a
608	Water	CH2Cl2	(Florisil) (S removal)	PGC/ECD	No	Area	0.04-0.15 µg/L	Yes	EPA, 1984e; Longbottom and Lichtenberg, 1982
625	Water	CH2Cl2	None	PGC/EIMS (CGC)	Yes	Area	30-36 µg/L	Yes	EPA, 1984f; Longbottom and Lichtenberg, 1982
304h	Water	Hexane/ CH2Cl2 (85/15)	Florisil/ silica gel (CH3CN) (S removal)	PGC/ECD or HECD	Yes	Summed areas or Webb-McCall	NS	Yes	EPA, 1978
EPA (by-products)	Water	Several	Several	HRGC/EIMS	Yes	Ind. peaks	NS	Yes	Erickson et al., 1982, 1983d; EPA, 1984c
ANSI	Water	Hexane	(H2SO4) (Saponification) Alumina	PGC/ECD	No	Single peak or summed peaks	2 ppm	Yes	ANSI, 1974
Monsanto	Water	Hexane	Alumina	PGC/ECD	No	Individual or total peak heights	2 ppb	No	Moein, 1976
UK-DOE	Water	Hexane	Silica gel	PGC/ECD	No	NS	106 ng/L	No	UK-DOE, 1979; Devenish and Harling-Bowen, 1980
D3304-74	Air Water Soil, sediment	DI Hexane H2O/CH3CN	(H2SO4) (Saponification) (Alumina)	PGC/ECD	No	Total area	NS	Yes	ASTM, 1981b
EPA (homolog)	Solids and liquids	Several	Several	HRGC/EIMS	Yes	Ind. peaks	NS	Yes	Erickson et al., 1985c
EPA 625-S	Sludge	CH2Cl2	Florisil, Silica gel, or GPC	HRGC/EIMS or PGC/EIMS	Yes	Area	NS	Yes	Haile and Lopez-Avila, 1984

Table 3-I (Continued)

Procedure Designation	Matrix	Extraction	Cleanup[c]	Determination Method	Qual.	Quantitation Method	LOD	QC	Reference
EPA (Halocarbon)	Sludge	Hexane/CH_2Cl_2/acetone (83/15/2)	GPC S removal	PGC/ECD	Yes	Peak area or peak height	NS	Yes	Rodriguez et al., 1980
Priority Pollutant	Sludge	CH_2Cl_2 (base/neutral and acid fractions)	GPC	PGC/EIMS	NS	NS	NS	Yes	EPA, 1979e
B100	Sludge	CH_2Cl_2 (3 fractions)	GPC Silica gel	HRGC/EIMS or PGC/EIMS	Yes	NS	NS	Yes	Ballinger, 1978
8080	Solid waste	CH_2Cl_2	(Florisil)	PGC/ECD	No	Area	1 μg/g	Yes	EPA, 1982e
8250	Solid waste	CH_2Cl_2	None	PGC/EIMS	No	NS	1 μg/g	Yes	EPA, 1982e
8270	Solid waste	$CHCl_2$	None	HRGC/EIMS	NO	NS	1 μg/g	Yes	EPA, 1982e
EPA (spills)	Unspecified	Hexane/acetone	(CH_3CN) (Florisil) (Silica gel) (Mercury)	PGC/ECD	No	Total area or Webb-McCall	NS	No	Beard and Schaum, 1978
EPA	Soil and Sediment	Acetone/Hexane	Florisil Silica gel (S removal)	PGC/ECD	No	Computer	NS	Yes	EPA, 1982d
Monsanto	Sediment	CH_3CN	Saponification H_2SO_4 Alumina	PGC/ECD	No	Individual or total peak heights	2 ppb	No	Moein, 1976
ANSI	Sediment, soil	CH_3CN	Saponification H_2SO_4 Alumina	PGC/ECD	No	Single peak or summed peaks	2 ppm	Yes	ANSI, 1974
EPA (by-products)	Air collected on Florisil or XAD-2	Hexane	(H_2SO_4) (Florisil)	HRGC/EIMS	Yes	Ind. peaks	NS	Yes	Erickson et al., 1982,1983d; Erickson, 1984c
EPA (ambient air)	Air near hazardous waste sites collected on PUF	Hexane/ether	Alumina	PGC/ECD	No	Total area or peak height	10-50 ng/m^3	No	Lewis, 1982

Table 3-I (Continued)

Procedure Designation	Matrix	Extraction	Cleanup[c]	Determination Method	Qual.	Quantitation Method	LOD	QC	Reference
EPA (stack)	Incinerator emissions and ambient air collected on Florisil	Hexane	(H_2SO_4)	Perchlorination PGC/ECD	No	Area	10 ng	No	Haile and Baladi, 1977; Beard and Schaum, 1978
EPA	Combustion sources collected on Florisil	Pentane or CH_2Cl_2	(Florisil/silica gel)	PGC/MS	Yes	Area/homolog	0.1 ng/inj	No	Levins et al., 1979
EPA (incinerators)	Stack gas	Pentane/methanol		PGC/MS	Yes	Single peak	NS	Yes	Beard and Schaum, 1978
ANSI	Air (toluene impinger)		(H_2SO_4) (Saponification) (Alumina)	PGC/ECD	No	Single peak	2 ppb	Yes	ANSI, 1974
NIOSH (P&CAM 244)	Air collected on Florisil	Hexane	None	PGC/ECD	No	Peak height or area from standard curve or Webb-McCall	0.01 mg/m³	No	NIOSH, 1977a
NIOSH (P&CAM 253)	Air collected on Florisil	Hexane	None	PGC/ECD Perchlorination	No	Peak height or area from standard curve	0.01 mg/m³	No	NIOSH, 1977b,c
EPA (gas)	Natural gas sampled with Florisil	Hexane	H_2SO_4	PGC/ECD	No	Total area, peak height or Webb-McCall (Perchlorination)	0.1-2 µg/m³	No	Harris et al., 1981
EPA [5,A,(3)]	Blood	Hexane	(Florisil)	PGC/ECD	No	NS	NS	No	Watts, 1980
EPA [5,A,(1)]	Adipose	Pet. ether/CH_3CN	Florisil	PGC/ECD	No	NS	NS	Yes	Watts, 1980
EPA (9,D)	Adipose	Pet. ether/CH_3CN	Saponification Florisil	TLC	No	Semiquant.	10 ppm	No	Watts, 1980
EPA (9,B)	Milk	Acetone/hexane	CH_3CN Florisil Silica acid	PGC/ECD	Yes	Ind. peaks	50 ppb	Yes	Watts, 1980 Sherma, 1981

Table 3-I (Continued)

Procedure Designation	Matrix	Extraction	Cleanup[c]	Determination Method	Qual.	Quantitation Method	LOD	QC	Reference
AOAC (29)	Food	CH_3CN/Pet. ether	Florisil MgO/ Celite Saponification	PGC/ECD	No	Total area or Ind. peaks	NS[a]	No	AOAC, 1980a
Japan	Food	Pet. ether/ CH_3CN	Silica gel Saponification (Florisil)	PGC/ECD	Yes	Summed areas perchlorination	NS	No	Tanabe, 1976
PAM	Food	Pet. ether/ CH_3CN	Silicic acid (Saponification) (Oxidation) (Florisil)	PGC/ECD (PGC/HECD) (NP-TLC) (RP-TLC)	No	Area	NS	No	FDA, 1977
AOAC (29)	Paper and paperboard	Saponification	Florisil MgO/ Celite Saponification	PGC/ECD	No	Total area or Ind. peaks	NS[a]	No	AOAC, 1980b
D3303-74	Capacitor askarels	DI[b]	None	SCOT HRGC/FID	No	Total area	2.8×10^{-8} mol/L	No	ASTM, 1980a
D4059-83	Mineral oil	Dilute with hexane or isooctane	Florisil slurry (H_2SO_4) (Florisil column)	PGC/ECD (PGC/HECD)	Yes	Ind. peaks or Webb-McCall	50 ppm	No	ASTM, 1983
EPA (oil)	Transformer fluids or waste oils	DI	(H_2SO_4) (Florisil) (Alumina) (Silica gel) (GPC), (CH_3CN)	PGC/HECD or /ECD or /EIMS (HRGC)	No	Total area or Webb-McCall	1 mg/kg	Yes	EPA, 1981 Bellar and Lichtenberg, 1981
EPA (by-products)	Products or wastes	Several	Several	HRGC/EIMS	Yes	Ind. peaks	NS	Yes	Erickson et al. 1982, 1983d; Erickson, 1984a
DCMA	3 pigment types	A. Hexane/ H_2SO_4 B. CH_2Cl_2	None Florisil	PGC/ECD	No	10 isomers	~ 1 ppm/homolog	Yes	DCMA, 1982
DOW	Chlorinated benzenes	DI	None	PGC/EIMS	Yes	Total peak height/homolog	NS	Yes	Dow, 1981
EPA (isomer groups)	Unspecified	Not addressed	Not addressed	HRGC/EIMS	Yes	Ind. peaks	NS	Yes	EPA, 1984d

a No specific details.
b Direct injection or dilute and inject.
c Techniques in parentheses are described as optional in the procedure.
d Or PGC with microcoulometric or electrolytic conductivity.

procedure is not specified. No validation data are given, although general discussions of the applicability of the techniques are presented. The ASTM procedure for water is similar.

The ASTM (1983) procedure for mineral insulating oils utilizes solvent dilution and a Florisil slurry cleanup prior to PGC/ECD determination. The procedure assumes that the composition of the PCBs present in transformer or capacitor oils closely resembles that of the Aroclor standards. It notes that the sensitivity of the ECD is reduced by mineral oil and instructs the analyst to make the amount of oil in the standard and sample equivalent to minimize the effects of the oil interference on the quantitative results.

II. EPA PROCEDURE FOR OILS

The EPA procedure for analysis of PCBs in transformer oils and waste oils (EPA, 1981a; Bellar and Lichtenberg, 1981) provides a generalized approach with respect to sample preparation, and instrumental analysis. Several cleanup techniques are provided as optional approaches in this procedure (see Chapter 6). For the instrumental analysis, GC with halogen specific, electron capture, or mass spectrometry detectors are all allowed, provided appropriate limits of detection can be achieved. A strong quality control program including control samples, daily quality control check samples, blanks, standard additions, accuracy and precision records, and instrumental and chromatographic performance criteria is required to support all data generated by the method.

III. EPA PROCEDURES FOR SPILLS AND INCINERATORS

The EPA procedures for PCB spills and incinerators (Beard and Schaum, 1978) are part of a manual for PCB disposal, primarily focusing on incineration methods. Although this interim report is badly flawed and incomplete, it has been widely used as the guidance document by the EPA Regional Administrators for testing incinerators.

The stack gas is sampled using the modified EPA Method 5 technique developed by Haile and Baladi (1977). PCBs are extracted from the sorbent material in a Soxhlet extractor using both pentane and methanol. The GC/MS analysis is taken from a tentative procedure for PCBs in water (Dudenbostel, 1978). Samples may be chromatographed on columns packed with 3% Dexsil 300, OV-1, or OV-101 and may be detected using either electron impact or chemical ionization mass spectrometry.

The "Tentative Method for Testing of Polychlorinated Biphenyls (PCBs) in Spilled Material" (Attachment A,
Beard and Schaum, 1978) directs the analyst to air-dry the
sample (matrix is not further specified), grind it, and then
extract a 100-g subsample in a Soxhlet extractor with hexane-
acetone (1:1). The procedure then patches into an unrefer-
enced industrial effluent method, which first specifies a
PGC/ECD screen. If necessary, various cleanup techniques are
specified. An acetonitrile partition is used to remove fats
and oils. A Florisil column cleanup fractionates out some
pesticides using 6%, 15%, and 50% ethyl ether/petroleum ether
eluates. Two alternate silica gel microcolumn cleanups are
presented, one of which provides for sulfur removal with
mercury.

IV. PROCEDURES FOR FOOD

The FDA (1977), AOAC (1980a), and Japanese (Tanabe,
1976) procedures for food are similar. Samples of food are
ground, extracted with petroleum ether, and the lipids removed by an acetonitrile partition. Various cleanup techniques are utilized prior to determination by PGC/ECD.

V. PROCEDURES FOR BY-PRODUCT ANALYSIS

The procedures for by-product analysis (Dow, 1981;
DCMA, 1982; Erickson et al., 1982, 1983d; Erickson, 1984a,
1984b, 1984c) all require strong QC programs. The EPA procedures (Erickson et al., 1982, 1983d; Erickson, 1984a,
1984b, 1984c) allow a maximum of flexibility in the extraction and cleanups to accomodate the wide range of matrices
(the product and product waste procedure is applicable to
liquids, gases, or solids of virtually any composition). In
lieu of method control, the procedures rely on the QC, notably the measurement of the recovery of four ^{13}C-labeled PCBs
spiked into each sample as recovery surrogates.

4

SAMPLE COLLECTION AND STORAGE

The first step in any successful analysis is the collection of a sample. The selection of sampling sites, frequency of sampling, number of samples, measurement of physical and chemical parameters of the sample, and the overall statistical design of sampling methods have been provided in extensive detail (see for example, Moser and Huibregtse, 1976; EPA, 1976; Mason, 1982; Kelso et al., 1985). The sampling design in most cases is directly related to the objectives of a specific research program or a regulatory action.

PCBs are an inert, non-polar class of semivolatile organic compounds. As such, they are reasonably well-behaved during sample collection and storage. Consequently, with the exceptions of the air and water sampling techniques which concentrate the PCBs from the matrix onto an adsorbent, most PCB sample collections have utilized the standard or customary methods for semivolatile organics in the subject matrix. For example, the ASTM procedure (1981b) references general methods for water sampling, sediment and soil sampling, and air sampling. The reader is referred to general sampling and storage procedures in the absence of a PCB-specific method. Sampling for chemical analysis has been reviewed (Kratochvil et al., 1984).

I. WATER

Water samples may be collected by grab or integration techniques. Grab sampling has been much more common. The integration techniques include automatic composite samplers, adsorption onto a solid (XAD resin, polyurethane foam, etc.), and liquid-liquid extraction. Since water sampling for PCB analysis may be readily adapted from general water sampling procedures for semivolatile organics, the reader is referred to these procedures for specific guidance. These include EPA's Priority Pollutant Methods 608 and 625 (EPA, 1979a, 1979b, 1984e, 1984f; Longbottom and Lichtenberg,

63

1982); ASTM's (1981b) Method D 3304; the EPA Handbook for
Sampling and Sample Preparation of Water and Wastewater
(Moser and Huibregtse, 1976) and an EPA document on Pro-
cedures for Handling and Chemical Analysis of Sediment and
Water Samples (Plumb, 1981).

A. Grab Sampling

    Most water procedures and methods have used simple
grab sampling. For example, EPA's Method 608 for organochlorine pesticides and PCBs in wastewater (EPA, 1979a) stipulates that grab samples be collected in glass containers. A
rigorous glassware cleaning method is described in the procedure. Samples must be iced or refrigerated from the time
of collection until extraction. If samples will be stored
for more than 48 hours, the pH is to be adjusted to between
6.0 and 8.0.

    The Bodman bottle can collect up to 90 L (Palmork
et al., 1982; Harvey and Steinhauer, 1976). As the sample is
lowered, water flows through a weighted aluminum cylinder.
At the desired depth, plates at either end are closed and the
sample is retrieved. The sample is transfered to steel drums
under nitrogen for storage. A glass sphere which collects a
10-L sample has the advantage of direct hexane extraction in
the sample vessel (Palmork et al., 1982). Extraction in the
sampling vessel not only reduces the volume of sample to be
stored, but also minimizes adsorptive losses to the container
walls. The use and specifications of two large-volume grab
samplers were described for sampling seawater (Pavlou et al.,
1980). The samplers were designed to be used in conjunction
with a filtering system (also described) to collect large
volumes of particulate.

    A gaslift system can collect unlimited water vol-
umes (Palmork et al., 1982). Water is aspirated through a
3/4 in. stainless steel pipe by injecting nitrogen near the
base of the pipe. Marine water can be collected at 8 to 10
L/min at a depth of 10 m and transferred directly to stainless steel drums to prevent contamination by the shipboard
environment.

B. Automatic Composite Samplers

    An automatic composite sampler generally consists
of a pump, tubing, a timer, and a collection vessel. Typically, the timer cycles the pump on for a fraction of every
hour, during which water is pumped into the collection vessel. This permits collection of an integrated sample from a
flowing water stream over a 1-day period or longer. The EPA

(1979a,b) stipulates that automatic samplers use refrigerated glass containers for the water sample and that the equipment be as free as possible of Tygon tubing and other potential sources of contamination.

C. Solid Adsorbent Sampling

A wide variety of solid adsorbent materials have been investigated for use in water sampling. The objective has been to preconcentrate PCBs from a large volume of water onto a small volume of solid adsorbent which may be easily transported, stored, and extracted. In addition to its convenience, preconcentration can enhance the method detection limit.

As discussed below, investigators have reported mixed results with adsorbent columns. Background from the sorbent, poor precision, and non-quantitative recovery have all been reported. Thus, investigators must demonstrate that results obtained with these sampling techniques are valid. Risebrough et al. (1976) reviewed early uses of solid adsorbents to sample seawater.

1. Polyurethane foam: The use of polyurethane foam (PUF) to adsorb PCBs from water samples was reported by Gesser et al. (1971). They reported 91 to 98% recovery from 1-L samples passed through a PUF plug in a glass column. The PCBs were recovered from the sorbent with 20 mL acetone, followed by 100 mL hexane. Bellar and Lichtenberg (1975), however, noted that this technique was not applicable to river water samples, since the suspended solids plugged the column. Uthe et al. (1974), reported success with PUF coated with DC-200 silicone grease. They used their plugs as indwelling monitors; the plug is submerged in a water system to collect PCBs as they come in contact with the sampler as shown in Figure 4-1. While the simplicity and low cost of this system make it appealing, the authors did not validate the PCB concentrations against an accepted method. Bellar and Lichtenberg (1975) noted that this method led to poorer precision and accuracy with dosed river water than with distilled water.

An active in situ seawater sampler using PUF plugs permits collection of PCBs from large water volumes (Risebrough et al., 1976). The sampler contains five PUF plugs in a 975-cm^3 tube. The sample is lowered to depth and water pumped at 500 mL/min by a vacuum hose connected to the ship. The PCBs are subsequently extracted by successive elution with 500 mL each acetone and hexane. The PCB concentrations obtained from 26 to 79 L samples by this sample compared

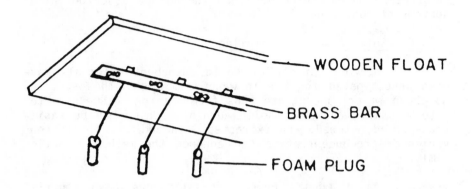

Figure 4-1. Passive Water Sampling Device

Polyurethane foam plugs are held just beneath the water surface.

Reprinted, with permission, from Uthe et al. (1974); copyright 1974 by Marcel Dekker, Inc.

---

favorably with those obtained by methylene chloride extraction and were about twice those obtained with hexane extraction.

Ahling and Jensen (1970) used PUF coated with n-undecane and Carbowax 4000 monostearate to effect a "reverse phase liquid-liquid partitioning." Water samples (up to 200 L) were concentrated onto 3 g of sorbent and then desorbed with 5 mL petroleum ether. Recoveries of 93 to 100% were observed for 10 µg of Clophen A50 added to 5-L water samples.

2. Macroreticular resins: The use of macroreticular resins (specifically the Amberlite XAD series) has been reported by several groups (Musty and Nickless, 1974a; Lawrence and Tosine, 1976; Harvey and Steinhauer, 1976; Osterroht, 1977; Coburn et al., 1977; Picer and Picer, 1980; Palmork et al., 1982; and Eisenreich et al., 1983a). Musty and Nickless (1974a) reported an overall recovery of 76% after one liter of tap water spiked at the ppb level was adsorbed onto XAD-4 (a styrene-divinylbenzene copolymer), and then eluted with diethyl ether-hexane mixture. Coburn et al. (1977) reported 78 to 86% recovery of an Aroclor mixture from 2-L natural water samples collected on XAD-2 (also a styrene-divinylbenzene copolymer), and then eluted with ether.

Recovery of chlorinated hydrocarbons, including PCBs, was reported to be low and variable by Picer and Picer (1980). In fact, they noted that the results of a collaborative study produced results varying by over two orders of magnitude from replicate XAD-2 resin cartridges which had been prepared by one laboratory.

A column containing 50 mL XAD-2 was used to extract PCBs from 50 to 200 L of seawater which had been collected in a 65-L sampler (Harvey and Steinhauer, 1976). The water was pumped through the column at a rate of 5 bed volumes/min. The authors noted that the flow rate was critical to selective adsorption of the organochlorines relative to other organic matter. PCBs were eluted from the column with acetonitrile. The precision, based on replicate analyses, was within ± 20%. The accuracy based on comparison to solvent extraction of 50-L aliquots of the same sample was also within ± 20%.

Eisenreich et al. (1983a) used XAD-2 to concentrate PCBs from Lake Superior water. The 40-L sample size permitted the authors to quantitate PCBs with average concentrations around 1 ng/L (parts per trillion). The resin was extracted in a Soxhlet extractor using a 1:1 mixture of hexane and acetone. No validation data were given.

3. Tenax GC: Leoni et al. (1976b) reported essentially quantitative recovery of 1.6 ppb of PCBs spiked into 10 L of seacoast water which were concentrated without filtration onto a column packed with a mixture of Celite (diatomaceous earth), and Tenax GC [poly(2,6-diphenyl-p-phenylene oxide)]. The PCBs were eluted with diethyl ether. They noted that it was often necessary to filter water samples, but did not measure PCB recovery under these conditions. Picer and Picer (1980) reported considerable background from Tenax columns using a variety of cleanup and desorption solvents.

D. Liquid-Liquid Extraction Sampling

Ahnoff and Josefsson (1973, 1974, 1976) reported the use of a continuous liquid-liquid extractor which concentrated PCBs from hundreds of liters of river water into 100 to 300 mL of lighter-than-water solvent. The sampler mixed the water and solvent with a stirring bar. Water entered from the top and exited from the bottom. Pumping rates were variable up to about 5 L/hr. Recoveries of chlorinated pesticides were > 80%. PCB concentrations in river water were measured as low as 0.1 ng/L.

E.   Rainwater Sampling

Rainwater sampling can employ simple apparatus. For example, stations for continuous collection of rain plus dry deposition (Bidleman et al., 1981a) consisted of 22-cm diameter stainless-steel funnels which emptied into 3.8-L brown-glass jugs. The funnels were placed about 2 m above a marsh surface and were surrounded with wire spikes to discourage perching birds. These "continuous" stations were tended at 2 to 3 week intervals. Event rain samples were collected by exposing stainless-steel bowls during rainstorms.

More elaborate apparatus designed to either concentrate the water sample as it is collected or to prevent dry deposition of particulate is used more often. For example, Murphy et al. (1981) used a sampler which concentrated PCBs onto a sorbent for their studies of PCB deposition in the Great Lakes. Rain fell on a 1.5 m² surface, was filtered through glass fiber, and then the PCBs sorbed onto polyurethane foam. This approach, however, was subsequently abandoned in favor of an integrated wet/dry sampler, which simply collected the rainwater in buckets. The sampler had a roof which automatically uncovered a bucket at the start of a rainfall.

Two samplers have been described which automatically collect rainwater and concentrate it onto a resin cartridge (Strachan and Huneault, 1984; Pankow et al., 1984). Both systems sense rainfall and automatically open a cover for the collection period. The rain then falls on a clean surface and flows toward the sorbent cartridge. Strachan and Huneault used XAD-2 or XAD-7 resin. Recoveries from the XAD-2 were higher than from the XAD-7 (86% versus 68% for several pesticides). Pankow et al. (1984) used Tenax-GC as the adsorbent.

F.   Water Sample Storage

Most general procedures (e.g., the EPA priority pollutant methods) merely specify cold storage, sometimes in the dark or in amber bottles. No special precautions are stipulated for PCBs.

The adsorption of PCBs from water onto the container wall has been reported (Pepe and Byrne, 1980; Muldrew et al., 1981; Sutcliffe and Nielsen, 1983). If precautions are not made to prevent these adsorptive losses during sampling and storage, then the extraction technique should include extraction of the interior of the sample container.

The use of formaldehyde has been shown to preserve water samples for PCB analysis as shown in Figure 4-2 (Bellar and Lichtenberg, 1975). Aroclor spiked in river water at 1 µg/L decreased steadily over a 15-day study in unpreserved samples, while no losses were observed when an unspecified amount of formaldehyde had been added. The temperature and light conditions were not specified. The authors noted greater losses with the congeners containing ≦ 3 chlorine atoms. Other preservation techniques were less effective: over the range of 2.7 to 10.5, pH had no effect on storage losses. Both refrigeration and the absence of light retarded PCB loss relative to storage at ambient temperature in the light, but still showed significant losses, as shown in Figure 4-2. The authors noted that the rate of loss appeared to be affected by the physical, chemical, and biological characteristics of the samples. They also documented a faster rate of loss with Teflon than with aluminum cap liners; although no PCBs could be recovered by extraction of the Teflon liners.

Storage temperature (4°C versus 24°C), pH (2, 7, and 10), and chlorine (0 or 2 ppm NaOCl) did not markedly affect the recoveries of seven different Aroclors from clean water after storage for 7 days (Millar et al., 1981, 1982). Most of the samples exhibited greater than 90% recovery.

Sorption of PCBs to glass and plastic surfaces has been shown to cause significant losses (Pepe and Byrne, 1980; Muldrew et al., 1981; Sutcliffe and Nielsen, 1983), although the first two studies are flawed in that the concentration of the ^{14}C-2,2',4,4',5,5'-hexachlorobiphenyl was well in excess of either the water solubility or environmentally significant levels. Nevertheless, adsorption onto the sample container (and the cap) should be considered as a potential source of loss from a sample.

Under most storage conditions, photochemical, chemical or biological degradation of PCBs in water samples appear unlikely. However, as noted in the two preceeding paragraphs, losses due to physical removal have been observed and can be significant. The sorption of PCBs onto glass, particulate, and other surfaces is only to be expected, given their low water solubility and high octanol-water partition coefficients. It may be that the preservation effects of formaldehyde noted by Bellar and Lichtenberg (1975) above, may have been simply the effect of increasing the solubility of the PCBs in the sample by the addition of a water-miscible organic "solvent."

Analysts can generally counteract sorptive losses by treating the entire interior of the sample vessel (water,

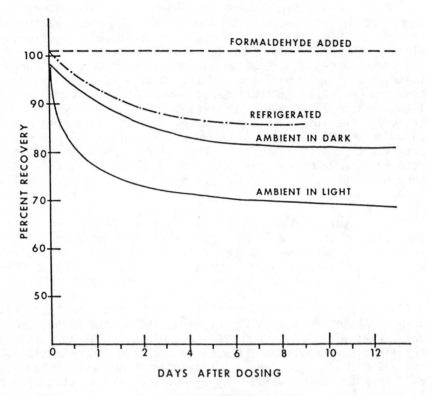

Figure 4-2.   Effect of Storage Conditions on Recovery
of Aroclor 1016 from River Water

Samples were dosed at 1 µg/sample, stored at ambient temperature (in light and the dark) under refrigeration, and preserved with formaldehyde.

Reprinted, with permission, from Bellar and Lichtenberg, 1975;
copyright 1975 by American Society for Testing and Materials.

surface, and cap liner) as part of the "sample." If the sample container is extracted and combined with the water extract, the adsorbed PCBs should be recovered. In addition, the use of spiked field controls and/or samples which are spiked (standard addition) in the field as part of the overall QC (see Chapter 9) should aid the analyst in assessing any losses during storage.

II. AIR

        The general category of air sampling encompasses a wide variety of objectives and techniques. Ambient (i.e., breathable) air includes both indoor and outdoor sites, and may be sampled using personal, fixed, and atmospheric deposition sampling techniques. The non-ambient air which has been sampled is stack gas from incinerators, power plants, etc. Regardless of the air type or sampling objective, nearly all reported procedures involve some technique of concentrating the PCBs from the air to a much smaller volume of solid or liquid sorbent; usually with an active pumping mechanism to draw the air through the sorbent medium. The only exceptions to active sampling are the techniques designed to monitor atmospheric deposition.

        Air sampling techniques must quantitatively concentrate the PCBs from the air. In addition, the PCBs must be recoverable, the sorbent medium must not generate interferences, and the entire process must be shown to accurately reflect the true concentration in air. This section presents the techniques used for air sampling and also discusses the validation and utility of the techniques.

    A. Ambient Air

        1. Solid sorbents: Several of the common solid sorbents have been used for collection of PCBs from air-- porous polyurethane foam (PUF), Florisil, and XAD-2. With all of these sorbents, the PCBs are rather loosely bound and migrate slowly through the medium with the air flow, just as they do through a gas chromatography column. Thus, a major task in characterizing a sorbent is assessing the breakthrough volume. The more volatile, lower-chlorinated PCBs break through first, so many of the recovery studies show poorer recoveries for these compounds than for the heavier homologs.

            a. Polyurethane foam: PUF plugs have been extensively studied by Bidleman and coworkers (Bidleman and Olney, 1974; Simon and Bidleman, 1979; Burdick and Bidleman, 1981; Bidleman and Leonard, 1982; Billings and Bidleman,

1980, 1983; Bidleman et al., 1981b, 1983, 1984). Commercially available PUF is cut into cylindrical plugs (e.g., 7.6 cm diameter x 7.6 cm thick). The plugs are then extracted in a Soxhlet (Billings and Bidleman, 1983), or by repeated manual compression (Erickson et al., 1980a) with organic solvents. The plugs are then dried in a vacuum desiccator at 40 to 45°C (temperature is not critical). The movement of 3,3'-dichlorobiphenyl and 2,4',5-trichlorobiphenyl through PUF has been studied (Burdick and Bidleman, 1981; Bidleman et al., 1983). They found that the penetration depths of the PCBs depended on the ambient temperature and volatility of the compound and were linearly related to the total air volume, i.e., the system behaves like a gas-solid chromatograph. Even for these lighter PCBs, breakthrough volumes for a 15-cm PUF plug at 20°C were over 1,000 m^3. Thus, PUF may be used for high-volume air sampling. Bidleman's group has typically collected 600 to 1,500 m^3 of air with PCB concentrations ranging from 0.08 to 100 ng/m^3, measured as Aroclor 1016 and 1254. The blank values for the PUF plugs were in the 5 to 10 ng/plug range for freshly cleaned plugs and 10 to 20 ng/plug range for plugs used after 3 months of storage.

Lewis et al. (1977a,b) reported collection efficiencies in the 70 to 85% range for different Aroclors when 200 to 325 m^3 of air containing 19 to 153 ng/m^3 PCBs were sampled through 5-cm diameter x 7.6 cm PUF plugs. The collection efficiency correlated with the degree of chlorination. Using PGC/ECD, they calculated a theoretical detection limit of 0.1 ng/m^3. Lewis and Jackson (1982) reported improved collection efficiencies with a dual sorbent cartridge consisting of a 25 cm^3 bed of granular sorbent sandwiched between two PUF plugs (5 cm thick upstream and 2.5 cm thick downstream). The granular sorbents tested were Chromosorb 102, Porapak R, XAD-2, Tenax GC, and Florisil. No specific sorbent was recommended. The sampling cartridge was Soxhlet-extracted without disassembly. The results, shown in Table 4-I, indicate improved collection for the lighter PCBs (di- and trichlorobiphenyls) over PUF alone. Lewis and MacLeod (1982) reduced the size of the cartridge to 2.2 cm diameter x 6 cm for use in personal sampling. At flow rates of 3.8 L/min and a total sampling volume of 900 L, recoveries of Aroclor 1242, 1254, and 1260 were 96%, 95%, and 109%, respectively. An analytical procedure has been prepared, which summarizes the method (Lewis, 1982).

Oehme and Stray (1982) and Oehme and Ottar (1983) used PUF plugs to sample arctic air for extremely low levels of PCBs. They reported a sampling efficiency of 80 to 100% for the first 11-cm diameter x 5 cm plug. The levels

Table 4-I. Collection Efficiencies of Sorbents

Chlorobiphenyl	Calcd Air Concn. (ng/m^3)	% Collected[a] After 24 hr at 225 L/min					
		PUF Alone	PUF/ Chromosorb 102	PUF/ Porapak R	PUF/ XAD-2	PUF/ Tenax GC	PUF/ Florisil PR
4,4'-Di	2.0-20	62	82	82	96	85	111
2,4,5-Tri	0.2-2.0	36	80	87	91		92
2,4',5-Tri	0.2-2.0	86	81	89	93	80	88
2,2',5,5'-Tetra	0.2-2.0	94	81	88	88	81	92
2,2',4,5,5'-Penta	0.2-2.0	92	79	92	96	84	97
2,2',4,4',5,5'-Hexa	0.2-2.0	86	84	92	95	85	93

a Average of 6 to 12 determinations.
Source: Lewis and Jackson, 1982. Reprinted with permission, copyright 1982, American Chemical Society.

found in arctic air using HRGC/EIMS ranged from 0.2 to 4.0 pg/m^3 measured as Cl_6 and Cl_7 homologs and from 0.6 to 5.0 pg/m^3 measured as Phenochlor DP6. Other investigators reporting successful use of PUF plugs include Erickson et al. (1980a), and Stratton et al. (1978). Although PCBs were not studied, Adams and Caro (1980) published an extensive study of the utility of PUF as a sorbent for pesticides from air. In a review of available methods for ambient air, Margeson (1977) recommended the use of PUF for sample collection.

b. Florisil: Florisil, a magnesium silicate salt, has been widely used for stack sampling applications, but its application to sampling PCBs from ambient air has been rather limited. Small sampling cartridges containing 0.3 g of deactivated Florisil (3% water w/w) and 1 g of anhydrous sodium sulfate were used to sample for up to 60 hr at 2 to 4 L/min air flow (Giam et al., 1975). PCB concentrations were in the 35 to 90 ng/m^3 range. Losses during sampling were negligible, even after 5 days of sampling at 2 to 3 L/min air flow.

The NIOSH (1977 a,b,c) methods for PCBs in air utilize Florisil tubes which are sampled with a personal sampling pump at 50 to 200 mL/min. The glass tubes are 4 mm ID x 7 cm long with two sections of 30/48 mesh deactivated Florisil containing 100 mg and 50 mg (backup). Glass wool preceeds the first section; PUF separates the sections and follows the backup Florisil. PCBs are solvent-desorbed and determined by PGC/ECD. A collection efficiency of 100% is reported for a 50-L air sample with PCB concentrations of up to 10 mg/m^3. This method was recently used to sample for 2,2',4,4'-tetrachlorobiphenyl as a by-product in 2,4-dichlorobenzoyl peroxide manufacture (Rubenstein, 1983). The PCB concentrations were in the 100 to 200 ng/m^3 range.

The Ontario Ministry of the Environment uses Florisil cartridges to sample air in their ambient air surveys (Singer et al., 1983). The cartridge blanks average less than 0.3 ng/m^3 PCBs/m^3 air.

c. XAD-2: The macroreticular resin XAD-2 is a styrene-divinylbenzene copolymer with a surface area of 300 to 350 m^2/g. The successful use of XAD-2 with a high volume sampler has been reported (Doskey and Andren, 1979). The XAD-2 was held in a resin capsule with 60-mesh screens. Two 70-g portions of the resin were sampled in tandem. The resin was cleaned up by first drying at 60°C overnight, then Soxhlet-extracting with petroleum ether for 72 hr, then drying as before. At a flow rate of 0.5 to 0.7 m^3/min (total air volume of 700 to 3,100 m^3), 90% collection efficiencies were reported for a tetrachlorobiphenyl and Aroclor 1221.

Under similar conditions, 90 to 95% recoveries of Aroclors 1221, 1242, and 1254 have been reported (Hollod and Eisenreich, 1981; Eisenreich et al. 1983b). Only 100-400 m^3 of air could be sampled before breakthrough occured.

d. Comparison of sorbents. PUF, silicone oil coated on PUF, Florisil, and XAD-2 were evaluated (Doskey and Andren, 1979) using ^{14}C-labeled 2,2',5,5'-tetrachlorobiphenyl. The retention of the PCB spiked (300 ng) onto the top of the sorbent was tested with flow rates of 3 to 7 L/min and total sample volumes of 7 to 26 m^3. XAD-2 and Florisil exhibited essentially quantitative retention of the PCB, while the PUF exhibited 80% retention and the silicone oil coated PUF exhibited 58% retention. The collection efficiency was then measured. The radiolabeled PCB (150 ng) was also vaporized into the air stream and then collected by the sorbents. The coated PUF was not evaluated due to its poor performance in the previous experiment. At flow rates of 5 to 16 L/min and total sample volumes of 5 to 17 m^3, the XAD-2 and Florisil collected the PCB at 99 and 100%, respectively. The efficiency of the PUF was measured at 50%. XAD-2 was selected over Florisil as the sorbent of choice because it was coarser, had a lower pressure drop, and thus permitted higher air sampling rates.

Billings and Bidleman (1983) compared PUF, Tenax GC, and XAD-2 in field studies. All three effectively collected Aroclor 1254 on a 10 to 20-g trap with negligible penetration to a backup trap. In a 24-hr sampling period (500 to 700 m^3 air) at 20°C, about 15% of Aroclor 1016 broke through the backup trap with PUF. The breakthrough was less for the other two sorbents. The ambient concentrations found with the three sorbents agreed well; generally within 10 to 15%.

2. Liquid sorbents: In methods involving liquid adsorbents, the air is bubbled through the liquid trapping medium. As reviewed by Margeson (1977), a wide variety of glassware geometries and liquids, ranging in volatility from hexane to ethylene glycol, have been used. The latter is used in an EPA (Watts, 1980) method for pesticides and PCBs. Air is bubbled through two impingers in series containing 100 mL of ethylene glycol each, with a glass fiber filter in front to trap particulate matter.

The ANSI (1974) procedure for PCBs in air uses toluene. An unspecified volume of air is drawn through one or more gas scrubbers containing toluene. The procedure notes that neither the capacity nor the collection efficiency has been evaluated. It further cautions the user to make only comparative measurements with samples collected under equivalent conditions.

3. <u>Sampling apparatus</u>: The sampling apparatus for PCBs is no different from that used for other semivolatile organics. A typical sampling train includes a filter, sorbent, pump, and a volume or flow-rate measurement device. A filter (e.g., glass fiber) often preceeds the collection medium to filter out particulate matter, insects, etc. The filter generally contains only a small fraction of the PCBs at normal temperatures. In cold climates, this may not be true and analysis of the filter should be considered.

Air is drawn through the filter and sorbent assembly by a pump. The size and type of pump depend on the desired detection limit and portability required. Collection of sufficient sample to detect PCBs at low concentrations requires either a high sampling rate (i.e., big pump), or long sampling periods. Personal sampling requires small, battery-powered pumps. In addition to the pump, most samplers include a volume or rate measurement device. This may be a dry gas meter or simply a pump cycle counter. Regardless, the system must be calibrated before use. It is important that the exhaust air be vented away from the intake to prevent recycling of the same air.

a. <u>High volume samplers</u>: A number of investigators have modified the classic "Hi-Vol" for PCB sampling by inserting sorbent cartridges in the throat between the 8 x 10 in. (20 x 25 cm) filter holder and the motor. These samplers generally operate at flow rates of about 1,000 L/min. Among those using these samplers are Eisenreich et al. (1983b), Bidleman and Olney (1974), Billings and Bidleman (1983), and Lewis et al. (1977a). A sampler based on the designs of Lewis and Jackson (1982) is commercially available (Model PS-1, General Metals Works Company).

b. <u>Medium volume samplers</u>: Erickson et al. (1980a) reported the use of a sampler which collected air at rates up to 250 L/min.

c. <u>Personal samplers</u>: A personal sampler, capable of sampling up to 4 L/min for at least 12 hr was developed by the EPA (MacLeod, 1979; Lewis and MacLeod, 1982). The air was pumped by a DuPont P-4000 constant flow sampling pump. PCBs were collected on a small PUF cartridge. Concentrations from < 10 to 10,000 ng/m^3 were reported.

4. <u>Atmospheric deposition</u>: The measurement of atmospheric deposition is an important link in environmental fate studies involving aerial transport of PCBs. Atmospheric deposition may be divided into rainfall (discussed above in the water section) and dry deposition. Dry deposition is generally measured by passively sampling on a flat surface.

The surface may be dry or wetted with mineral oil (McClure, 1976; Heesen et al., 1979), glycerin (Christensen et al., 1979), a mixture of diols and water (Murphy et al., 1981a) or other liquids. Bidleman et al. (1981a) and Christensen et al. (1979) collected PCBs on large aluminum baking pans. They compared the collection efficiency of dry, water-filled, and water/glycerin-coated (50:50) pans. The wet surfaces collected 1.5 to 3 times more than the dry pans. The use of coated horizontal surfaces appears to be the only common dry deposition collection technique (Andren, 1983), although its validity has not been established and is, in fact, open to considerable question (Andren, 1983). An exchange of comments by Murphy et al. (1981b) underscores both the theoretical and practical differences in the collection mechanisms of wet versus dry surfaces. They also note that the polarity of the wetting agent can affect the collection efficiency. It is possible that wet surfaces collect PCBs not only by deposition but also by adsorptive scavenging of vapor-phase components which would not normally settle out.

An innovative approach to obtaining realistic atmospheric deposition samples is ice coring (Murphy and Schinsky, 1983). Multiple cores (7.6 cm dia. x 10 to 80 cm in length) were composited to get representative samples of sufficient volume for detection. A net deposition rate of 2.0 $g/km^2/mo$ was measured for Saginaw Bay in Lake Huron.

5. Direct sampling: Direct introduction of an air sample into a mobile mass spectrometer system has been reported (Thomson et al., 1980; Thomson and Roberts, 1980, 1982). The system allows a 2-min average concentration to be measured at 3- to 4-min intervals. The detection limit was estimated to be in the nanogram per cubic meter range.

6. Discussion of ambient air sampling techniques: There is no clear mandate for one particular sampling technique. The use of solid sorbents is preferable to liquid sorbents for several reasons. Higher air volumes may be sampled. The solid sorbent is more portable and more adaptable to personal monitoring. The apparatus is simpler.

Regardless of the sorbent or the apparatus used, background contamination, breakthrough losses, and sample recovery must all be monitored by careful validation and quality control. Before sampling, the volume or flow rate device must be calibrated and the system checked for leaks.

An interesting observation by Billings and Bidleman (1983) may serve as a good rule of thumb: "Because vapor pressures of pesticides and PCB isomers increase rapidly with temperature, a 5°C rise in temperature has nearly the same

effect on sample penetration [into the sorbent] as doubling
the air volume."

    B. Source Sampling

        Stationary source emissions (stack or flue gas)
represent the point of entry into the environment for many
pollutants, including PCBs which may be in stack gas as a result of incomplete combustion during PCB incineration, or may
be passed through from contaminated fuel. Since stack emissions of PCBs are controllable, measurement of PCBs and stack
gases is important. In addition, the measurement of PCBs in
the stack gas during trial burns of PCB incinerators is required in the United States to assess the destruction efficiency (EPA, 1979d; EPA, 1983a; Erickson and Shah, 1983;
Ackerman et al., 1983).

        Stack gas differs from ambient air in several re-
spects. The gas is generally hot (70°C to 500°C), flowing
rapidly (5 to 20 m/sec), and hostile. The gas can contain
large amounts of particulate, is often corrosive, and is
nearly always laden with water. All of these properties must
be considered when collecting stack gas samples.

        1. Sampling techniques: Sampling methods for PCBs
have been adapted from the general stack sampling methods
used to measure particulate, acids, and other stack effluents. The sampling train used most often in the U.S. is
the modified EPA Method 5, shown in Figure 4-3. The stack
gas is drawn in through a probe. The sampling rate is adjusted so that the flow into the probe matches that in the
stack (isokinetic sampling) to minimize the flow disturbances
which would discriminate the gas sampled according to part-
icle size. The filter collects particulate at the same temperature as the stack. The resin cartridge (generally XAD-2)
is designed to collect PCBs and other semivolatile organics.
The impingers collect water and vapors (e.g., HCl). The geometry and sequence of the resin cartridge and impingers
differ among investigators. Different impinger styles and
sequences have been employed to deal with specific stack sit-
uations (high temperature, high particulate loading, etc.).
The modified Method 5 train is generally operated at 1 cfm
(28 Lpm) to collect a 2 to 10 m^3 sample. The modified
Method 5 uses all glass or glass-lined tubing, so corrosion
is not generally a problem.

        The filter for the Modified Method 5 should not be
used to obtain the Method 5 total particulate emissions from
the stack in addition to measuring the PCBs. The particu-
lates are measured gravimetrically after the filter has been
dried to a constant weight. This drying process can vaporize
the PCBs off the filter, resulting in low PCB recoveries.

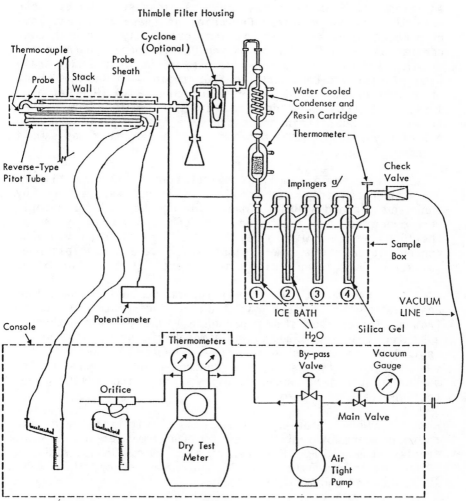

g/ Impingers 1,3 and 4 are of the Modified Greenburg-Smith Type
   Impinger 2 is of the Greenburg-Smith Design
   Impinger 1 and 2 Contain 100 ml Water
   Impinger 3 Empty
   Impinger 4 Contains 200-300 Grams Silica Gel

Figure 4-3.   Modified Method 5 Train for Organics Sampling
              of Stack Gas

Reprinted from Haile et al. (1983a).

Another sampling train used in the United States, the Source Assessment Sampling System (SASS) train (Feairheller et al., 1976; Lentzen et al., 1978) has not been widely used for PCB sampling. Quantitative collection and recovery of PCBs may not be possible with this system. In addition, the SASS train has many stainless steel parts, notably the sorbent module. Corrosion of these components has been noted to be a serious problem, especially with high concentrations of HCl, such as during PCB incineration (Ackerman et al., 1983b). A side-by-side comparison of the MM5 train with Florisil sorbent and the SASS train with XAD-2 sorbent at a utility oil-fired boiler was inconclusive (Hunt et al., 1984). No PCBs were detected in the samples from either train. The SASS train demonstrated a higher PCB destruction efficiency solely on the basis of the larger stack gas sample volume.

A simple sampling device, consisting of a filter, one condensate trap, and an XAD-2 cartridge was reported by Junk and Richard (1984). Mono- through hexachlorobiphenyls were quantitatively collected from 200°C air by the system at the 10 ng/m^3 level with a collection volume of 5 m^3. The PCB concentrations in a power plant stack were comparable when collected by either this simple sampling train or SASS.

Lovett et al. (1983) reported a direct sampling/ analysis system. Stack gas from an incinerator is pumped from an incinerator stack through a 10 µm filter and through a heated transfer line to an atmospheric pressure chemical ionization mass spectrometer (see Chapter 7) mounted in a van. Using this system, the concentration of PCBs in the stack gas could be measured every 3 min with a method detection limit of 8 µg/m^3.

More detailed discussions of sampling trains and their use are presented elsewhere (Ackerman et al., 1983b; Stanley et al., 1982; Erickson et al., 1982, 1983d; Erickson, 1984b; Haile and Baladi, 1977; Beard and Schaum, 1978; EPA, 1977; Johnson and Merrill, 1983).

2. Solid sorbents: The sorbent cartridge of the modified Method 5 and, presumably, other trains can accomodate any granular sorbent.

Adams et al. (1977) studied the breakthrough of Aroclor 1242 on XAD-2 in a study of sorbents for use in SASS and modified Method 5 trains. They found no breakthrough under experimental conditions and projected that XAD-2 would quantitatively trap PCBs under stack sampling conditions.

Haile and Baladi (1977) recommended Florisil over Tenax GC and XAD-2 for PCB sampling in a modified Method 5 train because of its lower background and high trapping efficiency. In laboratory studies, they found sampling efficiencies of 86 to 92% for Aroclors with Florisil. At flow rates of 17 to 20 L/min and ambient temperatures, Florisil and Tenax-GC exhibited much better recovery from an adsorption/desorption experiment as shown in Table 4-II. Subsequent adsorption/desorption experiments at 120°C found only 50 to 70% recoveries for Florisil while interferences prevented quantitation of the dichlorobiphenyl from the Tenax. Thus, they recommended cooling the gas before the sorbent to improve adsorption efficiency. The combined sampling efficiency and method recovery of the Florisil in the field sampling train is shown in Table 4-III. A recovery of 88% for Aroclor 1221 from XAD-2 in the sampling train was also reported.

Hanneman (personal communication, 1982) reported that PCBs were not retained at acceptable levels on common solid adsorbents when the flue gas temperature was greater than 150°C or in cases where the air contained an aerosol of a nonpolar material in which PCBs are very soluble. Hanneman reported successful collection of PCBs in these instances using PUF plugs coated with liquid polydimethylsiloxane. Several plugs of the coated polyurethane were placed in a water-cooled jacket to sample the air at elevated temperatures. A PCB congener was added to the surface of the foam plugs as a surrogate prior to sampling. A second PCB congener was added to the foam plugs after sampling to monitor surrogate recovery and collection efficiency.

More recently, Haile et al. (1983a) examined the PCB collection recovery efficiency for a modified Method 5 train with XAD-2 as the sorbent. Aroclor 1254 was spiked at two levels (110 and 1,100 μg total) into a simulated flue gas during an 8-hr laboratory test. The recovery was measured by GC/MS as total tri-, tetra-, penta-, and hexachlorobiphenyls. The total recoveries from both the probe rinse and train extract ranged from 68 to 99%. While there was no notable trend with homolog in the total recovery, the distribution between the probe rinse and train extract was most illuminating. Only the trichlorobiphenyls were volatile enough to collect appreciably in the train (~ 30%). The rest of the PCBs apparently adsorbed to the first cooled surface they encountered--the probe. These data suggest that the type of sorbent is not nearly as important as the provision of a cool surface for the PCBs to condense onto. Thus, sample collection apparatus geometry and temperature may be of much greater importance than is commonly realized.

TABLE 4-II

COMPARISON OF ADSORPTION AND RECOVERY EFFICIENCY
OF THREE SORBENTS

| | Adsorbent[a] | | |
	Florisil	Tenax	XAD-2
Sampling rate (L/min)	17[b]	20	20
Recovery (%)			
2,2'-Dichlorobiphenyl	71.4	82.7	34.0
2,2',4,5'-Tetrachlorobiphenyl	90.5	92.8	59.2
2,2',3,3',4,4'-Hexachlorobiphenyl	80.6	91.0	57.0
Mean	80.8	88.8	50.1

a Similar volumes of sorbent in a 22-mm ID tube sampled at
   ambient temperatures. PCBs vaporized in air upstream of
   sorbent.
b Maximum flow rate obtainable.
Source: Haile and Baladi (1977).

TABLE 4-III

SAMPLING EFFICIENCY OF FLORISIL SAMPLING TRAIN

PCB Mixture	Total Spike (μg)	Recovery[a] (%)
Aroclor 1221	23.8	86 ± 9
Aroclor 1242	18.2	88 ± 10
Aroclor 1254	11.6	92 ± 3

a Average and standard deviation for six tests.
Source: Haile and Baladi (1977).

Based on the work by Haile and Baladi (1977) which was recommended by EPA's interim manual (Beard and Schaum, 1978), Florisil has often been used to trap PCBs from stack gas. For example, it was used in the first (October 1979) trial burn at the ENSCO Incinerator in El Dorado, AR (EPA, 1981b), and at two industrial boiler tests (Hall et al., 1982; Polcyn et al., 1983). One disadvantage is its relatively fine mesh which results in a high pressure drop and lower flow rates during sampling. Another disadvantage is its intolerance of water. In high humidity, Florisil will hydrate, cake up, and block the air flow. The use of Florisil in four PCB incineration trial burns was reviewed by Ackerman et al. (1983a).

A dual trap system with Florisil followed by XAD-2 was employed at the Rollins Environmental, Deer Park, TX (EPA, 1981), second ENSCO, El Dorado, AR (EPA, 1981b), and Vulcanus MT trial burns (Ackerman et al., 1983b). The lack of a consensus on sorbents has apparently led some sampling teams to use both XAD-2 and Florisil to ensure the acceptability of the data.

A number of studies have employed XAD-2 in the sorbent cartridge in a modified Method 5 train (Stanley et al., 1982; Haile et al., 1983a,b, 1984). Its use in PCB incineration trial burns has been reviewed by Ackerman et al. (1983b). XAD-2 was recommended by the EPA for sampling during PCB trial burns (Beard and Schaum, 1978) and also by a standards working group (ASME, 1984).

3. Liquid sorbents: Despite some early use, liquid sorbents have not been extensively used for sampling stack gas. The primary liquid sorbent has been ethylene glycol. Liberti et al. (1980) used toluene in two tandem impingers to sample organochlorine compounds, including PCBs, from an urban incinerator. The subject has been reviewed (Margeson, 1977; Ackerman et al., 1983a).

4. Sampling design: The sampling design must meet the objectives of the study. The sample volume, number of samples, waste feed rates, etc., must all be carefully considered beforehand. It is particularly important to understand all of the related variables which impact on the measurable destruction efficiency. This subject has been presented in more detail (Erickson et al., 1984a). Another aspect of the study design is distinguishing between PCB emissions and background. A background or baseline run may be an appropriate part of the QC program. Haile et al. (1983b) found that the PCBs emitted from seven coal-fired utility boilers were higher than the levels in background

air, but that the two levels were generally within one standard deviation. Furthermore, the homolog distributions were
similar. These two facts indicate that the PCB emissions
from these plants may have just passed through the plant with
the combustion air.

5. Discussion: Stack sampling for PCBs is generally done using a complex sampling apparatus designed to sample isokinetically and to collect several fractions for a variety of analytes. In the U.S., the apparatus of choice is
the modified Method 5 train. The exact geometry of the modified sampling train and the choice of sorbent (XAD-2 or
Florisil) differ among sampling groups although XAD-2 appears
to have been more preferred in recent years. It appears that
the chemical properties of the sorbent may be less important
than the physical presence of a cool surface for condensation
of the PCBs. Since it has been shown that substantial
amounts of PCBs are collected in the probe and other parts of
the train plumbing (Haile et al., 1983a) it is particularly
important to validate the collection and recovery efficiency
with the full train under realistic conditions. Better validation techniques are needed to fully assess the collection
and recovery efficiency of a sampling system under a given
set of sampling conditions.

Unless further method validation studies indicate
an acceptable alternative, source sampling should utilize a
modified Method 5 train with XAD-2 as the sorbent. The contents of the entire train (probe, rinse, filter, any upstream
impingers, and the sorbent cartridge) must be analyzed for
PCBs. As noted above, the modified Method 5 filter should
not be used to measure the Method 5 total particulate.
Proper experimental design and QC are necessary to discriminate between unreacted PCBs from the incinerator and PCBs
collected from background air.

III. NATURAL GAS IN PIPELINES

A procedure (Harris et al., 1981) for the sampling
and analysis of natural gas for PCBs utilizes the NIOSH Florisil tubes (NIOSH, 1977a,b,c). The Florisil tube is connected to a valved port in the line through appropriate fit-
tings. A Magnahelic, rotometer or dry gas meter downstream
monitors the flow rates or volume.

IV. SOLIDS

Soil, sediment, biota, and tissue sampling for PCBs all utilize general trace organic sampling techniques. Sampling equipment and containers must be glass, steel, TFE, or other non-contaminating materials. The samples collected must be representative of the system, and the sample volume must be sufficient for the analyst's needs. Documents on sampling hazardous waste streams (deVera et al., 1980), soil (Mason, 1982), and PCB spill sites (Kelso et al., 1985) give additional guidance.

Using a mobile atmospheric pressure chemical ionization mass spectrometer, Lovett et al. (1983) demonstrated a real-time sampling/analysis technique for soil and other solids. Air from the surface of a spill, or soil core was pumped through a heated transfer line, "surface sniffing," to the spectrometer. A detection limit of 500 µg/g was reported.

V. SURFACES

Solid surfaces may need to be sampled to assess either PCB contamination or the effectiveness of cleanup after a PCB spill. These solid surfaces may be smooth and impervious, such as a drum interior, or rough and porous, such as an asphalt driveway. No standard surface sampling technique has been issued by an organization.

In an EPA guidance document on PCB spill cleanup, Kelso et al. (1985) recommended that nonporous surfaces be sampled by wiping. Surface wipes are taken with a moistened piece of filter paper with toluene, isooctane, or other appropriate solvent. The filter paper is held with a pair of stainless steel forceps and used to thoroughly swab a 10 cm x 10 cm area of the surface to be sampled. A template should be used to define the area. The wipe technique should be performed reproducibly. The wipe sample is stored at approximately 4°C in a precleaned glass jar.

Wipe samples are not appropriate for porous surfaces which may absorb the PCBs. These surfaces such as wood, asphalt, and concrete should be sampled by physical removal of a representative portion (Kelso et al., 1985). The sample can be collected by chipping, drilling, coring, chiseling, etc.

VI. OIL, DIELECTRIC FLUIDS, ETC.

A large number of PCB analyses involve transformer oil, hydraulic fluid, askarels, and other similar oils which may be contaminated with PCBs. Since these oils are generally contained in a transformer, drum, tank, etc., obtaining a sample may be as simple as opening a drain valve. The only consideration in sampling is representativeness. Especially where the oil is highly contaminated, the PCB content may not be homogeneous. For example, a drum of waste oil may contain several phases--a sludge, a water layer, and an oil layer. The PCB content of the three layers would differ markedly. Thus, the sampler must attempt to obtain a representative sample. Small containers may be mixed. With larger containers, subsamples from various depths may need to be taken.

5

EXTRACTION

Reliable trace organic analysis begins with the quantitative extraction or the analytes from the sample matrix. The general objective of an extraction technique is to separate the analyte (e.g., PCBs) from the sample into a matrix which is more compatible with the rest of the analytical procedure. The exact separation process is dependent on the complexity of the physical and chemical nature of the matrix. The general principles and techniques of extraction for trace organic analysis have been reviewed (Poole and Schuette, 1983). PCBs are readily extracted from matrices such as water, but are difficult to extract from oil and other matrices in which they are readily soluble.

This chapter reviews the literature and discusses applicable extraction techniques by matrix. After a discussion of general physical and chemical considerations, extraction techniques for water, sewage and sludge, sediment and soil, air, blood, animal and plant tissue, paper products, and oils are presented. A section at the end of the chapter discusses solvent evaporation, losses of PCBs through sorption onto glass containers, and sources of contamination.

Many of the extraction techniques discussed in the literature are derived from traditional pesticide analytical methods, and their adaptation to PCB analysis was made with little or no reported research or validation. Thus, most of the PCB extraction techiques discussed in this chapter may be best described as "workable" but not "optimized."

I. GENERAL CONSIDERATIONS

As noted in Chapter 2, PCBs are nonpolar, semivolatile organics. Thus, they are highly soluble in nonpolar solvents such as hexane and only slightly soluble in polar solvents such as water and acetonitrile. This property is advantageous for extraction from water samples, since the PCBs will readily partition from the water to most nonpolar (i.e., immiscible) organic solvents. However, when the PCBs are dissolved in a nonpolar matrix such as oil, the extraction process becomes much more difficult, if not impossible.

The physical mechanism of the extraction can also be important. The extraction solvent must come into contact with the entire sample to reliably extract the PCBs. With soil, tissue, and other solids, physical mixing or maceration is necessary to assure effective contact. Even more harsh techniques such as ultrasonic disruption or chemical degradation (e.g., saponification with base) may be required to break up cells, macromolecules, or other matrix components which could entrain PCBs. The rigor of the technique must be balanced between efficient extraction and degradation or loss of the analyte.

As with any partition scheme between two phases, PCB extraction relies on a favorable partition of the PCBs from the sample matrix into the extraction matrix. The more favorable the partition coefficient, the higher the extraction efficiency. Efficiency is also improved by repetitious extractions. If, for example, the partition coefficient, K, is 9, then 90% of the PCBs will extract from the sample to the solvent in the first extraction (at equilibrium). The second extraction will also yield 90% of the remaining PCBs for a total extraction of 99%. After three extractions, the combined extracts should contain 99.9% of the sample. With a lower partition coefficient, more repetitions are required for a similar total extraction. For most matrices, K has been presumed to be high and the traditional number of repetitions is 3.

II. WATER

Extraction of PCBs from water is generally straightforward, since the solubility is so low. A simple liquid-liquid extraction with any water-immiscible solvent should yield adequate results. As shown in Table 3-I, the standard procedures prescribe hexane, methylene chloride, or mixed solvents for water extraction. The sections below describe considerations for liquid-liquid extractions and also present some of the other extraction techniques reported in the literature. A steam distillation technique has been used for extraction of water samples, but was validated primarily for fish samples and is discussed in Section VII.B.3, below.

A. Liquid-Liquid Extraction

The classic liquid-liquid extraction techniques involve a simple shaking of the water and solvent in a separatory funnel. Continuous liquid-liquid extraction is simply

an "automation" of the separatory funnel shakeout. More eso-
teric extraction techniques include steam distillation and
sorbent column extraction. The latter is particularly appealing for on-site extraction of large volume water samples
to achieve very low detection limits. On-site water extraction was covered under "sampling" (Chapter 4).

A study of water extraction solvents and conditions
by Millar et al. (1981; 1982) found no distinctly advantageous combination of solvent and pH for all PCBs. In the
study, Aroclors 1016, 1221, 1232, 1242, 1248, 1254, and 1260
were spiked into unchlorinated well water. The spiked samples were then adjusted to pH 2, 7, and 10 and extracted with
either dichloromethane/hexane (15:85) or pure dichloromethane. The results were analyzed by analysis of variance
(ANOVA). For some PCB mixtures either one or the other solvent was preferable. The effect of pH was similarly con-
founding; neutral, basic, and "no preference" were statistically shown to be the best conditions for various Aroclors.
It appears from these data that there is no significant difference in these conditions for all PCBs.

A liquid-liquid extraction followed by a KOH saponification technique has been developed for paper mill effluents (Easty and Wabers, 1978; Delfino and Easty, 1979).
Water samples are extracted three times with hexane and then
cleaned up on a Florisil column prior to PGC/ECD determination. After the hexane extraction, the water sample is filtered and the isolated paper fibers are refluxed in alcoholic
KOH to remove any PCBs. Without the KOH saponification,
about 10% of the PCBs remained on the fibers after the hexane
extraction.

B.   Continuous Liquid-Liquid Extraction (CLE)

Continuous liquid-liquid extraction (CLE) is a
labor-saving technique to replace the common separatory funnel. In addition CLE is less likely to cause emulsion problems with very dirty matrices. A wide variety of apparatus
have been described to effect CLE. Most involve refluxing
solvent from a flask, which then drips through a water sample
and returns to the flask.

Godefroot et al. (1982a,b) demonstrated the applicability of a combined steam distillation/solvent extractor
for PCBs. The technique, a micro version of the Nickerson
and Likens (1966) apparatus, simultaneously steam distills
and gas-phase extracts PCBs and similar organics from 50 mL
water into 1-mL pentane. The recovery for Aroclor 1260 averaged 95%.

C.   Sorbent Column Extraction

With this technique, a water sample is passed
through a sorbent column where the PCBs and other organics
are "extracted" onto the sorbent. The adsorbed organics are
then eluted from the column with an organic solvent. The
distinct advantage of sorbent column extraction is the ability to extract large water volumes to enhance the method detection limit. The sorbent column extraction of large water
volumes (over two liters) has been employed in the field, as
discussed under "Sampling" (Chapter 4).

Coburn et al. (1977) reported an XAD-2 column technique for extraction of 2-L samples with subsequent elution
with ethyl ether. At the 250-ppt level, 78-86% recoveries
were observed for a mixture of Aroclors. A polyurethane foam
column technique gave 91-98% recovery at the 20-ppb level
from 1-L water samples (Gesser et al., 1971). The PCBs were
eluted with acetone and then hexane. Similar results have
been shown using XAD-2 or XAD-4 for sea water (Osterroht,
1974) and tap water (Musty and Nickless, 1974a). Picer and
Picer (1980) compared XAD-2, XAD-4, and Tenax for extraction
of PCBs from sea and tap water. The Tenax yielded many more
peaks at larger intensity, which more closely resembled an
Aroclor mixture than the other resins. However, severe PGC/
ECD interferences were noted with all of the sorbents. Leoni
et al. (1976b) achieved 100% recovery of PCBs at 1.6 ppb in
10-L samples of surface water. The PCBs were collected on a
column containing Tenax and Celite and then eluted with three
10-mL portions of ethyl ether.

A C-18 reversed phase partitioning cartridge
(Sep-Pak, Waters Associates) was used by Gallis et al. (1983)
to adsorb PCBs from water samples. The cartridges were pre-
conditioned with methanol.

D.   Purge and Trap

A purge and trap technique was demonstrated to
yield greater than 90% recoveries for Aroclor 1221, 1248, and
1254 (Colenutt and Thorburn, 1980). Water samples (2.0 L)
were purged at room temperature for 4 hr at 1 L/min. The
PCBs and other compounds were trapped on 5-25 mg activated
carbon. The carbon trap was subsequently desorbed with 50-
1,000 μL of pentane, carbon disulfide, carbon tetrachloride,
or diethyl ether. This extract could then be analyzed by
PGC/ECD.

E. Comparison of Extraction Techniques

Solvent extraction gave better results than XAD-4, a "partition system" (Carbowax 4000 monostearate and n-undecane coated on Chromosorb W) or polyurethane foam (Musty and Nickless, 1976). Recovery of PCBs at the 10-20 ppb level from water with the partition system ranged from 97% to 48%, decreasing with increasing chlorine content of the PCBs. The concentration of PCBs, measured as Aroclor 1260, in a water sample with the solvent extraction (diethyl ether/hexane, 15:85) technique was over twice that found with any of the three sorbent column techniques.

Bellar and Lichtenberg (1975) found separatory funnel liquid-liquid extraction to be the most efficient extraction technique for recovery of PCBs from natural waters. The use of polyurethane foam plugs--both in a column-elution mode and where the plug is soaked in the water sample--gave good recoveries with distilled water. With natural waters, however, the particulate matter stopped flow through the column. With natural waters, the recoveries from the soaking technique had poor precision. In addition, the PUF contributed significant background interferences to the GC/ECD analysis. A vortex extractor gave lower and less reproducible results, although it was not thoroughly evaluated.

III. SEWAGE AND SLUDGE

These ill-defined matrices range from "dirty water" to high-organic solids. Thus, many different extraction techniques have been employed. For raw municipal sewage with relatively low organic content, the sample can be extracted using a water technique, such as solvent extraction in a separatory funnel. More viscous samples can also be treated this way by simply diluting the matrix to the desired consistency--at a sacrifice of the method detection limit.

The effects of the high levels of organics on extraction efficiency were illustrated with a sorbent-column technique. Only 23 or 60% of the PCBs spiked into raw sewage were extracted with XAD-2 or XAD-4, respectively (Lawrence and Tosine, 1976). Apparently, the sorbent overloaded with this high organic-content matrix. Surprisingly, a column of polyvinyl chloride chips gave the best (73%) adsorption of PCBs and was recommended by the authors.

Four extraction techniques were compared by Rodriguez et al. (1980) in the development of a method for analysis of municipal sewage sludge for PCBs and chlorinated pesticides. The extraction techniques evaluated were:

(1)   Centrifuge.   Acetone/dichloromethane/hexane
       (2:15:83) mixture and then centrifuged to sep-
       arate the emulsified mixture.   The upper sol-
       vent layer is removed and the process repeated
       twice more.

(2)   Column Elution.   The sludge (20 g) is mixed
       with 80 g anhydrous sodium sulfate and then
       packed into a liquid chromatographic column.
       The PCBs are then eluted with 150 mL of
       acetone/hexane (20:80).

(3)   Soxhlet Extraction.   The sludge (20 g) is
       mixed with 180 g anhydrous sodium sulfate and
       then Soxhlet-extracted with dichloromethane/
       hexane (15:85) for about 40 cycles.

(4)   Continuous Liquid-Liquid Extraction.   The
       sludge (20 g), diluted with 10 mL water during
       transfer, was extracted overnight with dichlo-
       romethane in a modified Soxhlet extractor.

The latter technique gave poor (< 50%) recovery, presumably
because of poor solvent-sample contact.   The first three
techniques gave high (> 80%) recoveries.   A variety of reasons, including potential interferences, cost, and ease of
use, led the authors to recommend the centrifuge technique,
which gave 98% recovery of Aroclor 1260 from primary sludge
and 80% recovery from digested sludge.

IV.   SEDIMENT AND SOIL

       Sediment and soil differ from sewage sludge in
their generally lower organic content.   As with sewage
sludge, the critical component of an extraction technique for
either sediment or soil is the contact between the solvent
and the matrix.   This has generally been accomplished by
physical mixing (e.g., manual shaking) and use of a "wetting"
solvent mixture (e.g., hexane and acetone).   With soil samples, especially, thorough mixing and pulverizing of chunks
is an important preextraction step.

A.   Solvent Extraction

       The classic work on extraction of chlorinated in-
secticides (PCBs were "co-extractives" which could be removed
in the chromatographic cleanup) from sediment is by Goerlitz
and Law (1974).   The sediment (50 g) is centrifuged to remove
excess water, wetted with 40 mL acetone, extracted with 80 mL
hexane, re-wetted with 20 mL acetone, and extracted again

with hexane. Between each solvent addition, the sample is shaken 20 min on a wrist-action shaker. The extraction should be repeated until at least 75% of the added solvent is recovered. PCB recoveries were 100% after 3 extractions.

This basic approach has been utilized in many other studies, with modifications in the solvent ratio, volume, agitation time, etc. (Eder, 1976a; Jensen et al., 1977; Chau et al., 1979). Other "wetting" solvents have also been used, such as acetonitrile (ANSI, 1974) or water/acetonitrile (ASTM, 1981b).

Wetting the soil prior to solvent extraction appears to increase the extraction efficiency. A Soxhlet extraction of dry soil with hexane for 10 hr gave 30% recovery of radiolabeled Chlophen A-30 (Seidl and Ballschmiter, 1976a), while 85% recovery was measured using the same techniques from wet soil. The soil was wetted with 1 g water per 15 g soil.

B. Collaborative Studies

Lee and Chau (1981a) conducted an interlaboratory validation for PCBs in wet sediments. Both native and spiked (about 1 ppm) samples were analyzed. The participants were permitted to use analytical methods of their choice for the analysis of the materials. Of the methods used in the extraction of PCBs from sediment, which included ultrasonic, Soxhlet, blender and shaker methods, the ultrasonic was the most popular. In this study, Soxhlet extraction did not seem to provide higher recoveries of PCBs in comparison with other extraction techniques. Most participants used a mixture of polar and nonpolar solvents, such as 1:1 acetone and hexane, as the extracting solvent, while others used a single polar solvent such as acetonitrile or acetone. No obvious relationship was observed between the recoveries and the extraction procedure. This suggested to the authors that all the extraction methods used in this study were equally efficient for the recovery of PCBs in spiked sediment samples. A second collaborative study (Lee and Chau, 1981b) of PCBs in naturally contaminated dry sediments exhibited too much variability for the authors to make inferences on the differences in analytical techniques. The study is described in more detail in Chapter 10.

C. Thermal Desorption

Thermal desorption is commonly used for volatile compounds, such as chloroform, but only rarely employed for semivolatiles such as PCBs. The higher desorption temperatures and possibly lower desorption efficiencies probably contribute to this lack of popularity. On the other hand, thermal desorption can yield fewer interferences and has the distinct advantage of introducing the entire sample to the instrument. This provides potentially much better method detection limits than with solvent extraction where only 1/1000 of the sample is typically injected onto the gas chromatograph.

Lovett et al. (1983) reported the use of both a surface-sniffing and thermal desorption techniques for rapid analysis of PCBs at spill sites. Samples were volatilized and then directly introduced into a mobile atmospheric pressure chemical ionization mass spectrometer (see Chapter 7). The surface sniffing technique had a detection limit of 500 µg/g, while thermal desorption could detect 10 µg/g. The thermal desorption technique used mini-core soil samples and had a total analysis time of 3 min. No details or validation was reported.

Thermal desorption has also been used to introduce PCBs to a conventional PGC/EIMS (McMurtrey et al., 1983). Samples were desorbed under a helium stream for 10 sec at 1000°C. The desorbed materials were trapped at the head of the cool GC column. PCBs were detectable at the 10 ppm level, although the MDL was not determined, nor was the quantitative reliability of the method presented. The authors mistakenly termed the PCB desorption technique "pyrolysis." Thermal desorption of PCBs from hazardous waste samples into a triple quadrupole MS/MS system has also been described (Hunt et al., 1985).

The above results indicate that thermal desorption may well be a viable technique for rapid screening analyses. Until validation data are presented, the technique cannot be recommended for quantitative analysis.

D. Comparison of Sediment and Soil Extraction
       Techniques

Three techniques were compared for the extraction of PCBs from bottom materials (Bellar et al., 1980); they were:

(1) Soxhlet extraction: The Soxhlet extraction was conducted overnight with acetone/hexane (10:90) and the extract concentrated with a Kuderna-Danish evaporator, cleaned up on Florisil, and then treated with mercury to remove sulfur.

(2) <u>Sonication</u>: The sonication technique involved a single 5-min sonication at a power of 150 watts with 150 mL acetone over a 60-90 g sample. The acetone was then decanted, diluted with water, and the organics extracted with hexane/dichloromethane (85:15). The extract was concentrated and cleaned up as with the Soxhlet extraction.

(3) <u>Steam distillation</u>: The steam distillation technique employed the Nielson-Kryger apparatus for simultaneous distillation and extraction with hexane.

Prior to extraction with all three techniques, samples were air-dried, debris (stones, leaves, twigs, etc.) was removed, the sample was mixed, ground in a mortar and pestle and then subsampled. All three extractions gave quantitative recoveries of Aroclor 1254 spiked onto lake bottom samples; however, the Soxhlet extraction gave 25-40% higher results than the other two techniqeus for environmentally contaminated samples. These results emphasize the importance of validating methods with real samples, where the PCBs have been thoroughly incorporated into the matrix.

Bellar and Lichtenberg (1975) found that Soxhlet extraction of air-dried, 10% water-added bottom materials (muck and sandy muck) with a mixture of acetone/hexane (10:90) was the most efficient method for extracting PCBs. The less-efficient techniques included shaking with acetone and then hexane, shaking with an isopropanol/hexane mixture, blending with an acetonitrile/acetone mixture, preparation of a column by mixing with sodium sulfate and then eluting with either hexane or hexane-acetone, and high frequency dispersion with acetone. All of the techniques tested were taken from the literature.

Water/methanol/hexane (10:40:50) gave the best recovery of Aroclor 1242 from dry sediment (Spittler, 1983, 1984) in a single extraction of the sediment for screening purposes. The other solvent systems, which gave poorer recoveries were hexane, water/hexane (50:50), water/ethyl ether/hexane (33:33:33), water/ethyl ether (50:50), water/methanol/ethyl ether (33:33:33), and methanol/hexane (50:50).

V. <u>AIR</u>

PCBs should be readily extracted from the sorbent materials used in air sampling. As discussed in Chapter 4, PCBs are generally "extracted" from the air sample onto a

sorbent material during the sampling. This sorbent is then
returned to the laboratory for analysis, the first step of
which is a solvent extraction. Chapter 4 presents a detailed
discussion of the various sorbents used in air sampling.
These include polyurethane foam (PUF), Florisil, XAD-2 and
other macroreticular resins.

PCBs are extracted from these sorbent matrices by
repeated extraction with a nonpolar solvent such as hexane,
benzene, or methylene chloride. Often a continuous extractor, such as the Soxhlet extractor, is used to effect the repeated extractions. An important consideration of the extraction technique is contact between the solvent and all of
the sorbent. Column elution or other techniques which may
develop channeling of the solvent and thus do not ensure complete contact must be scrutinized carefully to assure quantitative extraction of the PCBs.

A.   Polyurethane Foam

PCBs are extractable from PUF plugs using nonpolar
or semi-polar solvents. Petroleum ether (a mixture of pen-
tanes and hexanes, now generally replaced with pesticide residue grade n-hexane) has been used to Soxhlet-extract PUF
plugs (Bidleman and Olney, 1974; Bidleman, 1981; Bidleman et
al., 1981a; Bidleman and Leonard, 1982). MacLeod (1979) used
ethyl ether/hexane (5:95) in a Soxhlet. Erickson et al.
(1980a) used toluene, which had been shown to be the most efficient for extraction of polychlorinated naphthalenes
(Erickson et al., 1978). Mechanical squeezing was used instead of Soxhlet extraction to improve the efficiency of extraction from the middle of the plug.

One study (Adams and Caro, 1980) has compared the
mechanical extraction techniques for PUF, although PCBs were
not tested, similar organochlorine pesticides make the data
relevant to this discussion. Soxhlet extraction (5 cycles)
squeezing (5 times with a metal plunger) and column elution,
all using acetone/hexane (50:50) were compared. The three
techniques gave 96 to 101% recoveries with 11 to 18% RSD.
Thus, for a series of 11 organochlorine pesticides, these
three mechanical extraction techniques appear to be equivalent.

B.   Florisil

Florisil (trademark, Floridin Company) is a synthetic magnesium silicate. Most of the authors using Florisil for air sampling have extracted the PCBs with hexane,
although one early report (Giam et al., 1975) used petroleum
ether followed by ethyl ether to elute PCBs from a column

prepared with the air sampling Florisil. Column elution has been reported when the amount of Florisil is small (Giam et al., 1975; Harris et al., 1981; Williams et al., 1980). The NIOSH method (1977a,b,c) directs the analyst to simply mix the hexane and Florisil for at least 10 min and then inject an aliquot of the supernatant hexane on the PGC/ECD. Haile and Baladi (1977) used a Soxhlet-extraction with hexane to desorb PCBs from a 7.5 g Florisil stack sampling cartridge.

C. XAD-2

The extraction of XAD-2 is generally done with a nonpolar solvent such as hexane, benzene (Stanley et al., 1982) or petroleum ether (Eisenreich et al., 1981a) in a Soxhlet extractor. The amount of XAD-2 used (typically 75 g of low-density polymeric resin) makes sample handling more difficult than with the small amounts of Florisil, so the Soxhlet technique has been more popular.

D. Dry Deposition Samples

Sample collectors (aluminum pans or glycerin-coated pans) are rinsed with solvent to remove the particulate and PCBs. Bidleman et al. (1981a) rinsed their pans with distilled water and acetone or dichloromethane and then scraped the surface repeatedly with a piece of Teflon® to ensure removal of adhered material. The combined rinses were then extracted with dichloromethane. Eisenreich et al. (1981a,b) washed the PCBs from dry deposition pans with PCB-free water only, which was subsequently extracted by steam distillation into toluene. It is surprising that only a water wash was employed, given the poor solubility of PCBs in water (see Chapter 2).

VI. BLOOD

The extraction of blood samples generally entails a simple liquid-liquid partition of whole blood, plasma, or serum with solvent. The techniques differ from those for other aqueous liquids in how the cells and proteins are handled to assure complete extraction and avoid emulsions. In addition, blood samples are generally small (e.g., 10 mL) relative to water and many other samples, so the mechanical techniques of agitation, etc., are different.

Whole blood is essentially the same matrix as obtained from the body, except for the possible addition of an anticoagulant, such as heparin, to retard clot formation. Plasma is the liquid portion of the blood obtained after

physical removal of the cells from whole blood by centrifugation. Serum is the fluid remaining after the cells and
platelets are allowed to coagulate. PCB analyses have been
conducted on all three "blood" matrices. The results may not
be comparable, since an unknown portion of the PCBs in whole
blood can be removed with the cells or clot.

        Blood extraction procedures have been issued by two
organizations: the U.S. Environmental Protection Agency and
the U.S. Centers for Disease Control. Most of the references
in the primary literature involve one or the other of these
procedures. Thus, this section has been divided into subsections describing these two procedures and their validation.

    A. Environmental Protection Agency

        The EPA manual for pesticide residue analysis (Sec-
tion 5,A,(3),(a), Watts, 1980) describes a hexane extraction
for serum:

        "A 2-mL aliquot of serum is extracted with 6
    milliliters of hexane in a round-bottom tube. The
    extraction is conducted for 2 hours on a slow-speed
    rotating mixer. The formation of emulsion is un-
    likely, but if it should occur, centrifugation may
    be used to effect separation of the layers. A 5-mL
    aliquot of the hexane layer is quantitatively
    transferred to an evaporative concentrator tube to
    which is affixed a modified micro-Snyder column.
    The extract is concentrated in a water or steam
    bath, and the final volume is adjusted to corre-
    spond to the expected concentration of the pesti-
    cide residue. A suitable aliquot is analyzed by
    electron capture gas chromatography."

The method was developed for organochlorine pesticides (Dale
et al., 1966) and PCBs are not listed as potential analytes
in the method (Watts, 1980). Nevertheless, the technique has
been adapted for the determination of PCBs (Curley et al.,
1971) and has been routinely used for PCB analysis (Erickson
et al., 1983e). In the original form (Dale et al., 1966),
the extraction entails a vigorous mixing for 3 min on a mini-
mixer, yielding an emulsion which is then broken by centrifugation. The EPA modification (Watts, 1980) recommends a
gentle mixing for 2 hr on a rack which gently rotates the
tubes end-for-end. This technique, while much slower, avoids
emulsions in most cases and thus saves an additional step.

        The EPA extraction involves only a single parti-
tion. In addition, although 6 mL hexane are added, only 5 mL
are recovered, since the hexane-serum interface is indistinct

due to a layer of protein. The lack of full solvent recovery is compensated in the calculations by multiplying the PGC/ECD results by 6/5.

B. Centers for Disease Control

Researchers at the Centers for Disease Control (CDC) have developed methods for determination of PCBs in serum which utilize a triple extraction with ethyl ether/hexane (50:50) (Needham et al., 1981; Burse et al., 1983a). Specifically, 4 mL serum and 2 mL methanol are mixed to denature the protein. The specimen is then extracted with 3 x 5 mL ethyl ether/hexane (50:50). Each extraction is conducted for 15 min on a rotary mixer at 50 rpm. The organic and serum layers are separated by centrifugation at 1800 rpm. The combined extracts are concentrated to 0.5 mL, cleaned on silica gel, and determined by PGC/ECD. No recovery data were presented; however, the precision of the entire method was ± 33% RSD at 2 ppb Aroclor 1254 and ± 12% RSD at 46 ppb. Using a similar extraction, McKinney et al. (1984) quantitatively (90-100%) recovered Aroclor 1254 except near the detection limit (10 ppb), where the recoveries were 77%. The precision was less than ±10% RSD.

An earlier publication (Needham et al., 1980) employed a similar extraction technique, except the extraction solvent was hexane alone. A recovery of 94 ± 5% for Aroclor 1260 spiked into serum at 41 ppb was measured for the entire method. Yet another version employed the ethyl ether/hexane extractions, but added a saponification step (Baker et al., 1980; Stratton and Geiszler, 1977). The concentrated organic extract was saponified by addition of 2 mL of a 2% KOH in methanol solution. The mixture was refluxed and concentrated to about 0.3 mL, taken up in 2 mL water/methanol (50:50), and then extracted three times with 2 mL hexane. The combined hexane extracts were then submitted to silica gel chromatography. Recoveries of 99 ± 1% and 108 ± 7% were reported by two laboratories (Stratton and Geiszler, 1977). Based on these limited results, the choice of hexane or ethyl ether/hexane does not appear to have a marked effect on the extraction.

Hexane was the favored extraction solvent in a collaborative study of PCBs in blood serum (Burse et al., 1983b). Of the 25 participants, 12 used hexane; 8 used ethyl ether/hexane; 2 extracted with acetonitrile and then partitioned into hexane or petroleum ether (see section on extraction of adipose tissue, above); 1 used a mixture of isopropanol/petroleum ether, and 1 adsorbed the blood on a Florisil column. Nine of the participants denatured the protein with methanol, while 15 did not. The scatter of the data did not

permit comparison of the efficiency of the extraction techniques. This study is discussed further in Chapter 10.

C. Comparison of Blood Extraction Techniques

The extraction of whole blood with hexane-saturated
acetonitrile was found to be quantitative (97%), while extraction with hexane alone achieved about 40% recovery
(Welborn et al., 1974). In addition, the hexane extraction
was selective, with higher recoveries for early-eluting PCB
peaks on the PGC/ECD. The hexane extraction involved vigor
ous shaking with three aliquots. The combined extracts were
dried with sodium sulfate, concentrated, cleaned on alumina,
and determined by PGC/ECD. The more efficient technique en-
tailed vigorous shaking three times with hexane-saturated
acetonitrile. The combined extracts were dried with sodium
sulfate, diluted with water, and extracted with three portions of hexane. The combined hexane extracts were concentrated, cleaned on alumina and determined by PGC/ECD. The
publication does not explain why both techniques were conducted on a macro scale. The solvent volumes were 50 mL/
extraction--the volume often used for extraction of 1-L water
samples.

VII. ANIMAL AND PLANT TISSUES

This broad sample matrix category spans a continuum
of polarity and extractability. At the one extreme, adipose
tissue can be almost entirely extracted into the organic solvent, leaving only a small residue of non-extractable matrix.
In this case, the matrix has simply been dissolved in the
solvent and the PCBs must still be extracted from the lipids.
At the other extreme, many plant tissues (food) can be easily
extracted with organic solvents, yielding a relatively clean
extract.

A. Adipose Tissue

Adipose tissue, from either humans or animals, consists of both lipids ("fat") and connective tissue. Spearman
(1982) has published a detailed review of the properties and
biochemistry of adipose tissue. Most extraction techniques
first separate the PCBs along with the lipids and any other
soluble organics from the connective tissue. The PCBs and
other compounds of similar polarity are then separated from
the lipids.

Most procedures also contain provisions for determining "percent fat" by evaporating the solvent from an aliquot of the original extract and then weighing the residue.

Knowledge of the fraction of the sample which is extractable is important in comparing the PCB content of different samples.

       1. Acetonitrile back-partition: A classic adipose and food extraction procedure developed by Mills et al. (1963) involves first extraction of the lipids from the connective tissue with petroleum ether and then extraction of the PCBs and pesticides from the petroleum ether into acetonitrile. Like many other techniques, it was originally developed for organochlorine pesticides and subsequently adapted for PCBs. This Mills-Onley-Gaither ("MOG") procedure has formed the basis of many techniques subsequently reported. For example, the EPA method (Watts, 1980) for pesticides in adipose involves:

> "A 5 g. sample is dry macerated with sand and Na_2SO_4 and the fat is isolated by repetitive extractions with petroleum ether. Pesticide residues are extracted from the fat with acetonitrile and then partitioned back into petroleum ether by aqueous dilution of the acetonitrile extract. Petroleum ether extract is concentrated to 5 mL by Kuderna-Danish evaporation and transferred to a Florisil column for successive elutions with 6% and 15% ethyl ether/ petroleum ether. The respective eluates are both concentrated to suitable volumes in Kuderna-Danish evaporators and the final extracts are examined by electron capture gas-liquid chromatography."

The PCBs and pesticides are separated in the Florisil step. PCBs are resolved from some co-eluting pesticides by silicic acid chromatography (see Chapter 6). Many users of this method now substitute pesticide residue grade n-hexane for the petroleum ether stipulated in the above procedure.

       The acetonitrile-hexane (or petroleum ether) partitioning step is reported to be time-consuming (Smrek and Needham, 1982). PCBs may also be lost during this step, since the partition ratio between the two solvents is probably relatively low.

       2. Acid digestion: An alternative approach was presented by Murphy (1972) in which the biological substances were removed from the hexane extract of adipose tissue by shaking the extract with concentrated sulfuric acid. The acid presumably degraded the lipids and other molecules, while leaving the relatively stable PCBs and chlorinated pesticides intact.

3. Column chromatography: Several groups have investigated the use of a column chromatographic step to "extract" PCBs from the lipids. Ernst et al. (1974) ground
frozen tissue samples with sand and sodium sulfate to form a
powder which was poured into a glass column. The PCBs were
then eluted from the column with acetone/n-hexane (33:67)
while the entire system was kept cold. PCB recoveries for
the entire procedure, including an alumina cleanup, were 96-
98%. A similar elution of a mixture of animal tissue and
sodium sulfate with hexane was judged better than other techniques (Bowes and Lewis, 1974). Specifically, lower recoveries were obtained for elution of the column with a
methanol/chloroform mixture (33:67), digestion with a hot
perchloric/glacial acetic acid mixture (40:60), and extraction with acetone followed by refluxing with hot isopropanol.

Smrek and Needham (1982) used a column of 10%
silver nitrate on silica gel to retain the lipids, DDT, and
DDT metabolites, while eluting the PCBs with hexane. Recoveries were greater than 90% with standard deviations of less
than 3%. Prior to the column chromatography, adipose samples
were ground with sodium sulfate to macerate the tissue and
adsorb water. The samples were then extracted with petroleum
ether three times. Porter and Burke (1973) mixed 8 g fat
with 25 g unactivated Florisil, placed the mixture in a column, and eluted with 150 mL water/acetonitrile (10:90). The
eluate was diluted with water and the PCBs partitioned into
petroleum ether, which was further cleaned up with a Florisil
column and determined by PGC/ECD. Eighty-five percent of
Aroclor 1254 was recovered from corn oil spiked at 100 ppb.
Similarly, Swift and Settle (1976) isolated PCBs by distrib-
uting the fat sample on the top of a column of unactivated
Florisil and eluting with water/acetonitrile (10:90).

4. Distillation: Sweep codistillation from animal
fat gave extracts which had PGC/ECD detection limits of 10 µg
Aroclor/g fat (Neidert and Saschenbrecker, 1984). With si-
lanized distillation tubes to prevent adsorptive losses, 98-
99% recoveries of Aroclors 1248-1268 were observed.

5. Low temperature precipitation: Low temperature
precipitation has also been used to remove lipids (McLeod and
Wales, 1972). Samples were extracted by refluxing in
acetone/ benzene (95:5) for 1 hr. The extract was then
cooled in a dry ice bath for 30 min with a nitrogen stream
bubbling through the solution. This caused lipids, waxes,
water, and other compounds to precipitate. The supernatant
was then separated from the precipitate by vacuum filtration
on cellulose. Although not validated for use with PCBs in
the original publication, the technique has been applied to
PCB analysis of tissue and milk samples (Mes and Campbell,
1976; Mes et al., 1977; Mes and Davies, 1978, 1979).

6. <u>Comparison of lipid removal techniques</u>:   Several mechanical techniques and extraction solvents were compared in a study by Mes and Campbell (1976). A Silverson mixer was found to be slightly more effective at lipid extraction and easier to use than a Waring Blender or a Virtis Model 23. They also evaluated nine solvents and found a acetone/benzene (95:5) mixture to give the highest PCB concentrations in unspiked human adipose samples. The other solvents were hexane, acetone/hexane (33:67), methanol/ dichloromethane (67:33 and 50:50), dichloromethane, benzene, water-saturated butanol, and diethyl ether/petroleum ether (50:50).

B. <u>Fish</u>

Fish samples can often be extracted by techniques similar to those used for adipose tissue, since fish can contain several percent lipids. Fish are of interest because of their human consumption, indication of PCB movement through aquatic and marine trophic levels, and the ability to study PCB transport by comparison of migratory and nonmigratory species.

1.   <u>Solvent extraction</u>:   Soxhlet extraction has been used extensively for extraction of fish samples (Zitko, 1971a; Zitko et al., 1974b; Frank et al., 1978; Kuehl et al., 1980a) and shellfish (Kilikidis et al., 1981). Average recoveries of 85-90% for PCBs (Frank et al., 1978), including cleanup and all other analytical steps, indicate that the extraction is generally adequate. Nevertheless, the lack of mixing cannot assure complete contact of the solvent with the fish tissue.

Extraction with hot solvents in a Soxhlet extractor was demonstrated to be more efficient for fish extraction than use of cold solvents in a glass column extraction (Hattula, 1974a). The study involved comparison of four solvent systems with three different fish (pike, perch and bream). The solvent systems were diethyl ether, diethyl ether/n-pentane (50:50), acetone/diethyl ether/n-hexane/petroleum ether (31:6:14:50), and methanol/chloroform (50:50). In the column extraction technique, 50 mL of the solvent was added to a glass column containing 5 g of loosely packed, ground fish tissue. After 2 hr of unagitated extraction, the solvent was drawn off and the tissue rinsed. Thus, only a single partition was effected. The Soxhlet extractions were carried out for 6 hr. The amount of native PCBs extracted from the fish were consistently higher with the Soxhlet extractor. The efficiencies of the different solvents were comparable. The author noted that the ±10 to ±20% RSD in the amounts extracted was high and cautioned that the extraction step is critical to the overall analytical precision.

Blending of the solvent and fish assures good contact. This technique is employed in the AOAC (1980a) procedure for extraction of fish (Method 29.012(e)). In this procedure, 25-50 g of fish are ground with Na_2SO_4 in a high speed blender to disintegrate the sample and bind any water. The sample is then extracted three times with petroleum ether. The supernatant solvent is filtered, combined, dried with Na_2SO_4, and concentrated in a K-D evaporator. A portion of the sample is removed for percent fat determination. The AOAC method is widely used, sometimes with minor modifications, such as substitution of n-hexane for petroleum ether. The collaborative validation was published by Sawyer (1973).

2. Column chromatography: The use of extraction columns has been reported for extraction of PCBs from fish (Stalling, 1971; Erney, 1974b; Hattula, 1974a). Fish samples are ground with sodium sulfate and sand to yield a dry powder and loosely packed into a column. The PCBs are then eluted with solvent. A minor variation reported by Stalling (1971) used dry ice during the grinding step to keep the tissue solid and therefore more amenable to pulverization. Although quantitative recoveries (97 ± 3%) have been reported by Stalling (1971), the lack of agitation and possible channeling of the column may lead to poor or irreproducible recoveries.

3. Distillation: A modification of the Nielsen-Kryger steam distillation apparatus was used for extraction of PCBs and other chemicals from fish, water and sediment (Veith and Kiwus, 1977; Dougherty et al., 1980). The apparatus (Figure 5-1) permits simultaneous steam distillation and solvent extraction. The final extract is amenable to analysis without further cleanup. A recovery of 82% from 10 g Ohio River catfish diluted with 2.5 L of water was reported for a 7-hr extraction. Kuehl et al. (1980b) reported success with a micro version of the extractor for analysis of 0.5 g of tissue. In contrast to the work by Veith and Kiwus, Kuehl et al. added 10% H_2SO_4 to the distillation flask, presumably to "digest" the matrix.

4. Saponification with base: Saponification has also been used to prepare samples of fish, shellfish, and other marine organisms (Castelli et al., 1983). The samples were homogenized with water, refluxed with ethanolic KOH and extracted twice with n-hexane. The hexane was washed with water, dried and concentrated samples were cleaned on Florisil and analyzed by HRGC/EIMS-SIM. The precision of the entire method was measured with Aroclor-spiked biological samples and found to be between 1.6-19%, depending on the homolog. The injection precision was similar, indicating that the instrumental determination contributed most of the measurement error.

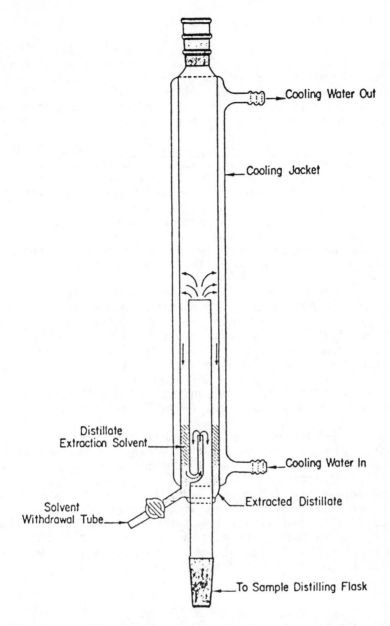

Figure 5-1. Exhaustive Steam-Distillation and Solvent-
Extraction Apparatus

Reprinted, with permission, from Veith and Kiwas (1977);
copyright 1977 by Springer-Verlag.

C. Milk

Milk is a fatty sample, which can retain PCBs and other pollutants. Cow's milk is of interest as a possible source of human consumption. Similarly, human milk is of concern with respect to consumption by infants. In addition, milk can be studied as a non-invasive sample collection procedure to measure body burden (Erickson et al., 1980b).

1. Acetonitrile back-partition: The AOAC (1980a) method for extraction of milk samples (Method 29.012(c)) uses 100 mL of milk. Ethanol (100 mL) and 1 g of sodium oxalate are added. The mixture is extracted three times with ethyl ether/petroleum ether (50:50), separating the layers by centrifugation. The combined organic layers are then washed with water three times, dried with sodium sulfate, and concentrated by evaporation. The PCBs and related compounds are separated from the fat by acetonitrile partitioning.

McKinney et al. (1984) validated a slight modification of the AOAC method, substituting hexane for petroleum ether. Five other solvent systems (all mixtures of a polar, water-miscible and nonpolar solvent) were investigated in lieu of the hexane-ether-ethanol combination. The latter yielded the highest lipid extraction and best reproducibility. At 20 and 40 ppb, PCB recoveries of about 102% with RSDs of ± 14 to ± 24% were reported. The method was applied to both human milk and infant formula samples.

EPA has utilized two methods for PCBs in human milk (Watts, 1980). The macro method employs an extraction with acetone, followed by hexane. The micro method uses an acetonitrile extraction, followed by a hexane partition. In the macro method, up to 25 g of milk are extracted three times with acetone and then twice with hexane. The combined extracts are washed with water twice to remove water-soluble materials, including the acetone. The extract is then dried and concentrated. The extract is then partitioned with acetonitrile as described for adipose tissue, above, and analyzed by PGC/ECD.

2. Saponification with base: A milk extraction technique similar to the AOAC method was published by Yakushiji et al. (1978). However, instead of the acetonitrile partition, they employed a reflux in ethanolic KOH to saponify the lipids. The resulting digestate was diluted with water and extracted with hexane. Saponification of milk samples has been reported by Tuinstra et al. (1980, 1981) and Tuinstra and Traag (1979a, 1979b).

3. <u>Acid digestion</u>: A single extraction of acidified milk with petroleum ether gave 90-95% recovery for PCBs
(Veierov and Aharonson, 1980). The milk was acidified by
slowly adding conc. H_2SO_4. The sample was then mixed until
the curds redissolved before the extraction. The extract was
then cleaned up by addition of sulfuric acid, three times the
quantity needed for decoloration. The organic layer was then
concentrated and analyzed by PGC/ECD.

4. <u>Column chromatography</u>: Savage et al. (1973a,b)
published procedures similar to those in Watts (1980) except
a Florisil column cleanup was used instead of the acetonitrile partition. In the micro method, 500 mg of milk are extracted three times with acetonitrile. The extraction is performed in a tissue grinder to effect mixing and the resulting
emulsion is broken by centrifugation. The combined extracts
are diluted with water and extracted three times with hexane.
The PCB-containing hexane extracts are concentrated, cleaned
on a Florisil column, fractionated with a silicic acid column
and analyzed by PGC/ECD.

A combination extraction/cleanup technique for milk
and dairy products used silica gel (Steinwandter, 1982a).
Milk was slurried with silica gel and added to a chromatography column on top of 10% water-deactivated silica gel. The
column was then eluted with dichloromethane/petroleum ether
(20:80), which extracted the PCBs from the milk and cleaned
up the eluate on the lower portion of the column. Samples
were then analyzed by HRGC/ECD or HRGC/EIMS.

5. <u>Extraction of freeze-dried samples</u>: Freeze-
dried milk samples have been Soxhlet-extracted with hexane
(Bush et al., 1983). Recoveries from the entire method,
which included a Florisil column cleanup and HRGC/ECD determination, were generally 60 to 80% for most congeners. However, recoveries in the 26 to 50% range were observed for
mono-, di-, and trichlorobiphenyls, presumably because of
volatilization losses in the freeze-drying step. The precision of the method was ± 5% or better for the major individual congeners. Bush et al. (1983) noted the poor recovery of
the lighter PCB congeners, but judged that the simplicity of
the technique made it worth using.

D. <u>Eggs</u>

Eggs from various species of birds have been extracted with hexane after grinding with sodium sulfate. The
lipids were removed by chromatography on alumina (Zitko,
1976).

A column elution technique (Wardall, 1977) combined
the extraction and lipid removal steps. Eggs were ground
with sodium sulfate and then mixed with Celite 545. This
mixture was added to a glass chromatography column on top of
a 5-g bed of alumina. The PCBs were then eluted with hexane.
The eluate was analyzed by GC/ECD without further cleanup.
Recoveries from 60-80% were observed for four PCB congeners.

E. Other Animal Organs

The above sections have described the extraction
techniques for fatty organs and samples which generally contain the highest PCB concentrations and are therefore of the
most interest. Other organs also contain PCBs (see Chapter
2) and are extracted by similar techniques. The lower lipid
content of these samples often allows the analyst to use less
stringent PCB/lipid extraction techniques.

Quail brains have been extracted using a column
technique after homogenization with Florisil and sodium sulfate. The eluent was dichloromethane/petroleum ether
(30:70). Whole bald eagle carcasses were homogenized and
20-g aliquots Soxhlet extracted to determine the PCB concentration in the entire bird (Bagley et al., 1970).

Tarradellas et al. (1982) describe an analytical
method for earthworms and their gut contents. The earthworms
were digested with a mixture of perchloric acid/glacial acetic acid (40:60) for 24 hr over a steam bath. The digestate
was then extracted three times with hexane. Sulfuric acid,
mercury, and Florisil cleanup steps prepared the samples for
HRGC/ECD analysis. The analysis of earthworms was promoted
as a sensitive indicator of the concentration of PCBs in
soil, since the earthworms exhibited five to eight times the
concentration of the soil. Furthermore, the earthworms appeared to "average" the PCBs as they migrated through the
soil, since the RSD of earthworm samples was much smaller
than the RSD of the PCB concentrations of soil samples taken
from different areas of a plot.

F. Plant Tissue

Plants, feed, grain, etc., must be ground and thoroughly mixed before extraction. This preparation step may be
combined with addition of sodium sulfate to bind water, as
with many other matrices. Corn silage has been extracted in
a blender with isopropanol/hexane (33:67), followed by a second extraction with benzene (Ernst et al., 1974). The extracts were filtered, combined, concentrated, cleaned by
Florisil chromatography, and analyzed by PGC/ECD.

1.   Acetonitrile back-partition: A   classic
procedure for organochlorine pesticides in nonfatty foods employs an acetonitrile extraction of the chopped sample, followed by a petroleum ether back extraction of the acetonitrile after dilution with water (Mills et al., 1963; FDA,
1977-Section 212).   After blending or chopping, the 100-g
sample is blended with 200-mL acetonitrile and 10 g Celite in
a blender.   The acetonitrile is separated from the solids by
filtration.   The filtrate is diluted with 600 mL water, 10 mL
saturated NaCl, and extracted with 100 mL petroleum ether.
The organic layer is washed with 2 x 100 mL water and dried
with sodium sulfate.   The extract is then cleaned with Florisil column chromatography and analyzed by gas chromatography.
The procedure has not been validated for PCBs, but quantitative recoveries of several organochlorine pesticides from
green vegetables, soups, fruits, and other foods (Mills et
al., 1963) indicate that it would be suitable for PCBs.

2.   Column chromatography/acid digestion: A column
extraction with a bed of sulfuric acid/silica gel (40:60,
v/v) yielded an extract which was sufficiently clean for silica gel cleanup and then PGC/ECD analysis, without the need
for acetonitrile partition, GPC, or other cleanup (Schwartz
and Lehmann, 1982).   The plant tissue was ground with sodium
sulfate and then added to a glass chromatography column on
top of the acid/silica gel mixture with a layer of sodium
sulfate in between.   The PCBs were eluted with hexane.   The
recoveries of Aroclor 1242 and 1254 were about 75 ± 6% at
10 ppb fortification level and about 90 ± 1% at 250 ppb fortification.   This extraction presumably combines matrix degradation by the sulfuric acid with chromatographic separation
in the column elution.

G.   Discussion of Tissue Extraction

Proper extraction of PCBs from animal and plant
tissue samples presents a challenge.   The matrix must be dis-
rupted, the PCBs must be removed, and finally the lipids and
other co-extractive material must be separated.   The tissue
can be macerated with a mechanical mixer, as long as the size
is appropriate, sufficient maceration is achieved, and no
contaminants are introduced from gaskets or other sources.
Sodium sulfate and/or sand are often added during this step
to adsorb any water and for "grit" to aid in the grinding.
The extraction solvent--often added prior to maceration--must
not only be a good solvent for PCBs but should also assist in
cell disruption.   Acetone and alcohols are good solvents for
cell lysis.   A mixed polar/nonpolar solvent such as acetone/
benzene, ether/hexane, or methanol/chloroform appears to be
the best extractant for PCBs.

The separation of the lipid materials has been achieved by many techniques, as discussed above. If PCBs are the sole analyte, a chemical destruction of the lipids may be the most straightforward. Sulfuric acid will destroy many biological (aliphatic) interferents, although losses of the lower-chlorinated PCBs have been reported (see Chapter 6). Saponification with base is also a useful technique for destroying triglycerides and other esters.

If additional analytes, such as the chlorinated pesticides, must be preserved, sulfuric acid digestion may not be advisable. The silver nitrate column of Smrek and Needham (1982) appears to be an elegant separation technique. The "classic" acetonitrile-hexane partition (Mills-Onley-Gaither) may be used, but recoveries from this step must be well-documented through validation and appropriate QC measures.

VIII. PAPER PRODUCTS

By virtue of their use in carbonless copy paper and other paper products and the extensive recycling of paper products, analysis for PCBs in paper products has been of considerable interest. A number of simple solvent extractions with hexane (Giacin and Gilbert, 1973; Serum et al., 1973; DeVoogt et al., 1984), petroleum ether (Shahied et al., 1973), and acetone (Kuratsune and Masuda, 1972) have been reported. Recoveries of 80-102% were reported by DeVoogt et al. (1984) from a variety of paper products ranging from toilet paper to paperboard.

An alcoholic KOH reflux was recommended as the technique for use with routine paper samples (Young et al., 1973) and ultimately adopted as an official method (AOAC, 1980b). While both the KOH saponification and a sulfuric acid digestion gave 96-97% recoveries from fortified paper samples, the latter technique was more tedious. In the KOH procedure, the samples (10 g) are cut up, mixed, and refluxed with 60 mL 2% KOH in ethanol or methanol for 30 min. The sample is diluted with water and repeatedly extracted with petroleum ether. The combined extracts are then washed with water, dried with sodium sulfate, concentrated in a Kuderna-Danish evaporator, cleaned on a Florisil column, and determined by PGC/ECD. Similar methods have been used by others (Stanovick et al., 1973; Easty, 1973; Becker and Schulte, 1976; Easty and Wabers, 1977).

IX. <u>OILS</u>

The determination of PCBs in oils has been of interest because of the high frequency of contamination of certain types of oils. PCBs have many similar chemical, physical, and use properties of mineral oil, silicone oil, and
other oils. Mixing PCBs with these oils and cross-contamination has led to broad-scale contamination of non-PCB fluids
with PCBs at low concentrations. For example, many askarel
transformers have been retrofilled with mineral oil or other
dielectric fluid to declassify the transformer from "PCB"
status. The resulting transformers generally have trace (50-
500 ppm) quantities of residual PCBs and are classified as
"PCB-contaminated." In addition, many electrical components
were contaminated from residual PCBs at the manufacturing
site. As discussed in Chapter 2, the PCB contamination of
these oils determines their classification, and thus use and
disposal rules, in the U.S.

PCBs have also contaminated other oils which enter
the animal or human food sources. A notable, classic example
is the Yusho incident (see Chapter 2 for a more detailed discussion), in which cooking oil which had been contaminated
with PCBs, was distributed in Japan. Many people were contaminated by the PCBs in this oil. As noted above, PCBs and
many oils have similar properties. For this reason, extraction techniques used for polar matrices, such as water, are
not appropriate for extraction of oils. Often, the "extraction" is simply a dilution of the matrix to lower the viscosity to make an injection on a GC. Some "extractions" are
conducted under cleanup steps, as described in Chapter 6.

A. Transformer and Related Oils

1. Organic oils: Liquid-liquid partition of PCBs
from oils is difficult. The similar polarity of the PCBs and
the matrix make unfavorable partition ratios. In addition,
the lack of chemical reactivity of the matrix generally pre-
vents the use of any chemical degradation techniques to convert the oil to an extractable matrix. Therefore, the most
common "extraction" technique for these matrices has been
simple dilution.

Hexane dilution has been successfully used in the
preparation of common PCB-containing oils for analysis by
PGC/ECD or PGC/HECD (Sonchik et al., 1984; Levine et al.,
1983). Samples were diluted either 1:25 or 1:100. Hexane
dilution is also recommended for analysis of transformer
fluid and waste oils by the U.S. EPA (1981a; Bellar and
Lichtenberg, 1981). The procedure specifies 1:100 or 1:1000

dilution of the oil with pesticide grade hexane. The procedure recommends screening the sample to determine the approximate concentration by X-ray fluorescence, microcoulometry, density measurement, or GC screening of a very dilute
(1:10,000) sample. Samples are then analyzed by PGC/HECD,
PGC/ECD, or PGC/EIMS. Several optional cleanup techniques
are presented. Several types of matrices are covered by the
simple dilution approach:

a. Transformer oils: The most common transformer oil which might be contaminated with PCBs is mineral
oil, which contains 20-30% aromatics and the balance hydrocarbons. Polydimethylsiloxane (silicone) fluids, discussed
below, are the next most common. Other transformer dielectrics which are used to retrofill PCB transformers are paraf-
finic hydrocarbons, high temperature esters, tetrachloroethylene (Perc, Wecosol®), and non-PCB askarels (chlorinated
benzenes). The properties and uses of these matrices are
discussed more thoroughly in a review (PEDCo, 1984). In
addition to these non-PCB dielectric fluids, old transformer
oil samples can be PCB askarels, containing up to 70% PCBs,
as discussed in Chapter 2.

b. Capacitor fluids: Capacitor askarels con-
tain high levels of PCBs such as Aroclor 1016, as described
in Chapter 2. Substitutes which may be contaminated with
PCBs include alkyl phthalate esters, 1,1-phenylxylylethane,
isopropylbiphenyl, and butylated monochlorodiphenyl ether.

c. Hydraulic fluids: Hydraulic fluids may be
petroleum based oils, phosphate esters, water glycols, and
invert emulsions. These matrices are most often contaminated
with Aroclor 1242 in the U.S. (Sonchik et al., 1984).

d. Waste oils: Waste oils can come from many
sources and have various compositions, including road oil,
automotive crank case oil, and recycled fuel oil.

e. Other oils: Water glycol and invert emul-
sion hydraulic fluids were immiscible with hexane. These matrices were extracted three times with hexane (Sonchik et
al., 1984).

A liquid-liquid partition of transformer oil
with acetonitrile/hexane (90:10) has been described (Gordon
et al., 1982). Specifically, 1.0 mL of the transformer oil
is shaken with 15 mL of the acetonitrile/hexane mixture, centrifuged, and the oil layer discarded. The acetonitrile is
then diluted with 10 mL water and the PCBs extracted into 10
mL hexane. The hexane is concentrated to 1.0 mL and cleaned
up with a silica gel cartridge (Sep-Pak®) and then determined

by HRGC/ECD. Recoveries for the total method were 70 to 100% for Aroclors 1254 and 1260 but only 40 to 75% for Aroclor 1242 over a concentration range of 5 to 500 ppm. Volatility of the lighter Aroclor 1242 was blamed by the study authors for the low recoveries, although different partition ratios of the lower PCB congeners must also be considered.

2. Silicone oils: Two extraction techniques have been used for silicone fluids: an acetonitrile partition for subsequent HPLC determination, and a carbon column extraction for PGC/ECD determination (Klimisch and Ingebrigtson, 1980). The acetonitrile partion was deemed necessary, since direct injection of the silicone fluid degraded the HPLC column efficiency. A 0.1 g sample was diluted with 2.9 g of clean silicone fluid and extracted with 3 mL of dry (< 0.5% water) acetonitrile. The acetonitrile was then diluted with water to the same composition as the HPLC mobile phase (62% acetonitrile). The authors noted that PCBs are only slightly soluble (0-2%) in acetonitrile and that low recoveries would be observed if the PCB concentration in the oil exceeded that concentration.

A charcoal extraction technique was used for samples in the 25 ppb to 5 ppm range (Klimisch and Ingebrigtson, 1980). A 1-2 g sample was dissolved in acetone/diethyl ether (25:75) and applied to a 1 x 15 cm column of 50-200 mesh activated coconut charcoal. A 75-mL portion of the acetone/diethyl ether mixture was eluted through the column. The PCBs were then eluted from the column with 75 mL toluene, which was concentrated, and then determined by PGC/ECD. Aroclor 1248 was quantitatively recovered (91-106%) from the column in the 1-20 μg range.

B. Vegetable Oils

Vegetable oil and related products have been analyzed by dilution with ethyl acetate/toluene (75:25), filtration if necessary, gel permeation chromatography, Florisil chromatography, and determination by PGC/ECD (Young and Kamps, 1982). The method was applied to crude soybean oil and its refinery by-products (soapstock, deoderizer distillate, and clabber stock). Specifically, 5.0 g of sample was diluted to 50 mL with ethyl acetate/hexane (75:25). Viscous or solid samples were liquified by gentle heating. The sample preparation technique was not specifically validated, although a recovery of 98% for Aroclor 1254 at 3 ppm was measured for the entire method.

The rice oils implicated in the Yusho incidents (both in Japan and in Taiwan) were prepared for analysis by saponification (Nagayama et al., 1975, 1976; Chen et al.,

1981). The oil was heated in ethanolic sodium hydroxide and extracted with n-hexane. Saponification is described in more detail in Section VII.C.2 in this Chapter.

X. ANCILLARY CONSIDERATIONS

   A. Solvent Evaporation

        Concentration of the sample extract by solvent evaporation is common to many of the extraction techniques discussed above for the various matrices. Common evaporative techniques involve either boiling of the solvent or blowing a dry gas stream (usually nitrogen) across the solvent surface. The former technique is often accomplished with a reflux column to reduce the chance of solute loss through vaporization or spattering. The most common evaporative apparatus is the Kuderna-Danish (KD) evaporator. Numerous studies have investigated the efficacy of the various concentration techniques with a common conclusion that the most important factor in preventing loss of analyte during this step is operator skill and attention. In short, solvent evaporation techniques are an "art."

        Caragay and Levins (1979) reported significant losses of Aroclor 1254 during KD concentration of dichloromethane/hexane (15:85). They noted that with proper attention to a rapid evaporation, "good recoveries" were obtained.

   B. Sorption onto Glassware

        As noted in Chapter 4, significant adsorptive losses onto both glass and plastic surfaces have been documented in water (Pepe and Byrne, 1980; Muldrew et al., 1981; Sutcliffe and Nielsen, 1983). Silanization appears to retard the losses (Muldrew et al., 1981; Neidert and Saschenbrecker, 1984). While data are available for water and adipose samples only, sorptive losses from any matrix or solvent is possible. For example, during an evaporative concentration in hexane, it is entirely possible that significant amounts of PCBs (and other organic analytes) could be deposited on the glass surface as the volume is reduced. Even with hexane and other "good" solvents, the low concentrations of PCBs could easily favor partition to the glass surface.

        Analysts can guard against sorptive losses through good analytical technique. The entire interior of a sample container (contents, glass surface, and cap liner) should be treated as the "sample." An extract of the container can easily be combined with the sample extract. Furthermore, all sample transfers should be accompanied by a quantitative rinse--including pipets. During the sample concentration steps, the sides of the container should be rinsed where possible and care should be taken to avoid spattering. If losses are observed or suspected, silanization may improve recovery. Finally, proper QC practices will monitor the recovery, so that any PCB losses will be detected (see Chapter 9).

C. Sources of Contamination

Contamination of samples by PCBs, interfering compounds, or non-specific interferences can lead to erroneous results and require repetition of the analysis, if the problem is detected. Interferences may come from solvents, reagents, glassware, the laboratory environment (contaminated air or work areas), or anything else that comes into contact with the sample. Generally, the analysis of laboratory reagent blank is sufficient to demonstrate that the samples are free from contaminants.

Preventing contamination of samples requires good general laboratory practice. Glassware must be scrupulously cleaned. It should be rinsed as soon as possible after use to remove gross contaminants from the sample and then subjected to a strict cleaning protocol. Many standard methods (see Chapter 3) give guidance on glassware cleaning. A good glassware cleanup protocol should reduce carryover from previous samples by at least 10^4 (i.e., only 0.01% of the previous sample should remain on the glassware). Nevertheless, a laboratory should segregate glassware and space for low and high level samples to prevent cross contamination of samples at the nanogram-per-gram level by samples at the percent level.

High purity solvents and reagents (e.g., pesticide residue grade) are generally free from interferences. Nevertheless, many standard procedures and many laboratories stipulate that each new lot of a reagent be checked for purity. In addition, most adsorbents used for sampling, extraction, or cleanup are purified prior to use by solvent extraction or thermal desorption. Some of the adsorbents commonly used for sample cleanup have been found to contain interferences, as discussed in Chapter 6.

Contamination of final extracts can also be a problem. Contaminants can leach from the vial cap, cap liner, or the glue that holds the two together. PCB contamination can occur if the syringe used to inject onto a GC is not scrupulously cleaned between injections. Syringes should be segregated for high and low level work, since cleanup to trace levels is extremely difficult once a syringe has been contaminated.

6

CLEANUP

The cleanup step in an analytical procedure removes other compounds which may interfere with the determination of specific analytes such as PCBs. A cleanup takes advantage of the difference in physical or chemical properties of PCBs and interferences to remove the unwanted constituents. The cleanup· process may be expressed in terms of enrichment, where the ratio of PCBs to interferents is increased. Ideally, a cleanup reproducibly achieves 100% recovery of PCBs in one fraction, with the interfering compounds relegated to other fractions.

The extent of cleanup required is dependent on the requirements of the determination step (see Chapter 7). With a highly selective detector such as mass spectrometry, less cleanup to remove other chlorinated organics would be required than for electron capture detection. On the other hand, low resolution electron impact mass spectrometry requires extensive cleanup to remove the oil matrix components prior to determination of trace levels of PCBs, while ECD is virtually blind to the components of a transformer oil matrix and little cleanup is required.

This chapter discusses the cleanup techniques available for PCBs, including adsorption column chromatography; high performance liquid chromatography (HPLC); thin layer chromatography (TLC); gel permeation chromatography; and chemical degradation with acid or base. When appropriate, adsorption column chromatographic fractionation techniques which isolate PCBs into different groups are also presented in this chapter. Partition techniques to remove bulk matrix interferences were presented in Chapter 5 (Extraction), since these techniques are highly matrix-dependent. Some of these techniques combine extraction and cleanup in one step.

I. ADSORBENT COLUMN CHROMATOGRAPHY

          Adsorption column chromatography is the most common
sample cleanup. In this technique, a solvent eluted a sample
extract through a column containing at least one adsorbent.
The differences in polarity, solubility and partition cause
the PCBs and other compounds to move at different rates.
Thus, the PCBs can be isolated in an appropriate fraction.
Common adsorbents include Florisil, silica gel, alumina, and
carbon. In addition, a combination of adsorbent materials in
one column, a column cleanup after liquid-liquid partition,
or a column cleanup after matrix destruction by sulfuric acid
or saponification have all been reported.

          Adsorption chromatography separates compounds by
liquid-solid partitioning. The affinity of the PCBs and
other components of the sample for the adsorbent depends on
their polarity and the surface activity of the adsorbent.
The adsorbent can be activated by heat (e.g., 130°C) or other
treatment, which makes more binding sites available. Con-
versely, adsorbents can be deactivated by tying up the sites.
A common deactivation for many of the adsorbents is adding
water to hydrate some of the binding sites, thereby making
them unavailable for PCBs or other organic sample constituents. The other aspect of liquid-solid partition is the
solubility of the sample components in the solvent. The solvent polarity can be precisely controlled to either enhance
or retard the elution of the organic components from the column.

     A. General Practices

          An adsorption column is generally prepared by
either a slurry-packing or dry-packing technique. The sample
is then applied to the top of the column in a small volume.
The PCBs and other components are eluted through the column
with an appropriate solvent. Air or nitrogen pressure can be
applied to accelerate the elution. The separation is often
enhanced by changing the polarity of the solvent during the
elution. The PCBs are eluted in a given, predetermined fraction. This fraction may include many other organics or may
include only a specific subset of the PCBs.

          Because of the differences in adsorbent activity
and packing efficiency, each batch of adsorbent should be
tested for the PCB elution volume. This is usually done by
passing a PCB mixture through the column and collecting the
eluent in small (e.g., 10 mL) fractions. The individual
fractions are then analyzed to determine where the PCBs elute.
This permits the analyst to define a routine collection fraction which will contain all PCBs. Azulene, a blue-colored

aromatic compound which is not detected by GC/ECD, has been found to be a useful visual indicator to monitor the elution of each individual Florisil, silica gel, or alumina column (Nowicki, 1981; Erickson et al., 1983e). This technique appears to greatly reduce the uncertainties in the appropriate volume of the PCB fraction. The position of the blue azulene band serves to mark the location of the end of the first fraction. The cut between fractions is made by the analyst when the azulene band reaches a prescribed point, not when a specified volume of solvent has eluted. Griffin et al. (1980) measured the movement of the azulene down a silica gel column as the fraction of the total column length, R_f. They found that the best cut point to separate PCBs from p,p'-DDE ranged only from an R_f of 0.32 to 0.38, while the absolute volume ranged from 90 to 150 mL. Clearly, the azulene indicator provides a more precise measure of the appropriate elution volume. The authors noted that azulene eluted from a packed OV-101 column well ahead of the earliest peaks in Aroclor 1221 or any other Aroclors and also exhibited a response of 3×10^{-4} relative to aldrin. Therefore, azulene should not interfere with PCB determination by GC/ECD.

    B. Florisil

        1. Properties: Florisil (trademark, Floridin Co.) is a synthetic magnesium silicate. The Florisil generally used in PCB analyses is 60/100 mesh pesticide residue ("PR") grade. It has typically been activated by heating to 650°C by the manufacturer. Although cleanup of the reagent with solvent may improve the blank values, most of the standard procedures simply prescribe heating the Florisil, as received, at 130°C until it is to be used (FDA, 1977; AOAC, 1980a; Watts, 1980). The U.S. EPA (Watts, 1980) specifically recommends storing pre-packed Florisil columns in a 130°C oven at least overnight to ensure column uniformity. It also recommends that the oven used to store sorbents should be restricted from general use to prevent contamination.

        While fully activated Florisil has been most widely used, the use of deactivated Florisil has been reported. A 2% deactivated Florisil column cleanup has been used by Bush et al. (1983, 1984) for cleanup of milk and blood samples, and by Bush and Barnard (1982) for cleanup of fish eggs, rat brain, and aquatic macroinvertebrates. Specifically, Florisil was activated at 450°C, deactivated by addition of 2% water (v/w), and equilibrated by shaking for at least 0.5 hr. Columns (1 cm I.D.) were dry-packed with 10 g sorbent and the PCBs eluted with 40 mL hexane. Mirex, photomirex, p,p'-DDE, o,p'-DDE, hexachlorobenzene, and octachlorostyrene eluted with the PCBs. Other pesticides were eluted with ethyl ether/hexane (10:90).

2. Evaluation of activity: As with other sorbents, the adsorption characteristics of Florisil can vary
significantly from lot to lot. Thus, it has often been recommended that each lot be evaluated. An evaluation of the
quality of Florisil has been described in detail in Section
3,D of EPA's pesticide residue analysis manual (Watts, 1980).
A representative sample of Florisil is thoroughly mixed and
packed into columns. A standard solution of pesticides (PCBs
could also be added if they are to be an analyte) is then
eluted through the column and the appropriate fractions collected. The elution pattern is then measured and the acceptability of the batch determined. Acceptable total recovery
of organochlorine pesticides from all fractions is 90 to 105%
(Watts, 1980; Sherma, 1981). No provision is made by Watts
(1980) for adjusting the volume or composition of the elution
solvents to optimize recovery. However, FDA (1977) permits
the analyst to adjust the amount of sorbent in the column
from the normal 4-in. depth to compensate for "over-
retentive" or "under-retentive" Florisil.

A lauric acid adsorption technique has also been
widely used to estimate the adsorptive capacity of Florisil
(Mills, 1968; FDA, 1977). An excess of lauric acid in hexane
is added to a weighed amount of Florisil and the amount not
adsorbed is measured by titration with sodium hydroxide. A
"lauric acid value" is then calculated as the milligrams
lauric acid adsorbed per gram Florisil. From this lauric
acid value, the amount of Florisil in the column is adjusted
from the normal 20-g column. The elution characteristics of
the batch are then verified by elution of a standard mixture
of pesticides (FDA, 1977), similar to that described for the
EPA procedure in the previous paragraph.

The elution of each column can also be visually
monitored with azulene. This technique is discussed in Section I.A, above.

3. Mills-Onley-Gaither technique: The Florisil
column cleanup in a classic pesticide analysis method (Mills
et al., 1963) was the basis for many of the standard PCB procedures presented in Chapter 3. These include food (FDA,
1977; AOAC, 1980a); adipose (Watts, 1980); soil and bottom
sediment (EPA, 1982d); and paper and paperboard (AOAC,
1980b). Specifically, the "Mills-Onley-Gaither" (MOG) method
used a large column (10 x 2.5 cm) of activated Florisil to
clean up extracts of 100-g samples of fruits and vegetables.
The elution solvents were ethyl ether/petroleum ether (6:94;
Fraction I), ethyl ether/petroleum ether (15:85; Fraction
II), and ethyl ether/petroleum ether (50:50; Fraction III).
The method was adopted for PCB analysis. Seven Aroclor mixtures (1221 through 1262) were shown to elute in Fraction I,

"the 6% fraction" (McMahon and Burke, 1978; Watts, 1980; Millar et al., 1981, 1982). This fraction is often submitted to further cleanup, as discussed in the section on silica gel (Section I.C, below), since many organochlorine pesticides (e.g., DDE, DDT, heptachlor) also elute in this fraction and interfere with PGC/ECD determination.

The MOG Florisil cleanup has been widely used to clean up fish (Erney, 1974; Sawyer, 1973); animal and human adipose (Sawyer, 1973; Erickson et al., 1983e); wastewater (Millar et al., 1981, 1982) and other matrices in addition to the food matrices for which it was originally validated.

4. Eluting solvent: It has been noted (Watts, 1980, Section 3, D, VIII, 2) that the polarity of the solvent dramatically affects the elution characteristics of many pesticides on a Florisil column. The standard elution characteristics have been obtained with ethanol/diethyl ether (2:98). The solvent composition should be tightly controlled to ensure reproducible results.

Ethyl ether/petroleum ether (6:94) or ethyl ether/hexane (6:94) is the classic solvent mixture used to elute PCBs and many organochlorine pesticides from Florisil (Mills et al., 1963; see Section I.B.3, above). A substitution of dichloromethane/hexane (20:80 to elute PCBs) has also been shown to be effective (Seidl and Ballschmiter, 1976b). PCB recoveries of > 90% from up to 1 g fat were observed. Methanol/hexane (2:98) has also been found effective for elution of PCBs and DDE from Florisil columns (McKinney et al., 1984).

Hexane has been found to be a satisfactory eluent for PCBs, in a cleanup of adipose (Erickson et al., 1983e), fish and shellfish (Castelli et al., 1983), milk and blood (Bush et al., 1984, 1984), and eggs, brain, and aquatic invertebrates (Bush and Barnard, 1982). Dichloromethane was used to elute PCBs from a Florisil column to clean up phthalocyanine blue, phthalocyanine green, and diarylide yellow pigments (DCMA, 1982).

5. Cartridges: A rapid cleanup using commercially prepared Florisil cartridges (Sep-Pak®, Waters Associates, Milford, MA) was demonstrated to yield quantitative PCB recoveries from fish samples (McKone and Daub, 1983). In addition, the Sep-Pak and conventional column Florisil cleanups were compared using eight fish samples with Aroclor 1260 concentration ranging from 2 to 178 ppm. The results from the two techniques compared within 10%. In the Sep-Pak cleanup a 5-mL petroleum ether extract of fish was flushed through the cartridge. The eluate, plus an additional 2-mL of petroleum

ether, was collected, diluted to a known volume and analyzed
by PGC/ECD. Repetition with a second cartridge was required
to effectively remove the lipids from samples containing more
than 4% fat. The use of the cartridges gave equivalent performance and was much faster and easier to perform.

        6. Applications: In addition to the applications
noted above, Florisil has been used to remove gross interferences from sample extracts from air, water, wastewater, tissue, dairy products, oil pigments, paper, paperboard, and
paper mill effluent (AOAC, 1980; Adams et al., 1979; Delfino
and Easty, 1979; Easty, 1973; EPA, 1979a; EPA, 1979b; EPA,
1978; EPA, 1980; Sonchik et al., 1984; Kamps et al., 1979;
Kuehl et al., 1980; Modi et al., 1976; Price and Welch, 1972;
Reynolds, 1969, 1971; Robbins and Willhite, 1979; Rodriguez
et al., 1980; Stijve et al., 1974; Swift and Settle, 1976;
Tessari and Savage, 1980; Yakushiji et al., 1978; Bagley et
al., 1970; Bagley and Cromartie, 1973; Bellar and Lichtenberg, 1975; Chau and Babjak, 1979).

        Florisil has also been used to provide additional
separation of sample extracts following initial cleanup of
matrices by low temperature precipitation, acetonitrile partitioning, oxidation, sulfuric acid digestion, alumina chromatography, or gel permeation chromatography (Eder, 1976a;
Ernst et al., 1974; Kohli et al., 1979; Mes et al., 1977a,
Mes et al., 1977b; Mulhern et al., 1972; Stanovick et al.,
1973; Swift and Settle, 1976; Tessari and Savage, 1980;
Trotter, 1974; Uk et al., 1972; Bagley et al., 1970; Bagley
and Cromartie, 1973; Copeland and Gohmann, 1982).

        7. Detailed procedure: As an example of the Flor-
isil column cleanup technique, the appropriate section of the
Bellar and Lichtenberg (1981) procedure for PCBs in transformer oils is given below.

        1. Variations among batches of Florisil (PR grade
            or equivalent) may affect the elution volume of
            the various PCBs. For this reason, the volume
            of solvent required to completely elute all
            PCBs must be verified by the analyst. The
            weight of Florisil can then be adjusted accord-
            ingly.

        2. Place a 20-g charge of Florisil, activated
            overnight at 130°C, into a Chromaflex column.
            Settle the Florisil by tapping the column. Add
            about 1 cm of anhydrous sodium sulfate to the
            top of the Florisil. Pre-elute the column with
            70 to 80 mL of hexane. Just before the expo-
            sure of the sodium sulfate layer to air, stop
            the flow. Discard the eluate.

3. Add the sample extract to the column.

4. Carefully wash down the inner wall of the column with 5 mL of hexane.

5. Add 200 mL of ethyl ether/hexane (6:94) and set the flow to about 5 mL/min.

6. Collect 200 mL of eluate in a Kuderna-Danish flask. All the PCBs should be in this fraction. Concentrate to an appropriate volume.

7. Analyze the sample.

C. Silica Gel

1. Properties: Silica gel is a granular form of silicic acid (H_2SiO_3). It is widely used as an adsorbent for organic molecules in both gas and liquid phases. It has been used both for primary sample cleanup and for fractionation of PCBs from similar organics after another cleanup.

2. Contaminants: Contaminated silica gel can present blank problems. Up to 160 ng PCBs/g silica gel were found in liquid-chromatographic grade silica gels from several manufacturers (Bergman et al., 1984a). The authors attributed the contamination to either the final cleanup or adsorption of PCBs from ambient air during storage. The PCBs were extracted from the silica gel by eluting a column with dichloromethane. This cleanup step was recommended by the authors as a satisfactory cleanup technique. Huckins et al. (1976) also reported contaminants, including bis-2-ethylhexyl phthalate, and PCBs. The occasional presence of H_2SO_4 in the sorbent may have produced other contaminants which interfered with PGC/ECD analysis. A purification of the silica gel by extraction with acetonitrile/dichloromethane (40:60) and then drying at 160°C for at least 48 hr was recommended.

3. Eluting solvent: The composition of the elution solvent can have marked effects on the elution of PCBs (and other organics) through silica gel. Zitko (1971b) demonstrated that the benzene content of different pesticide grade hexanes could markedly affect the elution of Aroclor 1254. Only 18% of the PCBs eluted with 10 mL of hexane containing 210 ppm benzene, while 56% of the PCBs eluted when the hexane contained 800 ppm benzene. Even higher recoveries were observed when more benzene was intentionally added. The benzene content of hexane has also been shown to decrease the resolution of PCBs from p,p'-DDE on silica gel (Griffin et al., 1980).

4. Elution characteristics

a. Activated silica gel: The source and activity of the silica gel are important factors in the elution of PCBs and other compounds. Griffin et al. (1980) compared several batches of silica gel and demonstrated a wide variation in their activity. The best cut point to separate Aroclor 1254 and p,p'-DDE ranged from 20 to 150 mL of hexane for different brands of fully activated silica gel. Mallinckrodt No. 2847 (100 mesh, re-sieved to 100 mesh), which had the highest cut point, was judged best since it gave the best resolution of the PCBs from the p,p'-DDE. Davidson No. 923 was also judged acceptable; Davidson No. 950, fair; Davidson No. 50, poor; and Merck Silica Gel 60, poor. The latter two adsorbents exhibited very low adsorbent activity. With the Mallinckrodt No. 2847, lot-to-lot variation did not affect the cut point, relative to an azulene visual indicator, although the absolute elution volumes did vary.

b. Deactivated silica gel: Intentional deactivation with distilled water is a common practice to speed up the elution of PCBs through a silica gel column. As illustrated in Figure 6-1, a less active sorbent (i.e., more water) will exhibit a shorter PCB retention, but will have poorer resolution (Griffin et al., 1980). Similar results were obtained by Armour and Burke (1970). The choice of the activity depends on the objective of the cleanup. If a gross cleanup of polar materials such as lipids is desired, a deactivated adsorbent may be practical, while a fractionation of PCBs from p,p'-DDE and other pesticides would be most effectively done with a fully activated adsorbent.

The elution volumes of PCBs and 50 pesticides on silica gel have been tabulated (Leoni, 1971). PCBs and several nonpolar pesticides such as hexachlorobenzene, aldrin, heptachlor, and several DDT analogs were eluted with n-hexane. The more polar pesticides required correspondingly more polar solvents. Davison 950 silica gel was activated for 2 hr at 130°C and then deactivated with 5% water.

c. Modified silica gel: An early application of silica gel to clean up samples for PCB analysis utilized an 80:20 mixture of 3%-activated silica gel/celite (Armour and Burke, 1970). A 25-g portion of the mixture was slurry-packed into a chromatographic column. PCBs were eluted with 250-mL petroleum ether, using air pressure to accelerate the elution. Fish extracts were first cleaned up on a Florisil column and the PCB fraction further cleaned up with the silica gel. The recoveries for Aroclor 1254 and 1260 were 95 to 100% at the 40-μg level in solvent. Recoveries of 100% and 76% were observed for the same PCB mixtures at a similar column loading when spiked into trout extract.

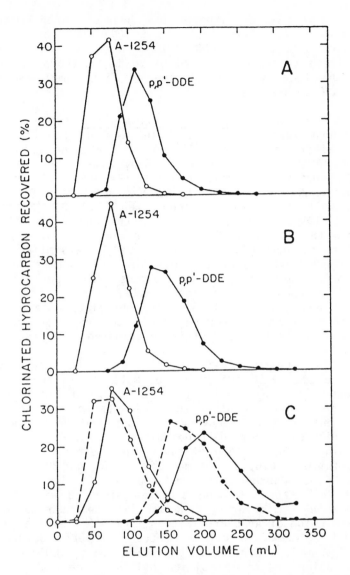

Figure 6-1.   Separation of p,p'-DDE from Aroclor 1254
by Column Chromatography With Different Activities
of Silica Gel

A - 1% Water-deactivated; B - 0.5% water-deactivated; and
C - 0% water-deactivated, either activated in column (___) or
bulk-deactivated and then cooled before packing (---). Columns were eluted with UV-grade hexane with 100 μg Aroclor 1254
or 10 μg p,p'-DDE.

Silver nitrate has been used to alter the properties of a silica gel column (Needham et al., 1980; Trevisani, 1980). The $AgNO_3$ (10%) acts as a "trap" for DDE and related compounds, according to the authors who originated the technique for cleanup of fish samples for TCDD analysis (Lamparski et al., 1979).

d. Alumina and silica gel in series: Silica gel columns were used to separate PCBs and pesticides into groups after an initial cleanup with alumina (Holden and Marsden, 1969; Musial et al., 1974; Zitko, 1971a). PCBs, DDE, DDT and several other pesticides eluted with 10-mL hexane, while the BHCs, dieldrin, endrin, and heptachlor epoxide eluted with 10-mL ethyl ether/hexane (10:90) (Holden and Mardsen, 1969). A careful cut of the hexane eluent could separate the PCBs and DDE (6-8 mL hexane) from the p,p'-DDT (14-16 mL hexane) (Musial et al., 1974). A similar separation scheme, using alumina and silica gel columns in series was used to separate phthalate esters, PCBs, pesticides and other compounds into appropriate fractions for analysis (Russell and McDuffie, 1983). The phthalate esters must be determined separately because they interfere with the GC/ECD detection of the PCBs and other chlorinated organics.

5. Column size: The size of the silica gel column should be scaled to the amount of material in the sample to be cleaned up. Steinwandter (1983) demonstrated that micro silica gel columns could effectively remove fat, while providing quantitative recovery of PCBs and pesticides when eluted with dichloromethane/petroleum ether (20:80). Columns containing 2, 3, and 4 g of silica gel retained 90, 140 and 190 mg fat with elution volumes of 20, 25, and 30 mL, respectively. The adsorbent was prepared by activating the silica gel at 450°C for 3 hr and then deactivating with 10% distilled water. Similarly, Erney (1974a) demonstrated quantitative elution of Aroclor mixtures from a 5-g silica gel column with 35 mL of petroleum ether. p,p'-DDE coeluted with the PCBs, while other common pesticides (e.g., DDT) eluted in a more polar fraction. Silica gel "as received" (i.e., no activation) was used for the validation studies after it was found that the "as received" material gave separations equal to or better than activated silica gel. This cleanup, following a Florisil cleanup, was used in a procedure for fish analysis (Erney, 1974b). The procedure gave comparable results, was faster, and used smaller amount of reagents than those in FDA's (1977) Pesticide Analytical Manual (PAM) standard procedure.

6. Applications: The ASTM (1981a) standard procedure for PCBs in water utilizes the silica gel microcolumn cleanup technique shown in Figure 6-2 after an initial

cleanup using Florisil. The PCBs in the 6% fraction (ethyl ether/petroleum ether; 6:94) from the Florisil column are separated from the other organochlorine compounds by elution with n-hexane. The pesticides can be eluted with ethyl ether/benzene (0.5:99.5). The amount of solvent needed to elute the PCBs is determined by collecting 1-mL fractions of the eluate of standard solutions of PCBs and pesticides. Figure 6-3 presents the Aroclor elution patterns given by ASTM. It is interesting to note that the more highly chlorinated mixtures (e.g., Aroclor 1260) elute before the less chlorinated mixtures (e.g., Aroclor 1242).

Silica gel column cleanup has been applied to the determination of PCBs in a variety of matrices, including fish (Armour and Burke, 1970; Erney, 1974b; Stalling, 1971; Huckins et al., 1976), adipose (Sawyer, 1973; Swift and Settle, 1976; Mes and Campbell, 1977), blood (Needham et al., 1980; Stratton and Geiszler, 1977), milk (Watts, 1980; Musial, 1974; Steinwandter, 1982a), food (Tanabe, 1976; FDA, 1977; Leoni et al., 1973; Nose, 1973; Vannuchi et al., 1976; Trevisani, 1980), biological matrices (Kveseth and Brevik, 1979), sewage sludge (Erickson and Pellizzari, 1977, 1979; Ballinger, 1978), soils (EPA, 1982d; Nose, 1973), sediment (Bellar and Lichtenberg, 1975), air and stack gas (Bidleman et al., 1978; Levins et al., 1979; MacLeod, 1979), water (EPA, 1978; ASTM, 1981a; Erickson et al., 1982, 1983d; Nose, 1973; United Kingdom Department of Environment, 1979; Derenish and Harling-Bowman, 1980), paper (Serum et al., 1973), transformer oils (Bellar and Lichtenberg, 1981; Gordon et al., 1982; Ogata et al., 1980; Steichen et al., 1982; Balya and Farrah, 1980) and industrial products and wastes (Erickson et al., 1982, 1983d, 1984d).

7. Detailed procedure: As an example of the silica gel cleanup technique, the appropriate section of the Bellar and Lichtenberg (1981) procedure for PCBs in transformer oils is given below.

1. Activate silica gel (Davison Grade 950 or equivalent) at 135°C overnight.

2. Variations between batches of silica gel may affect the elution volume of the various PCBs. For this reason, the volume of solvent required to completed elute all of the PCBs must be verified by the analyst. The weight of silica gel can then be adjusted accordingly.

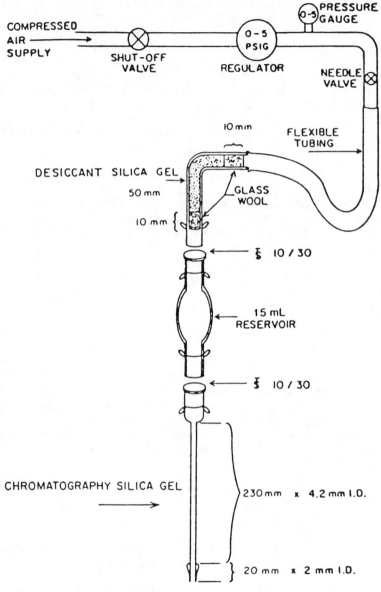

Figure 6-2. Apparatus for Pressure-Assisted Silica
Gel Microcolumn Chromatographic Separation of
Organochlorine Pesticides from PCBs
Following Florisil Cleanup

The sample is added to the top of the column and the 15 mL
reservoir filled with sufficient hexane to elute the PCBs.
The flow is adjusted to 1 mL/min using the air pressure.

Reprinted, with permission, from ASTM (1981a); copyright 1981
by American Society for Testing and Materials.

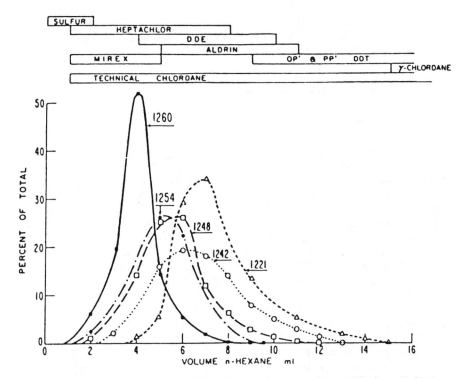

Figure 6-3. Aroclor Elution Patterns from Silica Gel
Microcolumn with Hexane as Eluting Solvent

See Figure 6-2 for column specifications.

Reprinted, with permission, from ASTM (1981a); copyright 1981
by American Society for Testing and Materials.

3. Place a 25-g charge of activated silica gel
into a Chromaflex column. Settle the silica
gel by tapping the column. Add about 1 cm of
anhydrous sodium sulfate to the top of the silica gel.

4. Pre-elute the column with 70 to 80 mL of hexane. Discard the eluate. Just before exposing
the sodium sulfate layer to air, stop the flow.

5. Add the sample extract to the column.

6. Wash down the inner wall of the column with
5 mL of hexane.

7. Elute the PCBs with 195 mL of diethyl ether/hexane (10:90; v:v).

8. Collect 200 mL of the eluate in a Kuderna-Danish flask. All of the PCBs should be in this fraction. Concentrate to an appropriate volume.

9. Analyze the sample.

D. <u>Alumina</u>

1. <u>Properties</u>: Alumina (Al_2O_3) is a common inorganic sorbent with a typical surface area of 100 to 400 m^2/g (Stahl, 1969). It is typically activated by heating to remove water (anywhere from 120°C to 800°C has been reported). The activated material is then often deactivated with water to varying degrees, sometimes referred to as Brockmann Activity I through V. Activity I is most active (i.e., 0% water) and Activity V (15% water) is least active (p. 203 in Stahl, 1969). Intermediate activities are II (3% water), III (6% water) and IV (10% water).

2. <u>Lipid removal</u>: A classic alumina cleanup, developed for organochlorine pesticides, (Holden and Marsden, 1969), has been successfully used to remove lipids from fish (Zitko, 1971a) and milk (Musial et al., 1979) for PCB analysis. Columns were prepared by dry packing 2 g of 5% water-deactivated alumina. PCBs, as well as many organochlorine pesticides, eluted in 20 mL hexane. The sample was then chromatographed on a silica gel column of the same size to separate the pesticides and PCBs into groups. A 2-g column of alumina has a capacity for 50 mg lipid (Hutzinger et al., 1974a), while at least 100 mg of fat are removed with both the silica and alumina columns (Holden and Marsden, 1969). A combination of alumina and silica gel in one column was used to simultaneously clean up fat and egg samples and concurrently separate PCBs p,p'-DDE from (Kveseth and Brevik, 1979). Hexane was used to elute the analytes from the columns which were packed with 2 g alumina on top and 4 g of fully activated silica gel on the bottom. Quantitative recoveries were observed.

PCBs were quantitatively recovered in the first fraction of hexane eluted from a column of 5%-deactivated neutral alumina (Teichman et al., 1978). Many pesticides such as DDE, DDT, aldrin, and heptachlor were also recovered in this fraction. The technique was used for the cleanup of soil, sediment, and oyster samples.

Telling et al. (1977) used two alumina columns for the cleanup of oily extracts from fish and fatty foods. The smaller column, 4 g alumina (activity II), had a capacity for at least 200 mg oil, with 100% recovery of PCBs in 5 mL hexane. A larger column with 22 g activity IV alumina could quantitatively elute PCBs in 10 mL hexane with 500 mg oil present. Some fractionation from the pesticides was achieved. The major co-eluting pesticides were p,p'-DDE and o,p'-DDT. Millar et al. (1981, 1982) demonstrated that the larger column gave quantitative recoveries for seven common Aroclor mixtures from wastewater (Millar et al., 1981, 1982). This and a Florisil cleanup (Mills et al., 1963) gave similar results, except the alumina column spread chlordane, toxaphene, and some other pesticides over a broad band, often in two or three fractions. The PCBs eluted quantitatively in the first 40 mL hexane.

3. <u>Cleanup of air samples</u>: Alumina column chromatography has been used to clean up extracts of air samples collected on polyurethane foam (Lewis et al., 1977; MacLeod, 1979; Lewis, 1982). The cleanup reduced interferences to < 1 pg/m^3 air (Lewis et al., 1977). A 1-mL concentrated extract was applied to a column of basic alumina (Brockman Activity IV) and eluted with 15 mL hexane. Recoveries of 88 to 107% were observed for five individual di- through hexachlorobiphenyls. Figure 6-4 illustrates the extent of the cleanup achieved. Clearly, the cleanup removes many ECD-active interferences.

4. <u>Separation of PCDFs and PCDDs from PCBs</u>: Column chromatography using alumina has been used to separate PCDFs and PCDDs from commercial PCBs and Yusho oil (Nagayama et al., 1975, 1976). After saponification of the Yusho oil (see Chapter 2) and an initial cleanup on silica gel, an alumina fractionation was performed. The alumina column was eluted with four solvents: (a) 20 mL n-hexane, (b) 120 mL carbon tetrachloride/n-hexane (20:80), (c) 10 mL n-hexane, and (d) dichloromethane/n-hexane (20:80). The PCDFs and PCDDs were recovered in the final fraction. A second fractionation was required in some cases to adequately remove the PCBs. A smaller column and smaller solvent volumes were used for the repetition of the alumina fractionation. A recovery of 90% was obtained for an unspecified PCDF.

5. <u>Other applications</u>: Alumina has been used for column chromatographic cleanup of a wide variety of matrices, including fish (Zitko, 1971a; Ofstad et al., 1978), human and animal adipose (Donkin et al., 1977); eggs (Wardall, 1977; Zitko, 1976), blood (Welborn et al., 1974), milk (Musial et al., 1972; Siyali, 1973; Tuinstra and Traag, 1919a), biological matrices (Keveseth and Brevik, 1979; Tuinstra and

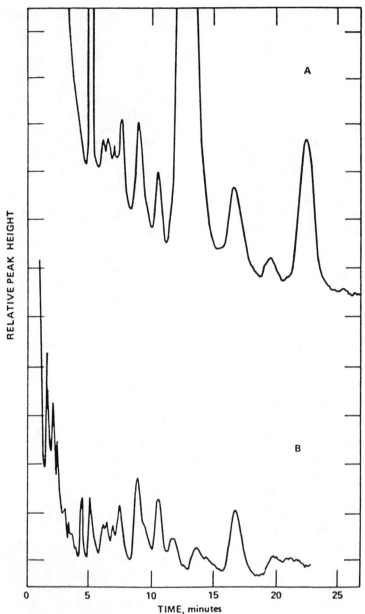

Figure 6-4.   PGC/ECD Chromatograms (A) Before and
(B) After Alumina Column Chromatographic Cleanup

The sample is a personal air monitoring sample collected at
Inez, North Carolina.

Reprinted from MacLeod (1979).

Traage, 1979a; Tuinstra et al., 1981; Teichman et al., 1978),
sediment (Goerlitz and Law, 1974; Teichman et al., 1978),
soil (Tuinstra and Traag, 1979a; Teichman et al., 1978), air
(Lewis et al., 1977; MacLeod, 1979; Lewis, 1982), water
(United Kingdom Department of Environment, 1979; Devenish and
Harling-Bowen, 1980), and oil (Kohli et al., 1979; Nagayama
et al., 1975, 1976; Telling et al., 1977; Sonchik et al.,
1984).

6. Detailed procedure: As an example of the alumina cleanup technique, the appropriate section of the Bellar
and Lichtenberg (1981) procedure for PCBs in transformer oils
is given below.

1. Adjust the activity of the alumina (Fisher A540
   or equivalent) by heating to 200°C for at least
   2 hr. When cool, add 3% water (wt:wt) and mix
   until uniform. Allow the deactivated alumina
   to equilibrate at least 1/2 hr before use.
   Store in a tightly sealed bottle.

2. Variations between batches of alumina may affect the elution volume of the various PCBs.
   For this reason, the volume of solvent required
   to completely elute all of the PCBs must be
   verified by the analyst. The weight of alumina
   can then be adjusted accordingly.

3. Place a 50-g charge of alumina into a Chromaflex column. Settle the alumina by tapping.
   Add about 1 cm of anhydrous sodium sulfate.
   Pre-elute the column with 70 to 80 mL of hexane. Just before exposure of the sodium sulfate layer to air, stop the flow. Discard the
   eluate.

4. Add the sample extract to the column.

5. Carefully wash down the inner wall of the column with 5 mL of hexane.

6. Add 295 mL of hexane to the column.

7. Discard the first 50 mL.

8. Collect 250 mL of the hexane in a Kuderna-
   Danish flask. All of the PCBs should be in
   this fraction. Concentrate to an appropriate
   volume.

9.   Analyze the sample.

E.   Carbon

    Carbon (or charcoal) has long been used to decolor reaction mixtures and otherwise clean up organic solutions. The chemical properties of the graphitic lattice make carbon not only a strong, but also a selective adsorbent. Thus, carbon can be used to both clean up samples and also fractionate PCBs and other organics according to their structural properties.

    The carbon column techniques exhibit excellent selectivity, but poor capacity. Thus, they are generally used as a second cleanup after major interferences have been removed by another technique. Dougherty et al. (1980) used gel permeation chromtography (see Section V, below) to remove the lipids and other major interferences from fish extracts before applying a carbon/foam cleanup. Smith et al. (1984) used a series of silica-based sorbents prior to the carbon/ fiber column, as described later in this section.

    1.   Separation of PCBs from other compounds: Chau and Bakjak (1979) used a carbon/foam mixture to separate PCBs from chlorinated pesticides. Following a general cleanup on Florisil column, mirex, photomirex, heptachlor and aldrin were quantitatively separated from PCBs and certain other organochlorines by elution of the carbon/foam column with cyclohexane. The cleanup scheme is shown in Figure 6-5. Greater than 95% of the target chlorinated compounds, including PCBs, were recovered in their respective fractions. The columns were prepared by chopping pesticide quality polyurethane foam (Analabs) in chloroform and slurrying with carbon (Norit C-170; four parts carbon per six parts foam, by weight). The mixture was then dried, dry-packed into a 5 mm ID column to a depth of 5 cm (about 0.2 g), and topped with 1 cm Na_2SO_4.

    A charcoal column has also been used to separate PCBs from several pesticides which co-eluted from an alumina column (Teichman et al., 1978). The column, 140 x 6 mm ID was slurry-packed to a height of 90 mm with 50-200 mesh charcoal (Fisher No. 5-690). Aldrin, heptachlor, p,p'-DDE, p,p'-DDT, p,p'-DDD, lindane, and chlordane eluted in a first fraction of 90 mL acetone/diethyl ether (25:75). Recoveries ranged from 81 to 112% at a fortification level of 1 to 4 ppb in soil. The PCBs eluted in a second fraction of 60 mL benzene. Recoveries of 100% were reported for Aroclor 1254 at a fortification level of 7 ppb in soil.

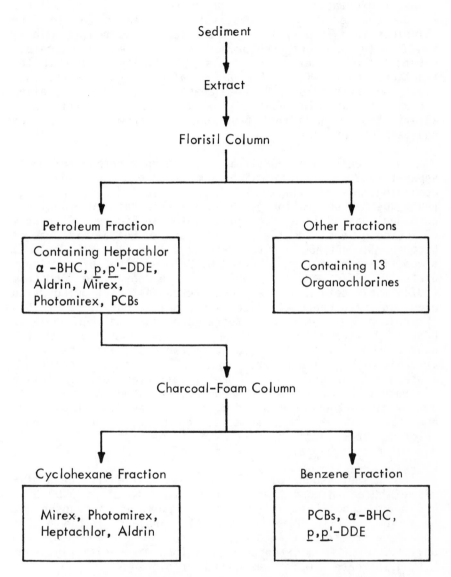

Figure 6-5.   Flow Chart of Extraction and Cleanup Using
Florisil and Carbon/Foam Column Chromatography to
Separate PCBs from Other Organochlorine
Compounds in Sediment Samples

Reprinted, with permission, from Chau and Babjak (1979); copyright 1979 by Association of Official Analytical Chemists,
Inc.

2. Separation of PCBs by structural features: Carbon has a high selectivity for those PCBs which can assume a planar conformation. These PCBs contain no ortho-chlorines. As the degree of ortho-substitution increases (up to four chlorines in o,o' positions), the retention decreases. Thus, a PCB with four ortho-chlorines would elute from a carbon column before other PCBs. This selectivity is useful for fractionation of PCBs. The degree of ortho-substitution affects the toxicity of PCBs (see Chapter 2 for a more detailed discussion and references). Therefore, isolation and characterization of different fractions from commerical mixtures has been of interest.

Jensen and Sundström (1974) used a carbon column to separate PCBs according to the number of o,o'-chlorines. By combining this procedure with high resolution gas chromatography, better separation and identification of individual PCB congeners was achieved. As illustrated in Figure 6-6, nearly 60 PCB congeners were identified in the technical mixtures of Clophen A50 and A60. This charcoal column (1.5 x 20 cm) was a modification of that reported by Berg et al. (1972) to separate DDT, DDD, and DDE from PCBs. The Jensen and Sundström (1974) modification of the procedure consisted of using Darco G-60 activated charcoal mixed with equal weight of Celite 545. The column was eluted with tetrahydrofuran and then benzene. PCBs with four ortho-chlorines eluted essentially with the dead volume of the column (10 mL tetrahydrofuran; Fraction 1; Trace B in Figure 6-6) and those with three ortho-chlorines eluted with an additional 20 mL of tetrahydrofuran (Fraction 2; Trace C in Figure 6-6). However, the compounds with only one or two ortho-chlorines required at least 100 mL of benzene for elution. The substitution pattern of additional chlorine atoms in the non-ortho positions of the PCB molecule did not noticeably affect the order of elution.

The carbon column cleanup was applied to the analysis of human adipose tissues following removal of DDD, DDT, DDE and metabolites by hydrolysis and oxidation (Jensen and Sundström, 1974). Most of the PCBs present in the pooled adipose extracts contained one to three ortho-chlorines. The only PCB with four ortho-chlorines that was positively identified in these samples was decachlorobiphenyl.

Jensen and Sundström (1974) suggested that the coplanarity of the phenyl rings might be affected by the number of chlorine atoms ortho to the biphenyl bridge. This difference in molecular conformation could explain the separation properties of activated charcoal based on the interactions between the graphite structure and aromatic character of the PCBs. The authors also suggested that this mechanism might explain the elution of o,p'-DDT and its metabolites before

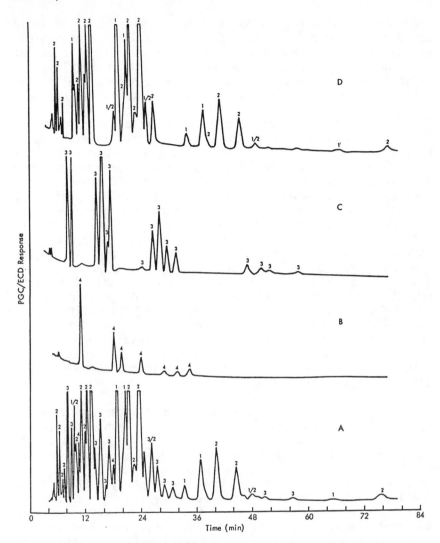

Figure 6-6. Chromatograms of PCBs Fractionated According to Number of Ortho Chlorines Using a Charcoal Column

The number of ortho chlorines is indicated above the peaks in (A) Chlophen A50 starting material; (B) Fraction 1, containing PCBs with 4 ortho chlorines, eluted with 10 mL tetrahydrofuran; (C) Fraction 2, containing PCBs with 3 ortho chlorines, eluted with 20 mL tetrahydrofuran, and (D) Fraction 3, containing PCBs with 2 and 1 ortho chlorines, eluted with 100 mL benzene. PGC/ECD chromatograms were obtained on a 5.2 m glass column packed with 4% Apiezon L on Chromosorb W, operated isothermally at 250°C.

Reprinted, with permission, from Jensen and Sundström (1974) copyright 1974 by the Royal Swedish Academy of Science, Stockholm, Sweden.

the corresponding p,p' isomers.   Jensen and Sundström (1974)
noted several considerations for working with activated carbon systems: (1) additional effort is required to analyze
more than one fraction of an extract containing PCBs (three
injections versus one); (2) and the elution profiles of each
batch of activated carbon adsorbent must be established.

Stalling et al. (1978, 1979a,b) and Huckins et al.
(1980) have used activated charcoal dispersed on either polyurethane foam or, more recently, on glass fibers (Smith et
al., 1984), to separate structurally similar components of
Aroclor mixtures in structure-toxicity correlation studies.
The results presented by Stalling et al. (1978) corroborated
the previous work by Jensen and Sundström (1974). Those PCBs
with more chlorines in the ortho positions eluted first from
a column of 1.75 g of activated carbon (Amoco PX-21) as shown
in Figure 6-7.   In addition, within each of the six possible
o,o'-chlorine substitution groups shown in Figure 6-7, elution volumes generally increased with additional chlorine
substitution.   This conflicts with the findings of Jensen and
Sundström (1974) and may be a function of solubility. Using
the activated charcoal cleanup procedure, separation and detection of Aroclor 1248 and 1254 components lacking o,o'-
chlorine substitution was feasible at concentrations less
than 1 µg/g Aroclor using high resolution gas chromatography/
election capture detection.

Huckins et al. (1980) determined the concentration
of non ortho-ortho'-substituted PCBs in several Aroclor mixtures (Table 6-I) and fish.   The non ortho-ortho'-substituted
PCBs are of interest because of the higher toxicological activity of these compounds relative to other PCB congeners.
Carbon-14-labeled 3,3',4,4'-tetrachlorobiphenyl, added to the
Aroclor mixtures, averaged 89% recovery from the carbon/foam
column.   As indicated in Table 6-I, the highest concentrations of the 3,3',4,4'-tetrachlorobiphenyl were found in Aroclors 1248 and 1242 which correlated well with the higher
toxicity of these mixtures to fish (Huckins et al. 1980).   In
addition, 3,3',4,4'-tetrachlorobiphenyl was isolated and
identified as a major constituent of the non ortho-ortho'-
substituted PCB fraction from composite fish samples.
Huckins et al. (1978) and Stalling et al. (1978) have also
used the carbon/foam chromatographic procedure to isolate
other planar polychlorinated aromatics such as dibenzo-p-
dioxins (PCDDs) and dibenzofurans (PCDFs) in formulations of
the Herbicide Agent Orange, Aroclors, and as trace environmental contaminants in fish tissues.

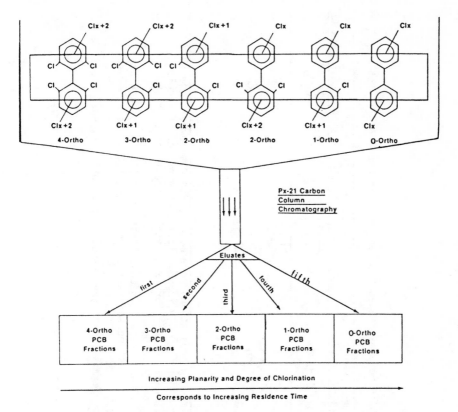

Figure 6-7. Elution Order of PCBs from Carbon Column,
Illustrating Dependance on Number of <u>ortho</u> Chlorines

Two 10 cm x 1 cm ID columns containing 1.75 g PX-21 carbon
(> 325 mesh) were eluted in series with a step gradient of
60-mL portions of toluene/cyclohexane (2:98 and 100:0).

Reprinted, with permission, from Stalling et al. (1979a);
copyright 1979 by New York Academy of Sciences.

Table 6-I. Concentration of Non-o,o-Chlorine Substituted PCB Congeners in Aroclor Mixtures[a]

| Aroclor | 3,4,4'-TriCB | | | 3,3',4,4'-TetraCB | | | 3,3',4,4',5,5'-PentaCB | 3,3',4,4',5,5'-HexaCB |
	N	Found, μg/g	Std. dev.	N	Found, μg/g	Std. dev.	Found, μg/g	Found, μg/g
1016	3	13,200	1,700		ND[b]		ND[c]	ND
1242	3	16,600	3,100	3	2,400	200	+	ND
1248	5	6,100	1,200	5	3,400	330	+	ND
1254	3	300	40	3	210	12	+	ND
1260	3	67	7		ND		ND	ND

a Aroclor sample size ranged from 50 to 103 mg and separations were made by using columns (1 cm ID × 10 cm) of Amoco PX-21 carbon dispersed on foam (15% w/w, carbon/foam). N = number of samples.
b ND = None detected; minimum detection limit was 0.4 μg/g for experimental conditions described in methods section, also see methods for recovery values.
c Plus sign indicates that 3,3',4,4',5,5'-PentaCB was present in concentrations < 250 μg/g; lack of standards of known concentrations prevented exact measurements. No 3,3',4,4',5,5'-HexaCB was detected in any of the five Aroclors.

Source: Huckins et al., 1980; reproduced with permission of the Association of Official Analytical Chemists, Copyright 1980.

The carbon/foam columns suffered from breakdown of the foam during use and a carbon/glass fiber system has been adopted. The most recent version of this system utilized the carbon/glass fiber column in series with other columns to extract, clean up and fractionate tissue samples in a two-part continuous process (Stalling et al., 1982; Smith et al., 1984). The serial columns are connected by tubing and valves to provide semiautomated operation with gravity flow. In part I (Figure 6-8) the sample, in a mixture with sodium sulfate, is extracted with dichloromethane/benzene (50:50) and the extract is, in the same process, passed through the sorbent columns. Specifically, the extract passes through silica-based adsorbents in the following order: potassium silicate, silica gel, cesium silicate, and finally silica gel. The residues of interest (PCDFs, PCDDs, specific PCB isomers, PCNs, as well as other aromatic chemical classes) are retained on the carbon/fiber adsorbent and are subsequently recovered by reverse elution with toluene. In part II (Figure 6-8), following a change of solvent to hexane, the sample is applied to a second series of adsorbents contained in two columns. The first column contains small amounts of cesium silicate and sulfuric acid-impregnated silica gel. The effluent from this column flows directly onto an activated alumina column on which several classes of residues are fractionated. Following reduction of sample volume, GC/ECD or GC/MS analyses are carried out. A similar system has been automated, using pressurized flow, solenoid values, and microcomputer control (O'Keefe et al., 1985).

II. HIGH PERFORMANCE LIQUID CHROMATOGRAPHY

A. Characteristics

High performance liquid chromatography (HPLC) can be used either as a cleanup technique, as discussed here, or as a final determination technique, as discussed in Chapter 7. As a cleanup technique, HPLC follows the same chromatographic principles as the open column adsorption column techniques discussed above. Molecules are selectively retarded by their adsorptive interactions with the solid phase. Under the proper conditions, PCBs are separated from interferences. If an appropriate fraction is collected, the PCB content may be subsequently determined by GC or other techniques.

The advantages of HPLC over the open column techniques are resolution, speed, reproducibility, and the ability to monitor the effluent. HPLC, as the name implies, has much better resolution than open column systems because the sorbent particles are smaller, more uniform, and more tightly

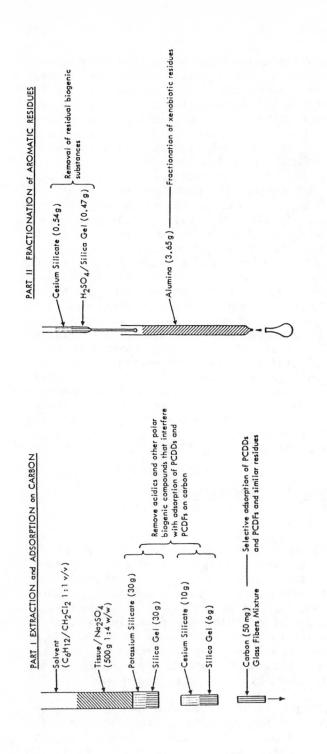

Figure 6-8. Enrichment and Fractionation of PCBs, PCNs, PCDDs, and PCDFs from Tissue Samples Using Carbon Column

Reprinted, with permission, from Smith et al. (1984); copyright 1984 by American Chemical Society.

142

packed. HPLC can be faster because the solvent flow is controlled by a high pressure pump, instead of gravity. Because
the same column is used repeatedly, the separations are reproducible. The UV detector normally associated with an HPLC
system provides a real-time indication of the compounds eluting from the column, which allows the analyst to make precise
fraction cuts.

The disadvantages of HPLC are low capacity and high
cost. In general, HPLC has less capacity for very dirty samples (e.g., fat extracts) than an open column system using
the same sorbent. In addition to the substantial cost of the
instrumentation and accessories, the per-sample cost may be
higher, since only one HPLC system is generally operated at a
time. In contrast, 8-12 open columns are typically monitored
by one analyst.

B. Applications

1. Tissue: Despite the aforementioned capacity
problems, HPLC has been successfully used to clean up animal
and plant samples for PCB and pesticide analysis (Rohlender
et al., 1976). PCBs and organochlorine pesticides from a
silica column with n-hexane and the triglycerides eluted with
acetone. Recoveries of about 95% were noted.

2. Paper: Figure 6-9 presents an example of an
HPLC cleanup of a paperboard extract (Dark and Crossman,
1973). The composition of the large peak after the PCB region was not identified. The sample was extracted with acetonitrile in a blender, filtered, and concentrated. The HPLC
conditions are given on the figure. The authors noted that
the PCB retention time was roughly proportional to the number
of chlorines, with dichlorobiphenyls eluting in the 3-5 min
region and trichlorobiphenyls eluting in the 8-10 min region.
Aitzetmüller (1975) used a 10-μm silica column with petroleum
ether as the solvent to clean up cardboard extracts for subsequent PCB determination by PGC/ECD. Large amounts of wax
present in the sample required additional cleanup. The wax
was saponified and the resulting wax alcohols removed by
Florisil column chromatography. Without the Florisil step,
the alcohols overloaded the HPLC column. DDE and DDT were
separated from Aroclors 1254 and 1260, indicating that, with
proper fraction collection, this HPLC system could be useful
for separation of DDE, DDT, and other interfering pesticides
from PCBs. Krull (1977) reviewed this and similar previous
work on HPLC fractionation.

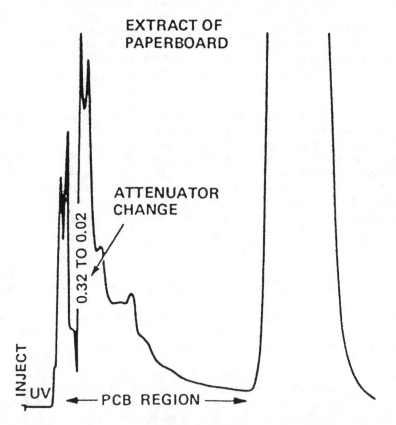

Figure 6-9.   Preparative Reversed-Phase HPLC Cleanup
of Paperboard Extract

A Bondapak C_{18}/Corasil column was eluted with acetonitrile
water.

Reprinted, with permission, from Dark and Crossman (1973);
copyright 1973 by Waters Associates.

3. Oil: Oil samples have also been cleaned up by HPLC for subsequent HRGC/ECD analysis (Chesler et al., 1979, 1981; Parris et al., 1984). The preparative aminosilane column (see Figure 6-10) removed more ECD interferences than solvent extraction, sulfuric acid treatment, or open column chromatography. In addition, the HPLC cleanup was more rapid. A total analysis time of 70 min was required for the HPLC cleanup and HRGC/ECD determination as compared to 8 hr for a procedure which employed solvent extraction, column chromatography, and sulfuric acid partitioning prior to the gas chromatographic analysis. The latter procedure did not clean up the sample sufficiently to yield an identifiable chromatogram of Aroclor 1254, which had been spiked into waste crankcase oil at 10 ppm. The HPLC cleanup of Chesler et al. (1979, 1981; Parris et al., 1984) was used in my laboratory to clean up transformer oil samples after chemical PCB destruction. The resultant oil was clean enough for GC/ECD determination, but did not remove sufficient mineral oil for HRGC/EIMS determination.

An HPLC cleanup for oils removed 96% of the oil background which was sufficient for analysis of PCBs by HRGC/EIMS at the 100 ppb level (Nero and Hudson, 1984). The NO_2-bonded column (Nucleosil 5 NO_2; 3-(4-nitrophenyl)propyl bonded to silica) was eluted with an isooctane/tetrahydrofuran gradient.

4. Commercial PCB mixture: Preparative HPLC has been used to characterize commercial PCB mixtures (Krupcik et al., 1977). A 42% chlorine PCB mixture was first fractionated into 70 fractions by vacuum distillation. Four of these fractions were further fractionated into 10-14 subfractions on a 25 cm x 8.0 mm ID column packed with 5 μm silica gel. The PCBs were eluted with n-pentane at a flow rate of 400 mL/hr. These subfractions were then analyzed by HPLC and HRGC/FID. Individual congeners were identified by comparison with authentic standards.

5. Separation of PCDDs from PCBs: PCBs are separable from PCDDs on an alumina HPLC column (Dolphin and Willmott, 1978). Using a 10 μm Alox T column (250 x 4.6 mm ID), n-hexane at 1.8 mL/min, and UV detection at 270 nm, Aroclor 1268 eluted with the solvent at about 2 min. PCDDs eluted from 2.9 to 4.0 min. Separations of PCBs and other chlorinated organics on silica columns were also presented.

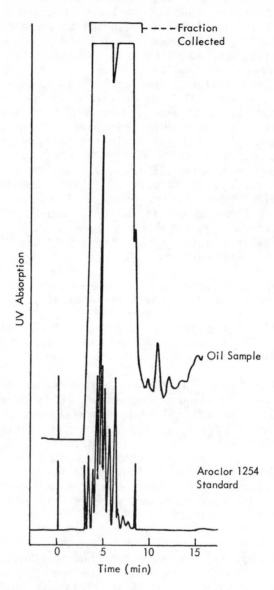

Figure 6-10.   Preparative-Scale HPLC Fractionation of Oil

Conditions: Column, preparative-scale aminosilane, 7.9 mm
ID x 30 cm; mobile phase, pesticide grade hexane; flow rate,
4 mL/min; detection, ultraviolet absorption, 254 nm; sample
injected, 100 μL.

Reprinted, with permission, from Chesler et al. (1981) and
Parris et al. (1984).

C. Detailed Procedure

As an example of the HPLC cleanup technique, the appropriate section of the Bellar and Lichtenberg (1981) procedure for PCBs in transformer oils is given below.

1. Quantitatively transfer the concentrated extract into the sample loop or the barrel of a syringe. Rinse the vial with several small portions of solvent. It may be necessary to inject several fractions.

2. Inject the extract and washes onto the amine column (Waters μBondapak 3.9 x 300 mm or equivalent) and elute the PCBs with 1.0 mL/min hexane. The UV at 254 nm or lower should be monitored.

3. Collect the eluent from 3 min to 9.5 min as it exits UV cell. The elution time should be verified using PCB standards covering a range from mono- to decachlorobiphenyls.

4. After collection, wash the column by eluting with methylene chloride until the absorbance attains a stable minimum. Return the system to hexane.

5. Concentrate the hexane eluate under a gentle stream of purified nitrogen to an appropriate volume and analyze.

III. THIN-LAYER CHROMATOGRAPHY

As with HPLC, thin layer chromatography (TLC) can be used either as a cleanup technique or as a final determination technique, as discussed in Chapter 7. The chemical separation mechanisms of TLC are also discussed in Chapter 7.

Silica gel (Kieselgel G) TLC plates were used to clean up fish extracts for PCB and organochlorine pesticide analysis by GC/ECD (Hattula, 1974b). The technique was a useful supplement to the routine sulfuric acid cleanup for confirming the concentrations of dieldrin, endrin, and the DDT-type compounds. Up to 15-mg fish fat could be applied per spot. The TLC cleanup involved a two-stage elution, first with dichloromethane to half of the plate height and second with n-heptane. Plates were sprayed with diphenylamine reagent and developed under UV light for 3 min to yield colored spots. PCBs were light violet. PCBs, aldrin, and p,p-DDE co-eluted in an upper spot, while p,p'-DDT, o,p'-DDT, p,p'-DDD, dieldrin, and endrin were separated into a lower spot. The fat remained much lower on the plate. The TLC technique gave PCB recoveries comparable to both a sulfuric acid cleanup and an alumina column cleanup. Nevertheless, the TLC technique was recommended for routine use only for samples with very low fat content (less than 10 mg) such as plankton, bottom invertebrates, and water plants. Silica gel TLC has also been used to clean up extracts of bird eggs (Koeniger et al., 1975) and bald eagle carcasses (Bagley et al., 1970) for PCB determination.

Animal feed extracts were cleaned up on alumina TLC plates using n-heptane as the developing solvent (Westoo and Noren, 1970). The PCBs, along with p,p'-DDE, o,p'-DDE, and o,p'-DDT were contained in one area of the plate, which was scraped from the plate and extracted. The extract could then be analyzed by GC or further cleaned up to remove p,p'-DDE by oxidation with chromium trioxide or by saponification with sodium hydroxide to remove o,p'-DDT.

A reversed phase TLC system was used to separate PCB mixtures into seven fractions for GC determination (De Vos and Peet, 1971). Paraffin-impregnated silica gel plates were developed with a solvent mixture of acetonitrile/acetone/methanol/water (40:18:40:2). Silver nitrate and UV light were used to visualize the spots. For preparative work, a small part of the plate was visualized and the remaining, unvisualized portions of the bands were scraped off the plates.

IV. ADSORBENT SLURRY TECHNIQUES

Adsorbent materials can be used in a simple slurry with the sample to effect a cleanup. As noted above, carbon has been used to decolor chemical reaction mixtures in a slurry, although the technique has not been reported for PCB analysis. The only adsorbent slurry technique commonly used for PCB analysis is the Florisil slurry for cleanup of transformer oil and similar matrices (EPA, 1981a; Bellar and Lichtenberg, 1981; ASTM, 1983). Although no articles have been published showing either the extent of cleanup or PCB recovery, this technique appears to be in common application. It may be speculated that the Florisil slurry removes ECD-active oxidation products formed during transformer oil use and also the phenolic and epoxide antioxidants which are added to askarels, mineral oil dielectric fluid, and other oil matrices.

As an example of the Florisil slurry cleanup technique, the appropriate section of the Bellar and Lichtenberg (1981) procedure for PCBs in transformer oils is given below.

1. Place the sample extract into a 20-mL narrow-mouth screw-cap container. Add 0.25 g of Florisil (PR grade or equivalent). Seal with a Teflon-lined screw cap and shake for 1 min.

2. Allow the Florisil to settle; then decant the treated solution into a second container with rinsing. Concentrate the sample to an appropriate volume. Analyze the sample.

V. GEL PERMEATION CHROMATOGRAPHY

A. Properties

Gel permeation chromatography (GPC), also called size-exclusion chromatography, separates molecules primarily by size. Large molecules are not well retained by the solid phase and elute early, while small molecules elute later. The stationary phase is a hydrophobic gel which is swollen with the elution solvent. Smaller molecules permeate into the gel particles, are retarded, and elute later than larger molecules. In addition to the separation based on molecular dimensions, adsorption phenomena in the GPC column can also separate compounds of similar molecular weight but different polarity. Thus, GPC cannot be regarded as solely a size separation technique. Common GPC packing materials are copolymers of styrene and divinylbenzene, often modified with different functional groups (e.g., Styragel, Bio-Beads); and polydextran (Sephadex). A more detailed description of GPC is available in general chromatography monographs (e.g., Zweig and Sherma, 1972).

Gel permeation chromatography (GPC) is a popular cleanup technique for complex matrices, especially those containing macromolecular interferents. Examples include biological materials containing high levels of lipid materials or oils with molecular weights in the range of 600 to 1500 amu. GPC has been fully automated to accommodate large number of sample extracts.

B. Eluting Solvents

The use of GPC to clean up biogenic extracts for PCB analysis was introduced by Stalling et al. (1971, 1972), using Biobeads SX-2 with cyclohexane as the solvent. Recoveries of PCBs as well as endrin, methoxychlor, lindane,

dieldrin, malathion, parathion, DDE, DDD and DDT were reported to be > 95% for samples containing up to 500 mg of
lipid materials.   Stalling et al.   (1971) recommended that
lipid material should not exceed 500 mg for a single analysis
with this size column.

A mixed dichloromethane/cyclohexane solvent was
used to elute polar compounds such as chlorophenols along
with the PCBs and organochlorine pesticides (Kuehl and
Leonard, 1978).   Retention volumes and recovery studies for
the polar and nonpolar compounds were measured on a Bio-Rad
SX-2 column using the following mixtures of dichloromethane/
hexane: (a) 100:0, (b) 10:90, (c) 50:50, and (e) 75:25.   The
50:50 mixture was the best compromise between high recoveries
and compound separation.   Figure 6-11 is an example of the
resolution with the 50:50 mixture on a similar column (Ribick
et al., 1982).

Dichloromethane alone was used as a rapid and efficient eluent for the bulk separation of lipids from low molecular weight organic compounds, while the dichloromethane/
hexane (50:50) solvent system was used to fractionate low
molecular weight organics into polar and nonpolar solvents.
Figure 6-12 is an example of the two-step cleanup.   The upper
trace (100% methylene chloride) represents bulk lipid separation for a fish extract and the lower trace (50% methylene
chloride) is the fractionation into polar and nonpolar constituents.   Fractions 1 and 2 from the second cleanup contained PCBs and chlorobenzene, while fractions 3 through 10
contained phenols, anisole, and heterocyclic aromatics.
Kuehl et al. (1980a,b) used the combination of GPC and negative chemical ionization mass spectrometry to analyze fish
tissues for PCBs, organochlorine pesticides and a number of
polar compounds.

A micro-GPC system consisting of a column of Bio-
Rad SX-2 beads (500 mm x 10 mm) using dichloromethane/cyclo-
hexane (50:50) as eluent was described by Kuehl et al.
(1980b) for the cleanup of 5 to 50 mg of human adipose tissue.   Larger sample masses overloaded the column and the PCBs
were not resolved from the fat.   Steinwandter (1982b) reported a similar GPC cleanup with dichloromethane as the elution solvent for a Bio-Beads SX-3 column.

C.   Calibration

A variety of substances have been used to calibrate
the elution of sample components on GPC.   A traditional cali-
brant is corn oil.   The PCBs are collected in the fraction
that elutes after the corn oil (Haile and Lopez-Avila, 1984).

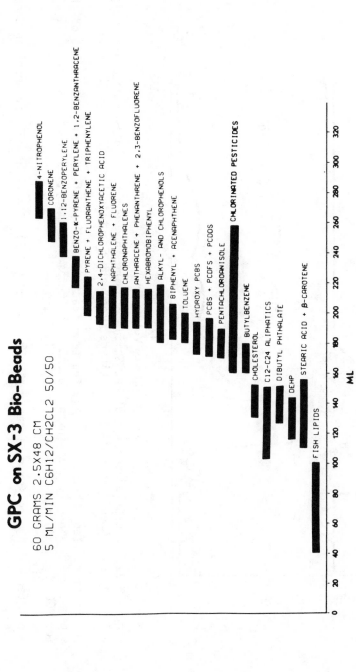

Figure 6-11. GPC Elution Profiles of Selected Biogenic Compounds and Environmental Contaminants

Conditions: 60 g SX-3 BioBeads, 2.5 cm × 48 cm column, cyclohexane/dichloromethane (1:1), 5 mL/min.

Reprinted, with permission, from Ribick et al. (1982); copyright 1982 by American Chemical Society.

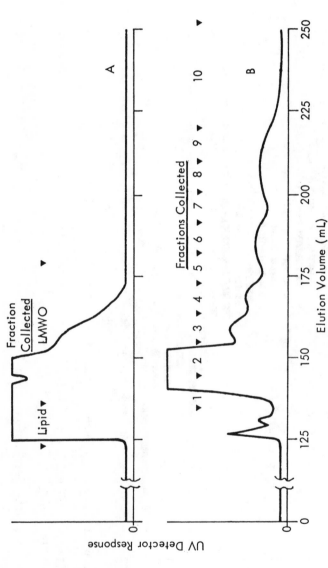

Figure 6-12. GPC Chromatograms of Fat Sample Showing the Separation of Low Molecular Weight Organic Chemicals (LMWO) from Lipids (Top) and Fractionation of LMWOs (Bottom)

In the first step (Chromatogram A), the LMWO fraction is collected, eliminating most of the lipids, which elute first. In the second step (Chromatogram B), 10 fractions were collected for PGC/ECD analysis. PCBs were in Fractions 1-4.

Reprinted, with permission, from Kuehl and Leonard (1977); copyright 1977 by American Chemical Society.

152

A more elegant calibration uses Vitamin E acetate and Vitamin K_3 to bracket the PCB window (Pellizzari et al., 1983a). The vitamins are detected in the column effluent by a UV detector at 254 nm. Degradation of the vitamins has been observed, so solutions should be fresh and their quality monitored (unpublished results, J. Stanley, Midwest Research Institute, Kansas City, Missouri).

D. Comparison to Other Cleanup Techniques

Griffitt and Craun (1974) compared GPC cleanup with acetonitrile partitioning for the analysis of PCBs and organochlorine pesticides in fat-containing food. In most cases 98% of the fat or oil eluted from the column before the pesticides or PCBs. Cleanup efficiency was better than that obtained with acetonitrile partitioning. Recoveries of Aroclor 1254 from milk fat were generally better with GPC (92-100%) than with a combined acetonitrile partitioning and Florisil column cleanup (77%).

Since a GPC column is generally used repetitively, Griffith and Craun (1974) investigated the potential for analyte carryover. High concentrations (500 µg each) of heptachlor epoxide, malathion, and Aroclor 1242 were loaded in alternate sample loops with the intermediate loops containing cyclohexane only as blanks. The analysis of the "blanks" showed that carryover was less than 0.10% (0.5 µg) for each of the spikes. The study authors concluded that this carryover was insignificant at the residue levels encountered in oils and fats.

The use of automated GPC was shown by Tessari et al. (1980) to be faster and more economical than the classic Mills-Onley-Gaither acetonitrile partioning and Florisil column chromatographic techniques (Mills et al., 1963; Watts, 1980) for cleanup of human adipose samples. Comparable results for PCBs and 19 organochlorine pesticides were obtained by the two techniques for 21 adipose samples.

E. Automation

Tindle and Stalling (1972) reported an automated apparatus for GPC cleanup in residue analysis with specific applications for fish lipids. The automated system allowed continuous operation with capability to process up to 23 samples, in sequence. Recoveries were reproducible (< 5% RSD) and cross-contamination from one sample to another was less than 1%. Since the introduction of the automated apparatus, gel permeation chromatography has been successfully used as a cleanup for high molecular weight matrices and has provided a cost-effective approach cleanup of large numbers of samples

(Albro, 1979; Caragay and Levins, 1979; Griffitt and Craun, 1974; Haile and Lopez-Avila, 1984; Hopper and Hughes, 1976; Kohli et al., 1979; Kuehl et al., 1980a, 1980b; Rodriguez et al., 1980; Stalling, 1971, 1976; Stalling et al., 1972, 1979; Tessari, 1980).

F. Applications

        The use of GPC cleanup in PCB analysis has been re- viewed (Krull, 1977). In addition to the applications cited in the paragraphs above, GPC has been used to clean up fish (Kloepfer, 1982; Kuehl et al., 1980a; Dougherty et al., 1980; Stalling et al., 1972; Stalling, 1971, 1976; Tuinstra et al., 1983); adipose (Egestad et al., 1982; Tessari et al., 1980); oil (Kohli et al., 1979; Young and Kamps, 1982); milk (Egestad et al., 1982); fatty foods (Griffitt and Craun, 1974); blood (Needham et al., 1981); sludge (Rodriguez et al., 1980; EPA, 1979e); and wastewater (Caragay and Levins, 1979).

G. Detailed Procedure

        As an example of the GPC cleanup technique, the ap- propriate section of the Bellar and Lichtenberg (1981) pro- cedure for PCBs in transformer oils is given below.

        1. Set up and calibrate the gel permeation chro- matograph with an SX-3 column according to the Autoprep instruction manual. Use methylene chloride/cyclohexane (15:85; v:v) as the mobile phase.

        2. Inject 5.0 mL of the sample extract into the instrument. Collect the fraction containing the PCBs (see Autoprep operator's manual) in a Kuderna-Danish flask equipped with a 10-mL ampul.

        3. Concentrate the PCB fraction to an appropriate volume.

        4. Analyze the sample.

VI. LIQUID-LIQUID PARTITIONING

        Liquid-liquid partitioning is used in both cleanup and extraction (see Chapter 5) steps. Partitioning is gen- erally used to remove polar interference which have much dif- ferent partition coefficients from PCBs. As described in Chapter 5, an acetonitrile-hexane partition is often used to

remove bulk lipids from hexane extracts of fatty samples.
These include adipose (Watts, 1980; Swift and Settle, 1976;
Porter and Burke, 1973), food (Mills et al., 1963; Leoni et
al., 1973; AOAC, 1980a; FDA, 1977; Tanabe, 1976; Leoni et
al., 1973), milk (Watts, 1980; Tessari, 1977; Tessari and
Savage, 1980), blood (Welborn et al., 1974) and eggs (Mulhern
et al., 1972).

Acetonitrile partition has also been used as part
of the extraction cleanup for both mineral oil (Gordon et
al., 1982) and silicone oil (Klimisch and Ingebrigtson, 1980)
transformer dielectric fluids, as described in Chapter 5.

Either a hexane-dimethylformamide (DMF) partition
or a Florisil column cleanup were recommended as cleanups for
determination of lighter PCB mixtures such as Clophen A-30
and Aroclor 1242 (Seidl and Ballschmiter, 1976b). Both techniques gave > 90% recovery of Clophen A-30 from olive oil
with only 5-10% of the matrix carried into the extract.
These cleanups were judged adequate for GC/ECD determination.
In the partition cleanup, 5-10 g oil were dissolved in 50 mL
hexane, and extracted 4 times with 15 mL DMF. The combined
DMF extracts were diluted with 100 mL water and back-
extracted with 2 x 20 mL hexane. The hexane layers were combined, dried, concentrated and then determined by HRGC/ECD.
Two other cleanup techniques gave inferior recoveries: hex-
ane/acetonitrile partition (45-60% recovery) and saponifica-
tion/sulfuric acid extraction (80% recovery).

As an example of a liquid-liquid partition cleanup
technique, the acetonitrile partition section of the Bellar
and Lichtenberg (1981) procedure for PCBs in transformer oils
is given below.

1. Place the sample extract into a 125-mL separatory funnel with enough hexane to bring the
   final volume to 15 mL. Extract the sample four
   times by shaking vigorously for 1 min with
   30-mL portions of hexane-saturated acetonitrile. Retain hexane layer for combination
   with other hexane extracts in step 3.

2. Combine and transfer the acetonitrile phases to
   a 1-L separatory funnel and add 650 mL of distilled water and 40 mL of saturated sodium
   chloride solution. Mix thoroughly for about 30
   sec. Extract with two 100-mL portions of hexane by vigorously shaking about 15 sec.

3. Combine the hexane extracts in a 1-L separatory
   funnel and wash with two 100-mL portions of

distilled water. Discard the water layer and
pour the hexane layer through an 8- to 10-cm
anhydrous sodium sulfate column into a 500-mL
Kuderna-Danish flask equipped with a 10-mL re-
ceiver. Rinse the separatory funnel and column
with three 10-mL portions of hexane.

4. Concentrate the extracts to an appropriate volume.

5. Analyze the sample.

VII. CHEMICAL DEGRADATION

Most of the cleanup techniques discussed in this
chapter involve physical separation of the PCBs from interferences. In this section, however, selective chemical degradation of the matrix is discussed as a technique for removing interferences. Chemical degradation techniques must
be used with caution to ensure that PCBs are not destroyed
along with the interferences.

A. Specific Reactions

Specific chemical reactions can be used to destroy
the matrix or interferents if they are already known. For
example, technical-grade products can be selectively degraded
during by-product PCB analyses (Erickson et al., 1982, 1983e,
1984d; Erickson, 1984a). Benzoyl chloride has been hydro-
lyzed using 1 M NaOH, with a small amount of hexane present
to extract any PCBs. After the hydrolysis, the aqueous layer
was extracted three times with hexane and the combined hexane
extracts back-extracted with 0.1 M NaOH to remove any residual benzoic acid. The hexane extract was dried and concentrated to an appropriate level for HRGC/EIMS determination.
Methyl esters and anhydrides have been similarly treated (unpublished data, Mitchell D. Erickson, Midwest Research Institute, Kansas City, Missouri).

B. Sulfuric Acid

This cleanup usually involves a simple shaking of
the sample extract with concentrated sulfuric acid for a
short time. The sulfuric acid oxidizes both potential GC
interferents and organic macromolecules. An organic-water
partition is sometimes used after the sulfuric acid treatment
to remove residual acid and also any polar materials which
did not fully partition into the acid. The technique has the
advantage of both speed and ease relative to most column
cleanups.

The technique was validated for the more acid-susceptible monochlorobiphenyls (Haile and Baladi, 1977). Specifically, 105 to 107% recoveries were observed for 2- and 4-chlorobiphenyl in 5 mL hexane after shaking for 1 min with 5 mL concentrated sulfuric acid. Additional cleanup with Florisil column chromatography was recommended. On the other hand, losses of mono- through trichlorobiphenyls were reported when pigment samples were heated with sulfuric acid for at least 15 min at 40-50°C to dissolve the matrix (DCMA, 1982).

A related technique utilized mixtures of sulfuric and nitric acids. Various reports prior to 1970, reviewed by Lincer (1973), conflicted on whether or not PCBs were lost by nitration. The use of sulfuric and nitric acid mixtures has not been reported since that time.

Sulfuric acid treatment is often used to cleanup transformer and other oil samples for PCB analysis (Bellar and Lichtenberg, 1981; Sonchik et al. 1984). It was recommended as the best cleanup for PCB fluid (askarel) and mineral oil; while column chromatographic cleanups were recommended for waste oil, hydraulic fluids, and capacitor fluids (Sonchik et al., 1984).

A sulfuric acid cleanup was found to be sufficient for PGC/ECD analysis and PGC/EIMS confirmation of PCBs in oil samples (Veierov and Aharonson, 1980). Unlike most other sulfuric acid cleanups, in which the sample and acid are simply shaken together, the sulfuric acid was eluted through the organic phase. Specifically, the sample was placed in a chromatographic column and concentrated sulfuric acid added dropwise. The heavier acid phase was drawn off occasionally and discarded. Acid was passed through the sample until twice the amount needed for the acid to emerge colorless had been added. This usually required about 10 mL acid/g fat. For cleanup of large samples, an alternating acid treatment-sample addition scheme was used. A small aliquot of sample was first dissolved in the solvent and acid-treated, then another aliquot of sample was added to the solvent and treated, and so on. This method allowed cleanup of up to 200 g fat in one day with no need for solvent evaporation, and with lipid carryover of only 0.02%. Greater than 85% recoveries were measured for soybean and safflower oil samples spiked with Aroclor 1254.

Another alternate configuration for sulfuric acid cleanup is to elute the sample through a column of acid-treated silica gel (Lamparski and Nestrick, 1980). At least 40% H_2SO_4 can be loaded onto a silica gel column. This technique has been found to be efficient and considerably less messy than the traditional shakeout, especially for large-volume samples (unpublished data, Mitchell D. Erickson, Midwest Research Institute, Kansas City, Missouri).

Sulfuric acid has been used to clean up fish (Hattula, 1974b; Ofstad et al., 1978); adipose (United Kingdom et al., 1972); biological materials (Murphy, 1972); oil (Kohli et al., 1979a; Sonchik et al., 1984; Levine et al., 1983; Veierov and Aharonson, 1980); stack gas (Haile and Baladi, 1977); paper products (Serum et al., 1973; Becker and Schulte, 1976). Fuming sulfuric (7%) has been used to clean up sewage sludge samples (Mattsson and Nygren, 1976).

As an example of the acid cleanup technique, the appropriate section of the Bellar and Lichtenberg (1981) procedure for PCBs in transformer oils is given below.

1. Place 5 mL of concentrated sulfuric acid into a 40-mL narrow-mouth screw-cap bottle. Add the sample extract. Seal the bottle with a Teflon-lined screw cap and shake for 1 min.

2. Allow the phases to separate, transfer the sample (upper phase) with three rinses of 1-2 mL solvent to a clean container.

3. Back-extract the sample extract with 5 to 10 drops of distilled water. Pass through a short column of anhydrous sodium sulfate and concentrate to an appropriate volume.

4. Analyze the sample.

5. If the sample is highly contaminated, a second or third acid cleanup may be employed.

C. Chromium Trioxide

The presence of p,p'-DDE, usually at a much higher concentration, can interfere with the determination of PCBs by PGC/ECD, since the p,p'-DDE peak elutes with pentachlorobiphenyls (Webb and McCall, 1974). Because of the chemical and physical similarity of p,p'-DDE and PCBs, most column cleanups yield both analytes in the same fraction. Often, analysts have simply quantitated the p,p'-DDE peak and ignored interference by co-eluting PCBs. In addition, the PCB quantitation is affected since some PCBs are buried under the large p,p'-DDE peak.

p,p'-DDE can be chemically degraded to p,p'-dichlorobenzophenone, which can then be readily fractionated with a column chromatographic cleanup. A chromium trioxide (CrO_3, chromic acid) degradation, followed by a silica gel column chromatography has been shown to remove the p,p'-DDE with 91% PCB recovery (Underwood, 1979). Specifically, the Florisil column eluate of fatty food sample (AOAC, 1980b) was shaken with a solution of 8% CrO_3 in glacial acetic acid. The chromium trioxide layer was back-extracted with hexane and discarded. The combined hexane fractions were back-extracted with water and then analyzed. The PCB peak at the retention time of p,p'-DDE was quantitated and subtracted from the p,p'-DDE value obtained before the chromium trioxide treatment to yield a "true" value for p,p'-DDE. The extract can also be further cleaned up using silica gel column. It was noted that high lipid content of some extracts would interfere with the p,p'-DDE degradation. Therefore, for such samples, GPC or another efficient lipid removal cleanup was recommended prior to the chromium trioxide cleanup. Chromium trioxide oxidation was also used to remove p,p'-DDE from pelican egg samples for TLC determination (Mulhern et al., 1972). p,p'-DDE had the same R_f as Aroclor 1254, while the dichlorobenzophenone product was well separated from the PCBs.

In a related technique, Mizutani and Matsumoto (1973) prepared liquid chromatographic column using chromium trioxide and acetic acid on a silica gel support, which quantitatively degraded DDE to dichlorobenzophenone to remove the DDE interference from the PCB chromatogram.

Chlorinated naphthalenes (PCNs) can be selectively oxidized by chromium trioxide to permit reliable determination of PCBs (Holmes and Walen, 1972). The PCNs, which occur in environmental samples as complex mixtures similar to PCBs, were oxidized by chromium trioxide in a boiling water bath for 20 min. No validation data were presented.

Losses of PCBs, especially the lower chlorinated homologs, during chromium trioxide cleanup have been reported (Szelewski et al., 1979). For the oxidation step, recoveries from spiked fish extracts ranged from 30 to 90% for eight replicates each of Aroclor 1016 and 1254, while no Aroclor 1221 was recovered. The lower PCBs may have been lost by oxidation, by volatilization due to the highly exothermic nature of the oxidative process, or a combination of the two. Similar losses and potential causes were observed by Trotter (1975).

A similar but more elaborate procedure separated DDT and its analogs from PCBs, as shown in Figure 6-13 (Trotter, 1975). The PCB-containing fraction from a Florisil

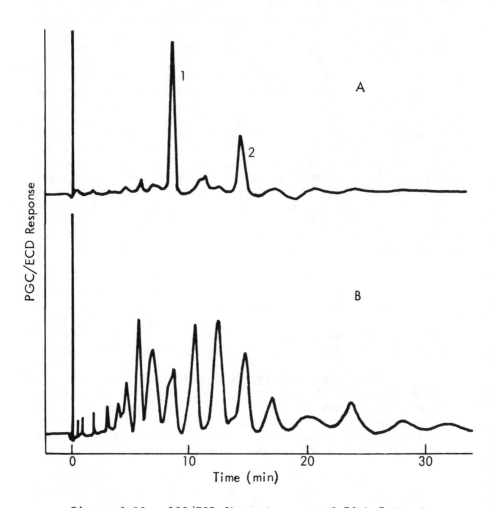

Figure 6-13.   PGC/ECD Chromatograms of Fish Extract
(A) Before and (B) After Treatment with KOH
and Chromium Trioxide to Degrade the
p,p'-DDE (Peak 1) and
p,p'-DDT (Peak 2)

The sample, Lake Michigan chub, contained 1.3 ppm p,p'-DDE
and 2.2 ppm p,p'-DDT as measured in Chromatogram A and 2.3
ppm PCBs, calculated as Aroclor 1254, from Chromatogram B.

column cleanup of fish extracts was first treated with ethanolic KOH (see below) to dehydrochlorinate DDT and related
compounds to their respective olefins. The DDT products,
DDE, and other olefins were then oxidized with chromium trioxide to dichlorobenzophenone. The PCBs were eluted in a petroleum ether fraction from a micro Florisil column. Recoveries for Aroclors 1254 and 1260 were > 80% in the ppm range,
but were poorer for lower chlorinated Aroclors and for lower
concentrations.

D. Base

Treatment of a sample with strong base can selectively degrade many interferences without affecting the PCBs.
The most common reaction is saponification of fats to their
corresponding glycerols and carboxylates. These products are
water-soluble and can be back-extracted. Another common reaction is dehydrochlorination of organochlorine pesticides.
In addition, and generally unreported, are a variety of other
reductive degradations which remove both chromatographable
and nonchromatographable interferences along with the fats or
organochlorine pesticides. As noted below, losses of the
lower chlorinated PCBs have been reported, so analysts must
exercise both caution and appropriate QC when using base
treatment to clean up samples.

Saponification of fat-containing samples with base
is a commonly used technique to eliminate the lipids, as discussed in Chapter 5. For instance, milk fat can be saponified by refluxing in ethanolic KOH. The digestate can then
be diluted with water and the PCBs extracted with hexane
(Yakushiji et al., 1978; Tuinstra et al., 1980, 1981;
Tuinstra and Traag, 1979a,b). A similar technique was applied to soil and tissue (Tatsukawa and Wakimoto, 1972).
Many of the standard procedures (Chapter 3) utilize saponification of sediment, soil, water, food and adipose matrices.

Another application of base to sample cleanup is
dehydrochlorination of organochlorine pesticides (Young and
Burke, 1972; Trotter, 1975). In conjunction with several
other cleanup techniques, Trotter used ethanolic KOH to degrade DDT and similar compounds to their corresponding olefins, which were then oxidized with CrO_3 to their corresponding dibenzophenones, as described above. Specifically,
the PCB fraction from a Florisil column was concentrated to
2 mL and 1 mL of 2% ethanolic KOH was added. The mixture was
refluxed for 15 min or until the volume reached 0.2 mL. The
PCBs and other organics were then extracted from the residue
with hexane. The dehydrochlorination reaction can also be
used to confirm the identity of pesticides by observing the
changes in the chromatograms (Young and Burke, 1972).

As an example of the base cleanup technique, the appropriate section of the Bellar and Lichtenberg (1981) procedure for PCBs in transformer oils is given below.

1. Quantitatively transfer the concentrated extract to a 125-mL extraction flask with the aid of several small portions of solvent.

2. Evaporate the extract just to dryness with a gentle stream of dry filtered nitrogen, and add 25 mL of 2.5% alcoholic KOH.

3. Add a boiling chip, put a water condenser in place, and allow the solution to reflux on a hot plate for 45 min.

4. After cooling, transfer the solution to a 250-mL separatory funnel with 25 mL of distilled water.

5. Rinse the extraction flask with 25 mL of hexane and add it to the separatory funnel.

6. Stopper the separatory funnel and shake vigorously for at least 1 min. Allow the layers to separate, and transfer the lower aqueous phase to a second separatory funnel.

7. Extract the saponification solution with a second 25-mL portion of hexane. After the layers have separated, add the first hexane extract to the second separatory funnel and transfer the aqueous alcohol layer to the original separatory funnel.

8. Repeat the extraction with a third 25-mL portion of hexane. Discard the saponification solution, and combine the hexane extracts.

9. Concentrate the hexane layer to an appropriate volume, and analyze the sample.

VIII. CLEANUP OF OIL SAMPLES

Determining the extent of PCB contamination in oil has been a major analytical application. While many laboratories have prescribed procedures for cleanup of specific matrices, few studies have been published recommending a given cleanup for these matrices. Table 6-II presents the cleanup techniques recommended by Sonchik et al. (1984) for a

Table 6-II. Recommended Sample Preparation
Procedures for GC/ECD Analysis

Oil Type	Procedure
Waste oil	Florisil column chromatography
Hydraulic fluid (excluding water glycols)	Alumina column chromatography
Water glycol hydraulic fluids	Hexane extraction
Capacitor fluids (excluding PCB fluid)	Alumina column chromatography
PCB fluid	Dilution; sulfuric acid wash
Transformer oil	Sulfuric acid wash

Source: Sonchik et al., 1984; reproduced from J. Chrom. Sci.
with permission of Preston Publications, Inc., Copyright
1984.

variety of oil matrices. For some matrices different cleanups were compared, but many of the recommendations appear to
be based on experience and subjective evidence.

A simple Florisil slurry cleanup (see Section IV)
is recommended by ASTM (1983) to remove interferences from
mineral insulating oils for PGC/ECD determination. Prior to
the cleanup, the sample is diluted with hexane or isooctane.
Florisil (0.25 g) is then added, the mixture shaken, and the
supernatant solution decanted to another vial for instrumental analysis. Shaking with concentrated sulfuric acid and
a Florisil microcolumn cleanup are given in the procedure as
alternative cleanup techniques. The Florisil slurry cleanup
was preferred because it is safer to use and dispose of than
the sulfuric acid and simpler than the adsorbent column
cleanup. ASTM (1983) also notes that a combination of the
Florisil slurry and acid treatment may be beneficial in some
cases.

IX. SULFUR REMOVAL

        Elemental sulfur frequently occurs in sediment, sewage sludge, and similar matrices. As seen in Figure 6-14, sulfur can significantly interfere with the early portion of a GC/ECD chromatogram. Several chemical treatments have been reported for sulfur removal, including mercury (Bellar and Lichtenberg, 1975, 1980; Goerlitz and Law, 1971, 1974; Rodriguez et al., 1980); tetrabutylammonium sulfite (Jensen et al., 1977; Bellar and Lichtenberg, 1980); cyanide (Mattsson and Nygren, 1976); and barium hydroxide (Mattsson and Nygren, 1976). Treatment with mercury appears to be the most widely used sulfur removal. A simple shaking for at least 1 min with 0.1 to 0.2 mL mercury removes sulfur (Goerlitz and Law, 1971, 1974). If the mercury darkens or causes precipitation, the sample is filtered with glass wool and the treatment repeated. In contrast, Rodriguez et al. (1980) found it advisable to shake sludge samples with 0.4 mL mercury for 2 hr.

        The tetrabutylammonium sulfite reagent is prepared by saturating a 0.1 molar aqueous solution of tetrabutylammonium hydrogen sulfate with sodium sulfite (Jensen et al., 1977). The reagent (1 mL) and 2 mL isopropanol are added to a 2-mL sample extract in isooctane and shaken for at least 1 min. Additional sodium sulfite is added, if necessary, until a solid residue persists. When the treatment is complete, 5 mL water is added, the mixture shaken, and the organic phase removed. Greater than 93% recoveries of PCBs were observed for both mercury and tetrabutylammonium sulfite treatment, and the techniques judged equivalent (Bellar and Lichtenberg, 1980).

        The cyanide treatment illustrated in Figure 6-14 was used by Mattsson and Nygren (1976), since mercury did not remove all of the sulfur. However, the cyanide degraded the hexachlorocyclohexane insecticides (BHCs) and a milder barium hydroxide treatment was recommended. Specifically, 1.5 mL of 0.1 M aqueous barium hydroxide is added to a 1-2 mL sample in hexane. Acetone (3 mL) is added dropwise and the solution will turn yellow-brown if sulfur is present. A second 3-mL aliquot of acetone is added and, upon shaking, a light green color appears. After 2 min the green color should disappear; if not, the treatment is repeated. When the color has disappeared, 10 mL water is added and the hexane phase separated and injected onto a gas chromatograph.

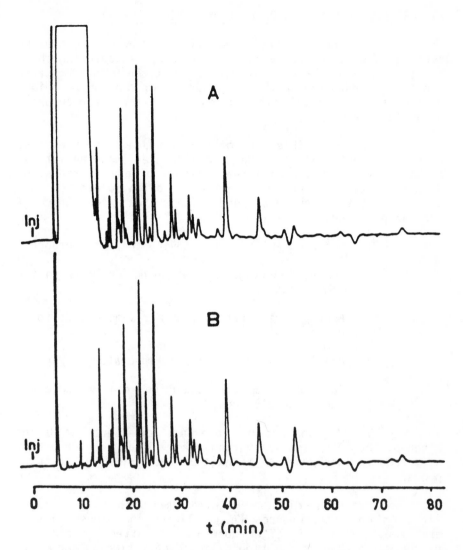

Figure 6-14.   HRGC/ECD Chromatograms Illustrating
Interference by Sulfur in the Early
Portion of Chromatogram A

A sewage sludge sample was extracted and the lipids removed
by shaking with 7% fuming sulfuric acid (Chromatogram A).
The sulfur was then removed by addition of potassium cyanide
(Chromatogram B).   The samples were analyzed on a 50-m SF 96
glass capillary column at 185°C isothermal.

Reprinted, with permission, from Mattsson and Nygren (1976);
copyright 1976 by Elsevier Science Publishers, B.V.

X. CRITERIA FOR CHOICE OF A CLEANUP TECHNIQUE

          This chapter has presented a review of the cleanup
techniques used for removing many different interfering chemicals from a variety of matrices. The confusing and even
conflicting data often makes the choice of cleanup technique
difficult. This section discusses the criteria for choosing
a sample cleanup.

          Where possible, one of the standard procedures dis-
cussed in Chapter 3 should be used. However, many analytical
problems do not fit within the confines of any of the standard procedures. Thus, the analyst is often forced to adapt
a cleanup to the problem at hand. The criteria for choice of
a cleanup include:

     1. Reported success at removing the interferences.

     2. Reported success at retaining any PCBs in the
         sample extract.

     3. Appropriate capacity for the sample size to be
         used.

     4. Previous experience in the laboratory.

     5. Cost of setup and execution relative to other
         candidate cleanups.

          If the analyst has previous experience with the
cleanup, the setup and validation time will be shorter and it
will require less practice to gain proficiency with the technique.

          Often a cleanup requires more than one stage.
First, major interferences (e.g., lipids in adipose tissue)
are removed. This is often done in the extraction step, as
discussed in Chapter 5. Liquid-liquid partitioning and macro
columns are widely used for this step. Second, a general
cleanup will separate the PCBs from other trace level interferences, such as organochlorine pesticides. Since these interferences are usually chemically and physically similar to
PCBs, the cleanup must involve a well-defined cut between the
interference and PCB fractions. Adsorbent column chromatography is most often employed for this step. The third stage
of a cleanup is fractionation of the PCBs by structural category. Since many analyses require only determination of total PCB content, this stage is not usually employed. Carbon
columns and other specialized chromatographic techniques are
generally used for fractionation of PCBs.

The choice of a cleanup technique is also dependent on the degree of purification required. In some cases, the concentration of the interferences is a million or more higher than the PCB concentration. In these cases, the cleanup and determination steps must effect a 10^6 concentration of the PCBs relative to the interferences. This will require a very efficient removal of the interferences with very little loss of the PCBs. Often a combination of techniques is used. For example, a chemical degradataion may change the bulk of the interferences into polar compounds which are easily removed in a solvent partition. An adsorbent column can then be used to remove the remaining interferences.

Unfortunately, there is insufficient agreement among the research reviewed in the preceeding sections to make specific recommendations for cleanup of individual matrices. Nevertheless, there is a general consensus on some of the more general approaches for specific interferences. These are discussed in the following paragraphs.

A. Lipids

Lipids and other polar, relatively fragile biological molecules have been most often removed by acetonitrile partition (see Chapter 5). As noted in Section V.D, above, the acetonitrile partitioning does not yield quantitative recoveries, so other techniques should be considered. Other candidate primary cleanups are gel permeation chromatography, Florisil column chromatography, and saponification with alcoholic KOH. Regardless of the primary cleanup, an adsorbent column cleanup will probably be necessary to fully remove the lipids.

Removal of a wide variety of less-stable interferences may be done with a chemical degradation cleanup (sulfuric acid, alcoholic KOH, or chromium trioxide). In the literature, these cleanups are generally targeted at a specific interference, such as lipids or DDE; however, in reality, many other interferences are often removed. This is quite often expressed by an instruction to repeat the treatment until all color is gone. Analysts should seriously consider the use of the chemical degradation cleanups (sulfuric acid, base, etc.) with PCB samples. Unlike many other organic analytes, PCBs are generally resistant to attack by these reagents and thus survive the cleanup. Since most aliphatic and many aromatic compounds are degraded, these chemical cleanups can be quite effective at removing matrix interferences. As long as the chemical degradation is shown to not affect the PCBs, these techniques should be considered for cleanup of most samples.

B. Macromolecules

        Macromolecules can be efficiently removed by GPC.
Applicable matrices include sediment, sludge, and biota of
all kinds. The macromolecules may be cellulose, sugars, proteins, or even synthetic polymers. The major impediment to
use of GPC appears to be the cost and effort of the initial
setup. If GPC cannot be justified, most of the adsorbent
column techniques will efficiently remove macromolecules, although they may suffer from capacity problems. In addition,
the adsorbent columns will probably not be reusable.

C. Organochlorine Pesticides

        Fractionation of PCBs from similar compounds such
as organochlorine pesticides usually requires one of the adsorbent columns. Florisil is the classic adsorbent for this
purpose and is still widely used. Silica gel and alumina
have also been extensively used. Arguments can be made for
the use of any one of these. Both silica gel and alumina can
be deactivated with water to alter the adsorbent properties
and control the elution volumes. On the other hand, "bad
batches" of alumina seem to be reported more often than with
the other adsorbents. Any of the three adsorbents will work
adequately for most cleanups, provided that the column and
solvent volumes are scaled to the sample size and the elution
volumes are carefully validated. A visual indicator such as
azulene can be effective in monitoring the elution characteristics of individual columns.

XI. VALIDATION OF CLEANUP TECHNIQUES

        Even when a well-documented technique is being
used, it must be validated for use by each laboratory and for
each sample type. Subtle differences in execution, reagents
(especially adsorbent activity), solvent composition, matrix,
and PCB composition can affect the effectiveness of a
cleanup.

        A thorough validation would include assessment of
the PCB recovery (accuracy), reproducibility (precision), and
enrichment factors. As noted in Chapter 9, these are all
part of good general quality control. Ongoing QC measures
constitute a reassurance that the cleanup remains valid.
With adsorbant column cleanups, the sorbent must be properly
activated and characterized (Edwards, 1974; Zitko, 1972).
The levels of interferences are assessed by eluting a blank
column with each sample set. In addition, deactivation of
the sorbent by the sample, column overloading, and impure
solvents can adversely affect the performance (Edwards,

1977).   Particular care must be taken with cleanups which use columns only once.   The column-to-column variability can often change the elution volume by several percent (Erickson et al., 1983e).   The elution volume must allow for the variability to assure full recovery of all PCB congeners in the PCB fraction.   Alternatively, a visual indicator such as azulene can be used to check the elution pattern for each individual column as discussed in Section I.A. of this chapter (Griffin et al., 1980; Nowicki, 1981; Erickson et al., 1983e).

7

DETERMINATION

All analytical methods are designed to answer "is the analyte present?", "how much analyte is in the sample?", or both questions. The identification and quantitation is generally accomplished in the same step. This determination step is the foundation of any method around which all other steps (cleanup, data reduction, QC, etc.) are centered. With PCBs, a chromatographic separation has almost always been an integral part of the determination technique. This chapter presents the three major separation techniques, gas chromatography (GC), thin layer chromatography (TLC), and high performance liquid chromatography (HPLC). The GC section contains subsections on separation, where both packed column (PGC) and high resolution (capillary) (HRGC) techniques are discussed, and detection, where electron capture (ECD), Hall electrolytic conductivity (HECD), mass spectrometry (MS), and other detectors are discussed. Other, non-chromatographic, techniques are presented separately.

Confirmation and screening represent the two extremes of analysis; the former striving for the maximum confidence in the results and the other sacrificing confidence for speed and/or simpler apparatus. These two topics are discussed, where appropriate, along with the determination techniques. Separate subsections at the end of this chapter discuss the techniques devoted specifically to either confirmation or screening.

Although often integral to the determination step, the reduction of data (interpretation of chromatograms and quantitation) is presented separately in Chapter 8.

I. CRITERIA FOR CHOICE OF TECHNIQUES

Most of the determination techniques used for PCBs employ a chromatographic separation coupled to a detector. The choice of technique depends upon:

171

1. anticipated PCB concentration (limit of detec-
    tion required),

2. anticipated number, level, and type of inter-
    ferences,

3. resolution needed (congener-specific or total
    PCB),

4. qualitative discrimination power (are false
    positives acceptable?),

5. quantitative accuracy and precision,

6. availability of instrumentation, and

7. analysis time and cost.

Clearly, no one technique is the best for all analyses, or
else the plethora of techniques discussed below would not exist. Needless to say, the extraction, cleanup, and determination techniques are all interrelated and must be appropriately mated in a method design.

In an analysis where "total PCB" is the desired
output, packed column GC, TLC, or HPLC may provide sufficient
resolution. On the other hand, if congener-specific analysis
is required for a metabolism study, HRGC would be the technique of choice.

The qualitative discrimination power of a detector
is a major factor in selection of a determination technique.
This is especially relevant when considering the variety of
PCB mixtures giving rise to complex chromatographic patterns.
If the concentrations are high enough (e.g., percent level)
and the interferences are minimal (e.g., transformer Askarels), a "universal" detector such as low resolution
(packed column) GC/FID or GC/TCD may be appropriate. If additional discrimination is required, GC/ECD may be appropriate if there are few other non-electron capturing compounds
(i.e., non-halogenated) in the matrix. In these cases, PCB
mixtures which fit the classic Aroclor patterns are identified by visual pattern recognition. When visual pattern
recognition cannot be used, where interferences are too complex, or where higher qualitative confidence is required, a
more discriminating technique such as HRGC/MS must be employed.

Another aspect of the qualitative discrimination
power of a technique is the acceptability of false positives
or negatives. A false positive may be acceptable in a survey
of transformers for PCB contamination, if the false positive
would simply result in the added expense of unnecessary

changing of the transformer dielectric fluid. On the other hand, false positives in human milk samples collected near a PCB incinerator would cause undue public concern and would therefore be highly undesirable. A false negative may arise from selection of a technique which has insufficient sensitivity for the anticipated concentrations (e.g., GC/EIMS analysis of blood samples as described above). False negatives may also arise from visual pattern recognition of GC/ECD chromatograms in which the PCB pattern is skewed from that of the standard due to weathering, retention time shifts, or other factors.

High quantitative accuracy and precision can, in theory, be met by most of the common techniques, provided that appropriate calibration, chromatographic separation, and data reduction steps are employed. One exception is TLC, which is generally regarded as "semiquantitative." Calibration using individual congeners is more difficult with ECD than EIMS because the ECD response can vary by an order of magnitude for different isomers of one homolog. Instrument availability is obviously a major factor in choice of technique. A laboratory with GC/EIMS capabilities is much more likely to choose this technique than one which must purchase instrumentation or employ an outside laboratory.

The analysis time and cost are also factors to be considered. TLC is quick, inexpensive, and requires no major capital equipment expenditures. At the other extreme, some HRGC/EIMS analyses can take well over an hour per sample, not counting the time required to set up and calibrate the instrument. Time-consuming analyses such as HRGC can be made more cost-effective by automation of the sample introduction and data reduction steps so that the instrumentation can be used beyond the customary 8-hr work day.

II. GAS CHROMATOGRAPHY

Gas chromatography (GC), also called gas-liquid chromatography, has been a workhorse technique in most analytical laboratories for over 20 years. The function of a GC is to separate complex mixtures and detect the components. The instrumentation consists of a pressurized gas (generally purified nitrogen, helium, or hydrogen) source, an injector, the separation column, and a detector. A very small (generally 1-10 μL) amount of sample is injected at the head of the column with a microsyringe, where it is vaporized. The vapors are swept by the carrier gas onto the column, where the components are separated, and then to the detector, where they are detected. The detection output consists of a series of peaks with time. The intensity of the peaks is generally proportional to the amount of compound present. The separation is effected by the interaction of the compounds with the gas and liquid phases. The more soluble the compound in the liquid phase, the more time it will spend dissolved in the liquid phase and the later it will elute. In addition, GC analyses use elevated temperatures or a programmed temperature range to enhance separation, so compound volatility also affects the retention time. PCBs generally elute in order of chlorination: $C_{12}H_9Cl$ first, $C_{12}Cl_{10}$ last; although there is considerable overlap in the middle homologs. Many liquid phases are available with different separating powers based on polarity, solubility, and other factors. The liquid phases are usually high molecular weight, low viscosity oils, gums, or waxes, which may be coated on the inside wall of a long, thin tube ("column") or they may be coated on an inert granular solid which is then packed into a column. In the former case, the columns are usually 0.2-0.5 mm ID and 10-100 m long and may be made of steel, glass, or, more recently, fused silica ("quartz"). GC using these "capillary" columns gives very high resolution and is therefore called high resolution gas chromatography (HRGC). Other terms for the same technique include capillary GC (CGC), glass capillary GC [(GC)^2], and fused silica capillary GC (FSCGC). The second alternative, packed column GC (PGC), utilizes columns which are usually 2-4 mm ID and 1-3 m long. PGC exhibits less resolution than HRGC, so more peaks tend to overlap, but is simpler to use and was preferred in the United States until the mid 1970's.

Common GC detectors include flame ionization (FID), which detects anything which burns and is therefore a "universal" detector, electron capture (ECD), which is selective for halogenated organics and a few other compounds, and mass spectrometry (MS), which detects all compounds and provides a characteristic spectrum for identification. Many other detectors are available, some of which are discussed below.

The separated peaks exit ("elute") from the GC column and are detected at different times. Measurement of the time required to elute through a given column yields a retention time (RT) which is reproducible for a given compound. To enhance the measurement precision, RTs are often measured relative to an internal standard to compensate for fluctuations in temperature or carrier gas flow rate. The relative retention time, RRT, can be used to identify components by comparison to RRTs of an authentic standard. Selective detectors provide an added dimension to the identification of PCBs. GC is discussed in detail in most analytical chemistry texts and in many monographs. Examples include McNair and Bonnelli (1969) and Jennings (1980).

Gas chromatography, in combination with various detectors, has been by far the most popular and useful analytical procedure for PCBs. In recent years, HRGC has been used increasingly, although many analysts still use PGC. The popularity of GC for PCB analysis lies in its resolution and speed (most PGC analyses take less than 30 min) and the sensitivity (ECD), selectivity (ECD, HECD), and specificity (MS) of the available detectors. This section is divided into separation, which is subdivided by PGC and HRGC techniques, and detection, which is subdivided by the various detectors.

A. Separation

As noted above, the separation of a complex mixture not only provides an identification of PCBs by their retention times, but also effects an in situ cleanup. The retention time of each component is generally measured relative to a standard run on the same system under the same conditions, preferably on the same day. This is not generally possible due to the large number of PCB congeners and their lack of availability. Several investigators have tabulated retention times or related parameters of individual congeners, as shown in Table 7-I. These data, especially the half-retention indices (Table 7-II) reported by Albro et al. (1977), may be useful to analysts who need to identify individual congeners. The analyst must exercise caution in using literature data without validating the reproducibility with selected authentic standards. Since many analyses center on identification of components of commercial mixtures, Table 7-III summarizes the literature references to peak identifications in these commercial mixtures.

1. Packed column GC (PGC): Packed column gas chromatography (PGC), has been the most widely used analytical separation technique for PCBs. The vast majority of the literature references have used PGC in a routine manner with a common liquid phase. The quality of PGC chromatography (resolution and tailing) is adequate for low resolution separation of Aroclor-derived samples into "fingerprints" for identification or quantitation, as shown in Appendix D and Figure 7-1. Since the Aroclor mixtures are too complex for resolution into peaks containing single congeners by PGC, little or no emphasis was placed on improving resolution. The most common PGC detector has been ECD. ECD has historically required isothermal GC operation (not so with modern instruments).

Table 7-I. Retention Times of PCB Congeners

No. of Congeners	Chromatographic Parameters			Reporting Mode[a]	Internal Standard	Reference
	Liquid Phase	Column Type	Temp. (°C)			
124	Apiezon L	0.02 in. × 50 ft[b]	205	RI	n-Alkenes	Sissons and Welti, 1971
27	SE-30	0.02 in. × 100 ft[b]	190	RRT	$\overline{DDE}$	Webb and McCall, 1972
45	c	2-3 m	200	RI	DDE	Albro and Fishbein, 1972a
60	Apiezon L, SF 96	2 mm × 5.2 m	250	RRT	2,2',3,4,4',5'-Hexachloro-biphenyl	Jensen and Sundstrom, 1974
All[d]	e	2-3 m	e	½ RI	DDE	Albro et al., 1977
85	SE-30	0.3 mm × 40 m	180	RI	n-Alkyltri-chloroacetates	Zell et al., 1978
21[f]	OV-1	0.25 mm × 20 m	220	RRT	DDE	Boe and Egaas, 1979
109	Apiezon L	0.3 mm × 40 m	40→140 @ 50 / 140→190 @ 1.6	RI	n-Alkanes	Ballschmiter and Zell, 1980
31	DB-1	30 m	190,200,210	RI	n-Alkanes	Hanneman, 1982
72	Apiezon L	0.29 mm × 20 m	70→130 @ 10 / 130→230 @ 4	RT	-	Bush et al., 1982
77	DB-5	0.255 mm × 15 m	110→325 @ 10	RRT	d_6-3,3',4,4'-Tetrachloro-biphenyl	Erickson et al., 1982
56	Apiezon M	0.2 mm × 45 m	100→240 @ 1	RRT	1,2-Dichloro-naphthalene 1,2,3,4-Tetra-chloronaph-thalene Octachloro-naphthalene	Pellizzari et al., 1983a,b
45	SP-2100	0.2 mm × 25 m	70→130 @ 10, 130→220 @ 3	RRT	DDE	Singer et al., 1983
209	SE-54	0.2 mm × 50 m	100→240 @ 1	RRT	Octachloronaph-thalene	Mullin et al., 1984

a RI = retention index; RRT = retention time relative to internal standard listed; RT = retention time in minutes.
b SCOT column.
c RIs were determined on OV-101, F-50, Apiezon L, OV-17, OV-225, and CHDMS packed columns.
d ½ RI values reported for substitution on one ring. RIs for all 209 congeners may be calculated.
e Ten packed columns with different phases, dimensions, and temperatures.
f 43 measured; 66 calculated.

Table 7-II. 1/2 (RI) Values for All Ring Substitution Patterns[a]

Substitution Pattern (1/2 PCB)	Column No.[b]												
	1	2	3	4	5	6	7	8	9	10	11	12	13
None	698	704	747	830	733	828	877	870	916	1,000	733	977	772
2	811	814	831	950	852	964	1,024	1,003	1,055	1,127	856	1,095	886
3	877	888	932	1,067	921	1,026	1,083	1,100	1,146	1,252	950	1,221	966
4	887	896	945	1,084	928	1,047	1,096	1,120	1,169	1,273	962	1,245	980
2,6	921	923	931	1,072	967	1,085	1,164	1,128	1,188	1,254	964	1,220	987
2,5	960	970	997	1,139	1,003	1,116	1,175	1,174	1,220	1,319	1,025	1,285	1,037
2,4	970	974	1,010	1,135	1,014	1,115	1,184	1,173	1,229	1,322	1,037	1,303	1,046
2,3	998	999	1,026	1,180	1,046	1,167	1,253	1,232	1,299	1,370	1,069	1,351	1,088
3,5	1,023	1,026	1,096	1,223	1,060	1,154	1,204	1,249	1,292	1,424	1,109	1,404	1,113
3,4	1,072	1,075	1,138	1,309	1,126	1,253	1,310	1,344	1,401	1,525	1,169	1,494	1,182
2,4,6	1,038	1,037	1,076	1,179	1,070	1,176	1,250	1,205	1,259	1,363	1,109	1,351	1,097
2,3,6	1,088	1,068	1,085	1,257	1,112	1,246	1,327	1,309	1,360	1,438	1,140	1,401	1,149
2,3,5	1,120	1,113	1,168	1,270	1,159	1,272	1,335	1,334	1,391	1,490	1,200	1,486	1,165
2,4,5	1,132	1,126	1,178	1,331	1,165	1,278	1,340	1,351	1,396	1,514	1,216	1,497	1,214
2,3,4	1,168	1,166	1,211	1,405	1,212	1,354	1,440	1,433	1,480	1,605	1,269	1,568	1,270
3,4,5	1,233	1,238	1,313	1,500	1,275	1,404	1,470	1,536	1,584	1,710	1,360	1,709	1,360
2,3,5,6	1,203	1,197	1,189	1,383	1,240	1,355	1,430	1,391	1,420	1,500	1,210	1,530	1,263

177

Table 7-II (concluded)

Substitution Pattern (1/2 PCB)	Column No.[b]												
	1	2	3	4	5	6	7	8	9	10	11	12	13
2,3,4,6	1,200	1,190	1,182	1,390	1,212	1,360	1,435	1,400	1,419	1,480	1,208	1,504	1,265
2,3,4,5	1,312	1,304	1,349	1,533	1,354	1,475	1,559	1,571	1,631	1,679	1,410	1,770	1,423
2,3,4,5,6	1,380	1,369	1,392	1,620	1,417	1,549	1,620	1,576	1,648	1,702	1,480	1,773	1,439
2,3,5,6[c]	1,257	1,256	1,273	1,444	1,314	1,393	1,481	1,471	1,536	1,612	1,276	1,637	1,307
2,3,4,6[c]	1,255	1,234	1,268	1,450	1,286	1,419	1,509	1,473	1,535	1,592	1,362	1,644	1,309
2,3,4,5[c]	1,341	1,339	1,380	1,556	1,377	1,502	1,593	1,581	1,654	1,750	1,467	1,772	1,422
2,3,4,5,6[c]	1,407	1,429	1,433	1,650	1,472	1,631	1,723	1,687	1,748	1,782	1,578	1,913	1,521

a To use the ½ RI value table, determine the substitution pattern on each ring; find the two entries corresponding to these substitutions in the appropriate column and add them together.

b Chromatography columns used.

Number	Packing	Dimensions (cm)	Temperature (°C)
1	10% OV-101, 80-100 mesh Chromosorb W HP	300 x 0.2	200
2	5% Versilube F-50, 80-100 mesh Chromosorb W HP	275 x 0.2	200
3	6% Apiezon L, 100-120 mesh Chromosorb W AW	200 x 0.2	205
4	10% OV-210, 80-100 mesh Supelcoport	330 x 0.2	200
5	10% OV-3, 100-120 mesh Gas-Chrom Z	300 x 0.2	200
6	10% OV-17, 80-100 mesh Supelcoport	300 x 0.2	200
7	10% OV-25, 100-120 mesh Gas-Chrom Z	300 x 0.2	200
8	10% AN-600, 100-120 mesh Chromosorb W HP	300 x 0.2	190
9	10% OV-225, 80-100 mesh Supelcoport	250 x 0.2	190
10	3% CHDMS, 100-120 mesh Gas-Chrom Q	400 x 0.2	200
11	5% Halocarbon K-352, 80-100 mesh Supelcoport	200 x 0.5	195
12	5% Poly MPE, 80-100 mesh Gas-Chrom Z	200 x 0.2	200
13	3% Dexil 410, 90-100 mesh Anakrom AS	200 x 0.2	200

c These values apply when only one ring is substituted.

Source: Albro et al., 1977; with errata noted in J. Chromatogr., 139, 404 (1977); reproduced with permission, copyright 1977, by Elsevier Science Publishers, B.V.

Table 7-III. Identification of PCB Congeners in Commercial Mixtures

Mixture	Technique	Number of Congeners Identified	Quantitated?	Reporting Mode[a]	Reference
Aroclor 1242	NMR, MS of fractions, authentic standards, ½ RIs	74	No	RI	Sissons and Welti, 1971
1254		116			
1260		124			
Aroclor 1242	PGC/FID on 12 columns, ½ RI, GC/MS	44	Yes		Albro and Parker, 1979
1016		31			
Aroclor 1248	HRGC/ECD, HRGC/FID, RIs	63	Yes	RI	Albro et al., 1981
1254		83			
1260		96			
Aroclor 1221	PGC/FID, IR	10	No	RRT	Webb and McCall, 1972
1232		16			
1242		27			
1248		43			
1254		27			
Aroclor 1221	Previous work, authentic standards, GC/MS	25	Yes	RT	Bush et al., 1982, 1983
1016		27			
1254		48			
1260		41			
Aroclor 1016/ 1254/ 1260	HRGC/ECD, HRGC/NCIMS, authentic standards	65[b]			Pellizzari et al., 1983a,b
Aroclor 1221	HRGC/EIMS of authentic standards	15	Yes	RRT	Tuinstra and Traag, 1983
1232		34			
1242		45			
1248		49			
1254		39			
1260		35			
Chlophen A50	HRGC/ECD of authentic standards	63	No	RI	Zell et al., 1978
A60		54			

Table 7-III (concluded)

Mixture	Technique	Number of Congeners Identified	Quantitated?	Reporting Mode[a]	Reference
Chlophen A30 A50 A60	Previous work, authentic standards, calculated RIs	59 71 67	No	RI	Ballschmiter and Zell, 1980
Chlophen A30 A60	HRGC/FID with column switching	70 52	Yes	NR[c]	Schulte and Malisch, 1983, 1984
Chlophen A30 A40 A50 A60	HRGC/ECD, HRGC/EIMS, authentic standards	63 57 62 62	Semi[d]	NR	Duinker and Hillebrand, 1983
Kanechlor 300 400 500 600	GC/FID and GC/MS	17 20 22 23		NR	Tanabe, 1976

a RI = retention index; RRT = relative retention time; RT = retention time.
b NR = not reported.
c Many peaks identified as isomer x and/or isomer y, with up to five possibilities for some peaks.
   Thirty-eight additional peaks identified only by homolog.
d Relative peak heights given in five categories.

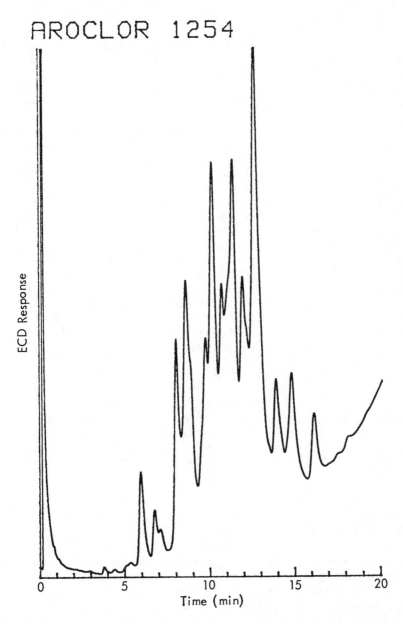

Figure 7-1.   Temperature-Programmed PGC/ECD Chromatogram
of Aroclor 1254

A 0.2 cm ID x 180 cm glass column, packed with 1.5% SP-2250/
1.95% SP-2401 on 100/120 mesh Supelcoport was programmed from
150°C to 250°C at 10°C/min.   The nitrogen carrier gas flow
rate was 30 mL/min.

By 1971 sufficient work in PCB analysis by PGC had been completed to merit a review (Reynolds, 1971). This was followed by several other reviews (Fishbein, 1972; Hutzinger et al., 1974a; Fuller et al., 1976; Krull, 1977; Margeson, 1977; and CMA, 1981). One review by Sherma (1975) was devoted to PGC analysis of PCBs and related chlorinated aromatic pollutants. PGC is the recommended analytical separation technique in most of the standard procedures listed in Table 3-I, a testimony to its reliability and popularity.

Albro et al. (1977) evaluated 13 packed columns ranging in polarity from Apiezon L to OV-225 (Table 7-II). The number of observed theoretical plates ranged from 491 to 3,833. None of the columns could successfully resolve all PCBs. It was calculated that of the 21,945 theoretically possible pairs of PCB congeners, 465 would be indistinguishable using the best column tested. The researchers discussed the use of multiple columns for resolving indistinguishable pairs and concluded that five columns were necessary to resolve all isomers. Thus, using this scheme, each sample would have to be analyzed once on each of five PGC columns to resolve all congeners. Albro and Parker (1979) applied this technique to the identification of the components in Aroclor 1016 and 1242. The identity of 44 congeners was reported. A report by Jensen and Sundström (1974) presents what may be the highest resolution PGC chromatogram of PCBs (Figure 6-6). Even though it was operated isothermally, this 5.2-m Apiezon L column resolved 59 peaks in a Chlophen mixture.

A recent development, bonded phases, gives more rugged and stable columns. The lighter loading of liquid phase also reportedly reduces the analysis time. In the example shown in Figure 7-2, a 1-hr PGC analysis was reduced to 18 min using the bonded liquid phase (Driscoll and Krull, 1983).

2.   High resolution gas chromatography: HRGC has not been as popular as PGC, although its use has increased dramatically in the past few years. This increase in popularity can be traced primarily to the advent of flexible fused silica capillary columns, which are easier to use, longer-lasting, and yield better chromatography than the glass and metal columns used previously. The quality of the HRGC separation currently achievable is illustrated in Figure 7-3 (Safe et al., 1983a). While this example represents the state of the art, a more "routine" chromatogram is presented in Figure 7-4 (Erickson and Stanley, 1982). Even the routine HRGC chromatogram provides substantially more resolution and information than a PGC chromatogram. As noted below, this can have both positive and negative ramifications. Generally speaking, any analysis which may be done by PGC may also be

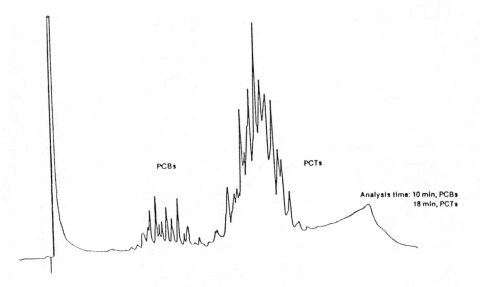

Figure 7-2.   PGC/FID Chromatogram of PCBs and PCTs
Using a Bonded Liquid Phase

A Permabond methyl silicone column was programmed from 140°C
at 10°C/min to 350°C.

Reprinted, with permission, from Driscoll and Krull (1983);
copyright 1983 by International Scientific Communications,
Inc.

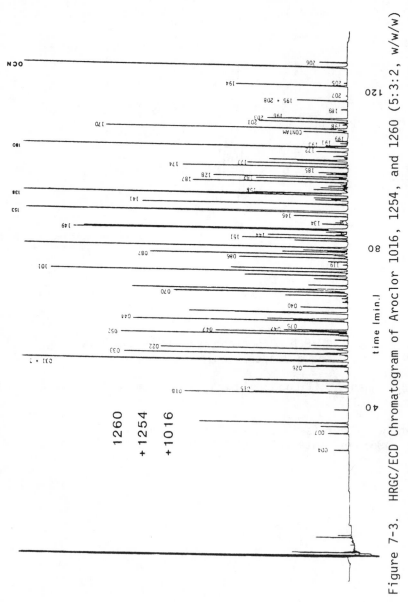

Figure 7-3. HRGC/ECD Chromatogram of Aroclor 1016, 1254, and 1260 (5:3:2, w/w/w)

A 50-m fused silica capillary column, coated with SE54 was programmed from 100°C at 1°C/min to 240°C. Numbers above peaks refer to PCB congener. The PCB congeners are numbered according to Ballschmiter and Zell (1980). The octachloronaphthalene internal standard is denoted by OCN.

Reprinted, with permission, from Safe et al. (1983a); copyright 1983 by Butterworth Publishers.

184

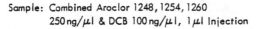

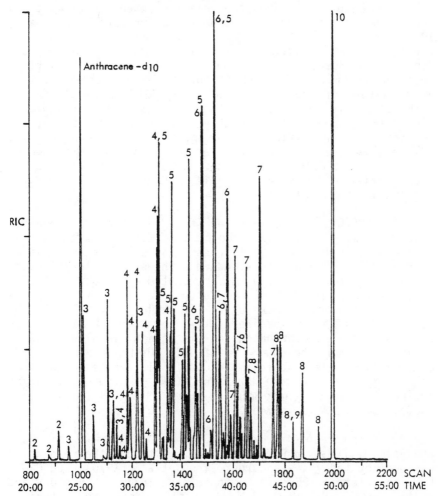

Figure 7-4. HRGC/EIMS Reconstructed Full Scan Ion
Chromatogram of PCBs and d_{10}-Anthracene
(Internal Standard)

The number of chlorines is denoted above each peak. Instrumental parameters: column - 15 m, DB-5, fused silica; column
temperature - 80°C for 2 min, 8°C/min to 300°C; helium carrier at 2.5 psi; 1 µL injected on J&W on-column injector.

Reprinted, with permission, from Erickson and Stanley (1982)
and Haile et al. (1983b).

achieved by HRGC, although the converse may not always be true. For instance, congener-specific analysis of complex PCB mixtures requires HRGC.

Figure 7-5 shows the relative retention times of 77 congeners using a DB-5 bonded phase column (Erickson et al., 1982; Stanley et al., 1983). This figure illustrates the overlap of the homologs. There is no way to separate congeners into homolog groups based solely on retention time. Relative retention times (RRT) for 77 PCB congeners as well as a mixture of Aroclors (1016, 1242, 1260) were determined with respect to the internal standard, 3,3',4,4'-tetrachlorobiphenyl-d_6, to establish relative retention windows that are required for identification of specific PCB homologs. The RRT data can also be used in selecting standard isomers which elute in the middle of the range as well as establishing the proper retention windows for HRGC/EIMS data acquisition for particular PCB homologs.

HRGC was briefly cited (five references) in one review (Sherma, 1975). An Aroclor HRGC/ECD chromatogram was included in a HRGC monograph (Jennings, 1980) as an application of HRGC. One of the standard methods in Table 3-I recommends HRGC, specifically a support coated open tubular (SCOT) column coated with FFAP (free fatty acid phase) for analysis of PCBs in capacitor Askarels. EPA Method 625 (EPA, 1979b) recommends PGC or if desired, capillary or SCOT columns may be used. High resolution gas chromatography is also allowed, if desired, for the analysis of PCBs in transformer fluids or waste oils (EPA, 1981a). HRGC/EIMS is the technique used for analysis of PCBs, PCDDs, and PCDFs in stack gas during incinerator tests (Ackerman et al., 1983a; Haile et al., 1983a, 1983b, 1984a, 1984b).

The resolution and column specifications for HRGC analysis of PCBs span a wide range. Although the resolution was poor by today's standards, Biros et al. (1970) used HRGC/EIMS to determine PCBs in human adipose in 1970. Sissons and Welti (1971) published an early article which characterized many of the PCB isomers in Aroclor 1254. Using an Apiezon L packed column, 23 peaks were resolved, while the same phase on a SCOT column (24,000 to 27,000 plates) separated 65 peaks.

Many investigators have used Apiezon L, a purified hydrocarbon grease, as an HRGC liquid phase (Albro et al., 1981; Stalling et al., 1980; Bush and Barnard, 1982; Bush et al., 1983; Jensen and Sundström, 1974; Nakamura and Kashimato, 1977; United Kingdom Department of Environment, 1979). Apiezon L has been reported by several groups to be the most selective phase for PCB congeners after comparison with other

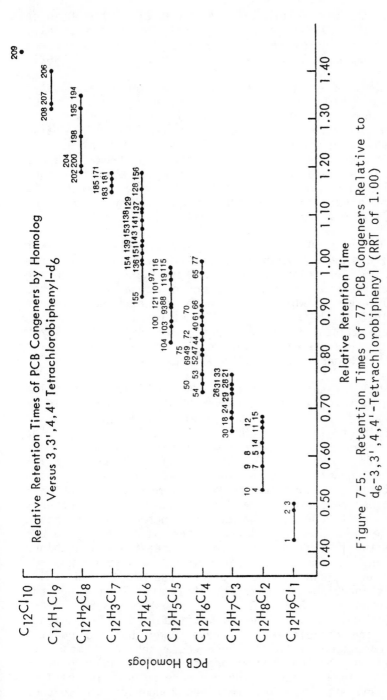

Figure 7-5. Retention Times of 77 PCB Congeners Relative to d₆-3,3',4,4'-Tetrachlorobiphenyl (RRT of 1.00)

The numbers refer to the IUPAC sequence number for each congener. Relative retention times were determined on a J&W DB-5, 15-m fused silica column in a Finnigan 4023 GC/EIMS system. Temperature program: 110°C for 2 min, then 10°C/min to 325°C.

Reprinted, with permission, from Erickson et al. (1982) and Stanley et al. (1983).

phases (Sissons and Welti, 1971; Albro et al., 1977; Bush et al., 1982, 1983, 1984; Pellizzari, 1981; Pellizzari et al., 1981, 1983b). Figure 7-6 presents examples of PCB separations on an Apiezon L capillary column (Bush et al., 1982).

Krupcik et al. (1976) evaluated metal wall-coated open tubular (WCOT) columns coated with Apiezon L or OV-101 and found them unsuitable. However, OV-101 on a glass WCOT column gave good results. Krupcik et al. (1982) have also reported the optimization of experimental conditions for the analysis of complex mixtures by capillary gas chromatography. The optimization procedure for complex materials was demonstrated with Aroclor 1242. Forty PCBs were separated at 170°C using a 40 m Carbowax 20M glass capillary column connected to a 76 m Apiezon L glass capillary column.

Using a 50-m Dexsil 410 glass capillary, Albro et al. (1981) achieved 175,000 effective theoretical plates for 2,2',3,3',5,5'-hexachlorobiphenyl. Resolution of Aroclor 1260, which required an isothermal chromatogram of 5 h, generated 110 peaks, of which only 4 were unidentified. Even at this resolution, the Dexsil 410 did not resolve all congener pairs. Less efficient columns coated with Silar 5C, Apiezon L, and OV-25 were used to provide different separations which resolved the congener pairs not previously resolved.

Mullin and co-workers have achieved impressive resolution by temperature-programmed HRGC/ECD on C-87 columns (Mullin and Filkins, 1981; Mullin et al., 1981) and SE-54 columns (Safe et al., 1983a; Mullin et al., 1983, 1984). The retention times on an SE-54 column of all 209 congeners are listed in Table 7-IV (Mullin et al., 1984). Figure 7-7 illustrates the general trend of increasing retention time with chlorine content. For isomeric PCBs (same degree of chlorination), the retention time is dependent on structure. Mullin et al. (1984) noted a general increase in retention time as the chlorines are placed further from the bridge between the two benzene rings (i.e., decreasing ortho-chloro substitution and increasing para-chloro substitution. For the monochlorobiphenyls, the elution order is 2- < 3- < 4-. For the dichlorobiphenyls with chlorines all on one ring, the elution order is 2,6- < 2,5- < 2,4- < 2,3- < 3,5- < 3,4-. The limited data on boiling points (Table 2-III) indicate that the more non-planar PCBs have lower boiling points, which is consistent with the observed retention times. In addition, it may be that those congeners which can more readily assume a planar conformation are more soluble in the liquid phase and are therefore retained longer in the column.

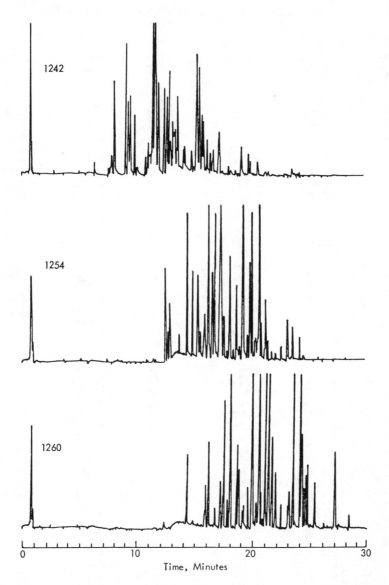

Figure 7-6. HRGC/ECD Chromatograms of Aroclors 1242, 1254,
        and 1260, on a 0.29 mm ID x 20-m Apiezon L Column

The column temperature was 70°C, programmed at 10°C/min to
130°C, then at 4°C/min to 230°C, with a 10-min hold.   Samples
(2 µL) were injected using splitless injection.

Reprinted, with permission, from Bush et al. (1982); copyright 1982 by Association of Offical Analytical Chemists,
Inc.

Table 7-IV. Relative Retention Times and ECD Response Factors[a] for 209 PCB Congeners

IUPAC No.[b]	Relative Retention Time[c]	Relative Response Factor[d]	IUPAC No.[b]	Relative Retention Time[c]	Relative Response Factor[d]
0	0.0997	0.0251	43	0.4587	0.503
1	0.1544	0.0393	44	0.4832	0.524
2	0.1937	0.04[e]	45	0.4334	0.54
3	0.1975	0.0193	46	0.445	0.468
4	0.2245	0.0374	47	0.4639	0.848
5	0.2785	0.119	48	0.4651	0.556
6	0.2709	0.38	49	0.461	0.648
7	0.2566	0.69	50	0.4007	0.6817[e]
8	0.2783	0.206	51	0.4242	0.6[e]
9	0.257	0.388	52	0.4557	0.418
10	0.2243	0.262	53	0.4187	0.3606
11	0.3238	0.0449	54	0.38	0.3643
12	0.3298	0.179	55	0.5562	0.829
13	0.3315	0.2[e]	56	0.5676	0.829[e]
14	0.2973	0.3047	57	0.5155	0.6[e]
15	0.3387	0.107	58	0.5267	0.609[e]
16	0.3625	0.447	59	0.486	0.6[e]
17	0.3398	0.412	60	0.5676	1.0164
18	0.3378	0.313	61	0.5331	1.2227
19	0.3045	0.3037	62	0.4685	1.1478
20	0.417	0.7238	63	0.529	0.728
21	0.4135	1.0598	64	0.4999	0.607
22	0.4267	1.0935	65	0.4671	0.8408
23	0.377	0.5[e]	66	0.5447	0.646
24	0.3508	0.793	67	0.5214	0.6[e]
25	0.3937	0.5[e]	68	0.504	0.726
26	0.3911	0.603	69	0.451	0.8024
27	0.3521	0.495	70	0.5407	0.658
28	0.4031	0.854	71	0.4989	0.468
29	0.382	0.6339	72	0.4984	0.5515
30	0.3165	0.8202	73	0.4554	0.5805
31	0.4024	0.562	74	0.5341	0.671
32	0.3636	0.278	75	0.4643	0.6461
33	0.4163	0.447	76	0.5408	0.5795
34	0.3782	0.6092	77	0.6295	0.3812
35	0.4738	0.3746	78	0.6024	1.1151
36	0.4375	0.2948	79	0.5894	0.881
37	0.4858	0.58	80	0.5464	0.7278
38	0.4593	0.4698	81	0.6149	0.7159
39	0.4488	0.347	82	0.6453	0.773
40	0.5102	0.722	83	0.6029	0.6339
41	0.499	0.5469	84	0.5744	0.386
42	0.487	0.792	85	0.6224	0.7396

Table 7-IV (continued)

IUPAC No.[b]	Relative Retention Time[c]	Relative Response Factor[d]	IUPAC No.[b]	Relative Retention Time[c]	Relative Response Factor[d]
86	0.6105	0.7968	131	0.6853	0.8492
87	0.6175	1.021	132	0.7035	0.7303
88	0.5486	0.6892	133	0.6871	1.148
89	0.5779	0.561	134	0.6796	0.7331
90	0.5814	0.611	135	0.6563	0.7031
91	0.5549	0.571	136	0.6257	0.444
92	0.5742	0.5375	137	0.7329	1.112
93	0.5437	0.6676	138	0.7403	0.827
94	0.5331	0.4514	139	0.6707	0.7219
95	0.5464	0.443	140	0.6707	0.6732
96	0.5057	0.4308	141	0.7203	1.352
97	0.61	0.631	142	0.6848	1.218
98	0.5415	0.6246	143	0.6789	0.7088
99	0.588	0.613	144	0.6563	0.8764
100	0.5212	0.5871	145	0.6149	0.6789
101	0.5816	0.668	146	0.6955	0.728[e]
102	0.5431	0.4561	147	0.6608	0.6[e]
103	0.5142	0.6068	148	0.6243	0.554
104	0.4757	0.4561	149	0.6672	0.572
105	0.7049	0.94	150	0.5969	0.5676
106	0.668	1.0046	151	0.6499	0.785
107	0.6628	0.8183	152	0.6062	0.5235
108	0.6626	1.0654	153	0.7036	0.688
109	0.6016	0.9625	154	0.6349	0.57
110	0.6314	0.65[e]	155	0.5666	0.586
111	0.6183	0.6601	156	0.8105	1.389
112	0.5986	0.8286	157	0.8184	1.1965
113	0.5862	0.604	158	0.7429	1.132
114	0.6828	1.0261	159	0.7655	0.9934
115	0.6171	1.1328	160	0.7396	1.1914
116	0.6132	1.3987	161	0.6968	0.9672
117	0.615	0.8895	162	0.7737	1.0322
118	0.6693	0.87	163	0.7396	0.9976
119	0.5968	0.8239	164	0.7399	0.9848
120	0.6256	0.7444	165	0.692	1.0777
121	0.5518	0.7659	166	0.7572	1.0421
122	0.6871	0.7247	167	0.7814	1.0658
123	0.6658	0.6645	168	0.7068	0.8375
124	0.6584	0.848	169	0.8625	0.8355
125	0.6142	0.556	170	0.874	0.75
126	0.7512	0.4757	171	0.8089	1.1712
127	0.7078	0.5834	172	0.8278	1.172
128	0.7761	1.188	173	0.8152	2.044
129	0.7501	0.997	174	0.7965	0.806
130	0.7284	0.952	175	0.7611	0.381

Table 7-IV (concluded)

IUPAC No.[b]	Relative Retention Time[c]	Relative Response Factor[d]	IUPAC No.[b]	Relative Retention Time[c]	Relative Response Factor[d]
176	0.7305	1.0589	193	0.8397	1.4167
177	0.8031	1.009	194	0.962	1.868
178	0.7537	0.621	195	0.9321	0.415
179	0.7205	0.8237	196	0.8938	1.2321
180	0.8362	1.295	197	0.8293	0.9522
181	0.7968	1.6046	198	0.8845	1.07
182	0.7653	1.1272	199	0.8494	1.1508
183	0.772	0.976	200	0.8197	0.369
184	0.7016	1.0046	201	0.8875	0.803
185	0.7848	1.437	202	0.8089	1.165
186	0.7416	1.2236	203	0.8938	1.629
187	0.7654	1.122	204	0.8217	0.8034
188	0.692	0.7337	205	0.9678	1.406
189	0.9142	1.5091	206	1.0103	1.673
190	0.874	1.31	207	0.9423	1.3257
191	0.8447	1.4741	208	0.932	1.1756
192	0.8269	1.599	209	1.0496	1.139

a   The high-resolution capillary gas chromatography was performed on a Varian Model 3700 gas chromatograph equipped with a ^{63}Ni electron capture detector. A 50-m fused silica capillary column (0.2 mm ID) coated with SE-54 (Hewlett-Packard) was used to separate the PCB isomers and congeners. The oven temperature was programmed at a rate of 1.0°C min^{-1} from 100 to 240°C. The injector and detector temperatures were 270 and 330°C, respectively. Sample volume, 6.0 μL, was injected by using an automatic sampler with splitting in the injector (10:1 split ratio, vented from 0.75 to 1.75 min). The hydrogen carrier gas was held at a constant pressure of 2.25 kg cm^{-2} to give the optimized linear velocity (μ) at 100°C of 45 cm s^{-1}.
b   Ballschmiter and Zell, 1980.
c   Retention times (RT) of the PCBs were expressed relative to the octachloronaphthalene (RT = 124.9 min) standard.
d   Response factors (by weight) for the PCBs expressed relative to octachloronaphthalene (R_f = 1.0 for 1 ng of OCN) by using integrated peak areas.
e   Estimated relative response factor based on other isomeric PCBs.

Source: Mullin et al., 1984; reproduced with permission, copyright 1984 by American Chemical Society.

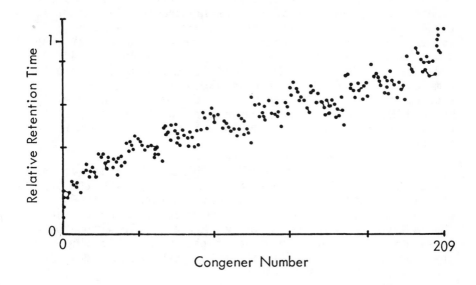

Figure 7-7.   Plot of HRGC Relative Retention Time Versus
Congener Number for all 209 PCBs

See Table 7-IV for more detailed data and chromatographic
conditions.

Reprinted, with permission, from Mullin et al. (1984); copyright 1984 by American Chemical Society.

Recently, bonded liquid phases have been made
available on capillary GC columns.   These exhibit low bleed
and background and have long lifetimes.   Figure 7-5 presents
a HRGC/EIMS chromatogram of a PCB standard on a DB-5 column.
Narrow-bore capillary columns produce both high resolution
and fast analyses, although the capacity is reduced since
less liquid phase is present.   For example, an 8-min chromatogram of Aroclor 1260 has been reported using a short
(4.1 m) capillary column operated isothermally at 222°C
(Schutjes et al., 1984).   A resolution of 70,000 theoretical
plates was obtained with the 55-µm ID fused silica column
coated with OV-1.   Similarly, Onuska (1984) demonstrated
nearly double the resolution with about half the analysis
time (35 versus 60 min) for a mixture of Aroclor 1242, 1254,
and 1260 with a 25 m x 104 µm ID column relative to a 50 m x
300 µm ID column.   Both columns were coated with OV-1, prepared in a similar way.

Despite the advances in column technology, no GC method reported or predicted will separate all 209 PCB congeners. As an example of the overlap problem, Mullin et al. (1984) noted that 11 pairs of congeners coelute on an SE-54 column. Using their conditions, as shown in Table 7-IV, congener numbers 94/61, 70/76, 95/80, 60/56, 145/81, 144/135, 140/139, 133/122, 163/160, 202/171, and 203/196 exhibited similar or identical retention times. In addition to the problem of congener separation, interferences may coelute. While EIMS can readily discriminate against non-PCBs, coeluting major components may affect the mass spectral response of PCBs.

3. Comparison of PGC and HRGC: The relative merits of PGC and HRGC are well-known (Jennings, 1980) and apply to the separation of PCBs. As seen in Figure 7-8 (Bush et al., 1982), HRGC provides better resolution, and thus higher qualitative reliability. PGC yields a simple chromatogram (less data reduction), permits higher sample loading (and therefore possibly lower limits of quantitation), and is generally considered easier to use.

The inherent low resolution of PGC has been further hindered since PGC analyses traditionally have been done isothermally due to requirements of the ECD (see below). This has not only degraded the resolution of later-eluting peaks (see Figures 7-1 and 7-8) but also lengthened the analysis time. On the other hand, HRGC chromatograms are generally temperature-programmed, which yields similar resolution throughout the chromatogram. Until recently, the emphasis with HRGC has been "ultimate" resolution, achieved by slow temperature program rates, low carrier gas flow rates, and, especially, long (> 50 m) capillary columns. This has resulted in very long chromatograms (see Figure 7-3) relative to PGC (see Figure 7-1). An extreme example is the 5-hr chromatogram published by Albro et al. (1981). In the past few years the trend has shifted toward practical applications of HRGC. Using shorter columns and faster temperature program rates, at the sacrifice of some resolution, chromatographers have produced rapid HRGC separations (Figure 7-9).

Properly utilized, HRGC transmits more of the sample injected to the detector than PGC. With less surface area, there are fewer active sites and less chance for adsorptive losses or catalytic degradation. This advantages translates into lower detection limits.

In a direct comparison of PGC and HRGC, no significant difference was observed in the results for the analysis of PCBs in oils at the 30-500 ppm levels (Levine et al., 1983). The PGC analyses were done on a 180 cm x 2 mm ID

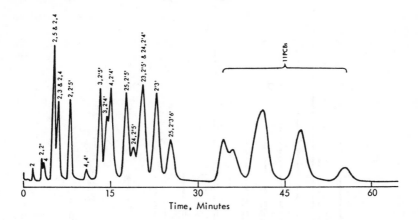

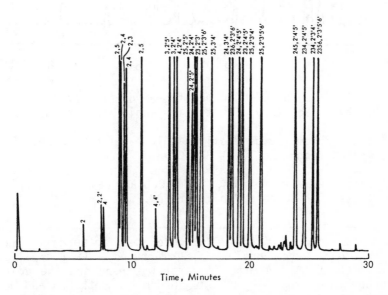

Figure 7-8.   Comparison of PGC/ECD (Top) and HRGC/ECD
             (Bottom) Chromatograms of 29 PCB Congeners

The PGC/ECD chromatogram was obtained on a 5.2 m Apiezon L
column operated isothermally at 250°C, as described by Jensen
and Sundström (1974).   The HRGC/ECD chromatogram was obtained
on a 20 m x 0.29 mm ID glass capillary coated with Apeizon L
and operated at an initial temperature of 70°C, programmed at
10°C/min to 130°C, then at 4°C/min to 230°C.

Reprinted, with permission, from Bush et al. (1982); copyright 1982 by Association of Official Analytical Chemists,
Inc.

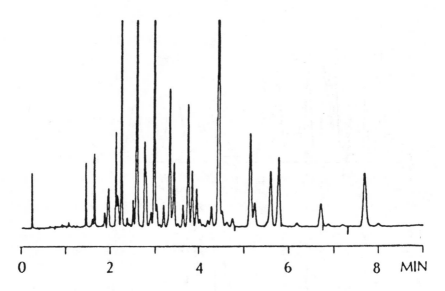

Figure 7-9.   HRGC/ECD Chromatogram of Aroclor 1260
Short Capillary Illustrating Rapid Separation

The 4.1 m x 55 µm ID fused silica column was coated with OV-1
and operated isothermally at 222°C.

Reprinted, with permission, from Onuska (1984); copyright
1984 by Elsevier Science Publishers BV.

---

glass column packed with 3% OV-1, operated isothermally. The
HRGC analyses were done on a 30-m fused silica capillary
coated with SE-54. A Grob injector was used and the column
was programmed from 50-250°C at 10°C/min. Both ECD and HECD
were used as detectors.

B. Injection

The injector is an integral and important part of
the chromatographic process. While often overlooked and not
even reported, the type of injector can affect resolution,
discriminations, and sensitivity. In PGC, most modern instruments have "on-column" injectors, while earlier work favored injection into a chamber, with the analytes being swept
onto the column after vaporization. This latter technique is
the basis of HRGC's split and splitless injectors. Recently,
on-column injectors have become available for HRGC and provide generally superior chromatography. One detriment of
on-column injectors is that, with dirty matrices, inorganics,

polymeric materials, etc., stay on the front of the column, degrading performance and increasing the background. The common solution is to break off the front portion of the column periodically.

C. Detection

The GC detector is a transducer, converting a chemical signal (molecules in a gas stream) to an electrical signal. Some detectors (e.g., FID) destroy the compounds in the detection process, while others (e.g., ECD) are non-destructive. GC detectors are discussed in more detail in several monographs and reviews (David, 1974; Sevcik, 1976; Adlard, 1978; McNair and Bonnelli, 1969).

GC detectors may be categorized as either universal or selective. The ECD and Hall electrolytic conductivity detector (HECD) are selective toward halogenated compounds. This selectivity, coupled with its extreme sensitivity, has made ECD very popular for analysis of trace levels (residues) of pesticides and PCBs and has, in fact, had a significant role in regulatory actions on these classes of compounds. FID is the most common GC detector and is an universal detector, giving similar responses for most organic compounds. Thus, FID would be unsuitable for detection of PCBs in a complex matrix.

Mass spectrometry and Fourier transform infrared spectrometry (FTIR) are in essence both universal and selective GC detectors. By focusing on a spectral property characteristic of a compound or class of compounds, these detectors can be quite specific. However, by using the full spectral range, any compound eluting from the GC will be detected. Due to the much higher information content of mass and infrared spectra, identifications made by GC/MS or GC/FTIR generally have much greater certainty than those made by other detectors.

The analysis of PCBs generally requires selectivity and sensitivity. Even after cleanup, PCBs are usually a minor component of the sample; mixed in with other halocarbons (e.g., DDE), hydrocarbons, lipids, etc. Thus, the detector often must selectively detect PCBs in the presence of other compounds present at orders of magnitude higher concentration. Furthermore, the levels typically observed in food, biota, tissue, soil, and other matrices of interest are in the parts per billion range. These levels strain the capabilities of even the most sensitive detection device such as ECD, resulting in a large number of "not detected" values in many reports.

The choice of detector often depends upon the level of analytes. Low concentrations demand a detector capable of detecting low amounts (high sensitivity). Figure 7-10 presents the typical range and detection limits for most of the GC detectors used in analysis for PCBs. The detection limit of the HECD is 10^{-11} g with a linear range up to about 10^{-2} g, as measured for lindane (Anderson and Hall, 1980). As can be seen, ECD exhibits the lowest limit of detection (LOD).

The reported LOD for PCBs in a variety of matrices are listed in Table 7-V. Comparison of the reported LODs is difficult because no standard definition of LOD was used. Glaser et al. (1981) followed a rigorous definition and experimentally determined the LOD with a fair degree of confidence, while other investigators clearly approximated the LOD. The issue is further clouded by inconsistency in presenting the LOD as a measure of the instrumental determination or the entire procedure. Some LODs are reported for standard solutions, while others take into account the interferences in the matrix which raise the detection limit considerably.

Every review article (Risebrough, 1971; Reynolds, 1971; Fishbein, 1972; Lincer, 1973; Hutzinger et al, 1974a; Sherma, 1975; Fuller et al., 1976; Margeson, 1977; Krull, 1977; Safe, 1976) has covered the subject of ECD detection of GC effluents. Fishbein (1972), Sherma (1975), and Hutzinger et al. (1974a) all reviewed the use of electrolytic conductivity detectors for PCB determination. Safe (1976) and Hutzinger et al. (1974a) discussed the use of flame ionization detection (FID), mostly with respect to calibration of ECD or establishing ECD response factors. Hutzinger et al. (1974a) noted that for the mono- and dichlorobiphenyls FID and ECD sensitivities are comparable.

As noted in Table 3-I, most of the standard methods specify ECD as either the detector or one of the options. FID is the detector prescribed in the American Society for Testing and Materials (1980) procedure for determining PCBs in capacitor Askarels. In this case, the matrix is well-characterized and generally contains no other compounds in the PCB retention window. HECD is permitted as an alternate detector in three procedures (EPA, 1978; EPA, 1981a; FDA, 1977).

1. Electron capture detection: The electron capture detector (ECD) detects the drop in current caused by the absorption of electrons by the sample compound. A radioactive source emits β particles (electrons) which are swept toward the anode by an applied voltage across the electrodes

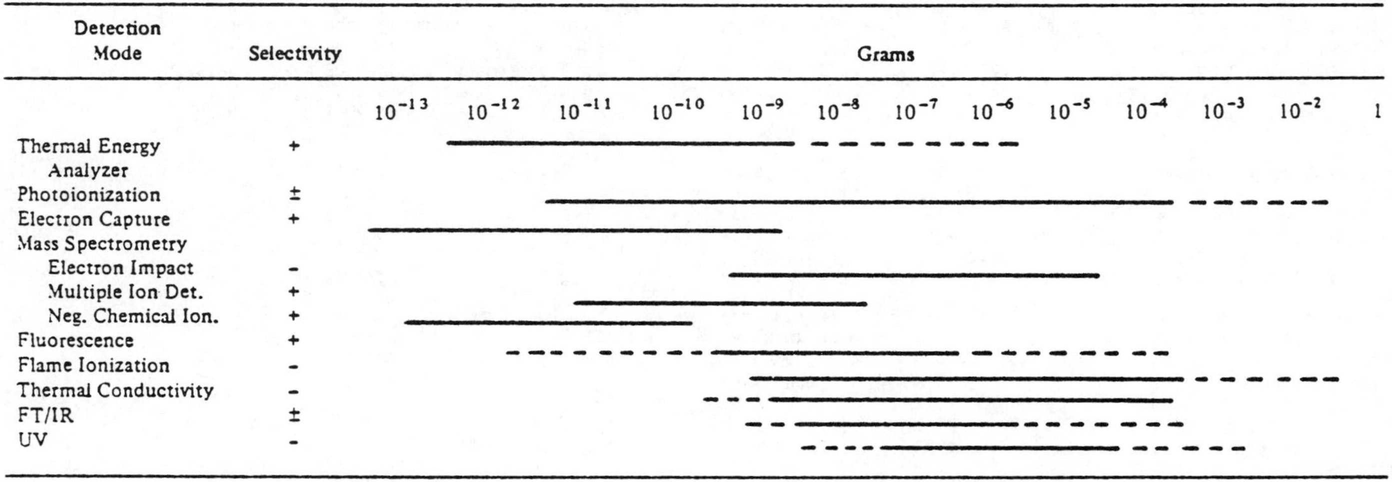

Figure 7-10. Detection Limits and Dynamic Range for Several Instrumental Methods

Reprinted, with permission, from Pellizzari (1981); copyright 1984 by Butterworth Publishers.

Table 7-V. Reported Limits of Detection for PCBs

Instrument	Reported LOD	Converted LOD[a] (µg/g or ppm)	PCB Type	Matrix	Reference
GC/ECD	0.065 µg/L	0.000065	Aroclor 1242	Dist. water	Glaser et al., 1981
	0.5 ppb	0.0005	Aroclors	River water	Kuehl et al., 1980a
	6.5 ppb	0.0065	Aroclors	Pure solution	Teichman et al., 1978
	50 ppb	0.05	Aroclors	Milk	Tessari and Savage, 1980
	1-0.1 ppb/isomer	0.001-0.0001	Isomers	Vegetable	Tuinstra et al., 1981
	0.5 ppm	0.5	Aroclors	Transformer fluid	Kirshen, 1981a,b
	1 ppm	1.0	Total PCB	Oil	Chesler et al., 1981
	0.5 ppm	0.5	Total PCB	Oils	Balya and Farrah, 1980
	0.6 µg/L	0.0006	Perchlorinated	Ground water	Stratton et al., 1979
	1 ng/m^3	NA[b]	Perchlorinated	Air	Stratton et al., 1978b
	0.1 ng/m^3	NA[b]	Theoretical per isomer	Air	Lewis et al., 1977a
	3 µg/L	0.003	Aroclor 1260	Blood serum	Kreiss et al., 1981
	1 ppm	1	10 homologs	Pigments	DCMA, 1982
	10 ppb	0.01	Aroclor 1254	Milk	McKinney et al., 1984
	4 ppb	0.004	Aroclor 1254	Serum	McKinney et al., 1984
GC/TCD	10 µg	-	Aroclor 1254	Air	Barton and Arsenault, 1982
GC/HECD	1 mg/kg	1.0	Aroclors	Oil	EPA, 1981a
GC/EIMS	30 µg/L	0.030	Aroclor 1221	Dist. water	Glaser et al., 1981
	36 µg/L	0.036	Aroclor 1254	Dist. water	Glaser et al., 1981
	0.01-0.2 µg/L	0.01-0.2	Single congener	Industrial sample extract	Tindall and Wininger, 1980
	1-4 ppb[c]	0.001-0.004	Single congener	NS	Westerberg et al., 1984
	5 ppm	5	Single congener	Chlorinated hydrocarbons	Collard and Irwin, 1982a,b, 1983
	1 µg/g	1	Single congener	Products and wastes	Erickson et al., 1983d
HREIMS	10 ppb	0.01	Aroclors	Biological extracts	Safe et al., 1975

Table 7-V (concluded)

Instrument	Reported LOD	Converted LOD[a] (µg/g or ppm)	PCB Type	Matrix	Reference
GC/NCIMS	> 10 ppb[c]	> 0.01	Mono- to penta- isomers	NS[d]	Westerberg et al., 1984
	3.8-0.09 ppb[c]	0.004-0.0001	Hexa- to deca- isomers	NS	Westerberg et al., 1984
Dir. Probe NCIMS	~ 1 ppb	0.001	NS	Biological extracts	Dougherty et al., 1980
TLC	0.5 ppm	0.5	Aroclor	Adipose	Bush and Lo, 1973
	< 0.04 ppm	< 0.04	Aroclor	Milk	Savage et al., 1973a
	0.1 µg	-	Aroclor	Animal tissue	De Vos and Peet, 1971
	0.05 µg	-	Aroclor	NS	Koch, 1979
	0.2 µg	-	Aroclor	Animal tissue	Mulhern et al., 1971
	1 µg	-	Aroclor	NS	Ismail and Bonner, 1974

a Converted to common units of micrograms per gram (parts per million) assuming 1 mL = 1 g density.
b NA = not applicable.
c See Table 7-XVI for additional details.
d NS = not specified.

(10-50 V). This electron migration produces a current, approximately 10^{-9} amperes. If a molecule or ion capable of absorbing an electron enters the detector, $M + e^- = [Me^-] +$ energy. The absorption or capture of electrons by M will reduce the current, since the species $[Me^-]$ migrates more slowly than an electron. In older ECDs the drop in current yielded the detector response. Most ECDs now sold use pulsing circuitry to maintain a constant current. The frequency of the pulses required to maintain the constant current is the detector response. Pulsed ECDs exhibit a greater linearity range than the old constant current models.

Because of its extreme sensitivity and selectivity toward halogenated compounds, ECD has been the most common detector for GC analysis of PCBs. While it is considered a selective detector, it does detect many non-PCB compounds (halogenated pesticides, PCNs, chloroaromatics, phthalate and adipate esters, and other compounds) which may be differentiated from PCBs only on the basis of retention time. Figure 7-11 illustrates the potential interferences from chlorinated pesticides. Figure 7-12 illustrates the actual interferences observed in a chlorinated organic process intermediate (Hanneman, 1982). Clearly, ECD was not a suitable detector for this sample.

In addition to ECD-active compounds such as halogenated organics and phthalate esters, there are other interferences which do not give discrete peaks. As mentioned in Chapter 6, elemental sulfur can interfere with PCB analysis in sediment and other samples which have been subjected to anaerobic degradation conditions. Another non-specific interference is mineral oil (ASTM, 1983). Mineral oil, a complex mixture of hydrocarbons, often contains PCBs as a result of cross-contamination of transformer oils. A typical analysis of mineral oil for PCBs entails simple dilution with hexane to reduce the viscosity and also achieve a concentration in the linear range of the ECD. The mineral oil in the diluted sample reduces the ECD response (ASTM, 1983). In order to minimize the effects of the mineral oil interference on the quantitation, ASTM (1983) recommends that the sample and standard contain the same amount of mineral oil.

A major disadvantage of ECD is the range of response factors (Tables 7-IV, 7-VI, 7-VII, and 7-VIII and Figure 7-13) which different PCB congeners exhibit. The earlier PGC/ECD work (Table 7-VI) has a response factor range of about 7000, while recent HRGC/ECD work (Table 7-VII) has a range of only about 100. Data sets similar to that in Table 7-VI were published by Zitko et al. (1971) and Hattori et al.

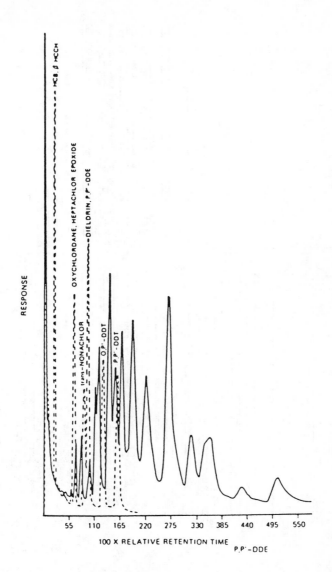

Figure 7-11. PGC/ECD Chromatograms of Aroclor 1260 (921 pg,
     Solid Line) and Nine Common Pesticides (38 pg Each,
          Dashed Line) Illustrating the Potential
                    for Interference

A 183 x 0.4 cm ID glass column packed with 3% SE-30 was operated at 195°C, isothermal with a nitrogen flow of 15 mL/
min.

Reprinted, with permission, from Needham et al. (1980); copyright 1980 by American Chemical Society.

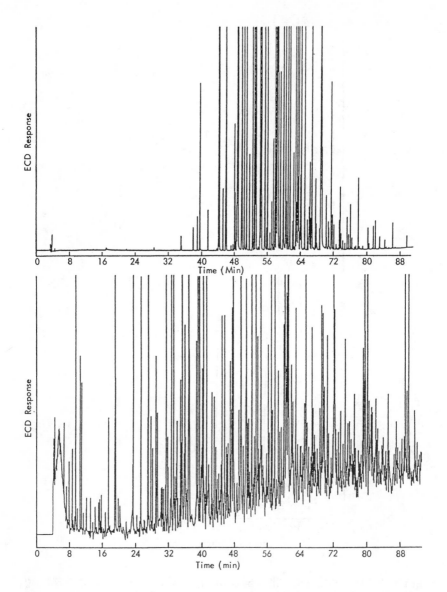

Figure 7-12.   HRGC/ECD Chromatogram of Process Intermediate
              (Bottom) and Aroclor 1248 (Top)

The sample contained mono- and dichlorobiphenyls and over 500
ECD-responsive interferences.   A 60-m DB-1 (bonded polydimethylsiloxane) fused silica capillary column was programmed
from 100°C to 290°C at 2°/min.

Table 7-VI. Relative Molar Responses of Electron Capture
and Flame Ionization Detectors to Some Chlorobiphenyls

| Chlorobiphenyl | Relative Molar Response | |
	Electron Capture	Flame Ionization
2-	1.00	1.00
3-	0.20	0.92
4-	1.10	0.87
2,2'-di	5.16	0.99
2,4-di	17.7	0.86
2,6-di	32.0	0.91
3,3'-di	6.10	0.94
3,4-di	15.2	0.86
4,4'-di	5.97	0.81
2,4,4'-tri	135	0.78
2,2',4,4'-tetra	106	0.87
2,2',6,6'-tetra	20.6	0.90
3,3',4,4'-tetra	396	0.87
3,3',5,5'-tetra	320	0.85
2,3,4,5-tetra	367	0.87
2,3,5,6-tetra	259	0.71
2,2',4,4',6,6'-hexa	347	
3,3',4,4',5,5'-hexa	726	
2,2',3,3',4,4',6,6'-octa	1,180	
2,2',3,3',5,5',6,6'-octa	1,150	
deca	1,410	
N	21	16
Mean	310	0.88
SD	438	0.07
RSD (%)	140	8.3

Table 7-VII. Summary of ECD Relative Response Factors[a]
(Mullin et al., 1984)

Homolog	No. of Isomers	Mean	SD	RSD (%)	Minimum Value	Maximum Value
0	1	0.0251	-	-	-	-
1	3	0.0329	0.0118	36	0.0193	0.04
2	12	0.2432	0.1825	75	0.0374	0.69
3	24	0.5631	0.2287	41	0.313	1.0935
4	42	0.6750	0.1992	30	-	-
5	46	0.7172	0.2115	29	0.4308	1.3987
6	42	0.8550	0.2567	30	0.444	1.389
7	24	1.1529	0.3705	32	0.381	2.044
8	12	1.0720	0.4452	42	0.369	1.868
9	3	1.3914	0.2551	18	1.1756	1.673
10	1	1.139	-	-	-	-

a Values summarized from Table 7-IV.

Table 7-VIII. Comparison of PGC/ECD Response Factors Obtained by Different Laboratories[a]

PCB Congener	Concentration[b] (mg/mL)	Laboratory Number						Mean	RSD (%)
		1	2	3	4	5	6		
2-Chlorobiphenyl	0.073415	1.00[c]	1.00	1.00	1.00	1.00	1.00	-	-
3,3'-Dichlorobiphenyl	0.088035	1.95	0.9939	0.729	0.7346	0.605	1.199	1.036	48
2,4,5-Trichlorobiphenyl	0.008180	0.19	0.139	0.065	0.0850	0.054	0.11	0.107	48
2,2',4,4'-Tetrachlorobiphenyl	0.018625	0.17	0.138	0.090	0.0671	0.058	0.095	0.103	42
2,3',4,5',6-Pentachlorobiphenyl	0.005670	0.11	0.110	0.032	0.0558	0.027	0.074	0.068	54
2,2',3,3',6,6'-Hexachlorobiphenyl	0.011265	0.17	0.141	0.081	0.0555	0.070	0.110	0.105	42
2,2',3,4,5,5',6-Heptachlorobiphenyl	0.005545	0.053	0.0625	0.026	0.0265	0.015	0.041	0.037	48
2,2',3,3',4,4',5,5'-Octachlorobiphenyl	0.006345	0.062	0.0489	0.026	0.0260	0.013	0.038	0.036	50
2,2',3,3',4,4',5,5',6-Nonachlorobiphenyl	0.006715	0.099	0.0695	0.032	0.0413	0.024	0.056	0.054	51
2,2',3,3',4,4',5,5',6,6'-Decachlorobiphenyl	0.004700	0.086	0.0564	0.026	0.0376	0.023	0.049	0.046	57
Reported value for 2-chlorobiphenyl		2.43	22.89	0.0310	40.70	0.2298	0.0715		
Reported ranged for 2-chlorobiphenyl		0.84	4.4	0.0247	15	0.0421	0.0054		

a   Study conducted as part of a collaborative validation of the Dry Color Manufacturer's Association method for by-product
PCBs in pigments (DCMA, 1982; see Chapter 10). All laboratories analyzed four dilutions over one order of magnitude
to obtain the response factor. Laboratories 3 and 5 used integrators to measure peak heights. The other laboratories
used manual measurement of peak heights in various units.

b   The stock standard mixture R-9427-184A was supplied to the laboratories at the concentration shown. The laboratories
selected the appropriate dilutions to obtain a working range.

c   All values were recalculated and normalized to 2-chlorobiphenyl to make the data comparable. The reported value and
range for 2-chlorobiphenyl are shown below to illustrate the scatter.

Sources: DCMA, 1982; reproduced with permission, by Dry Color Manufacturers' Association.

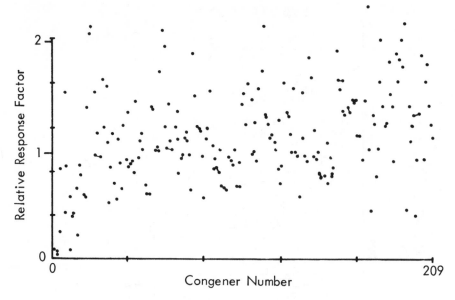

Figure 7-13.   Plot of HRGC/ECD Relative Response Factor
               Versus Congener Number for All 209 PCBs

See Table 7-IV for more detailed data and chromatographic
conditions.

Reprinted, with permission, from Mullin et al. (1984); copyright 1984 by American Chemical Society.

(1981) with response factors ranges about 540 and 9000, respectively. The opposite trend in response factors in Table
7-VIII, relative to the other tables, presumably results from
differences in the equations used (i.e., whether the PCB response is in the denominator or numerator). Boe and Egaas
(1979), Onuska et al. (1983) and Singer et al. (1983) have
also published ECD response factors. The range of response
factors seriously inhibits reliable quantitation.

        The difference in response factors noted above may
be a function of the differences in detector design and GC
column throughput. In addition, the HRGC is temperature-
programmed, while PGC data were presumably obtained isothermally. Despite these differences, all four tables clearly
illustrate that, even within a homolog, the RSD is very large
and would result in poor accuracy if quantitation involves
extrapolation from one isomer to another. For example, the
ECD relative response factors for all 12 octachlorobiphenyls
showed a range from 1.007 to 2.644 (range of 2.6X) with a RSD
of 35% (Mullin et al., 1981). A more recent tabulation
(Table 7-IV and 7-VII) of the response factors for these same

compounds by the same authors (Mullin et al., 1984) yielded much different results. While the values would be expected to differ by virtue of changing the internal standard (2,2',4,4',5,5'-hexachlorobiphenyl in the former publication and octachloronaphthalene in the latter), the trends among the sets of response factors were not similar (i.e., the highest in one set was not the highest in the other). This illustrates the importance of calibration of instruments at the time of the analysis.

The ECD response factors for a solution of one isomer of each homolog were compared for six laboratories as part of a collaborative validation of the Dry Color Manufacturers Association method for by-product PCBs in pigments (DCMA, 1982; see Chapter 10 for further discussion). The laboratories reported a mean value for the response factor (RF) and the range of the RFs obtained by analysis of four dilutions of the stock solution ranging from one order of magnitude in concentration. As shown at the bottom of Table 7-VIII, the intralaboratory range was quite large. The study authors attributed the wide range to the nonlinearity of ECD detectors and lack of amplifiers with linearizers in older instruments. They noted that samples should be concentrated or diluted to within ± 25% of the standard to get reliable results. The results presented in Table 7-VIII were recalculated from the original data to normalize the response factors. These normalized RFs permit direct comparison of the data from the different laboratories. The subject of ECD response factor variability is also discussed in the Quantitation section of Chapter 8.

To further complicate its quantitative use, ECD has notoriously variable sensitivity. On the same day, an instrument's response can drift enough to dramatically affect the quantitation of PCBs. The sensitivity (i.e., limit of detection) of GC/ECD is affected by the brand, individual instrument, daily instrumental response, attenuation, injection volume, and detector temperature (Rust, 1984).

Aue and Kapila (1978) presented a novel dual GC where selected peaks from the first ECD were "heart-cut" routed to a second PGC column, and detected by a second ECD. The chemical degradation of PCBs in the first detector yielded new electron-capturing species and provided confirmatory evidence of PCBs. The system probably is not suited to routine application.

PGC/ECD is generally the method of choice for analysis of transformer oils, hydraulic oils, askarels, mineral oil dielectric fluid, and other similar matrices which must

be assayed for PCB content prior to incineration or other destruction (Copland and Gohmann, 1982). The PCBs generally
resemble Aroclor standards, halogenated interferences are almost nonexistent, GC/ECD is highly selective against the hydrocarbon matrix, and the technique is relatively inexpensive
to operate.

A field-portable PGC/ECD was used to obtain rapid
measurements of PCBs in sediment and soil (Spittler, 1983,
1984). The sample preparation consisted of a single solvent
extraction and the PCBs were eluted within 9 min. In a 6-hr
period, 40 soils and 10 QC samples were analyzed, with concentrations ranging from 0.2 to 24,000 ppm. The use of field
analysis permits rapid decisions in a cleanup operation and
reduces the need for either return visits to a site by a
cleanup crew or excessive excavation of uncontaminated soils.
Similar portable systems have been reported (Colby et al.,
1983; Picker and Colby, 1984).

The only novel aspects of most articles deals with
qualitative or quantitative aspects of the detector and are
discussed in Chapter 8. Two studies comparing ECD with the
electrolytic conductivity detector are discussed below.

2. Electrolytic conductivity: The Hall electrolytic conductivity detector (HECD) measures the change in
conductivity of a solution containing HCl or HBr which is
formed by pyrolysis of halogenated organic GC effluents. The
column eluent is oxidized in a microcombustion furnace in a
quartz tube. The reaction products are absorbed into the
liquid electrolyte in the gas-liquid contactor and the electrolytic conductivity of the liquid measured between the two
electrodes. The reaction products of non-halogenated organics are CO_2, H_2O, N_2, and SO_2. The SO_2 is scrubbed out
with CaO and the other components give little or no response,
leaving HCl, HBr, and the other hydrogen halides as the detected species. The HECD exhibits 10^5-10^6 selectivity for
halogenated compounds over other compounds. It also gives a
linear response over at least a 10^3 range. It is much less
subject to interference from nonhalogenated compounds than
ECD and the response is proportional to the number of chlorines. The high limit of quantitation and difficulty of operation are the disadvantages of this detector.

Webb and McCall (1973) and Sawyer (1978a) used HECD
in the characterization of Aroclor standards. Serum et al.
(1973) used HECD, ECD, and electron impact mass spectrometry
as PGC detectors in analysis of paper products for PCBs and
other compounds. Hofstader et al. (1974) determined that

sulfur compounds in certain petroleum oils gave positive interferences in PGC/ECD determinations of PCBs. Flame photo-
metric, microcoulometric, and Hall detectors were used to
characterize the PCBs and interferences. Chesler et al.
(1981) characterized oil products in the preparation of National Bureau of Standards standard reference materials for
PCBs in oil. They used both ECD and HECD as HRGC detectors.
The ECD was found to be more sensitive than the HECD by two
orders of magnitude and easier to maintain in a noncontami-
nated state. However, ECD response factors varied for different PCB isomers, while the molar response to chlorine
which is obtained from the HECD appeared to be constant. The
HECD exhibited a wider linearity range and was more selective
as it responded only to halogenated compounds. Butler (1981)
demonstrated the application of HECD coupled to both packed
and HRGC columns in several matrices: milk, fish, transformer oil, and water. Detection of 1 ng of Aroclor 1254 was
shown.

An interesting, though tangential, use of HECD was
presented by Dolan et al. (1972), Dolan and Hall (1973), and
Su and Price (1973). By adjusting the HECD operating parameters they selectively detected organochlorine pesticides in
the presence of PCB interferences.

HECD and ECD were compared for their use in detecting PCBs in waste oil, hydraulic fluid, capacitor fluid, and
transformer oil (Sonchik et al., 1984). They found both detectors acceptable, but noted that the HECD gave higher results with less precision than the ECD. The method detection
limits ranged from 3-12 ppm for HECD and 2-4 ppm for ECD.
Greater than 100% recovery of spikes analyzed by the HECD indicated a non-specific response to non-PCB components, since
extraneous peaks were not observed. Nevertheless, the
authors recommended HECD for general applications, because
simple dilution may be employed for the sample preparation.
They noted, however, that injection of such large amounts of
oil was injurious to both the column and the reactor tube in
the detector. It was especially difficult to analyze butylated monochlorodiphenyl ether and phthalate ester dielectrics
without sample pretreatment. They also noted that ECD is
easier to operate, maintain, and troubleshoot than the HECD.

Another comparison of HECD and ECD for the analysis
of PCBs in oils at the 30-500 ppm levels found that the type
of detector made no significant difference in the results
(Levine et al., 1983). The authors noted that higher accuracy had been expected from the more specific HECD. They
postulated that the cleanup procedures (Florisil, alumina,
and sulfuric acid) all had effectively removed the non-PCB
species which would have caused interferences in the ECD and
degraded its accuracy.

3. <u>Mass spectrometry</u>: Mass spectrometers have only recently come into common use as GC detectors, although they have been widely used for decades in other areas. Mass spectrometers contain three major components: a region where ions are generated (source), a mass analyzer (magnet or quadrupole), and an ion detector. Molecules introduced to a mass spectrometer via a GC are generally ionized by a beam of high-energy electrons ("electron impact") or by reaction with ionized molecules such as methane ("chemical ionization"). The ionized molecule and/or its fragments are then swept to the analyzer section. In a magnetic sector instrument, the strength of the applied magnetic field controls the mass (actually mass-to-charge ratio, m/z) of the ions which can pass through the curved flight path. A quadrupole analyzer has a flight path down the center of four rods. Oscillating RF and DC fields of opposing polarities are applied to the rods. Only those ions of the desired mass pass through the quadrupole; the others oscillate out of the path and strike the rods. Ions passing through either type of analyzer are focused on an electron multiplier for detection. The polarity of the applied voltages determine whether positive ions (usually) or negative ions are transmitted and detected. Associated electronics control all of the components and rapidly change the mass analyzer conditions to scan a mass range.

A GC/MS produces a chromatogram consisting of data points at about 1-sec intervals, which are actually full mass spectra. The data are stored by a dedicated computer and may be retrieved in a variety of ways. The data file contains information on the amount of compound (signal intensity), molecular weight ("parent" ion), and chemical composition (fragmentation patterns and isotopic clusters). A reconstructed ion chromatogram (RIC or total ion current profile) is the sum of all measured ions and is analogous to the response of a flame ionization detector (see Figures 7-4 and 7-14). Extracted ion current profiles (EICPs) or ion plots are chromatograms of only selected portions of the data; usually a single ion. As illustrated in Figure 7-15, the EICPs for PCBs allow comparison of the isotopic ratios and also exhibit characteristic patterns for commercially derived PCBs. Finally, the individual spectra may be used to identify compounds. The spectrum in Figure 7-16 is typical of a hexachlorobiphenyl. More complete descriptions of GC/MS instrumentation, principles, and data interpretation are available from many monographs and analytical text books. One example is McLafferty (1980).

MS is particularly suited to detection of PCBs because of their intense molecular ion and the characteristic

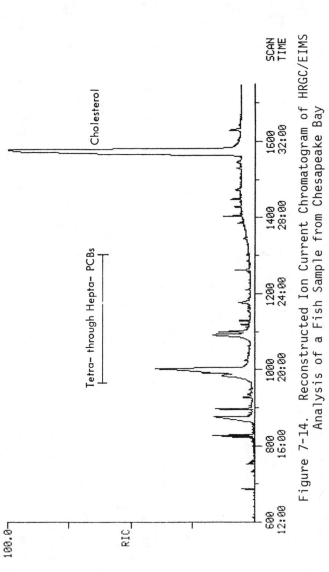

Figure 7-14. Reconstructed Ion Current Chromatogram of HRGC/EIMS Analysis of a Fish Sample from Chesapeake Bay

The area where the tetra- through heptachlorobiphenyls would elute is marked on the chromatogram. The PCBs in the sample are not apparent in this figure because of the higher levels of interferences. The fish was extracted with hexane and cleaned up with gel permeation chromatography. The chromatogram was obtained on a 30-m DB-5 column, with a temperature of 60°C for 2 min, programmed at 10°C/min to 410°C. Full scan, low resolution electron impact (70 eV) data were collected for masses from m/z 143 to 517.

Unpublished data, Mitchell D. Erickson and Stephen E. Swanson, April 2, 1984, Midwest Research Institute, Kansas City, Missouri.

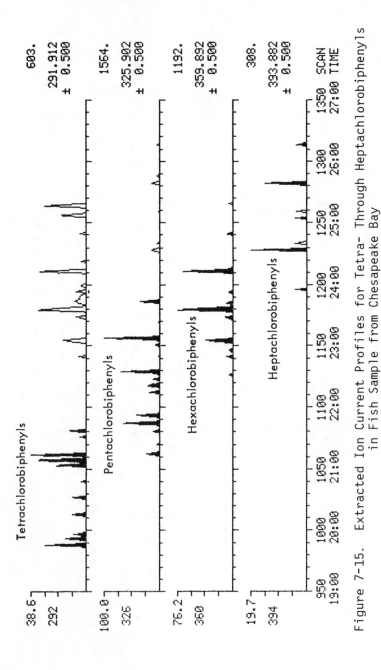

Figure 7-15. Extracted Ion Current Profiles for Tetra- Through Heptachlorobiphenyls in Fish Sample from Chesapeake Bay

See Figure 7-14 for analysis details. Shaded peaks are PCBs. Unshaded peaks are either not PCBs or fragments of higher chlorinated homologs. For example, the peaks at Scan Nos. 1155, 1180, and 1211 in the m/z 292 EICP are fragments (M-70) of hexachlorobiphenyls.

Unpublished data, Mitchell D. Erickson and Stephen E. Swanson, April 2, 1984, Midwest Research Institute, Kansas City, Missouri.

214

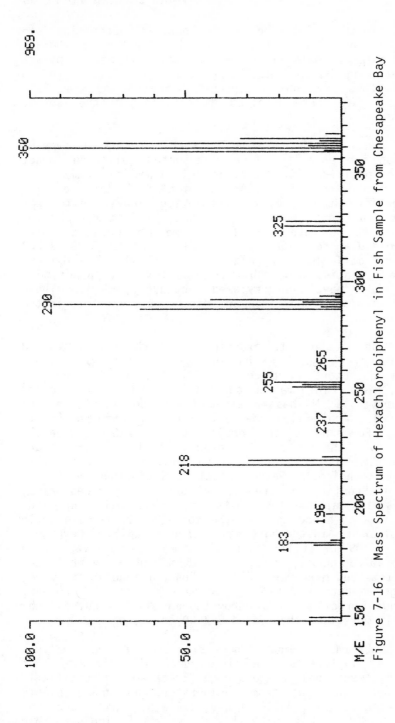

Figure 7-16. Mass Spectrum of Hexachlorobiphenyl in Fish Sample from Chesapeake Bay

Spectrum No. 1180 in Figures 7-14 and 7-15; see Figure 7-14 for details on analysis.

Unpublished data, Mitchell D. Erickson and Stephen E. Swanson, April 2, 1984, Midwest Research Institute, Kansas City, Missouri.

215

chlorine cluster. Chlorine has two naturally occurring isotopes, ^{35}Cl and ^{37}Cl, which occur in a ratio of 100:33.
Thus, a molecule with one chlorine atom will have a parent
ion, M, and an M+2 peak at 33% relative intensity. With two
chlorine atoms, M+2 has an intensity of 66% and M+4, 11%.
Appendix C gives more detailed presentations of the isotope
ratios.

Mass spectrometry may be subdivided by the type of
ionization and polarity of ions detected (electron impact
ionization/positive ion detection, EI; chemical ionization/
positive ion detection, CI; and chemical ionization/negative
ion detection, NCI) or by the resolution, low (able to separate at least unit masses, i.e., m/z 321 from m/z 322) or
high (able to separate ions of the same unit mass, but different molecular formulae, i.e., $C_{12}Cl_5H$, m/z 319.8529--a PCB
fragment--from $C_{12}H_4O_2Cl_4$, m/z 319.8967--TCDD. The differences and relative applicabilities to toxic compounds, including PCBs, have been reviewed (Dougherty, 1980). These
different modes of operation are discussed separately in the
subsections below.

Because of its expense, complexity of data, and
lack of sensitivity, GC/MS has not been used as extensively
as other detectors (particularly GC/ECD), despite its in-
herently higher information content. As the above factors
have improved, GC/MS has become much more popular for analysis of PCBs, and will probably continue to increase in importance. For example, the sensitivity of GC/MS has steadily
improved over the years. As noted in Table 7-V and Figure
7-10, GC/EIMS is still best characterized as a moderately
sensitive technique. Several factors including the introduction of "routine" instruments without costly accessories,
decreases in data system costs, and mass-marketing techniques, have combined to keep the costs of GC/MS down while
prices of other instruments have risen steadily. Nevertheless, a GC/MS is still considerably more expensive than a
GC/ECD ($40,000 and up versus $10,000-$20,000). With larger
data systems and more versatile and "user-friendly" software,
the large amount of data is more easily handled. However,
data reduction of a GC/MS chromatogram still requires substantially more time than for a GC/ECD chromatogram.

GC/EIMS has found increasing use in trace analysis
of PCBs as pollutants, including human milk (Yakushiji et
al., 1978), municipal sewage sludge (Erickson and Pellizzari,
1979), and stack gas from incinerators and power plants
(Levins et al., 1979; Haile et al., 1983a,b, 1984). One area
where GC/EIMS (or possibly other MS modes) is indispensible
as the primary analytical technique is for samples which contain large amounts of other chlorinated organics. In these

samples, chlorine-specific detectors (ECD or HECD) cannot discriminate between PCBs and interferents. An example is the analysis of chlorinated organic products and wastes in which the PCBs are generated as by-products. GC/EIMS has been recommended as the technique of choice for these types of samples (CMA, 1981; Erickson and Stanley, 1982).

a. Electron impact mass spectrometry: Electron impact mass spectrometry (EIMS) ranks second only to ECD in popularity as a GC detector for PCBs. Electron impact has been and continues to be the most widely used MS ionization technique. While the chemical ionization (CI) and negative chemical ionization (NCI) techniques are often more sensitive (Table 7-V, Figure 7-10), their operation is more complicated and the spectral patterns and response factors are much less reproducible.

EIMS has been applied to PCB determination using both direct probe and gas chromatography for sample introduction. Early work generally employed the then-exotic technique for confirmation of GC/ECD results. In recent years, as GC/EIMS has become more routine, analysts have increasingly chosen GC/EIMS as the primary technique. As listed in Table 3-I, several standard procedures use GC/EIMS, either as the primary analytical technique or as the confirmatory technique. The application of EIMS to analysis for PCBs has been reviewed by Fishbein (1972), Oswald et al. (1974b), Hutzinger et al. (1974a), Safe (1976), and Stan (1981).

Among the pioneers, Biros et al. (1970) used HRGC/EIMS to determine PCBs in human adipose tissue, Bagley et al. (1970) determined PCBs in bald eagles by PGC/EIMS, and Bonelli (1972a,b) presented PGC/EIMS data for an Aroclor 1254/chlorinated pesticide mixture. In addition, Sissons and Welti (1971), Webb and McCall (1972, 1973), Ugawa et al. (1973), Duinker and Hillebrand (1983) and Tuinstra and Traag (1983) employed GC/EIMS in characterization of commercial PCB mixture. Using both electron impact and chemical ionization mass spectrometry, Oswald et al. (1974a) were able to differentiate some isomers in complex mixtures from their spectra.

While full spectra provide the most qualitative information, the use of selected ion monitoring enhances both instrument sensitivity and selectivity and simplifies data interpretation. Examples of this technique have been presented by Beggs and Banks (1976), Eichelberger et al. (1974), Tressl and Wessely (1976), Martelli et al. (1981), Collard and Irwin (1982a,b, 1983), and Erickson and Pellizzari (1977, 1979). Eichelberger et al. (1974) gave ion selection criteria which were based on their intensity and

the probability of interference from higher homologs or other
compounds. Table 7-IX presents a set of SIM ions appropriate
for PCBs originally published by Rote and Morris (1973) and
expanded upon by Erickson et al. (1982, 1983d). Generally,
only the ratio of the primary to secondary ions is necessary
for qualitative identification. The tertiary ion is used
only when the other data are questionable. The analyst must
also include ions for the internal standards and recovery
surrogates added to the sample.

A compromise between full scan and SIM techniques is mass chromatography, also called extracted ion current profiles. Full spectra are collected and then ion intensity versus file position plots are extracted from the
data by the computer. Thus, mass chromatography has the ease
of interpretation of SIM but higher LOQs since full spectra
are collected. These full spectra are available for qualitative use if needed. Canada and Regnier (1976) presented a
technique which used mass chromatography to monitor the ion
ratios in the PCB isotopic clusters.

Another compromise technique, limited mass
scanning (LMS), involves scanning the spectrometer only over
the mass range of interest (e.g., molecular ion cluster).
This permits the spectrometer to spend more time on the ions
of interest and thus achieve better sensitivity than the full
scan mode. Figure 7-17 presents an example of an LMS analysis (Erickson et al., 1983b). The lower portion of the figure, the "reconstructed ion chromatogram" (RIC), is a sum of
all of the ranges scanned. The plots of the individual ions
for the octachlorobiphenyl and ^{13}C-octachlorobiphenyl clearly
show fewer peaks and thus, less complexity than the RIC.

Tindall and Wininger (1980), Erickson et al.
(1982, 1983a,b,d) and Westerberg et al. (1984) utilized LMS
in their GC/EIMS analysis of commercial products for by-
product PCBs. Table 7-X presents a set of suggested LMS
ranges, developed by Tindall and Wininger (1980) and modified
by Erickson et al. (1982). The analyst must adjust these
ranges or add new mass ranges to cover internal standards and
recovery surrogates. The mass ranges cover at least the ions
for SIM analysis (Table 7-VIII) and also include the two
masses below the parent ion. These ions are included both to
monitor the background, since M-1 and M-2 losses are uncom-
mon, and also to permit the system to settle down electron-
ically before it is measuring a mass which would be used for
quantitation. A similar approach was used by Westerberg et
al. (1984).

Table 7-IX. Characteristic SIM Ions for PCBs

| Homolog | Ion (Relative Intensity) | | |
	Primary	Secondary	Tertiary
$C_{12}H_9Cl$	188 (100)	190 (33)	-
$C_{12}H_8Cl_2$	222 (100)	224 (66)	226 (11)
$C_{12}H_7Cl_3$	256 (100)	258 (99)	260 (33)
$C_{12}H_6Cl_4$	292 (100)	290 (76)	294 (49)
$C_{12}H_5Cl_5$	326 (100)	328 (66)	324 (61)
$C_{12}H_4Cl_6$	360 (100)	362 (82)	364 (36)
$C_{12}H_3Cl_7$	394 (100)	396 (98)	398 (54)
$C_{12}H_2Cl_8$	430 (100)	432 (66)	428 (87)
$C_{12}HCl_9$	464 (100)	466 (76)	462 (76)
$C_{12}Cl_{10}$	498 (100)	500 (87)	496 (68)
$C_{10}H_9I$[a]	254 (100)	-	-
$C_{12}D_6Cl_4$[a]	298 (100)	300 (49)	296 (76)
$C_{18}D_{12}$[a]	240 (100)	-	-
$^{13}C_6{}^{12}C_6H_9Cl$[b]	194 (100)	196 (33)	-
$^{13}C_{12}H_6Cl_4$[b]	304 (100)	306 (49)	302 (76)
$^{13}C_{12}H_2Cl_8$[b]	442 (100)	444 (65)	440 (87)
$^{13}C_{12}Cl_{10}$[b]	510 (100)	512 (87)	508 (68)

a Internal standards added to sample before HRGC/EIMS
   analysis.
b Recovery surrogates added to sample before extraction.
Source: Erickson et al., 1985c.

ANALYSIS OF CHLORINATED AROMATIC WASTE

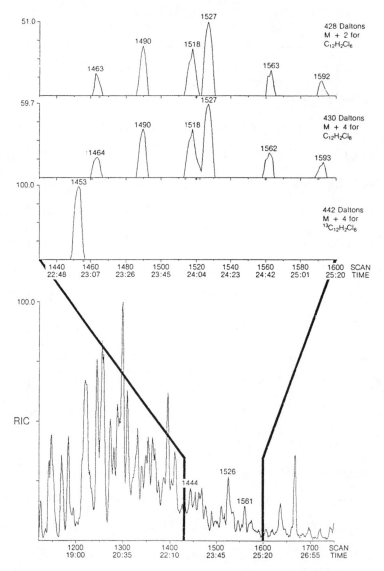

Figure 7-17. HRGC/EIMS Data for a Chlorinated Aromatic
Waste Showing Presence of Octachlorobiphenyls
as By-products

Extracted ion current profiles (upper) of octachlorobiphenyl
congeners identified (428, 430 Daltons), the ^{13}C-octachloro-
biphenyl surrogate (442 Daltons), and portion of reconstructed ion chromatogram.

Reprinted, with permission, from Erickson et al. (1983b);
copyright 1983 by Battelle Press.

Table 7-X.   Limited Mass Scanning (LMS)
Ranges for PCBs

Compound	Mass Range (m/z)
$C_{12}H_9Cl_1$ + $^{13}C_6{}^{12}C_6H_9Cl$[a]	186-198
$C_{12}H_8Cl_2$	220-226
$C_{12}H_7Cl_3$	254-260
$C_{12}H_6Cl_4$ + $C_{12}D_6Cl_4$[b] + $^{13}C_{12}H_6Cl_4$[a]	288-310
$C_{12}H_5Cl_5$	322-328
$C_{12}H_4Cl_6$	356-362
$C_{12}H_3Cl_7$	390-396
$C_{12}H_2Cl_8$	426-434
$C_{12}HCl_9$	460-468
$C_{12}Cl_{10}$	496-502
$C_{10}H_9I$[b]	254
$C_{18}D_{12}$[b]	240
$^{13}C_{12}H_2Cl_8$[a]	440-446
$^{13}C_{12}Cl_{10}$[a]	508-514

a   Recovery surrogates added to sample before extraction.
b   Internal standards added to sample before HRGC/EIMS
analysis.
Source: Erickson et al., 1985c.

In contrast to ECD, the responses of the PCB congeners are relatively well-behaved. As seen in Tables 7-IV, 7-VI, 7-VII, and 7-VIII, the ECD response factors can range over at least two orders of magnitude and can even vary widely among isomers of one homolog. The EIMS data of Martelli et al. (1981) are presented in Table 7-XI. These response factors are somewhat confusing, in that the lowest response for each homolog was set at 1.000. Thus, there is no way to compare the responses of the different homologs.

A more complete set of response factors (RFs) is presented in Table 7-XII (Erickson et al., 1982, 1983b; Stanley et al., 1983). Comparison of the data (Table 7-XIII and Figure 7-18) indicated that there was a statistically significant difference in the RF values from the quadrupole and magnetic instruments for all but the mono-, tetra-, and pentachlorobiphenyl homologs. Differences between instrument types were expected due to differences in mass discrimination and hence sensitivity between the quadrupole and magnetic sector instruments. Further comparison of the data showed no significant difference in the variance of the RF within each homolog. Based on the consistency of the RF data, standards were selected for calibration and quantitation of all PCB isomers for each homolog (Table 7-XIV). The RF values indicate that HRGC/EIMS should provide more accurate quantitation of PCBs than can be obtained by other instrumental methods.

b.   Positive chemical ionization mass spectrometry. Positive chemical ionization (CI) mass spectrometry (CIMS) is one of the "soft" ionization techniques which tend to produce fewer fragments. Thus, the spectra are simple and the molecular ion is generally one of the most intense peaks. However, with PCBs, the electron impact spectra generally exhibit good molecular ions, reducing the advantages of CI. Another problem with CI is that the ionization process depends on a reagent gas introduced with the sample into the source. Slight changes in gas pressure, source temperature, and electronic conditions can affect the reaction conditions and thus the spectrum (both fragmentation patterns and overall intensity). Thus, CI is not as reproducible as electron impact, either qualitatively or quantitatively.

Several researchers have utilized GC/CIMS for determination of PCBs. Oswald et al. (1974a), Sawyer (1978a), and Cairns and Siegmund (1981a) characterized standard solutions. Oswald et al. (1974b), Iida and Kashiwagi (1975), Stalling (1976), Cairns and Jacobsen (1977), and Iida et al. (1983) applied GC/CIMS to PCB metabolites, environmental samples, and food samples.

Table 7-XI.   Molecular Ion Response of PCBs
             Congeners to EIMS[a]

Compound	Relative[b] Response Mean ± SD, N = 4
Monochlorobiphenyls	
4-	1.000 ± 0.004
3-	1.060 ± 0.015
2-	1.090 ± 0.015
Mean[c]	1.050 ± 0.046 (4.4)
Dichlorobiphenyls	
2,2'-	1.000 ± 0.078
2,6-	1.505 ± 0.148
2,3-	1.689 ± 0.021
3,4-	1.738 ± 0.016
2,5-	1.821 ± 0.023
2,4-	1.851 ± 0.021
4,4'-	1.868 ± 0.033
3,5-	1.909 ± 0.140
3,3'-	1.922 ± 0.082
2,4'-	2.062 ± 0.035
Mean	1.736 ± 0.30 (17.2)
Trichlorobiphenyls	
2,5,2'-	1.000 ± 0.066
2,3,4-	1.273 ± 0.064
2,4,6-	1.288 ± 0.087
2,3,6-	1.315 ± 0.122
3,4,2'-	1.319 ± 0.079
2,4,4'-	1.356 ± 0.143
2,5,3'-	1.358 ± 0.103
2,4,5-	1.474 ± 0.097
2,5,4'-	1.627 ± 0.081
Mean	1.334 ± 0.221 (16.4)
Tetrachlorobiphenyls	
2,3,2',3'-	1.000 ± 0.039
2,3,2',5'-	1.253 ± 0.094
2,4,2',4'-	1.315 ± 0.092
3,4,3',4'-	1.418 ± 0.146
2,4,2',5'-	1.478 ± 0.090
2,5,2',5'-	1.536 ± 0.086
2,4,3',4'-	1.749 ± 0.097
2,6,2',6'-	1.766 ± 0.045
2,5,3',4'-	1.828 ± 0.133
2,3,4,5-	1.854 ± 0.208
2,3,5,6-	2.146 ± 0.092
Mean	1.577 ± 0.32 (20.7)

Table 7-XI (concluded)

Compound	Relative[b] Response Mean ± SD, N = 4
Pentachlorobiphenyls	
2,4,5,2',3'-	1.000 ± 0.041
2,4,5,2',5'-	1.001 ± 0.072
2,3,4,2',5'-	1.013 ± 0.047
Mean	1.005 ± 0.007 (0.7)
Hexachlorobiphenyls	
2,3,5,6,2',5'-	1.000 ± 0.077
2,3,4,5,2',5'-	1.092 ± 0.100
2,3,4,2',3',4'-	1.100 ± 0.047
2,3,4,2',4',5'-	1.107 ± 0.071
2,3,6,2',3',6'-	1.184 ± 0.038
2,4,6,2',4',6'-	1.265 ± 0.022
2,4,5,2',4',5'-	1.321 ± 0.103
Mean	1.153 ± 0.13 (10.8)
Octachlorobiphenyls	
2,3,4,5,2',3',4',5'-	1.000 ± 0.056
2,3,5,6,2',3',5',6'-	1.359 ± 0.034

a   Data obtained on an LKB 2091-051 gas chromato-
    graph low resolution mass spectrometer oper-
    ated in the EI mode with selected ion moni-
    toring acquisition, equipped with an LKB-2130
    computer for data acquisition and calculation.
    The GC conditions were as follows: glass
    column, 2 m x 2 mm ID, packed with 3% OV-1
    on Gas Chrom Q (100-120 mesh); helium flow,
    25 mL/min[1]; electron energy, 70 eV; trap
    current, 100 μA; ion temperature, 250°C;
    separator temperature, 250°C.
b   Relative to the isomer with the lowest re-
    sponse, for each homolog.
c   Mean ± standard deviation (relative standard
    deviation) of the responses for the con-
    geners in the homolog.
Source: Martelli et al., 1981; reproduced with
    permission, copyright 1981 by John Wiley and
    Sons, Ltd.

Table 7-XII. HRGC/EIMS Relative Response Factors[a]

Congener No.	Degree of Chlorination	Quadrupole (4 Measurements)[b,c]			Quadrupole[b,d] (Single Measurement)	Magnetic Sector[d,e] (Single Measurement)
		Average Relative Response Factor	Standard Deviation	Coefficient of Variation (%)		
1	1	4.073	0.118	2.9	2.708	2.536
2	1	2.951	0.056	1.9	2.506	2.139
3	1	2.969	0.028	1.0	3.011	2.313
4	2	1.232	0.008	0.6	1.294	1.237
5	2	1.959	0.035	1.8	1.727	1.619
7	2	2.008	0.027	1.4	2.195	1.648
8	2	2.049	0.023	1.1	2.157	1.748
9	2	2.148	0.061	2.8	2.149	1.692
10	2	1.880	0.031	1.7	1.946	1.550
11	2	3.073	0.073	2.4	2.288	2.170
12	2	1.929	0.036	1.9	2.081	1.608
14	2	2.083	0.098	4.7	2.304	1.745
15	2	1.909	0.089	4.7	2.337	1.611
18	3	1.104	0.012	1.1	1.144	0.927
21	3	1.586	0.018	1.1	1.395	1.148
24	3	1.051	0.033	3.1	1.144	0.661
26	3	1.714	0.013	0.7	1.759	1.297
28	3	1.587	0.028	1.7	1.836	1.207
29	3	2.195	0.048	2.2	1.680	1.544
30	3	1.526	0.067	4.4	1.700	1.254
31	3	1.706	0.024	1.4	1.853	1.248
33	3	1.688	0.031	1.9	1.821	1.221
40	4	0.597	0.013	2.2	0.595	0.600
44	4	0.712	0.007	0.9	0.654	0.768
47	4	1.062	0.059	5.6	0.914	1.009
49	4	0.831	0.019	2.2	0.843	0.830
50	4	0.957	0.025	2.6	1.009	0.974
52	4	0.732	0.011	1.5	0.771	0.758
53	4	0.750	0.008	1.0	0.730	0.783
54	4	0.958	0.013	1.3	0.904	0.939
61	4	0.975	0.069	7.1	0.992	0.887
65	4	1.086	0.022	2.0	0.960	0.903
66	4	1.139	0.068	6.0	1.131	1.056
69	4	1.058	0.012	1.1	1.090	1.065

Table 7-XII (continued)

Congener No.	Degree of Chlorination	Quadrupole (4 Measurements)[b,c]			Quadrupole[b,d] (Single Measurement)	Magnetic Sector[d,e] (Single Measurement)
		Average Relative Response Factor	Standard Deviation	Coefficient of Variation (%)		
70	4	1.091	0.050	4.5	1.135	0.868
72	4	0.980	0.048	4.9	0.994	0.932
75	4	1.185	0.061	5.1	1.221	1.032
77	4	1.095	0.050	4.6	1.199	1.036
87	5	0.617	0.011	1.7	0.610	0.594
88	5	0.611	0.005	0.7	0.591	0.644
93	5	0.574	0.010	1.7	0.572	0.615
97	5	0.719	0.008	1.1	0.650	0.693
100	5	0.727	0.003	0.4	0.716	0.804
101	5	0.653	0.004	0.5	0.733	0.724
103	5	0.566	0.009	1.6	0.656	0.697
104	5	0.824	0.025	3.0	0.816	0.869
115	5	0.853	0.061	7.1	0.992	0.594
116	5	0.785	0.013	1.7	0.875	0.908
119	5	0.762	0.022	2.9	0.855	0.882
121	5	0.948	0.020	2.1	0.797	0.987
128	6	0.499	0.005	1.1	0.448	0.553
129	6	0.431	0.004	0.8	0.329	0.482
136	6	0.689	0.016	2.3	0.573	0.884
137	6	0.533	0.008	1.6	0.500	0.625
138	6	0.433	0.008	1.9	0.482	0.607
139	6	0.462	0.026	5.7	0.440	0.526
141	6	0.419	0.010	2.4	0.469	0.561
143	6	0.490	0.005	1.0	0.455	0.578
151	6	0.473	0.013	2.8	0.440	0.573
153	6	0.549	0.050	9.1	0.573	0.679
154	6	0.511	0.010	2.0	0.463	0.624
155	6	0.587	0.011	1.8	0.673	0.828
156	6	0.599	0.044	7.4	0.659	0.800
171	7	0.346	0.002	0.6	0.275	0.466
181	7	0.383	0.009	2.4	0.315	0.581
183	7	0.380	0.010	2.5	0.334	0.496
185	7	0.336	0.006	1.7	0.307	0.445

Table 7-XII (concluded)

Congener No.	Degree of Chlorination	Quadrupole (4 Measurements)[b,c]			Quadrupole[b,d] (Single Measurement)	Magnetic Sector[d,e] (Single Measurement)
		Average Relative Response Factor	Standard Deviation	Coefficient of Variation (%)		
194	8	0.221	0.001	0.6	0.159	0.372
195	8	0.263	0.003	1.2	0.217	0.497
198	8	0.262	0.008	2.9	0.213	0.414
200	8	0.301	0.007	2.4	0.250	0.463
202	8	0.250	0.007	2.7	0.272	0.579
204	8	0.221	0.007	3.2	0.237	0.451
206	9	0.193	0.003	1.7	0.153	0.346
207	9	0.237	0.008	3.5	0.210	0.538
208	9	0.259	0.003	1.3	0.200	0.516
209	10	0.213	0.006	2.8	0.179	0.586

a Relative to d_6-3,3',4,4'-tetrachlorobiphenyl. Calculated as the average of four replicate measurements made on the same day. Compounds separated on a 0.255 mm ID x 15 m DB-5 (0.25 μm thick) fused silica capillary column (S&W Scientific) with 45 cm/sec helium carrier gas, on-column injection (J&W) of 1.0 μL hexane solutions. The column temperature was programmed from 110 to 325°C at 10°C/min. The column outlet was placed in the source, with a transfer line temperature of 280°C.

b Finnigan 4023 Quadrupole Mass Spectrometer with electron impact ionization. The spectrometer was scanned from m/z 95-550 with a 1-sec cycle time, unit resolution, source temperature of 280°C, 70 eV electron energy, 0.2 mA trap current, -1600 V multiplier voltage, and 10^{-6} A/V preamplifier sensitivity. The mass spectrometer was tuned daily according to rigorous criteria (Erickson et al., 1982) to ensure system reproducibility.

c Four replicate measurements made on the same day for each congener.

d Single measurement for each congener; all data collected on a single day to minimize effects of tuning, drift, etc., which have day-to-day variance.

e Finnigan MAT 311A magnetic sector mass spectrometer with electron impact ionization. The spectrometer was scanned from m/z 98-550 exponentially with a 1.2-sec cycle time, resolution of 1000, source temperature of 280°C, 70 eV electron energy, 1-2 mA emission current, and -1600 V multiplier voltage.

Source: Erickson et al. (1982, 1983b); Stanley et al. (1983); and unpublished data, Midwest Research Institute, Kansas City, Missouri.

Table 7-XIII. Summary of HRGC/EIMS Response Factors in Table 7-XII[a]

Homolog	No. of Isomers Measured	Quadrupole (4 measurements/congener)			Quadrupole (1 measurement/congener)			Magnetic Sector		
		Mean	SD	RSD %[b]	Mean	SD	RSD %	Mean	SD	RSD %
Cl_1	3	3.331	0.643	19.3	2.742	0.254	9.3	2.329	0.199	8.5
Cl_2	10	2.034	0.447	22.0	2.048	0.322	15.7	1.663	0.229	13.8
Cl_3	9	1.573	0.341	21.7	1.592	0.289	18.1	1.167	0.248	21.2
Cl_4	16	0.951	0.175	18.4	0.946	0.189	20.0	0.903	0.130	13.2
Cl_5	12	0.720	0.120	16.7	0.739	0.130	17.6	0.751	0.135	18.0
Cl_6	13	0.513	0.078	15.1	0.500	0.096	19.1	0.640	0.124	19.3
Cl_7	4	0.361	0.024	6.6	0.308	0.025	8.0	0.497	0.060	12.0
Cl_8	6	0.253	0.030	11.9	0.224	0.039	17.3	0.463	0.071	15.4
Cl_9	3	0.230	0.034	14.6	0.188	0.030	16.2	0.467	0.105	22.5
Cl_{10}	1	0.213	-	-	0.179	-	-	0.586	-	-

a Relative to (d_6)-3,3',4,4'-Tetrachlorobiphenyl. See footnotes in Table 7-XII for experimental conditions.
b Relative standard deviation.
Source: Erickson et al. (1982, 1983b), Stanley et al. (1983), and unpublished data, Midwest Research Institute, Kansas City, Missouri.

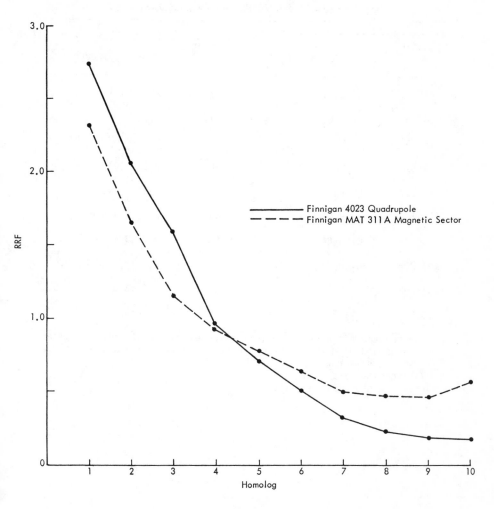

Figure 7-18.   Plot of Average Response Factors
Versus PCB Homolog

Response factors were determined relative to d_6-3,3',4,4'-
tetrachlorobiphenyl for 77 congeners on a single day to minimize instrumental effects.   See Table 7-XII for instrumental
conditions.

Reprinted, with permission, from Erickson et al. (1982,
1983b) and Stanley et al. (1983).

Table 7-XIV. Pairings of Analyte and Calibration Congeners for
Homolog-Specific GC/EIMS Determination of PCBs

Analyte		Calibration Standard[a]	
Congener[b] No.	Compound	Congener No.	Compound
1	$C_{12}H_9Cl$	1	2
4-15	$C_{12}H_8Cl_2$	7	2,4
16-39	$C_{12}H_7Cl_3$	30	2,4,6
40-81	$C_{12}H_6Cl_4$	50	2,2',4,6
82-127	$C_{12}H_5Cl_5$	97	2,2',3',4,5
128-169	$C_{12}H_4Cl_6$	143	2,2',3,4,5,6'
170-193	$C_{12}H_3Cl_7$	183	2,2',3',4,4',5',6
194-205	$C_{12}H_2Cl_8$	202	2,2',3,3',5,5',6,6'
206-208	$C_{12}HCl_9$	207	2,2',3,3',4,4',5,6,6'
209	$C_{12}Cl_{10}$	209	$C_{12}Cl_{10}$

a The congeners are prepared in a mixture along with internal standards and used to generate the response factors for the analytes
in the same row.
b Ballschmiter and Zell, 1980.
Source: Erickson et al., 1985c.

The fragmentation patterns of hydrogen CI mass spectra are isomer-dependent for the lower homologs (Cl_4 and lower) and may be useful in identification of PCB isomers (Harrison et al., 1981). The higher homologs did not fragment enough to be of qualitative value.

Dougherty et al. (1973) reported the use of direct probe positive and negative CIMS for the analysis of human adipose tissues for PCBs. Stalling et al. (1980b) reported an HPLC/MS technique for PCBs which is presumed to use the CI mode. This preliminary report speculated that HPLC/MS could be useful as a screening technique for environmental samples.

A related (but often defined as separate) technique, atmospheric pressure chemical ionization (APCI) has been reported for PCB determination. Dzidic et al. (1975) reported subpicogram detection of 2,3,4,5,6-pentachlorobiphenyl. An instrument in a van has been used for in situ detection of PCBs in clay and soil (Thomson et al., 1980; Thomson and Roberts 1980, 1982; Lovett et al., 1983). It has been used for direct sampling and analysis of mono- through hexachlorobiphenyls in stack gas (Lovett et al., 1983) and ambient air (Thomson et al., 1980). Data were available about 2 min after the sample was collected. A detection limit for total PCBs of 8 $\mu g/m^3$ was reported.

c. Negative chemical ionization mass spectrometry: Negative chemical ionization (NCI) mass spectrometry (NCIMS) is similar to both CIMS and ECD. The basic difference between negative and positive CI is the polarity of the various voltage potentials in the spectrometer and the detector. Many of the chemical reactions in the NCI source and the ECD are the same. NCI and ECD exhibit similar detection limits and selectivities toward chlorinated compounds, thus the interest in NCI. The reproducibility problems of CI are also present in NCI. The range of response factors found with ECD are also found with NCI (see Table 7-XV). NCIMS, only recently available, is still considered to be a research technique.

The major reasons for use of NCIMS for PCB analysis are its sensitivity and selectivity. The sensitivity is highly dependent on the degree of chlorination. As shown in Table 7-XVI, the sensitivity of NCIMS is much worse than EIMS for the lower homologs and up to 40 times better for the higher homologs (Westerberg et al., 1984). Nevertheless, the lower MDL for the higher homologs can be a decided advantage for trace work. It should be noted that the magnitude of the homolog discrimination may be dependent on conditions or instrument configuration.

Table 7-XV. Relative Response Factors for HRGC/NCIMS Detection
of PCBs (m/z 35) for Homologous Series of PCBs

Homolog	No. of Isomers Possible	No. of PCB Isomers Measured	Range[a]	Mean ± SD	% RSD
1Cl	3	3	0.456-1.787	0.924 ± 0.75	81
2Cl	12	8	2.881-21.199	8.343 ± 6.17	74
3Cl	24	7	0.721-10.901	2.921 ± 3.64	125
4Cl	42	16	0.102-4.267	2.058 ± 1.02	50
5Cl	46	12	0.465-1.216	0.805 ± 0.27	33
6Cl	42	16	0.369-1.440	0.817 ± 0.29	36
7Cl	24	13	0.236-1.192	0.703 ± 0.30	43
8Cl	12	8	0.241-1.116	0.573 ± 0.26	46
9Cl	3	3	0.066-0.565	0.354 ± 0.26	73
10Cl	1	1	-	0.418	-

a All values are relative to octachloronaphthalene.
Source: Pellizzari et al., 1983b.

Table 7-XVI. Limits of Detection for PCBs

PCB Isomer	MW	EI MDL[a] (ppb)	NCI MDL[a] (ppb)
2-Monochlorobiphenyl	188	1.3	> 10
4,4'-Dichlorobiphenyl	222	3.1	> 10
2,4,5-Trichlorobiphenyl	256	2.6	> 10
2,2',4,4'-Tetrachlorobiphenyl	290	2.0	> 10
2,3',4,5',6-Pentachlorobiphenyl	324	1.2	> 10
2,2',4,5,5'-Pentachlorobiphenyl	324	1.9	> 10
2,2',3,3',6,6'-Hexachlorobiphenyl	358	1.3	3.5
2,2',3,3',4,4'-Hexachlorobiphenyl	358	2.8	1.8
2,2',3,4,5,5',6-Heptachlorobiphenyl	392	2.2	0.16
2,2',3,3',4,4',5,5'-Octachlorobiphenyl	426	3.2	0.09
2,2',3,3',4,4',5,5',6-Nonachlorobiphenyl	460	4.5	0.13
2,2',3,3',4,4',5,5',6,6'-Decachlorobiphenyl	494	4.3	0.10

a MDL = Amount which corresponds to a peak height of twice the average noise
      level above baseline.
Source: Westerberg et al., 1984; reproduced with permission, copyright by
      Elsevier Science Publishers, B.V.

The selectivity of NCIMS was illustrated by Kuehl et al. (1980a), who used both HRGC/EIMS and HRGC/NCIMS to analyze fish samples for a variety of chloro-organics, including PCBs. The electron impact spectra were used for primary identification, although the NCI spectra were also of great value. Figure 7-19 presents the NCI and electron impact RICs for comparison. The NCI is much more selective toward the halogenated compounds, eliminating the broad hump which is presumably a complex mixture of lipids and oils from the fish matrix. Other investigators have applied GC/NCIMS to analysis for PCBs in Lake Ontario sediment (Kaminsky and Hites, 1982) and marine sediments (Lewis and Jamieson, 1983).

The group led by Dougherty has published extensively on the methods and application of (direct probe) NCIMS (Dougherty, 1980, 1981a,b; Dougherty et al., 1973, 1980; Kuehl et al., 1980b). The technique is described as rapid and highly selective toward halogenated compounds. The latter advantage reduces the need for cleanup and, according to Dougherty (1981a), permits the analysis without the customary GC separation.

HRGC/NCIMS proved much more sensitive than HRGC/EIMS for PCBs in the analysis of ambient air samples collected during a demonstration of PCB destruction at the ENSCO incinerator in El Dorado, AR (Erickson et al., 1980a). Extracts of the polyurethane foam air sampling sorbent contained no detectable PCBs when analyzed by HRGC/EIMS, whereas the analysis of the same extracts by HRGC/NCIMS found mono-through hexachlorobiphenyls in most of the samples at concentrations up to 51 ng/m^3/homolog.

The HRGC/NCIMS instrumental operating parameters have been characterized (Pellizzari et al., 1981, 1983a, 1983b). The choice of reagent gas and its pressure markedly affect the relative intensities of the major peaks (m/z 35 and 37, molecular ion, etc.). The response factors for several PCB congeners are summarized in Table 7-XV (Pellizzari et al., 1983b). As with ECD, the range of the response factors is broad. Thus quantitation by extrapolation from a single calibration isomer presents similar problems. They have compared the quantitation of single congeners obtained by HRGC/ ECD and HRGC/NCIMS (Pellizzari et al., 1983b). In both cases, there was a one-to-one correspondence between the calibration and analyte congeners. For nine congeners in serum and 38 in adipose, the analyses generally correlated well. For some congeners, however, there was a distinct bias toward one or the other technique, which may have been due to discrepancies in calibration. They also note that the HRGC/ECD is more sensitive than HRGC/NCIMS: 109 versus 50 peaks were quantitated by the two techniques, respectively.

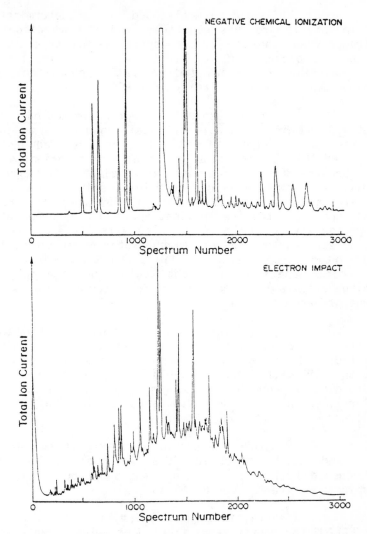

Figure 7-19. Comparison of HRGC/NCIMS (Top) and HRGC/EIMS
(Bottom) Total Ion Current Profiles for a Fish Sample

The fish sample was extracted with dichloromethane/hexane
(50:50), cleaned up by Florisil column chromatography and
further cleaned up by gel permeation chromatography. The
sample was injected via a Grob injector onto a 30 m x 0.25 mm
glass capillary column coated with SE-30 which was programmed
from 100°C to 225°C at 4°C/min with a 30-min hold. A Finnigan 4000 quadrupole mass spectrometer was operated at 70 eV
ionization energy for the EIMS mode and with 0.5 torr methane
for the NICMS mode.

Reprinted, with permission, from Kuehl et al. (1980a); copyright 1980 by Association of Official Analytical Chemists,
Inc.

While not directly used for PCB determination, HRGC/atmospheric pressure negative chemical ionization mass spectrometry was shown to be both sensitive and selective for PCDDs in the presence of PCBs (Mitchum et al., 1982). With proper selection of masses and ionization conditions, this technique may be highly selective for PCBs.

d. High resolution electron impact mass spectrometry: HREIMS is capable of obtaining precise and accurate mass measurements of a peak. As reviewed by Safe (1976), HREIMS is particularly useful for chlorinated compounds because the chlorine mass defect clearly distinguishes a halocarbon from a molecule containing only carbon, hydrogen, nitrogen, and oxygen. Safe (1976) and Safe et al. (1975) have reported the application of direct probe HREIMS to the analysis of crude goat urine extracts and other biological samples for PCB and polychloroterphenyl metabolites. The reported 10-ppb detection limit and the rapid analysis time (no GC separation is used) would appear to make this technique a suitable technique for rapid screening of samples for the presence of PCBs.

Figure 7-20 illustrates the need for HREIMS to separate interferences if they are not chromatographically separated. The direct probe mass spectrum in Figure 7-20 shows that DDE, TCDD, and PCB would have given one peak under low resolution conditions (Baughman and Meselson, 1973). Similar spectra have been published by Hass and Friesen (1979) and Dougherty (1980).

HRGC/HREIMS has been applied to the analysis of fat and blood samples for PCBs (Voyksner et al., 1983). As discussed in the next section, the technique proved more reliable than direct probe MS/MS analysis.

Several factors have inhibited the wide usage of GC/HREIMS for routine analytical work. Instrumentation is more expensive, more difficult to use, and much less available. Nevertheless, HREIMS does provide much higher qualitative confidence than most other detectors and should be considered as an excellent candidate for confirmation, when required.

e. Mass spectrometry/mass spectrometry (MS/MS): MS/MS couples two or more mass analyzers in one instrument so that a fragment of a molecule (e.g., M-70 for a PCB) may be selected out of the entire spectrum, further fragmented and, in a subsequent analyzer, its fragments analyzed. MS/MS may be operated in several different modes to produce different outputs from this multidimensional ion map. The technique has been reviewed (Kondrat and Cooks, 1978; Yost

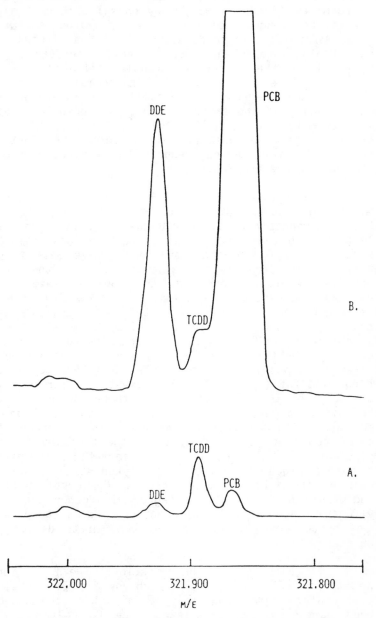

Figure 7-20.   HREIMS Spectrum of Fish Sample After Sulfuric
       Acid and Alumina Column Chromatographic Cleanups

The CH_2Cl_2/hexane (20:80) fraction was analyzed after preelu-
tion with A - CCl_4/hexane (20:80) or B - CH_2Cl_2/hexane
(1:99).

Reprinted, with permission, from Baughman and Meselson
(1973).

and Enke, 1979). A triple quadrupole was used to analyze marine sediments (Bonner, 1983). By normal GC/EIMS analysis, PCBs were indistinguishable from the hydrocarbon background, while GC/MS/MS was able to detect (but not quantitate) tetra- through heptachlorobiphenyls with little interference. For each homolog, the first quadrupole filtered only the $C_{12}H_n{}^{35}Cl_{10-n}$ (i.e., the lowest ion in the molecular cluster) ion. The second quadrupole, the collision chamber, generated daughter ions, and the third quadrupole scanned the spectrum of the daughter ions ($M-Cl^+$, $M-HCl^+$, $M-Cl_2^+$, etc.). The major advantage cited was the ability to use the instrument to filter out interferences, reducing or eliminating the often lengthy sample preparation.

Voyksner et al. (1983) also found MS/MS useful in analyzing complex samples for PCBs; however, they noted that interferences caused the PCB quantitation to be erroneously high. In the first stage of the MS/MS analysis, $[M]^+\cdot$ ions (e.g., 358 for hexachlorobiphenyl) were passed by the magnetic sector. The electrostatic analyzer was then scanned to observe the loss of one and two chlorines. Samples were introduced by direct probe. The values by MS/MS were 2 to 10 times larger than the GC/HREIMS values. The results obtained by direct probe HREIMS on the blood samples were higher than those obtained by GC/HREIMS. These results suggest that the direct probe HREIMS and MS/MS techniques are detecting more interferences, possibly due to aliphatics (cholesterol, etc.) in blood and fat (large $[M-CH_3]^+$ present) or from higher PCB homologs. The GC/HREIMS was presumed to be the more accurate method since it gave lower quantitative results, which indicated less influence from the matrix. The accuracy of the analyses could not be checked since the true levels in the samples were not known a priori. The advantages of speed and less sample preparation were, in Voyksner's opinion, outweighed by the fact that the results were consistently and unpredictably high and did not agree with other techniques. They further noted that GC introduction reduces the probability of encountering interferences compared to direct probe techniques.

4. Flame ionization detection: The flame ionization detector (FID) measures the change in electrical conductivity of a flame which is proportional to the number of charged particles in the flame. The GC column effluent enters the base of a hydrogen/air microburner and is burned. An electrode at the base and one at the top measure the current. FID is the most commonly used GC detector because of its sensitivity and universality. Although some investigators have used FID for determination of PCBs in samples, it has generally been used only for calibration of response factors, to check purity of standards, or other method development work.

FID has been used for determination of PCBs in environmental samples (Mizutani and Matsumoto, 1972; Modi et al., 1976; Lao et al., 1976; Onuska and Comba, 1980). Biros (1971) split the GC effluent to FID for quantitation and EIMS for identification. Cook et al. (1978) and Zimmerli (1974) used FID to detect biphenyl following dehydrochlorination of PCBs; a technique termed carbon skeleton chromatography.

Most of the FID applications have been in establishing response factors, characterizing Aroclors, or other method development areas (Webb and McCall, 1972; Albro and Fishbein, 1972a; Ugawa et al., 1973; Dexter and Pavlou, 1976; Boe and Egaas, 1979; Pavlou et al., 1980; Albro and Parker, 1980; Albro et al., 1981; Stalling et al., 1982). An example of the use of FID is presented in Table 7-V, where the molar responses of FID and ECD were compared (Hutzinger et al., 1974a; Safe, 1976).

FID is not selective enough for general application to PCB problems.

5. <u>Photoionization</u>: The photoionization detector (PID) uses a high intensity UV source to ionize molecules in the GC effluent. The ions are then detected at an electrode. The energy of the UV source (measured in electron volts) determines the selectivity of the PID.

GC/PID was studied for possible application as a portable PCB monitor (Bostick et al., 1983; Denton et al., 1981). PID was found to be about 40 times more sensitive than FID. However, using the standard 10.2 eV lamp, the PID was not selective for PCBs in hydrocarbon matrices. Better selectivity was obtained with an experimental 8.3 eV lamp. The lack of selectivity and problems with portability made the technique impractical. Therefore, the approach was not pursued further.

6. <u>Thermal conductivity (TCD)</u>: Hirwe et al. (1974) used TCD to characterize Aroclor mixtures. This application is similar to many of the FID applications. GC/TCD was used to determine PCBs in ethylene glycol impingers used to collect the gaseous effluent from a bench-scale plasma arc destruction test (Barton and Arsenault, 1982). A 10 µg/10 µL detection limit for Aroclor 1254 was reported, which was adequate to demonstrate > 99% destruction efficiency.

Since TCD is neither selective nor sensitive, it is not generally considered a detector of choice for PCB analysis.

D.   Perchlorination

          Perchlorination methods are based on the exhaustive
chlorination of the biphenyl ring of the PCB congeners.   The
major disadvantage of the perchlorination reactions is that
biphenyl can also be perchlorinated.   Thus, the presence of
biphenyl can lead to erroneously high levels of quantitation.
Quantitative analysis is typically accomplished by GC/ECD
(Figure 7-21) although GC/MS identification has been used in
some instances.   Perchlorination reactions are reportedly
troublesome because of contamination of reagents with decachlorobiphenyl or brominated compounds (Trotter and Young,
1975).

          Perchlorination reaction methods were first studied
using antimony pentachloride (Berg et al., 1972; Masumoto,
1972; Armour, 1973) and thionyl chloride in the presence of
aluminum chloride (Nose, 1972).   Armour (1973) reported
greater than 90% recovery of PCBs by perchlorination and
found the technique comparable to PGC/ECD comparison with
Aroclor standards.   Nose (1972) reported approximately 100%
conversion of tri-, tetra-, and hexachlorobiphenyls to decachlorobiphenyl with the thionyl chloride system.   Antimony
pentachloride is apparently the most frequently used reagent.
Hutzinger et al. (1973) studied trichlorosulfur tetrachloro-
aluminate to quantitatively convert Aroclor 1254 to decachlorobiphenyl.   A rapid perchlorination technique, which utilizes an iron catalyst, has also been reported (Steinwandter
and Bruene, 1982; Steinwandter, 1984).   Complete perchlorination was reported in 10 min after addition of 10 mg iron powder and 0.2 mL $SbCl_5$ and heating to 205°C.

          One of the major disadvantages of perchlorination
arises from blank problems (Trotter and Young, 1975).   This
has resulted in the need to carefully characterize perchlorination reagents prior to reaction (Huckins et al., 1974).
The other major disadvantage of perchlorination is the conversion of biphenyl to decachlorobiphenyl.   Chlorine-37 labeled perchlorination reagents have been studied as a means
to clarify this problem and at the same time distinguish the
contribution of various PCB homologs to the final decachlorobiphenyl by computer assisted isotope dilution interpretation
(Burkhard and Armstrong, 1981).   This technique, although
unique in approach, requires optimum reaction and MS conditions for successful analysis.   A recent study claimed that
the perchlorination yield is constant regardless of the degree of chlorination of the starting material and that a constant factor (0.9X) could be used to convert the decachlorobiphenyl mass back to the original commercial mixture
(Takamiya, 1983).   This method was reported to be an accurate

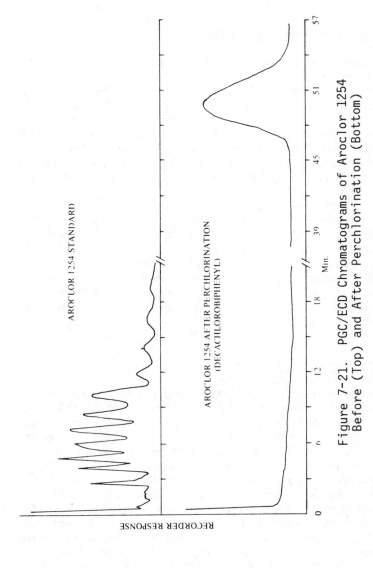

Figure 7-21. PGC/ECD Chromatograms of Aroclor 1254 Before (Top) and After Perchlorination (Bottom)

The sample was chromatographed on a 6 ft x 4 mm glass column containing 4% SE-30 on acid-washed Chromosorb W 60-80 mesh at 260°C with a nitrogen carrier gas at 60 mL/min.

Reprinted, with permission, from Hutzinger et al. (1974a); copyright 1974 by CRC Press, Inc., Boca Raton, Florida.

241

and rapid screen for PCBs. Perchlorination has been used successfully for numerous studies in recent years (Leoni et al., 1976a; Vannucchi et al., 1976; Crist and Moseman, 1977; Haile and Baladi, 1977; Margeson, 1977; Mes et al., 1977; Brinkman et al., 1978; Stratton et al., 1978a,b, 1979; Kohli et al., 1979a; Mes and Davies, 1979; Robbins and Willhite, 1979; Albro et al., 1979; Trevisani, 1980; Sherma, 1981).

E. Carbon Skeleton Chromatography

Carbon skeleton chromatography is based on the dechlorination of PCBs to biphenyl. Catalysts for the dechlorination are typically platinum or palladium. The disadvantage of carbon skeleton chromatography is that background levels of biphenyl in the sample extract will yield erroneously high concentrations of total PCBs as noted for perchlorination. Also, since the product of dechlorination is biphenyl, mass spectrometry must be used to reliably identify the compound, especially in extracts from complex matrices.

Quantitative carbon skeleton chromatography by catalytic decomposition of the PCBs over platinum or palladium to biphenyl has been discussed in three articles (Berg et al., 1972; Zimmerli, 1974; Cooke et al., 1978). Zimmerli (1974) and Cooke et al. (1978) studied conversion of PCBs as well as halogenated terphenyls, napthalenes, dioxins, furans, and DDT. Effective catalysts were found to be effective as 3% palladium at 305°C and 5% platinum at 180°C. Reaction products for the various compounds were identified by GC/MS.

III. THIN-LAYER CHROMATOGRAPHY

Thin-layer chromatography employs a liquid as the mobile phase and a thin layer (e.g., 100-250 μm) of solid adsorbent as the solid phase. The thin layer is generally adhered to a glass plate for mechanical stability. The TLC plate is spotted with the mixture solution near one end. The plate is then placed vertically, spot down, in a developing tank containing a small amount of the mobile phase in the bottom. The mobile phase climbs the plate by capillary action and draws components of the mixture upward. Since the components interact with the mobile phase and adsorbent differently, they migrate at different rates, thereby effecting the separation. The different components of the mixture are subsequently detected as spots either visually or with an optical scanner. Occasionally derivatizing reagents are used to enhance visualization. Compounds are identified by comparison of the height they climb the plate (R_f) with the R_f of authentic standards, preferably run on the same plate. Quantitation is generally only approximate and is done by comparison of the intensity of the color with that of a standard. TLC is discussed in more detail in most analytical chemistry texts and many monographs. One example is Stahl (1969).

In addition to its use as a cleanup technique (Chapter 6), TLC has been used as a determination technique. TLC was used extensively in early work (latter 1960s, early 1970s) because HPLC was not readily available and the GC techniques were not well-developed. Most of the early TLC reports were normal phase (silica gel) and included elaborate cleanup steps to remove interferents (e.g., oxidation of DDE to a benzophenone derivative). In the mid-1970s when packed column gas-liquid chromatography/electron capture detection (PGC/ECD) became the method of choice, emphasis on TLC methods dwindled. Several articles have been published which take advantage of modern TLC techniques: high performance TLC, two-dimensional TLC, reverse phase TLC, and new detection methods. TLC has been shown to be an effective technique for determination of (Aroclor) PCBs in a wide variety of matrices. The advantages included its ease of use and the simplicity of the apparatus. The disadvantages include lack of resolution, moderate sensitivity, and low specificity.

A. Historical Perspective

TLC analysis of PCBs was reviewed by Fishbein (1972). TLC is included as an alternate technique for "semiquantitation" analysis of PCBs in human adipose tissue in EPA manuals (Watts, 1980; Sherma, 1981). It is also included in the Association of Official Analytical Chemists methods for confirmation of identity (AOAC, 1980a,b). TLC is mentioned by the Food and Drug Administration (1977) as a technique which they feel may also be useful. The TLC properties of commercial polychlorinated terphenyls have also been investigated (De Kok et al., 1982).

Since the publication of a TLC method for PCBs by Mulhern (1968) and Mulhern et al. (1971), several researchers have used a similar method for analysis of PCBs in food (Stijve and Cardinale, 1974), animal feeds (Westöö and Noren, 1970), food packaging (Zimmerli et al., 1973), bald eagles (Bagley et al., 1970), Aroclor mixtures (Willis and Addison, 1972), animal tissue (Collins et al., 1972; Koeniger et al., 1976; Bush and Lo, 1973; Hattula, 1974b; Mes et al., 1977), human adipose tissue (Price and Welch, 1972; Lucas et al., 1980), human milk (Savage et al., 1973a, 1973b; Mes and Davies, 1979), soil (Piechalak, 1984), and oil (Stahr, 1984). Many of these researchers employed TLC in conjunction with other techniques such as GC/ECD. Often, TLC has been used as a qualitative confirmation technique.

Bruggeman et al. (1982) used reverse phase TLC (C_{18} bonded phase) to study the relationship between PCB retention and hydrophobicity (water solubility and octanol-water partition coefficients). Anomalous behavior was observed for ortho-substituted PCBs relative to other PCBs, chlorobenzenes, alkylbenzenes, and polynuclear aromatic hydrocarbons. The authors attributed the results to the non-planarity of the ortho-substituted PCBs, which apparently reduces the ability of the solute molecule to interact with the stationary phase.

Several developments have improved the technique. Circular TLC reportedly improves sensitivity by an order of magnitude with a PCB limit of detection of about 0.05 μg (Koch, 1979). Fused glass TLC has been reported as yielding longer plate life (Okumura et al., 1973). Proper selection of the solid phase and eluting solvent permit separation of Aroclor components into discrete bands, as shown in Figure 7-22 (Brinkman et al., 1976a). Reverse phase (Figure 7-22) gives better resolution, but normal phase is more convenient and less time-consuming. Reverse phase TLC has been reported to yield better separation of PCBs from interferences (DeVos and Peet, 1971; DeVos, 1972; Stalling and Huckins, 1973; Brinkman et al., 1976a). An impregnated silica gel plate has been reported (Bergman et al., 1976) which improves selectivity apparently on the basis of ion-pairing. The use of surfactant micellar solutions as the mobile phase is certainly novel and reportedly has potential for separation of chlorinated aromatics, including decachlorobiphenyl (Armstrong and Terrill, 1979). Improvements in detection have included an $AgNO_3$ spray followed by UV irradiation (DeVos and Peet, 1971; DeVos, 1972; Kawabata, 1974) and fluorescence (Kan et al., 1973; Ueta et al., 1974; Stahr, 1984). A two-dimensional TLC method was developed which barely separated the DDT analogs from PCBs, as shown in Figure 7-23 (Fehringer and Westfall, 1971).

This last reference points to one of the major problems with TLC determination of PCBs. Many common interferences (e.g., DDE in biological tissues) have similar elution characteristics and are not easily resolved. One common technique for removal of DDE prior to TLC is oxidation of the DDE to dichlorobenzophenone with chromium trioxide or other oxidant (Biros et al., 1972; Sherma, 1981; Watts, 1980; Collins et al., 1972). Thielemann (1976) reported separation of PCBs from DDE on paraffin-impregnated Kieselguhr 9 plates.

Quantitation can be improved with the use of a densitometer (Stahr, 1984). Reverse-phase TLC was performed on C_{18} plates with methanol/water (95:5) as the eluting solvent. A limit of detection of 10 ng was reported, with 5% repeatability in the linear quantitation range of 1-4 μg.

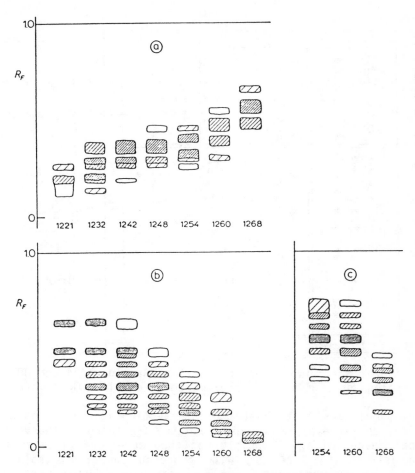

Figure 7-22. TLC of Aroclors 1221 Through
1268 in Three Systems

(a) Silica gel/n̲-hexane; (b) Kieselguhr impregnated with paraffin oil/acetonitrile-methanol-water (8:9:3); (c) Kieselguhr
impregnated with paraffin oil/acetonitrile-methanol-acetone-
water (20:20:9:1)

Reprinted, with permission, from Brinkman et al. (1976a);
copyright 1976 by Elsevier Science Publishers, B.V.

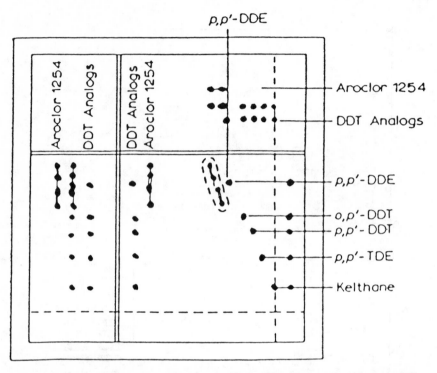

Figure 7-23. Two Dimensional TLC of Aroclor 1254 and DDT
Analogs on a Silver Nitrate-Impregnated Silica Gel Plate

The sample was spotted at the intersection of the two dashed
lines and several standards along the top third of the vertical dashed line. The plate was then developed (from right
to left in this figure) with n-heptane until the solvent
front had reached 10 cm, as denoted by the double vertical
line. The plate was then turned 90° to the orientation
shown, additional standards spotted along the bottom dashed
line, and the plate developed with acetone/n-heptane (2:98)
to the horizontal double solid line. The Aroclor 1254 from
the sample is within the dashed oval. The DDT analogs from
the sample are in a diagonal line to the right and below the
Aroclor 1254.

Reprinted, with permission, from Fehringer and Westfall
(1971); copyright 1971 by Elsevier Science Publishers, B.V.

B.   Comparison to Other Techniques

        Two studies (Bush et al., 1975; Collins et al.,
1972) compared TLC and GC/ECD. In both studies the PCB values obtained were comparable, although in the study by Bush
et al., the TLC results were generally lower than GC/ECD.

        Lucas et al. (1980) reported a statistical analysis
of semiquantitative determinations of PCBs in human adipose
tissue generated by the EPA's National Human Monitoring Program (Kutz and Strassman, 1976) during FY 1972 to 1976. Results were reported only as ranges (not determined, < 1, 1 to
3, and > 3 ppm) for 5,259 samples. The EPA TLC technique
(Watts, 1980; Sherma, 1981) was used in this study through
November 1974 and a GC/ECD technique involving a single PCB
peak quantitation was used thereafter. A total of 3,802 TLC
results and 1,457 PGC/ECD results were compared and found to
be not significantly different.

        Reverse-phase TLC compared favorably with GC/ECD
for the analysis of PCBs in transformer oil in the 4-55 ppm
range (Stahr, 1984). The difference in the results of the
two methods averaged ± 20%.

C.   Current and Potential Applications

        TLC lacks the congener resolution of GC, so it is
not applicable to detailed analysis for individual PCBs.
However, the low setup and per-analysis costs (no capital
equipment) and rapid analysis make it ideal for screening
samples where a simple "yes" or "no" answer for total PCBs is
sufficient. Examples could include screening of industrial
products for by-product PCBs and screening of soil or hazardous waste samples for PCB contamination. In samples where
PCBs are ubiquitous, such as human adipose, TLC may be of
less utility, since more detailed qualitative and quantitative information is generally sought. However, it should be
noted that the LODs quoted for TLC are not as sensitive as
those for other techniques, so it will be less applicable
where trace level analysis is required.

IV. HIGH PERFORMANCE LIQUID CHROMATOGRAPHY

        High performance liquid chromatography, also called
high pressure or high speed liquid chromatography (HPLC), is
essentially an instrumental version of the common open column
chromatographic techniques used for sample cleanup (see
Chapter 6). The instrumentation consists of a pumping system, injector, separation column, and a detector. All components are linked by tubing, so the separation and detection

are done in one continuous operation. The separation may be based on liquid-solid partitioning (e.g., hexane on silica gel), liquid-liquid partitioning (e.g., bonded alkane columns such as C_{18}), size exclusion (gel permeation), or chemical functionality interactions (e.g., amine columns). Liquid-solid and liquid-liquid chromatography are collectively known as adsorption chromatography, since the interaction with the stationary phase occurs at the surface. Separation of analytes by adsorption chromatography may be effected using either of two modes of operation controlled by the nature of the mobile phase: normal or reverse phase. In normal phase adsorption chromatography, the mobile phase or solvent (e.g., hexane, methylene chloride, benzene) is less polar than the stationary phase (e.g., silica or alumina). Reverse phase chromatography utilizes a more polar solvent (e.g., water, acetonitrile, methanol) relative to the stationary phase (e.g., chemically bonded C_8 or C_{18}- silica gel).

Common detectors include ultraviolet (not very selective), fluorescence (somewhat selective), and electrochemical (selective, depending on compound classes). Several other detectors are employed less commonly, including mass spectrometry. Compounds are identified by their retention time (RT) when compared to that of a standard and by detection with a selective detector. The intensity (height or area) of the peak is used for quantitation by comparison to the response obtained from a standard.

HPLC is discussed in detail in most analytical chemistry texts and in many monographs. Two examples are Yost et al. (1980) and Snyder and Kirkland (1979).

A. Literature Citations

High performance liquid chromatography (HPLC), with ultraviolet and other detectors, has been reported in the characterization of commercial PCBs, as a cleanup technique, and as a determination technique. Despite its general applicability in analytical chemistry, HPLC has not been as popular as gas chromatography for PCB analysis. The major reason is that GC detectors, especially those selective toward halogens, exhibit much lower limits of detection.

Since HPLC is basically an instrumental version of the column chromatographic cleanup techniques, described in Chapter 6, it is applicable both as a cleanup and a determination technique. Some researchers have exploited this and combined cleanup and determination into one step with HPLC (Hanai and Walton, 1977; Van Vliet et al., 1979).

Krull (1977) discussed HPLC and its utility as a cleanup technique, especially for removing similar chlorinated hydrocarbons such as the DDT family. Lawrence and Turton (1978) reviewed the HPLC data on pesticides and PCBs. Their review provides a useful tabulation of HPLC chromatographic systems (column packings, dimensions, mobile phases, detectors) and elution volumes for 166 pesticides and PCBs.

Although HPLC has been used for measurement of PCBs from a variety of matrices discussed below, this technique has not been used with any of the standard procedures identified in Chapter 3.

1. Characterization of commercial mixtures: Several authors (Brinkman et al., 1976a,b; Veith and Austin, 1976; Albro and Parker, 1979; Brinkman and De Vries, 1979) have used HPLC in characterization of commercial PCB products or establishing the chemical behavior of PCBs. Krupcik et al. (1977) used HPLC/UV and HRGC/FID to characterize fractions obtained by vacuum distillation of an Aroclor 1242 mixture. The HPLC separation was performed on silica gel with n-pentane as the elution solvent. Figure 7-24 illustrates the chromatography and also the effect of different UV wavelengths on sensitivity. About 20 congeners were identified in this and other fractions by comparison of retention times to those of authentic standards. Brinkman et al. (1976a,b) used a similar system to characterize Aroclors and listed retention times and UV data for 51 congeners.

Kaminsky and Fasco (1978) used reverse phase (RP) HPLC/UV to characterize Aroclor 1221, 1016, and 1254. The retention times on a µBondapak C_{18} column with a water/acetonitrile gradient and relative response at 254 nm were reported for 48 congeners. Figure 7-25 illustrates the separation power of RP HPLC. Clearly the reverse phase is much better at resolving PCBs than normal phase (Figure 7-24). Issaq et al. (1984) also used a C_{18} bonded column to obtain an RP HPLC/UV separation of Aroclor 1254 into 15 peaks.

Brinkman and De Vries (1979) used silica gel and alumina columns with n-hexane as the eluent to characterize a variety of haloaromatics, including PCBs, relating chromatographic behavior to structure. Planarity and linearity of the molecule were found to affect adsorption on alumina, but not silica gel. The presence of substituents ortho to each other or the central C-C bond promotes retention on both adsorbents. Veith and Austin (1976) found that the HPLC retention time on a C_{18} column with methanol/water eluent was proportional to the octanol/water partition coefficient.

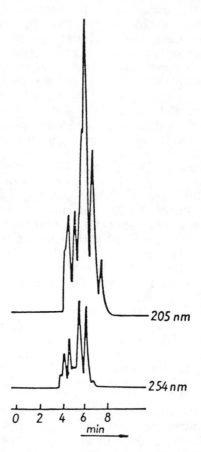

Figure 7-24.   HPLC Chromatogram of PCBs with UV Detection
            at Two Wavelengths (205 nm and 254 nm)

The sample was the last fraction (No. 70) from a distillation
of Aroclor 1242.   A 25 cm x 4.7 mm ID glass column was packed
with 5 μm spherical silica gel.   The solvent was n-pentane at
40 mL/min.

Reprinted, with permission, from Krupcik et al. (1977); copyright 1977 by Elsevier Science Publishers B.V.

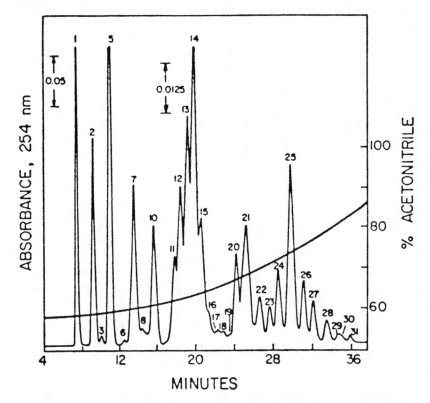

Figure 7-25.   Reverse Phase HPLC/UV Separation of Aroclors
1221, 1016, and 1254 (1:1:1, w/w/w) in Tetrahydrofuran
on a µBondapak C_{18} Column Monitored at 254 nm

Initial conditions, 40% water-acetonitrile (9:1) and 60%
water-acetonitrile (1:9); final conditions, 100% water-
acetonitrile (1:9); gradient time, 40 min; flow rate, 2 mL/
min; injection volume, 10 µL; amount injected, 50 µg total.

Reprinted, with permission, from Kaminsky and Fasco (1978);
copyright 1978 by Elsevier Science Publishers B.V.

Recently, high resolution HPLC using capillary or
micropacked columns has revolutionized the resolving power of
HPLC.   The pioneers in this field, Ishii and Takeuchi (1983)
have illustrated the high resolution RP HPLC of PCBs, as
shown in Figure 7-26.   This is by far the highest resolution
HPLC chromatogram of those in the literature reviewed.   The
high resolution, however, is achieved only at a cost in time.
The analysis in Figure 7-26 took about 8 hr to elute all of
the PCBs.

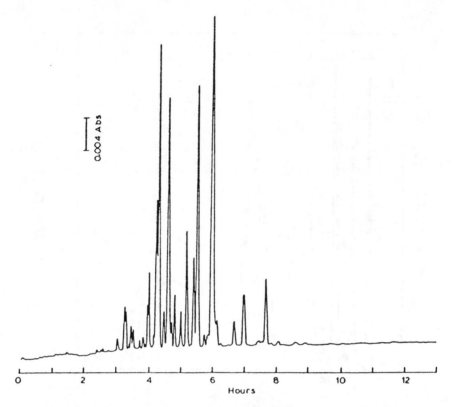

Figure 7-26.   High Resolution Reversed-Phase HPLC/UV
Chromatogram of PCB Mixture Containing 48% Chlorine

The column was a 1.5 m x 0.26 mm ID fused silica capillary
packed with 5 μm silica ODS SC-01.   Acetonitrile/water
(85:15, v/v) was pumped at 0.6 μL/min.   The sample was 5% PCB
in acetonitrile; 0.2 μL was injected.   The UV detector wave-
length was 254 nm.

Reprinted, with permission, from Ishii and Takeuchi (1983);
copyright 1983 by Elsevier Science Publishers B.V.

        De Kok et al (1982b) used HPLC to characterize com-
mercial polychlorinated terphenyls (PCTs).   Hernandez and
Walton (1982) reported the retention volumes of polychlorinated biphenylols by RP HPLC/UV using a C_{18} column and
methanol/water as the eluent.

        HPLC has been used as a cleanup technique prior to
gas chromatographic determination (Aitzetmüller, 1975; Dark
and Crossman, 1973; Rohleder et al., 1976; Krupcik et al.,
1977; Dolphin and Willmott, 1978).   More recently it has been

used on a preparative scale to clean up waste and transformer oils prior to HRGC/ECD determination (Anonymous, 1982a; Chesler et al., 1981). In the course of these investigations, the researchers noted that the HRGC/ECD limit of detection was about 100 times lower than the HPLC/UV limit of detection.

2. Trace analysis: As HPLC became increasingly popular in the early 1970s, Eisenbeiss and Sieper (1973) performed preliminary investigations of the use of HPLC for pesticide (and PCB) residue analysis. They concluded that HPLC can be regarded as "an alternative or supplementary method to conventional methods such as gas chromatography," and also would be applicable as a confirmatory analysis. Electron capture detection of HPLC effluents has been described (Willmott and Dolphin, 1974) for the analysis of PCBs. The LOD of HPLC/ECD was reported to be about 10 times higher than for GC/ECD in a study of decachlorobiphenyl following perchlorination (Brinkman et al., 1978).

Room temperature phosphorescence in liquid solutions (RTPL) was used as a RP HPLC detector for PCBs (Donkerbroek et al., 1982, 1983). Detection limits were reported for nine congeners ranging from 0.21-5.6 ng. Ortho-substituted PCBs are poorly detected, so the technique may be useful for qualitative identification of compounds when used in conjunction with UV detection. Stalling et al. (1980b) gave a preliminary description of an HPLC/MS (presumably the chemical ionization MS mode) system for rapid screening for PCBs.

Hanai and Walton (1977) developed an HPLC/UV method for determining PCBs in water. No LOD was determined, but good recoveries were obtained for 250 µg/L of Aroclor 1232 spiked into distilled water. The water was pumped directly through the HPLC system and the PCBs subsequently eluted by gradient elution. A similar application (Van Vliet et al., 1979) used an HPLC precolumn to concentrate PCBs from water and then elute them onto the analytical column for separation and determination. The example presented was for 20 µg/16.5 mL of water or 1,200 µg/L.

Belliardo et al. (1979) developed a RP HPLC/UV procedure for PCBs in oil and compared it with a PGC/ECD method. The HPLC method was judged suitable to approximate, but not quantitate, the PCB content. Compared with GC/ECD methods, the RP HPLC/UV was termed rapid, convenient, and applicable to routine analysis. Klimisch and Ingebrigtson (1980) reported a RP HPLC/UV method for determination of PCBs in polydimethylsiloxane (silicone) fluids. PCBs were extracted with acetonitrile and then injected on a C_{18} column with acetonitrile/water eluent. A method detection limit (MDL) of 100 ppb and repeatability of less than ± 4% at the 0.1-3% level were reported. A PGC/ECD method had an MDL of 25 ppb and was judged to be preferable for low level analyses and for routine screening where a single dilution is the only preparation required. For PCB levels over 1%, HPLC was recommended for quantitative work since the serial dilutions required to get within the PGC/ECD linearity are more time-consuming.

Seidl and Ballschmiter (1979) used silica gel HPLC/UV to detect biphenyl after dehydrochlorination of PCBs in soil and olive oil. A detection limit of 100 ng absolute was reported, which translates to about 0.05-0.5 µg/g depending on sample size and other factors.

A simple, rapid method for quantitation of PCBs removes interferences by the DDT family by oxidation to dichlorobenzophenone and then determination by normal phase HPLC/UV (Chiosi et al., 1982). The PCB detection limit (as Aroclor 1242) was reported as 2.57 ng. The precision of the HPLC step was in the range of ± 2%. The method was applied to snails and tuna with no observed interferences.

B.   Current and Potential Applications

HPLC has found little use in analysis for trace PCBs in environmental samples. With the shift toward analysis of commercial products and assessment of transformer and other fluids for PCB contamination (often at the high ppm to percent levels), HPLC should be more useful. The poor inherent sensitivity of most HPLC detectors is partially compensated for by the large injection volumes (often more than 100 µL). Another drawback of HPLC is that the specific detectors available for GC (e.g., ECD and MS) are not as widely applied to HPLC. Thus, most applications have utilized the UV detection, which is not very selective. Perhaps the greatest potential advantage of HPLC is when it can be used as a one-step cleanup/determination technique. This could be easily automated to provide PCB analysis with virtually no labor costs. Sample matrices which are much different from PCBs, such as water, would be particularly amenable to this approach.

V.   NONCHROMATOGRAPHIC METHODS

This section presents a variety of miscellaneous methods reported for the determination of PCBs. Some of the MS techniques (notably HREIMS and MS/MS) are used either as GC detectors, or as stand-alone techniques with direct probe sample introduction. Both applications were discussed in the respective subsections above. While many of the nonchromatographic techniques are of great use in characterizing PCBs, few of them have the required specificity and sensitivity for trace determinations.

A. Nuclear Magnetic Resonance (NMR) Spectrometry

Wilson and Anderson (1973) used both ^{13}C and ^{1}H nuclear magentic resonance (NMR) to characterize the chemistry of selected PCBs. No attempt at analysis of real samples was made. Levy and Hewitt (1977) reported the analysis of PCB mixtures by ^{13}C NMR, but noted that the technique was not as useful for higher homologs. Hutzinger et al. (1974a) included a discussion of the NMR characteristics of PCBs in their review book. Synthetic congeners have been characterized by proton NMR (Mullin et al., 1981, 1984).

B. Infrared (IR) Spectrometry

Hutzinger et al. (1974a) discussed the infrared (IR) spectral properties of PCBs. Webb and McCall (1972) used IR and other techniques to identify 24 PCB congeners in Aroclor 1221. The spectra of 14 pentachlorobiphenyls and two trichlorobiphenyls were studied in detail by Nyquist et al. (1983). Spectra were obtained on a Fourier transform infrared spectrometer (FTIR) using the diffuse reflectance technique. In addition to spectra, major peaks were assigned to the various bending and stretching modes and the group frequency contributions presented. The authors noted that this data base should be useful in the identification of other congeners.

Chen and Gardner (1983) used the higher sensitivity and data manipulation capabilities of FTIR to identify and quantitate the individual congeners in mixtures. The method was applied to fractions collected from a gas chromatograph. Up to three components were accurately identified and quantitated. FTIR has been used as an on-line GC detector (Erickson, 1979) and could probably be applied to PCB analyses, where the concentrations are sufficient and the identity of individual congeners is needed. This technique would be especially applicable as a confirmatory technique.

FTIR has been studied as a field-usable instrumental technique for rapidly determining PCBs in transformer oil (Nordstrom, 1983; Nordstrom and McIntosh, 1981). For regulatory purposes (EPA, 1979d), transformer oils must be categorized as "clean" (< 50 ppm), "contaminated" (50-500 ppm), or "PCB-containing" (> 500 ppm). Transmittance spectra are collected and the concentration determined by a least-squares fit of the absorbance to a standard curve. In order to clean up the sample sufficiently for reliable measurement in the 50-500 ppm concentration range, an automated dimethyl formamide extraction and concentration apparatus is attached to the FTIR spectrometer. The entire procedure can analyze a sample in 10 min with ± 10% accuracy in the 50-500 ppm range. The technique was judged impractical and further research discontinued (Hinganori, 1984).

A filter IR instrument has been studied for use as a portable field monitor (Denton et al., 1981; Bostick et al., 1983; Denton and Walker, 1983). The authors selected IR because of its ability to detect PCBs in the presence of mineral oil. In fact, mineral oil is the well-known Nujol used to mull solid samples in classic infrared spectroscopy. The authors found the 8.5 μm (1,180 cm^{-1}) and 9.2 μm (1,090 cm^{-1}) bands selective for Aroclor 1260 in the presence of mineral oil or trichlorobenzene (a common component of transformer askarels). The major limitation of the technique was the high limit of detection--500-1,000 μg/g. The authors also used IR to detect PCBs in soil. The PCBs were extracted from the soil matrix with a volatile solvent (e.g., acetonitrile) and then spotted onto the window of a multiple internal reflectance (MIR) cell. After the solvent had evaporated, the absorbance was measured. The authors were able to detect a "few dozen micrograms" of Aroclor 1260.

C. Radioimmunoassay

Albro and coworkers reported preliminary results in the development of a radioimmunoassay (RIA) method for PCBs (Albro et al., 1979; Kohli et al., 1979a; Luster et al., 1979, 1981). The evidence indicated the feasibility of employing radioimmunoassays for determining the Aroclor number and concentration in environmental samples (Luster et al., 1979). The assay required an antiserum for each isomer but was termed fairly specific.

A radioimmunoassay was developed capable of determining Aroclor 1260 in milk at levels of from 20 to 80 ppb and in blood from 2 to 16 ppb (Newsome and Shields, 1981). The values obtained by radioimmunoassay correlated well with those determined by gas-liquid chromatography but were up to 25% lower. Antiserum was produced in rabbits and was specific for 2,2',4,4',5,5'-hexachlorobiphenyl. It cross-reacted with congeners and isomers in Aroclor 1254 and 1260 to the extent that a 20% decrease in binding was observed with 0.1 ng of either mixture. The method required preliminary cleanup of the extract on alumina.

D. Other Techniques

Interrupted-sweep voltametry has been applied to the identification of PCBs, yielding positive identifications (Farwell et al., 1975). Plasma chromatography has been reported to give characteristic qualitative data for PCBs (Karasek, 1971). One report utilized neutron activation analysis for the determination of PCBs in dosed rats (Manri et al., 1971). Low temperature luminescence has been proposed as a simplified method for the identification and quantitation of PCBs (EPA, 1972; Brownrigg and Hornig, 1974, 1976). The limit of detection was reported to be as low as 0.01 ppm.

VI. CONFIRMATION

Confirmatory techniques have been used frequently in PCB analysis. The term confirmation may be loosely defined as any operation performed to increase the confidence of the results beyond the primary analysis. Qualitative confirmation is much more often reported than quantitative confirmation. Confirmatory techniques involve variation of the same technique (PGC/ECD on two dissimilar columns), confirmation by a lesser technique (PGC/ECD with TLC confirmation), or confirmation by a more advanced technique (PGC/ECD with PGC/EIMS confirmation). A review on confirmatory tests presents a general overview of confirmation as it relates to pesticides (Lawrence, 1981).

A. Literature Citations

Hutzinger et al. (1974a) reviewed confirmation. While mass spectrometry was briefly mentioned, most of the discussion centered on perchlorination. Table 3-I lists all of the standard methods and notes the type of confirmation suggested. All of these confirmations are optional and qualitative.

As early as 1969, the need for confirmation of PCB findings was discussed (Reynolds, 1969). An exchange of comments following a presentation by Risebrough (1971) led to a proposal for confirmation, covering mass spectrometry, dechlorination, and perchlorination. Price and Welch (1972) are typical of many early investigators who backed up their PGC/ECD analysis with a TLC confirmation (see also the standard methods: AOAC, 1980a; FDA, 1977). Hannan et al. (1973) utilized a cumbersome ultraviolet irradiation method to confirm PGC/ECD results. A dual GC to heart-cut a chromatogram and separate the decomposition products from the first ECD has been proposed as a confirmation technique for pesticides and PCBs (Aue and Shubhender, 1978). A HPLC/room temperature phosphorescence system has been reported which not only provides a second detection in addition to UV, but also aids in identification of isomers, since ortho-substituted PCBs are not detected by the phosphorescence technique (Donkerbroek et al., 1982, 1983).

Mes and co-workers have utilized a variety of techniques to confirm the PCB concentration in the analysis of adipose and milk samples (Mes et al., 1977, 1980; Mes and Davies, 1979). The methods include two dissimilar GC columns, perchlorination, and GC/EIMS.

GC/EIMS was used by Biros et al. (1972) and Kutz and Strassman (1976) to confirm TLC results. GC/EIMS confirmation has also been reported (Haile and Baladi, 1977; Teichman et al., 1978; Musial et al., 1974; Lucas et al., 1980; Pastel et al., 1980; Rodriguez et al., 1980; Erickson et al., 1983e). HREIMS has been reported as a confirmatory technique (Safe et al., 1975; Safe, 1976; Musial et al., 1974). Kuehl et al. (1980b) used HRGC/NCIMS to qualitatively confirm their HRGC/EIMS PCB identifications in fish. Hass and Friesen (1979), placing particular emphasis on polychlorinated dibenzodioxins, reviewed the advanced mass spectrometric techniques for both high sensitivity and high reliability analysis: HREIMS and NCIMS.

B. Current and Potential Applications

The choice of a confirmation technique depends on (1) the information content from the primary technique, (2) the PCB and interferent concentrations, (3) the level of confidence needed, and (4) availability of instrumentation. Clearly, the confirmation technique must increase knowledge about the sample. Confirmation by GC/ECD after a successful analysis by GC/EIMS therefore makes little sense, while the reverse may often make sense. The analytical technique must be sufficiently sensitive for the level of PCBs in the sample. This frequently means that GC/EIMS cannot be used to confirm residue levels in trace environmental samples. The higher the level of interferences, the more selective the confirmation technique must be. Even with the high selectivity of MS, high levels of dissimilar compounds (e.g., an oil matrix) can totally obscure PCBs at the part-per-million level in a GC/EIMS confirmation. The level of analytical confidence required can often be a political or financial decision. In addition, it depends on the prior knowledge of the sample. Detection of PCBs at 10 µg/g in human adipose by GC/ECD would not normally require confirmation, since this is a typical level and they are ubiquitous (Lucas et al., 1982).

On the other hand, confirmation would most certainly be required if an Aroclor-like pattern were observed in a GC/ECD chromatogram of a commercial product sample which should not be contaminated and had a negative assay for chlorine.

With ECD detection of either GC or HRGC, second-column confirmations are often appropriate. All of the more advanced MS techniques (NCIMS, HREIMS, MS/MS), with direct probe or preferably as GC sample introduction, are useful confirmation techniques.

Quantitative confirmation has rarely been noted in the literature. Confirmation of the quantitation is almost as important as the confirmation of the identity of the analyte. Not only can interferences mask or augment the peak identified as a PCB, but calibration by a second technique is often sufficiently different to minimize systematic bias. Quantitative confirmation can be viewed as a portion of a good QC program since it verifies the reported values.

VII. SCREENING

   A. Screening for PCBs

Screening techniques sacrifice the confidence in the analysis for speed and/or simplicity of apparatus. Often a screening analysis provides only qualitative or semiquantitative information. Samples should be screened where immediate analysis is needed, such as during an incinerator trial burn to make sure that the PCBs are being destroyed, or where most of the samples should contain no PCBs above the detection limit of either the screening or primary analytical technique and may be efficiently eliminated by the screen.

1. Chromatographic screening: As discussed earlier, TLC, HPLC, and GC all have application for screening samples. In addition, the perchlorination and carbon skeleton chromatography techniques can serve for screening samples. Finally, abbreviated analytical procedures can be used to quickly screen samples. An example is a PGC/ECD analysis of fish tissue with a quick extraction/cleanup using miniature chromatographic columns (Erney, 1974a).

Another aspect of screening is simple range-finding. If there is a possibility of an extremely high concentration sample, such as in transformer oil samples or in hazardous waste samples, very dilute or very small volume injections can prevent a catastrophic overloading of the analytical system.

2. Total organic halide: An increasingly popular screening technique is total organic halide (TOX) or total organic chlorine (TOCl or RCl). TOCl values are required for incinerator testing for PCBs (EPA, 1979d). While TOX is one of the least selective techniques since it detects "all" organic halides, it is quite sensitive and can be useful when there are low levels of other chlorinated compounds relative to the PCBs. TOX have been monitored using a very short column (2.5 cm long) PGC/HECD method, shown in Figure 7-27 (Stanley et al., 1982; Haile et al., 1983a; Nulton et al., 1984), or extraction/GC/EIMS method (Beard and Schaum, 1978). Both employ a Soxhlet extraction of the XAD-2 resin from the modified Method 5 train (EPA, 1977; Haile and Baladi, 1977). The TOX values for stack gas and fly ash from a power plant and an incinerator obtained by HRGC/EIMS averaged about 14% higher than the values obtained by the short column GC/HECD technique (Nulton et al., 1984). It should be noted that these methods do not in fact measure total chlorinated organics, but rather semivolatile, gas chromatographable, chlorinated organics. The GC/HECD TOX measurement was applied to background air particulate, stack gas particulate, and ash samples from a municipal incinerator and a co-fired power plant (Haile et al., 1983a,b; Nulton et al., 1984). Values ranged from 0.9 to 46,000 ng/g. In water samples they ranged from 100 to 1,000 ng/L.

Two techniques for total chlorinated organics involve concentration of the organic halides on a sorbent trap, and reduction to HCl at 950°C. In one system the HCl gas is detected by electrolytic conductivity (Model 610 Total Organic Halogen Analyzer, O.I. Corporation, College Station, Texas). In the other system, the HCl gas is detected by microcoulometry (Model DX-20 Total Organic Halide Analyzer, Dohrmann Xertex, Santa Clara, California). Both techniques have the advantage over previously used methods in that volatile, semivolatile, and non-volatile organic chlorides can be detected. The extraction/GC methods detect only the semivolatile organic chlorides. The electrolytic conductivity technique was characterized by Bernard and Russell (1983). As shown in Figure 7-28, the analyses with the electrolytic conductivity technique are quite rapid and reproducible. The response is linear with concentration. The coefficients of variation at both PCB levels were less than 2% and about 2.6% for the blank. This technique features an optional dedicated data system. The microcoulometric technique was characterized by Berger (1984).

3. Chemical determination of total chloride: The classic organic reduction of organochlorine to free chloride ion with metallic sodium has been used to develop screening techniques for PCBs. The free chloride ion can be detected by a chloride ion-specific electrode or colorimetrically.

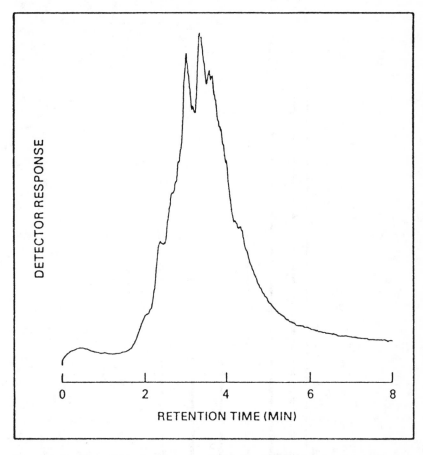

Figure 7-27.   Total Organic Halide (TOX) Analysis Using a
Short Column PGC/HECD

The sample (5-20 µL) is injected onto a 1-m column containing
2.5 cm of 10% SP-2100 on Ultrabond packing with a helium flow
rate of 60 mL/min.   The column temperature was 60°C for 3
min, then programmed at 40°C/min to 230°C.   The total area
under the chromatogram is integrated and compared to the response for monochlorobiphenyl.

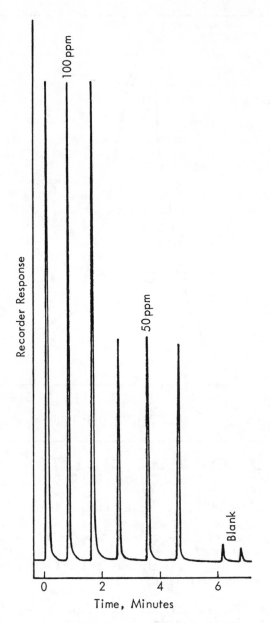

Figure 7-28.   TOCl Measurements of Aroclor 1248 Using
                Electrolytic Conductivity

Eight sample injections (5 μL) are shown.

Reprinted, with permission, from Bernard and Russell (1983).

Using the colorimetric detection principle, an inexpensive, rapid, self-contained kit has been developed for field-testing transformer oil samples (Fisher et al., 1984). The object is to determine whether the oil is "contaminated" (50-500 ppm) with PCBs and therefore requires special handling and disposal in the United States (EPA, 1979d). The kit (Chlor-N-Oil®), developed for the Electric Power Research Institute and marketed by Dexsil Corporation, is based on the quantitative conversion of the chlorine atoms on PCBs to chloride ions which in turn are extracted into an aqueous solution and measured colorimetrically. Chlorine is converted to chloride ions by sodium salts formed by naphthalene together with the dimethyl ether of diethylene glycol ("diglyme") as stabilizing ligand. The chloride ions are extracted into an aqueous buffer solution and reacted with a carefully controlled amount of dissolved mercuric nitrate. Diphenylcarbazone is added. Reaction of any excess mercuric ion with the diphenylcarbazone will form a vivid blue complex. If the chloride ion content exceeds that taken up by the available mercuric ion, the complex is not formed and the reaction mixture remains colorless to pale yellow. The reactions are carried out in soft plastic test tubes containing premeasured reagents in breakable glass ampules. Proper control of the sample size and of the quantity of mercuric nitrate allows the blue-colorless response level in the mineral transformer oil to be set at levels from a few ppm to several thousand ppm.

The lowest ratio of chlorine to PCB found in an askarel is 0.42 (Aroclor 1242). Therefore, an oil sample containing less than 21 ppm chlorine cannot contain more than 50 ppm PCB. A color response level set at 21 ppm chlorine for the kit should assure that no contaminated oil (i.e., 50-500 ppm) gives blue responses. Samples giving colorless responses can be checked by gas chromatography to determine whether they actually contain more than 50 ppm PCB. It has been estimated that the use of a colorimetric test kit can reduce the number of GC/ECD analyses required to determine whether or not a transformer oil is contaminated by 50-60% (Walsh, 1983). This would result in a significant reduction in cost of a monitoring program.

The test was validated by 40 utilities with a total of 824 samples tested. Using a 50-ppm regulator cutoff, 27% of the samples yielded false positives and only 2.3% were false negatives when compared to GC/ECD results, which were assumed to be accurate (Tahiliani, 1984). Minor changes in the kit and instructions promise to improve the accuracy of the test.

4. X-Ray fluorescence: X-ray fluorescence (XRF) has been studied as a PCB screening technique. When an atom like chlorine is bombarded with x-rays, electrons are dislodged from inner orbitals, creating "holes." These holes are rapidly filled by electrons from outer orbitals. The energy difference between an inner and outer orbital results in the emission of a secondary x-ray when a hole is filled. This secondary x-ray is measured by XRF. McQuade (1982) showed that XRF could accurately detect and quantitate chlorine down to a concentration equivalent to about 10 ppm of an Aroclor. The technique cannot differentiate between PCBs and other chlorine species (including inorganic chlorides). The total analysis time is about 5 min/ sample and the instrument is small enough (40 kg) for field use. The portable analyzer was used to test transformer oils at electrical substations (Schwalb and Marquez, 1982). The main objective was to categorize the oils as "clean" (< 50 ppm), "contaminated" (50-500 ppm), or "PCB-containing" (> 500 ppm) for EPA regulatory purposes (EPA, 1979d). The XRF results compared well with those obtained off-site by GC, although there were occasional false negatives.

B. Screening for Interferences

Samples may also be screened to assess the effectiveness of cleanup before submission to a final determination technique such as GC/EIMS. The objective is to assess the overall level of chromatographable compounds, not to specifically detect PCBs. Background screening for samples which will be analyzed by a gas chromatographic technique is best accomplished using GC/flame ionization detection (FID). FID is a "universal" detector and thus provides a relatively uniform response to all eluting components of the mixture.

Interference screening is especially applicable for unfamiliar samples, when major interferences may contaminate the analytical instrumentation. Indications for screening include: highly colored samples or extracts; evidence of cleanup technique overloading; precipitation on solvent evaporation; sample history (e.g., solid hazardous waste of unknown composition); and matrices which have similar physical properties to PCBs (e.g., oils).

VIII. SUMMARY

As discussed in this chapter, a wide variety of instrumental techniques are available to determine the PCB content of a sample. The choice of the technique depends on a number of factors, as presented in "Criteria for Choice of Techniques" at the beginning of this chapter. For routine analysis, GC/ECD, GC/HECD, or GC/EIMS would probably be most appropriate. The selection of PGC or HRGC depends on the need for isomer specificity and, to some extent, individual preference. Several screening techniques may be applicable if the probability of PCB occurrence is low and the matrix composition permits their use. TLC, TOX, GC/FID, and GC/ECD are all candidate screening techniques under the right circumstances. Confirmation generally involves either reanalysis on a second column using the same detector, or stepping up in instrumental sophistication to improve the qualitative reliability of the analysis. Thus, EIMS, HREIMS, MS/MS, and NCIMS are often considered confirmatory techniques.

8

DATA REDUCTION

Data reduction is a key element in sample analysis. In this step, the analyst converts the instrumental output into information for the user. Specifically, any PCBs present in the samples are identified and quantitated. Depending on the detection and output system, data may be presented to the analyst as analog chromatograms, numerical tabulations, MS extracted ion current plots, etc. Computers and integrators can reduce the analyst's work in data acquisition and reduction; however, the judgement of a qualified analyst is critical to reliable data reduction.

The importance of data reduction cannot be overemphasized, especially with PCBs. In a collaborative study, Delfino and Easty (1979) reported an RSD of ± 15.6% for direct injection of an Aroclor 1242. They noted that the PGC/ECD analysis appeared to provide the principal source of variation in the overall determination. Similarly, Erickson et al. (1983c) noted that data reduction constituted about one-third of the error associated with a HRGC/EIMS procedure for by-product PCB analysis. See Chapter 10 for more details on both studies.

The first task in data reduction is to qualitatively identify the analyte, answering the question "is the analyte present?" Quantitation can be attempted only after a compound has been identified, although the required level of confidence in the identification can vary widely, as discussed below.

I. QUALITATIVE

A. The Importance of Proper Qualitative Data Interpretation

The qualitative aspects of the analysis are all too often overlooked. Especially with complex mixtures of PCBs, differences in the qualitative assessment of a sample can

dramatically affect the number of peaks quantitated. Qualitative assessment of results depends to a large extent on
sample type. For samples where the presence of PCBs has been
well-established (e.g., human or adipose tissue) the qualitative burden is not nearly so great as for samples in which
PCBs are not expected.

The cleanup and determination techniques used to
generate the data also dictate the level and type of data assessment needed. PCB-specific methods reduce the probability
of interference and ease the qualitative burden. In some
cases, the cleanup involves a rather specific liquid chromatographic separation which separates PCBs from most organochlorine pesticides and other potential interferences. In
addition, the use of specific GC detectors (ECD, HECD) reduces the probability of interferences and increases confidence in the identification. Better still, MS provides spectra of the eluent which may be compared with those of authentic compounds to give higher confidence in the identifications. The retention time of the unknown should match that
of a standard or at least be within a PCB window. HRGC gives
much more precise retention times than PGC and increases
qualitative confidence. In the case of samples contaminated
by commercial mixtures (e.g., Aroclor), the pattern of chromatographic peaks often resembles the pattern of a standard.
This visual pattern recognition has been a common qualitative
technique in residue analyses, especially when PGC/ECD is the
analytical procedure.

For many analyses, qualitative identification of
PCBs is trivial. For example, human adipose samples will
most assuredly have a characteristic PCB pattern in sample
after sample. In cases where the presence of PCBs is less
likely, the qualitative criteria should be established before
the analysis, generally as part of the QA plan. To some extent, qualitative criteria are controlled by external factors: economics, politics, organizational policy, etc. For
example, a regulated industry may set relatively low qualitative criteria, so that samples even suspected of containing
PCBs will be properly disposed of. Also, if confirmation of
suspected PCBs in a waste is more expensive than disposal,
then further analysis is clearly not warranted; the waste is
simply labeled "PCB-contaminated" and shipped off for disposal. Not only should the qualitative criteria establish
limits (retention time windows, ion ratios, etc.), but they
should direct the analyst to alternate courses of action
(consult supervisor, confirm by alternate technique, analyze
by standard addition, etc.).

In addition to the various gas chromatographic identification techniques discussed here, thin-layer chromatography and high performance liquid chromatography yield qualitative information, as discussed in Chapter 7. More exotic techniques such as specialized mass spectrometric techniques, Fourier transform infrared spectrometry, and nuclear magnetic resonance spectroscopy are not used routinely for PCB analysis and were discussed in Chapter 7.

B.   Interpretation of Retention Data

Regardless of the detector used, the retention time data from a gas chromatogram provides the first dimension of information used to identify PCBs. The peaks must be within the PCB window before any of the other qualitative criteria are applied. With ECD and HECD data, the detector selectivity reduces, but does not eliminate, the probability that non-PCB peaks will interfere with the qualitative interpretation. With mass spectromtric detection, the mass spectrum provides a second qualitative dimension, as discussed in Section I.C, below.

Only a few of the references using ECD or other analog detectors have mentioned the qualitative criteria used in identification of PCBs. In PGC/ECD procedures, visual pattern recognition is normally the qualitative technique. Often two GC columns of different polarity are used to enhance the confidence of the identification. With HRGC data, individual congeners may be identified by use of retention time or retention index tables or by comparison to a characterized commercial mixture. Increasingly, formal computerized pattern recognition routines are used to compare the PCB composition of samples.

1.   Low resolution chromatograms: The low resolution chromatograms generated by PGC/ECD or PGC/HECD can be compared to the retention windows established with standards (either congener mixtures, or commercial mixtures). The only other qualitative assessment which can be made is comparison of the pattern with that of a commercial mixture. A representative qualitative criterion in the literature that the chromatogram exhibit a "typical Aroclor pattern" (Gordon et al., 1982; Giam et al., 1972; Ofstad et al., 1978; Kirshen, 1981a,b). For many purposes, visual pattern recognition is entirely satisfactory. However, the PCB mixtures in many samples do not resemble a single Aroclor mixture, so identification is difficult.

Computerized pattern recognition has been applied to the relatively simple task of identifying which Aroclor is present in transformer oils and related samples (Colby and Picker, 1983). The goal was to minimize both the analysis time and operator intervention with an automated field analyzer (Colby et al., 1983; Picker and Colby, 1983). An algorithm was written for the dedicated microprocessor which identified PGC/ECD peaks in the Aroclor retention windows and then converted the retention time-intensity data pairs into an n-dimensional vector. The cosine of the angle of this vector in n-space was calculated and compared with the cosine of the angle for the various Aroclor standards. Pure and major-component Aroclors in a sample were readily distinguished. The algorithm was unreliable for components of less than 20% relative to the total amount of Aroclor. The authors noted that visual interpretation was also unreliable at this level.

Lerman et al. (1982) developed an algorithm for analysis of PCBs in transformer oils which calculates the concentration of an unknown against standard Aroclors 1242, 1254, and 1260 using both the total area and a mean of five key peaks for each. An error factor is calculated and an "error score" reported. The analyst can then review the data and decide which Aroclor best fits the unknown. The article does not present the routine in detail. Another routine (Lea et al., 1983) to identify Aroclors 1242, 1254, and 1260 is designed to be used with common chromatographic data systems (e.g., Varian Vista 401) and integrators (e.g., Varian CDS-111). Peaks are identified by retention time and then integrated. The peak areas are compared to those in the standard Aroclors by a ratio technique. The relative standard deviation of these ratios indicates how well the unknown matches the standard. Statistical tests ("Q test") are also incorporated to test for outliers, which can then be eliminated from the calculation.

A novel data reduction approach is to treat a PGC/ECD chromatogram as a spectrum and use infrared spectral subtraction software to match the unknown to a standard(s) in an interactive mode. Gossman (1983) presented this concept as applied to PCB-contaminated wastes. The ability to reject peaks which did not fit with an Aroclor standard was used to fit "only the good data." The concept, used with discretion, has particular appeal in analysis of mixed or degraded Aroclors. After a subtraction of one Aroclor, the residual peaks are observable on a screen and the analyst can visually assess the data.

2.   High resolution gas chromatograms

        a.   Use of retention times and retention indices: Several researchers have compared retention times (RTs) or relative retention times (RRTs) between the sample and an Aroclor standard for PCB identification (Webb and McCall, 1972; Onsuka and Comba, 1978; Erickson et al., 1983e; Pellizzari et al., 1983a,b; Tuinstra et al., 1980). Another identification technique involves use of one of the retention index (RI) schemes (e.g., Kovats). Several publications contain tabulations of RIs of PCB congeners as shown in Table 7-I (Sissons and Welti, 1971; Zell et al., 1978; Ballschmiter and Zell, 1980; Albro et al., 1981; Albro and Fishbein, 1972a,b; Hanneman, 1982). Since all 209 PCB congeners are not readily available, a scheme of predicting RIs has been developed based on the half-RI values (see Table 7-II) for the various chlorination positons on one of the benzene rings. Sissons and Welti (1971) first proposed this system, which was expanded upon and further validated by Albro and Fishbein (1972a) and Albro et al. (1977). The use of half RIs permits the analyst to qualitatively identify all 209 PCBs on the basis of their retention time, although the level of confidence in this identification has not been determined. Using state-of-the-art chromatography, RI measurement precision of ± 0.05% has been reported for PCBs (Neu et al., 1978), and with full optimization, precision of ± 0.01% has been predicted (Neu and Zinburg, 1979).

b. <u>Individual congener identification</u>: Several publications, dating back to the landmark work of Sissons and Welti (1971), concentrated on the identification of PCB congeners in commercial mixtures such as Aroclor or Chlophen (Tas and de Vos, 1971; Tas and Kleipool, 1972; Armour, 1972; Willis and Addison, 1972; Paasivirta and Pitkänen, 1975; Jensen and Sundström, 1974; Neu et al., 1978; Zell et al., 1978; Ballschmiter and Zell, 1980; Pellizzari et al., 1981; Tuinstra et al., 1981; Bush et al., 1982; Duinker and Hillebrand, 1983). The objective of most of these papers was to characterize the commercial mixture as an aid to quantitation in environmental samples or for toxicological information. The recent work by Bush et al. (1982) expanded on previous work and assigned 72 peaks in a mixture of Aroclors 1221, 1016, 1254, and 1260 (2 µg/mL each). Where there were ambiguities in previous work which they could not resolve, only the homolog is listed (e.g., Cl_5). They note that the confidence of the peak identities differs, depending on availability of standards, number of isomers eluting in the same region, etc. They also note that the confidence in the assignments will increase with time as more standards become available and further work is done to corroborate the assignments. Using the four-Aroclor calibration mixture and the peak tables, Bush et al. (1982) can identify all of the major and most of the minor PCB peaks found in environmental samples from the northeast United States. They state that:

"...although chromatographic matching of retention parameters does not necessarily constitute
perfect authentication of peak assignment, several
authors are reaching a consensus on the structure
of compounds separated on Apiezon L (Mullin et al.,
1981; Ballschmiter and Zell, 1980) and other phases
(Albro et al., 1981). We consider that the structures of the major peaks are now well enough established to warrant reporting them quantitatively
as described here. This will enable the task of
determining the toxicological significance of residues of PCB to be started, a hopeless task when results are expressed in terms of Aroclor mixtures as
has been the practice hitherto."

For environmentally derived samples where specification of
congeners is useful and where PCB concentrations are very
low, this HRGC/ECD method holds great promise.

Zell and Ballschmiter (1980) interpreted any
deviation of an environmental PCB pattern from the pattern of
combinations of commercial mixtures as the result of degradation or weathering. These authors established which congeners are indicative of metabolism, or other degradation
process for different types of environmental samples. This
method allows the analyst to focus attention on those components of interest--either because of their constancy from
matrix to matrix, or because of their change with environmental conditions.

c. Comparison of retention times on two HRGC
columns: Singer et al. (1983) used two HRGC columns (OV-1
and SE-54) with ECD detection for both qualitative and quantitative analysis. The data from the two analyses were correlated and the following criteria supplied using a program
written on the chromatograhpic data system:

"1. The retention time of the peak must have
been within limits (usually ± 0.1%) of the expected
retention time, otherwise the peak was rejected.

2. If the peak for a given PCB was identified
on both columns and the quantities were within limits (usually ± 20%), the average was calculated and
printed followed by the word 'confirmed.'

3. If the peak for a given PCB was identified
on both columns, but the quantities were not within
given limits, then the lower value was taken as the
result, followed by word 'interference' (we assumed

that the higher value was caused by an impurity co-eluting with the PCB).

4. If the peak for a given PCB was identified on one column only, the value was rejected and identified by the words 'not PCB.'

5. Although the capillary columns have very high resolving power, some PCBs could not be re-solved at all or could be resolved on one column only. If this happened, then the determined quan-tities of unresolved PCBs on one or both columns were summed up and evaluated under identical cri-teria."

d. <u>Pattern recognition</u>: As noted at the be-ginning of this section, GC/ECD data have traditionally been evaluated by visual pattern recognition. In the past few years some analysts have used computerized pattern recogni-tion. Bush et al. (1983) have used a rather simple technique to study differential concentrations of PCB congeners in ma-ternal and fetal cord blood. They used histograms of the frequency of detection at different concentration intervals to compare the two matrices. They were able to detect sev-eral congeners which are differentiated by the placenta. Gassiot et al. (1982) compared the Zobel and simplex computer algorithms for the identification and quantitation of up to three Aroclors in fish sample. The simplex routine was judged easier and more flexible to use.

Dunn et al. (1982) have used a computerized pattern recognition technique to evaluate HRGC/ECD data on PCBs. HRGC/ECD data for 69 congeners in about 700 samples of sediment, suspended sediment, benthos, and fish were examined using the SIMple Classification by Analogy (SIMCA) principal components modeling technique. SIMCA performs a vector anal-ysis of all of the relationships (e.g., concentration of a congener in water) and derives a set of artificial coordi-nates which best separate the data into classes. The two di-mensional eigenvector plots of the data readily indicated samples that were (a) either incorrectly assigned to a class, i.e., fish instead of water, or (b) those that were experi-mentally abnormal. SIMCA proved to be especially valuable for identifing outlier samples for reanalysis and also pro-vided a basis for defining "trace" concentration levels. Dunn et al. (1984) also compared SIMCA, K-nearest neighbor (KNN) and partial least squares (PLS) techniques to cate-gorize HRGC/ECD data by Aroclor. A transformer oil from a dump site was found to contain predominantly Aroclor 1260 with about 8% Aroclor 1254 (Figure 8-1). Pattern recognition appears to be a most promising technique for interpretation of large numbers of PCB determinations.

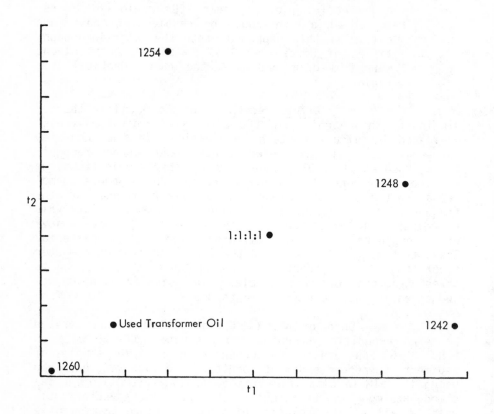

Figure 8-1.   Principal Components Plot of PCB Data

The data for four Aroclors, a transformer oil, and a 1:1:1:1 mixture of the Aroclors showing that the transformer oils are similar, but not equivalent, to Aroclor 1260. The axes de-noted t_1 and t_2, are arbitrary, unitless scales depicting the relationship of the data in n-dimensional space.

3. Recommended qualitative techniques for GC data:
Where "total PCBs" or similar general identification is desired, simple pattern recognition (visual or computerized) of
the PCBs relative to Aroclor standards may be appropriate.
However, as noted above, many types of samples can be weathered or metabolized to skew the Aroclor patterns. In these
cases, more advanced identification techniques are necessary.
The precise relative retention times on HRGC columns represent a high level of confidence in the identity of the peaks.
Use of a dual column analysis and correlation of the data
provide additional confidence.

Automated data quality assessment is becoming increasingly popular as old strip chart recorders and integrators are replaced by chromatographic data systems, which
are becoming increasingly sophisticated. Retention time
windows, peak height ratios, and other criteria are already
in use. More sophisticated statistical techniques, correlation and pattern recognition, will become more popular as the
programs become more available and chemists become familiar
with their utility. Automated injectors, better instrumentation control, and possibly improved columns can all be utilized to improve the retention time precision. As the precision improves, the time window for an identification can be
narrowed, reducing the possibility of other compounds being
identified as PCBs.

C. Interpretation of Mass Spectrometric Data

1. General: When a mass spectrometer is used as
the GC detector, a second qualitative dimension is available
in addition to the retention time. The mass spectra of PCBs
are distinctive due to the cluster of masses generated by the
presence of two chlorine isotopes in nature (see Appendix C).
If sufficient material is present to obtain full mass spectra, an unknown can be reliably identified by comparison with
spectra of authentic standards or from spectral compilations
(Stenhagen et al., 1974; Mass Spectrometry Data Centre, 1970;
Heller and Milne, 1978).

As mentioned above, the natural isotopic abundance
ratios yield a characteristic pattern (Appendix C). The ratios have been tabulated for PCBs (Appendix C; Erickson et
al., 1983d; Rote and Morris, 1973). The use of these ratios
in selected ion monitoring can provide qualitative information when full mass spectra are not obtained (Canada and
Regnier, 1976; Erickson and Pellizzari, 1977, 1979; Erickson
et al., 1982). Even though the natural isotopic abundance
ratios are constant, instrumental variances and interferences
can affect the observed ratio. Thus, ratios observed with

standards may be more appropriate than the natural ratio for comparison to an unknown (Erickson et al., 1983b).

2.   Specific criteria: Tindall   and   Wininger (1980), in a method designed to determine PCBs even if they are not "Aroclor-derived," established qualitative criteria:

> Each peak in the chromatogram is evaluated to determine if it is a PCB peak. Peaks must meet these criteria to be labeled PCB peaks for quanti- tation: (1) the peaks of the characteristic ions must maximize at the same retention time; (2) the peak must be in the proper retention time window; and (3) the relative peak intensities of the mo- lecular ions must be within ± 15% of the theoret- ical ratio. This tolerance is arbitrary and can be made larger for very low concentrations of PCBs where statistical variations in peak intensity be- come large.

Work by Collard and Irwin (1982a,b, 1983) and Dow (1981) established similar qualitative criteria:

> Identify the chlorinated biphenyl homologs by their mass ion response, relative retention time, and ion intensity ratio (± 20% relative). Secon- dary confirmation of trichloro- through decachloro- biphenyl may rely upon the M-70+ ion response.

The procedure developed for EPA's enforcement of by-product PCBs in chemical products and wastes (Erickson et al., 1982, 1983d; Erickson, 1984a) includes similar qualitative criteria for data collected under full scan, selected ion monitoring (SIM), or limited mass scan (LMS) conditions. For full scan data

> "1.   The peak must elute within the retention time windows set for that homolog.

> 2.   The unknown spectrum should be compared to that of an authentic PCB. The intensity of the three largest ions in the molecular cluster (two largest for monochlorobiphenyls) must match the ra- tio observed for a standard within ± 20%. Fragment clusters with proper intensity ratios should also be present. System noise at low concentration or interferences may skew the ion ratio beyond the ± 20% criteria. If the analyst's best judgement is that a peak, which does not meet the qualitative criteria, is a PCB, the peak may be included in the calculation, with a footnote explaining the data and the reason for relaxing the criteria.

3. Alternatively, a spectral search may be used to automatically reduce the data. The criteria for acceptable identification include a high index of similarity."

The criteria for selected ion monitoring and limited mass scanning data are similar, but add the specific requirement that the analyst search higher mass windows, in particular M+70 to prevent misidentification of a PCB fragment ion cluster as the parent. If there is reasonable doubt as to the identity of a peak as a PCB, "the analyst must either identify the peak as a PCB or proceed to a confirmational analysis." This approach for marginal data reflects regulatory constraints to err on the high side of the true value. These three works (Tindall and Wininger, 1980; Collard and Irwin, 1983; and Erickson et al., 1983d) suggest a new awareness that qualitative criteria must be stipulated in any method if the results are to have any significance.

A novel use of GC/MS data in identifying the relative concentrations of different Aroclors was described by Liu et al. (1983). A multiple regression algorithm identified the percent of each Aroclor (1242, 1248, 1254, or 1260) contributing to each of 40 GC peaks. This data base was then used to compare unknowns and identify the relative concentrations of the different Aroclors. The authors noted that lower correlations were obtained with samples which had been subjected to degradation.

3. Recommended qualitative techniques for GC/MS data: The qualitative criteria of Tindall and Wininger (1980), Collard and Irwin (1983), and Erickson et al. (1983d) are the most complete guidance on mass spectral identification of PCBs. These criteria cannot cover all cases. At low levels, or with interferences, the PCB clusters can become skewed. In addition, data massaging techniques (summing spectra, background subtract, etc.) can be used (and misused) to bring a peak ratio which had been out of the proper ion intensity ratio requirement (e.g., ± 20% relative) within the requirement. Rules for data manipulation have not been well-defined for general GC/MS analysis a well as for PCBs. Better guidance for data acceptance are needed.

Future software packages will undoubtedly permit automated identification of PCBs based on isotopic abundance ratios. Although the technology is available, high precision retention times with GC/MS, have not been widely used. As noted above, HRGC/ECD can give fairly high confidence identifications of over 70 congeners, based solely on relative retention times. With the added dimension of the mass spectrum, data of very high qualitative confidence can easily be generated.

II. QUANTITATIVE

Quantitation (or less accurately, quantification) is the final step in a chemical analysis sequence. Some measure of signal intensity (peak height, or peak area) is converted into concentration. For most detectors used in PCB analysis, the mass of analyte in a peak, M_a, is proportional to the signal for the analyte, A_a.

$$M_a = RF \times A_a \qquad \text{Eq. 8-1}$$

The response factor, RF, is a constant which accounts for instrument attenuation, response of the compound, and other factors. RFs are derived by injection of a standard of known M_a and back-calculating Equation 8-1. Quantitation can be improved by injection of several standards of different M_a to give a plot of response versus amount (or concentration). Then RF can be read off the response curve at the precise area for the unknown. Since there can be instrumental variation from run to run (different injection volumes, instrumental drift, etc.) additional precision can usually be obtained with the internal standard (IS) method. A known amount of an internal standard, M_{is}, is added to each sample. Then the equation becomes

$$M_a = RF \times A_a \times \frac{M_{is}}{A_{is}}. \qquad \text{Eq. 8-2}$$

For this equation, the RF is derived using the internal standard areas, and would not have the same value as in Equation 8-1. Once the mass of the analyte in the peak is known, the concentration in the extract, C_e, can be derived.

$$C_e = \frac{M_a}{V_i} \qquad \text{Eq. 8-3}$$

where V_i is the volume injected onto the instrument. The concentration in the extract may be converted to concentration in the original sample, C_s, by

$$C_s = C_e \times \frac{V_e}{M_s} \qquad \text{Eq. 8-4}$$

where M_s is the mass of the sample (volume may be used for water and air samples). V_e, the volume of the extract, is often 1.0 mL and care must be taken to ensure that proper units are used to prevent miscalculation by a factor of 1,000, since V_i is often 1 µL.

Equations 8-3 and 8-4 are often combined with either Equations 8-1 or 8-2 so that the calculation is done in one equation.

$$C_s = RF \times A_a \times \frac{M_{is}}{A_{is}} \times \frac{1}{V_i} \times \frac{V_e}{M_s} \qquad \text{Eq. 8-5}$$

If all of the values for the terms in Equation 8-5 were known, the only error in quantitation could be a mistake in calculation or transcription. Unfortunately, deriving the value for RF (the calibration step) and A_a (the determination step) from the raw data can easily induce significant errors in the overall analysis. This is particularly true for PCBs, as discussed below.

With most organic compounds, quantitation is relatively straightforward. The instrumental response is calibrated using standard solutions of the compound. The amount of unknown is measured by comparison of the signal it generates with the calibration factor or curve. Quantitation of PCBs is not nearly so simple since the analyte is not a single compound but rather a complex mixture of 209 possible congeners. In addition, standards of all 209 congeners are not readily available for calibration. Given these problems, analysts have devised alternate quantitation methods, often based on the similarity of the sample PCB mixture to a commercial product (e.g., Aroclor). Aroclor-based quantitation schemes may be appropriate if the sample and standard "fingerprints" are similar. As the similarity diverges, the quantitative confidence diminishes.

A. Calibration

Three calibration techniques are available: external standard, internal standard response factors, and internal standard multipoint calibration.

1. External standard calibration: Calibration of the analysis system versus an external standard and then quantitation using the absolute intensities of the peaks lacks precision (Haefelfinger, 1981) and is not generally recommended for gas chromatographic analysis. Often, a major source of imprecision is the reproducibility of injection volume. Nevertheless, many PCB analyses, especially those using PGC/ECD, have successfully used external standard calibration.

2. Internal standard calibration: In this technique, internal standard(s) are added to the sample extract immediately prior to the instrumental determination, and the analytes are quantitated using the ratio of the analyte and

internal standard responses. A previously determined response factor (essentially a one-point calibration curve,
with an assumed intercept at the origin) is used in converting the response ratio to the mass.

For PCBs, which can span a large retention time
range, three or four internal standards which span the PCB
window may improve the precision of the response factors, and
therefore the final quantitation. Response factor precision
is related to how close the analyte peak and internal standard elute (Haefelfinger, 1981; Bickford et al., 1980).
Other factors to be considered in the selection of internal
standards are chromatographic resolution from analytes and
interferences, different mass spectral properties to assure
identification in GC/MS analysis, chemical similarity to
analyte (to minimize effects of changes in system selectivity), very low probability of occurrance in samples, and
chemical stability. Candidates for internal standards in PCB
analysis include PCB congeners known not to be present in the
matrix, other halobiphenyls (e.g., tribromobiphenyl), related
haloaromatics (e.g., chloronaphthalenes), and isotopically
labeled compounds (e.g., d_6-3,3',4,4'-tetrachlorobiphenyl or
d_{12}-chrysene).

Since the internal standard technique is a one-
point calibration, the response factor must be determined at
a concentration close to that of the analyte. Differences of
more than one order of magnitude may induce significant error.

3. Internal standard multipoint calibration: This
technique is essentially the same as the response factor
technique, above, except multiple calibration points (typically three, spanning up to two orders of magnitude) are
used to establish a calibration curve. This has the potential for greater precision, but requires much more time and
several standard solutions. In cases where detector sensitivity (signal response versus amount or concentration) is
either nonlinear or the curve does not intercept close to the
origin, a multipoint curve is especially advisable.

4. Selection of compounds for calibration: Since
PCBs consist of 209 separate congeners, most of which are not
readily available, a subset must generally be employed for
calibration. This subset must be judiciously selected, since
quantitation based on a calibration factor obtained for
another congener introduces an error. The options for selection of compounds to be used in calibration are:

1. Establish and use relative responses for
all 209 congeners.

2. Establish and use relative responses for several congeners and extrapolate the responses for the other congeners.

3. Characterize a secondary standard prepared from commercial mixtures to span the range of congeners.

4. Calibrate against one or more Aroclor mixtures.

5. Calibrate for only a few selected available congeners.

Option 1 is the ultimate technique; however, all 209 congeners are not readily available. Option 2 is a compromise. Option 3 would utilize a well-characterized mixed Aroclor or similar mixture. This has the advantages of low cost (once the characterization has been completed) and uniformity. One disadvantage is that the concentrations of the congeners range over two or more orders of magnitude, so calibration of the instrument would be difficult. Another problem is that non-Aroclor constituents cannot be quantitated. Option 4 has been utilized extensively, especially with PGC/ECD analysis. As discussed elsewhere, this approach is valid only if the standard and the unknown "fingerprints" are similar. Option 5 will not yield a "total PCB" value, but may be the most appropriate approach for many applications where information about selected congeners is sufficient.

B. Quantitation Techniques

It is obvious that PCBs were quantitated in most references in the bibliography, since quantitative data were presented. However, many authors neglected to mention how the detector signal was converted into a concentration value. Many other articles only made a brief mention of "integration" or "comparison with Aroclor 1260 standard" with respect to the quantitation.

As shown in Table 3-I, all standard procedures give at least cursory instructions on quantitation. At one extreme, the general purpose semivolatile organic procedures (EPA, 1978, 1979a,b; Ballinger, 1978) contain vague direction to "integrate the area under the peak." Much more complete quantitation guidelines are given in EPA's (Bellar and Lichtenberg, 1981; EPA, 1981a) procedure for analysis of PCBs in transformer fluids and waste oils.

1.   Packed column gas chromatography/electron capture detection

a.   Webb-McCall: The most prominent PGC/ECD
quantitation technique was originated by Webb and McCall
(1973). The weight percent and homolog identification (relative proportions where more than one homolog was present)
were determined PGC/EIMS for several Aroclors, and retention
times relative to p,p'-DDE were specified. An example is
presented in Table 8-I and Figure 8-2. The general procedure
is as follows:

1.   Chromatograph known amounts of the
standards and measure the area for each peak.

2.   Using the tables of data determine
the response factor for each peak.

3.   Chromatograph the sample and measure
the area of each peak.

4.   Multiply the area of each peak by the
response factor for that peak.

5.   Add the nanograms of PCB found in
each peak to obtain the total nanograms of PCB
present.

6.   Samples containing one or more Aroclors can be quantitated by comparison with
appropriate standards.

Regarding the last point, Webb and McCall devised the chromatogram division scheme shown in Figure 8-3.
This scheme accounts for the chromatographic overlap of the
three common Aroclors. Their article presents a detailed ex-
planation of the rationale for this flowchart. Validation of
the multi-Aroclor quantitation with nine known mixtures found
recoveries ranging from 96 to 107%.

Following an interlaboratory survey, Chau and
Sampson (1975) recommended that the Webb-McCall technique be
adopted as the uniform quantitation technique. They cited
the general applicability, elimination of mixed standards,
the more realistic results, and simplicity of the method as
reasons for their recommendations. Another interlaboratory
study (Lee and Chau, 1981a) also found Webb-McCall quantitation preferable. Half of the 14 participants used Webb-
McCall, while the others used either selected peaks or a summation of all peaks. The mean of the results by the Webb-
McCall quantitation was only 3% higher than the design value,
while the other quantitations averaged 22% higher.

Exact replication of the Webb-McCall quantitation requires either reproducing the chromatographic pattern using the same lot of Aroclor standards as Webb and McCall used or determining the composition of the peaks obtained with different chromatographic conditions or Aroclor lots. These stringent requirements have led most researchers to characterize their quantitation practice as a modified Webb-McCall (Sawyer, 1978a; Kreiss et al., 1981; Harris et al., 1981; Steichen et al., 1982; Erickson et al., 1983e). These users have not replicated the Webb-McCall chromatography or Aroclor lot number, but have decided that the chromatographic patterns are similar enough to use Webb-McCall's data tables. The error induced by this practice is probably not significant, since participants in the interlaboratory studies discussed in the previous paragraph reported a variety of chromatographic conditions and undoubtedly used several lots of Aroclors. Ugawa et al. (1973) devised a quantitation technique similar to Webb-McCall which was based on Kanechlors, the Japanese commercial PCB mixtures. A scheme similar to Webb-McCall (Dexter and Pavlou, 1976; Pavlou et al., 1980) used PGC/FID to characterize the Aroclor mixtures, with analysis of samples by PGC/ECD. Several standard procedures have adopted the Webb-McCall quantitation technique for analysis of PCBs in a variety of matrices as summarized in Table 3-I (NIOSH, 1977b, 1977c; Beard and Schaum, 1978; EPA, 1978, 1981a; Bellar and Lichtenberg, 1981; Harris et al., 1981).

The calculations required with the Webb-McCall technique can be easily automated using common GC integrators or data systems (Needham et al., 1981; Kirshen, 1981a,b; Newton and Laski, 1983; Erickson et al., 1983e). Newton and Laski (1983) reported a computer routine for quantitation of Aroclor 1242, 1254, and 1260 and their combinations. The routine, essentially an automation of the Webb and McCall (1973) procedure using BASIC, compared favorably with manual calculation by peak height or peak area. About 5 minutes of operator time is required per analysis. One apparent flaw of the routine, in addition to the assumption that the analyte PCBs are unmodified Aroclors, is that it does not consider the chromatographic overlap of the Aroclors. The three Aroclors are segregated into non-overlapping time windows.

b. Total areas: Several researchers (Collins et al., 1972; Bellar and Lichtenberg, 1975) and standard methods (AOAC, 1980a,b; ASTM, 1981a,b) advocate comparison of the total areas under the "Aroclor region" in the sample and standard chromatograms. This is a simple approach and has been recommended by Sawyer (1973) as the most reliable method for obtaining interlaboratory precision. In a later collaborative study (Sawyer, 1978b), the individual peak height,

Table 8-I.   Composition of Aroclor 1254 According to
Webb and McCall (1973)

RRT[a]	Mean Weight Percent	Relative Std. Dev.[b]	No. of Chlorines[c]
47	6.2	3.7	4
54	2.9	2.6	4
58	1.4	2.8	4
70	13.2	2.7	4 (25%)
			5 (75%)
84	17.3	1.9	5
98	7.5	5.3	5
104	13.6	3.8	5
125	15.0	2.4	5 (70%)
			6 (30%)
146	10.4	2.7	5 (30%)
			6 (70%)
160	1.3	8.4	6
174	8.4	5.5	6
203	1.8	18.6	6
232	1.0	26.1	7
Total	100.0		

a   Retention time relative to p,p'-DDE = 100.   Measured from
first appearance of solvent.
b   Standard deviation of six results as a percentage of the
mean of the results.
c   From GC/MS data.   Peaks containing mixtures of isomers
are bracketed.
Source: Webb and McCall (1973); reprinted with permission,
copyright 1973 by Preston Publications, Inc.

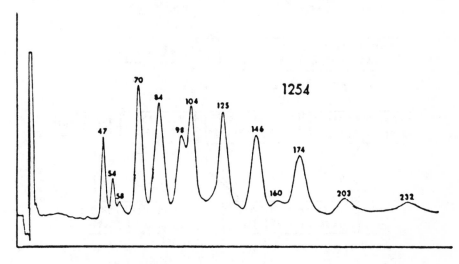

Figure 8-2.   PGC/ECD Chromatogram of Aroclor 1254

The sample was chromatographed on SE-30 with a Ni-63 detector operated in the DC mode. The peak identification numbers correspond to the retention time relative to $\underline{p},\underline{p}'$-DDE = 100. See Table 8-I for peak compositions.

Reprinted, with permission, from Webb and McCall (1973); copyright 1973 by Preston Publications, Inc.

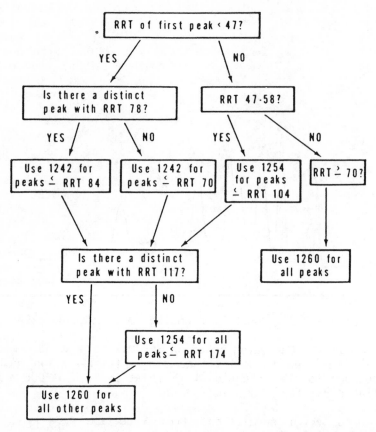

Figure 8-3.   Flow Chart for Division of PGC/ECD Chromatograms
Into Retention Time Regions for Quantitation of Samples
With Mixed Aroclor Patterns

Reprinted, with permission, from Webb and McCall (1973);
copyright 1973 by Preston Publications, Inc.

total peak height and total peak area methods were all compared and gave similar results, although the individual peak
method (Webb and McCall, 1973; Sawyer, 1978a), was judged
slightly better. On this basis, AOAC (1980a,b) permits
either individual peak (Webb-McCall) or total area quantitation of PCBs. Bellar and Lichtenberg (1975) used either
the total peak height for samples closely resembling Aroclors
or Webb-McCall for patterns "not representing a single Aroclor."

        Transformer oils must often be analyzed to
comply with regulations regarding their use and disposal.
The objective in the United States has been to classify the
oil as "PCB-containing" if it contains over 500 ppm PCBs and
"PCB contaminated" if it contains 50 to 500 ppm PCBs. Thus,
quantitation has focused on deriving a "total PCB" concentration. Transformer oil analysis is relatively simple, the
sample matrices are relatively consistent and unmodified Aroclor patterns are almost always observed. Thus, sophisticated analytical techniques have not generally been necessary. In addition, rapid results from on-site laboratories
have often been desired.

        The EPA (Bellar and Lichtenberg, 1981; EPA,
1981a) has issued an analytical method for PCBs in transformer fluid and waste oils. If the parent Aroclor is
identifiable, it may be used as the standard for quantitation:

> "The concentration of the PCBs in the
> sample is calculated by comparing the sum of
> the responses for each PCB in the standard to
> the sum of all of the PCBs in the sample.
> This is particularly important as sample con-
> centrations approach within 20% of 50 mg/kg or
> any other EPA-regulated concentration. If
> calculations are based upon a single PCB peak
> or upon a small percentage of the total PCB
> peaks, serious errors may result. Peaks com-
> prising less than 50% of the total can be dis-
> regarded only if (a) interference problems
> persist after cleanup; (b) the source of PCBs
> is obvious; or (c) the concentration of PCBs
> are not within ± 20% of an EPA-controlled
> value such as 50 mg/kg."

The method directs the analyst to use the following formula
to calculate the concentration of PCBs in the sample:

$$\text{"Concentration (mg/kg)} = \frac{B \times V_t}{A \times W} \qquad \text{Eq. 8-6}$$

where:

$$A = \frac{\text{Sum of Standard Peak Heights (Areas)}}{\text{ng of Standard Injected}} \times \text{mm/ng},$$

$$B = \frac{\text{Sum of Sample Peak Heights (Areas)}}{\mu L \text{ Injected}} = \text{mm/}\mu L,$$

V_t = dilution volume of sample in milliliters, and

W = weight of the sample in grams."

If the parent Aroclor is not apparent, the analyst is di-
rected to calculate the concentration according to the procedure of Webb and McCall (1973). The concentration of the
PCBs in each peak is determined individually. These concentrations are then added together to determine the total PCB
content of the sample. Each PCB identified in the sample
must be included in these calculations. Specific instructions are given.

2.   High resolution gas chromatography/electron
capture detection

a.   Single congener quantitation: The application of HRGC to PCB determination complicates an already
difficult quantitation problem: more peaks are present.
Since the peaks are presumably single congeners instead of
the mixtures obtained by PGC, quantitation of single congeners has been emphasized by many authors. Boe and Egaas
(1979) devised a calibration factor system that permits the
analyst to calculate the ECD response factor for a given congener, once its structure is known. More recently, the ECD
response factors for all 209 congeners were measured (Mullin
et al., 1984; Tables 7-IV and 7-VII). As discussed in
Chapter 7 the ranges over homologs and within a homolog indicate that calibration with each congener would be necessary
for accurate results.

b.   Calibration with commercial mixtures: One
option for calibration is to use a commercial mixture (i.e.,
Aroclor) as a secondary standard, as mentioned in Section
II.A.4. This is the approach taken with the Webb and McCall
(1973) quantitation for PGC/ECD data (see Section II.B.1.a,
above). With HRGC/ECD data, similar approaches can be used,
although identification and quantitation of all of the components in the Aroclor mixture is much more tedious. The
various publications which characterize commercial PCB mixtures are reviewed in Table 7-III and Appendix B. Among the
more recent and complete tabulations, Albro et al. (1981) determined the relative molar percentages of the individual

components of about 100 different PCB congeners in Aroclors 1248, 1254, and 1260. They recommend using the Aroclor mixtures as secondary standards to determine HRGC/ECD response factors. Schulte and Malisch (1984) have published a similar approach based on the known composition of Chlophen A60. This approach has been further refined by Bush et al. (1982, 1983) and the mass for 72 peaks in four common Aroclors determined (Table 8-II). The accuracy was assessed by comparison of the gravimetric versus GC-calculated concentrations. The total amount calculated by the chromatographic data system was 12% higher than the gravimetric value. The precision, based on replicate injections of a mixture of 27 authentic congeners, ranged from ± 1.17% RSD to ± 8.26% RSD for individual peaks, with a precision on the total of ± 2.25% RSD.

A menu-driven computer program was recently reported which gives congener-specific quantitation of over 100 components of Aroclors 1242, 1248, 1254, and 1260 (Schwartz et al., 1984). The data may be presented in several ways, such as by congener, by homolog, or by number of ortho chlorines. The data may also be fed into a pattern recognition program for additional qualitative studies (Dunn et al., 1984).

The use of a well-characterized secondary standard has several advantages. The preparation of standards is relatively simple and cheap. All of the congeners likely to occur in environmental samples will be calibrated and will be in roughly similar proportions in the samples and standards. A disadvantage is that, like the Webb-McCall quantitation, it presupposes that all PCBs are derived from the commercial mixtures and does not quantitate all PCBs. This can be detrimental in analysis of true unknowns, especially where by-product PCBs or partially destroyed PCBs may be present.

c.   Statistical evaluation of HRGC/ECD data: A rigorous statistical quantitation was described (Kafadar and Eberhardt, 1983) for the certification of the NBS standard reference material of Aroclors in oil (Uriano, 1982). The linear statistical model recognized that the data for the individual peaks determined by HRGC/ECD were not independent. Each of four SRMs were analyzed six times as described by Chesler et al. (1981) and Parris et al. (1984), yielding 10 PCB peaks and 3 internal standard areas. The statistical analysis yielded the certified concentrations shown in Table 8-III.

d.   Quantitation using selected diagnostic peaks: Zell and Ballschmiter (1980) presented a simplified

Table 8-II.　Analysis of 1:1:1:1 Mixture and Separate Aroclor Mixture

Retention Time, min	Structure	Calib. Amt. µg/mL	Aroclor (2.0 µg/mL) 1221	1016	1254	1260	Sum of Aroclors
5.33	2	0.794	1.264				1.264
6.59	2,2'	0.182	0.118	0.094			0.212
6.79	4	0.425	0.400				0.400
7.86	2,5	0.026	0.018	0.008			0.026
7.98	2,4	0.035	0.033	0.008			0.041
8.10	2,3'	0.092	0.069	0.034			0.103
8.21	2,3	0.047	0.030	0.026			0.059
8.36	2,4'	0.323	0.213	0.166			0.379
9.37	2,2',5'	0.216	T[d]	0.185			0.202
9.62	2,2',4'	0.074	T	0.065			0.073
9.79	2,2',3' + 3,2',6'	0.096	T	0.094			0.102
10.18	2',4,6'	0.074	T	0.057			0.074
10.41	4,4'	0.158	0.104	0.064			0.168
11.09	2,2',4',6'	0.018	T	0.015			0.018
11.32	2',3,5'	0.040	T	0.032			0.039
11.39	2,3',5'	0.038	T	0.034			0.037
11.49	Cl_3	0.021	T	0.017			0.020
11.55	Cl_3	0.025	T	0.023			0.024
11.65	2',3,4'	0.167	T	0.149			0.166
11.85	2',3,3' + 2',4,4'	0.267	T	0.238			0.271
12.12	2',3',4	0.140	T	0.127			0.147
12.62	2,2',5,5'	0.233	T	0.115	0.133		0.268
12.90	2,2',4,5'	0.151	T	0.113	0.042		0.161
13.07	2,2',3,5'	0.166	T	0.105	0.067		0.179
13.22	2,2',4,4'	0.057	T	0.047	0.011		0.063
13.40	Cl_4	0.050		0.039	0.008		0.047
13.56	2,2',3,3'	0.049		0.039	0.011		0.050
13.65	Cl_4	0.050		0.043	0.015		0.058
13.82	Cl_4	0.110		0.107	0.057		0.164
14.52	Cl_5	0.165			0.115	0.081	0.196
15.03	2,2',3,3',6'	0.085			0.078	0.025	0.103
15.45	2,3',4',5	0.134			0.105	0.013	0.118
15.66	2,3',4,4'	0.042			0.032	0.006	0.038
16.03	2',3',4,4'	0.053			0.059	0.015	0.074
16.13	2,2',3,3',6,6'	0.086			0.041	0.056	0.097
16.36	2,2',4',5,5'	0.181			0.136	0.072	0.208
16.68	2,2',4,4',5'	0.070			0.069	0.006	0.075
16.85	2,2',3,4',5'	0.080			Not integrated		
16.92	2,2',3',4',5	0.116			0.149	0.024	0.173
17.37	2,2',3,3',4'	0.269			0.289	0.049	0.338
17.66	2,2',3',5,5',6'	0.112			0.037	0.087	0.124
17.97	2,2',3,3',5',6'	0.029			0.012	0.021	0.033
18.16	2,2',3,3',4,6'	0.206			0.083	0.145	0.228

TABLE 8-II (concluded)

Retention Time, min	Structure	Calib. Amt. μg/mL	Aroclor (2.0 μg/mL)				Sum of Aroclors
			1221	1016	1254	1260	
18.50	Cl$_5$	0.014			0.013	0.007	0.020
18.78	2,2',3,3',5',6,6'	0.096			0.051	0.054	0.105
18.95	2',3,4,4',5'	0.058			0.015	0.051	0.066
19.28	2,2',3,3',4',6,6'	0.135			0.128	0.017	0.145
19.44	2,2',3,4',5,5'	0.032			0.015	0.020	0.035
19.72	Cl$_5$	0.051			0.024	0.034	0.058
19.87	2',3,3',4,4'	0.082			0.080	0.005	0.085
20.06	2,2',4,4',5,5'	0.369			0.127	0.253	0.380
20.29	Cl$_6$	0.025			0.015	0.011	0.026
20.46	Cl$_6$	0.045			0.027	0.021	0.048
20.66	2,2',3,4,4',5'	0.266			0.130	0.165	0.295
20.87	2,2',3,3',5,5',6'	0.051			0.035	0.028	0.063
21.01	2,2',3',4,5,5',6'	0.010				0.008	0.008
21.18	Cl$_7$	0.118			0.009	0.127	0.136
21.27	2,2',3,3',4,4'	0.053			0.040		0.040
21.51	2,2',3,3',5,5',6,6'	0.193			0.022	0.170	0.192
21.79	2,2',3,3',4,4',6'	0.068			0.011	0.060	0.071
22.13	2,3',4,4',5,5'	0.048			0.008	0.047	0.055
22.58	2,2',3,3',4',5',6,6'	0.026			0.009	0.018	0.027
23.13	2',3,3',4,4',5'	0.047			0.033	0.019	0.052
23.27	2,2',3,3',4',5,5'	0.029			0.005	0.023	0.028
23.63	2,2',3',4,4',5,5'	0.278			0.027	0.250	0.277
24.22	2,2',3,3',4,4',5'	0.120			0.020	0.102	0.122
24.37	2,2',3,3',4,5,5',6'	0.064			T	0.059	0.064
24.56	Cl$_7$	0.033			T	0.028	0.035
24.71	2,2',3,3',4,4',5,6'	0.035			T	0.032	0.036
24.86	2,2',3',4,4',5,5',6'	0.042			T	0.038	0.043
25.49	2,2',3,3',4,4',5',6'	0.033				0.030	0.030
27.27	2',3,3',4,4',5,5'	0.065			T	0.062	0.063
	Total	8.238	2.249	2.044	2.393	2.339	9.225

---

a T = Trace.
Source: Bush et al., 1982; reprinted with permission, copyright 1982 by Association of Official Analytical Chemists.

Table 8-III. Quantitation of NBS Standard Reference Material 1581 -
              Polychlorinated Biphenyls in Oil

Matrix	Aroclor Type	Certified Concentration $(\mu g/g)^{a,b}$	Statistical Concentration $\mu g/g^{c}$	95% Confidence Units $(\mu g/g)^{c}$
Motor oil	1242	100 ± 1	100.07	98.65, 101.48
Motor oil	1260	100 ± 2	100.69	98.70, 102.74
Transformer oil	1242	100 ± 1	100.39	99.18, 101.62
Transformer oil	1260	100 ± 3	100.07	98.65, 101.48

a From Uriano, 1982.
b Uncertainty is expressed at the 95% confidence level.
c From Kafadar and Eberhardt, 1983.

approach to quantitation using "diagnostic peaks." The rationale for selection of these diagnostic peaks is discussed
in Section I.B.2.b, above. Although subject to some error,
the authors consider the inherent error small relative to
total PCB quantitation at the parts per billion range. They
also assert that the small, unresolved peaks are more likely
to be (or contain) nonPCB components such as polychloro-
terpenes (toxaphene). The validity of the approach has not
been reported.

                Tuinstra et al. (1983) presented an extension
of the above approach. For regulatory analyses, where the
full quantitation of samples below the regulatory cut-off
level is of no interest, they selected six PCB congeners
(Table 8-IV) for use in quantitation. The six are present in
at least one Aroclor mixture, tend to accumulate in biological samples, are commercially available, and are chromatographically resolved from other congeners. This approach may
be especially useful in large sample screening programs,
where the Aroclor-derived PCB patterns are similar and compliance with a regulatory cut-off is the primary concern.

                Simplistic quantitation routines are still used
with HRGC, even though most analysts choose it over PGC for
the increased information content. Gordon et al. (1982) used
only three peaks from each Aroclor standard to quantitate
PCBs in transformer oil by HRGC/ECD. While PCBs do not
weather extensively in transformer oil and are thus more
likely to resemble the parent Aroclor, this method utilizes
only a small portion of the available information. Schulte
et al. (1976) recommended quantitation of HRGC/ECD chromatograms based on two selected characteristic peaks in food extracts.

                3. Comparison of quantitation by PGC/ECD and HRGC/
ECD: Wolff et al. (1982a) used one tri-, penta-, and hexachlorobiphenyl as standards for HRGC/ECD quantitation of tri-
through heptachlorobiphenyls in plasma and adipose samples of
occupationally exposed people. Quantitation by this sum of
individual peaks gave comparable results to the Webb-McCall
method using PGC/ECD. Both methods gave lower values than
the sum of peak areas method using PGC/ECD data.

                A collaborative study of PCBs and organochlorine
pesticides in open ocean waters come to an emphatic conclusion that PCB concentrations in seawater should not be reported in terms of Aroclor 1254 (Palmork et al., 1982). Almost all of the literature had previously reported seawater
concentrations as an Aroclor 1254 equivalent. The study
showed that the measured amounts of individual PCB congeners

Table 8-IV. Six PCBs Used for Regulatory Tolerance Purposes

Compound	IUPAC No.	Maximum Percentage in Technical Aroclors	Derived Tolerance[a] (mg/kg)
2,4,4'-Trichlorobiphenyl	28	10 (In Aroclor 1242)	0.5
2,2',5,5'-Tetrachlorobiphenyl	52	4 (In Aroclor 1254)	0.2
2,2',4,5,5'-Pentachlorobiphenyl	101	8 (In Aroclor 1254)	0.4
2,2',3,4,4',5'-Hexachlorobiphenyl	138	10 (In Aroclor 1260)	0.5
2,2',4,4',5,5'-Hexachlorobiphenyl	153	10 (In Aroclor 1260)	0.5
2,2',3,4,4',5,5'-Heptachlorobiphenyl	180	12 (In Aroclor 1260)	0.6

a Derived from The Netherlands' official tolerance of 5 mg/kg in fish, assuming (worst case) that only one technical Aroclor mixture is present in a sample.

Source: Tuinstra et al. (1983), reproduced with permission; copyright 1983, Gordon and Breach Science Publishers, Ltd.

in a single sample varied from the equivalent of 0.06 to 1.57 ng/L Aroclor 1254 indicating severe distortion of the Aroclor pattern. The study authors recommended that congener-specific PCB measurement was the only valid method for determining PCBs in open ocean water.

The PCB concentrations in air samples were measured by PGC/ECD, HRGC/ECD on three different columns, and by dual column HRGC/ECD, as shown in Table 8-V (Singer et al., 1983). The dual column approach involved simultaneous injection of the sample onto two columns in one GC oven. The quantitative results decreased about one order of magnitude for each of the levels of increased analytical sophistication. The HRGC analyses on the different single columns agree fairly well and are roughly an order of magnitude less than the PGC data and an order of magnitude greater than the dual column HRGC data. Singer et al. believe that the higher values result from erroneous quantitation of interferences along with the PCBs and speculate that most of the data for PCB concentrations in ambient air may be biased high. This conclusion should be verified by independent confirmatory techniques. It is unclear from the article whether the dual column HRGC approach is eliminating only interferences, as the authors claim, or applying overly-stringent identification criteria (see Section I.B.2.c, above).

4.   Gas chromatography/electron impact ionization mass spectrometry: The ability of EIMS to easily sort PCBs by homolog has led to a tendency among GC/EIMS users to quantitate by homolog (i.e., summing all peaks for each homolog). Another major difference from ECD is the ability to quantitate using either a single PCB-specific m/z peak or the total ion current. The latter corresponds to an analog detector output.

The first reported GC/EIMS quantitation of PCBs was a simple translation of classical GC/ECD quantitation: comparison of "the area under one or more of the eight PCB peaks to the area of a known amount of a standard" (Bonelli, 1972a,b). Eichelberger et al. (1974) chose what they termed "the conventional approach" and assumed that the PCB mixture was one of the commercial mixtures. The total peak area for each selected ion monitoring (SIM) mass in the sample and standard were compared using an internal standard to normalize the peak areas. Williams and Benoit (1979) used the summed total integrated area for six to eight selected peaks for quantitation of PCBs in several household products.

A multiple regression statistical analysis program quantitated HRGC/EIMS data for sediment samples using standard areas for 40 peaks in Aroclors 1242, 1248, 1254 and 1260

Analytical Chemistry of PCBs

Table 8-V. Comparison of PCB Concentrtions in Air Samples Determined
by PGC, HRGC, and Dual Column HRGC[a]

| No. | Sample Code | Packed | Single Capillary Column | | | Dual Column |
			SP-2100	OV-1	SE-54	OV-1/SE-54
1	HAM-S1-12-16	66	4.2	5.3	1.4	0.4
2	HAM-S1-12-17	44	1.0	2.7	3.0	0.7
3	HAM-S1-12-18	7.1	2.2[b]	2.6	1.2	0.0
4	SAR-S1-U1-16	58	4.6[b]	6.1	4.3	0.6
5	SAR-S1-U1-18	6.2	1.6[b]	3.2	1.0	0.02
6	SUD-S1-S1-18	52	3.8[b]	2.3	2.1	0.0
7	SUD-S1-S1-17	53	1.7[b]	2.9	2.0	0.0
8	SUD-S1-S1-4	47	4.1[b]	3.9	2.8	0.3
9	SUD-S1-S1-1	66	3.9[b]	3.9	3.1	0.8
10	SAR-S1-U1-15	115	3.5[b]	3.7	14	0.6
11	SAR-S1-U1-17	19	3.7[b]	3.3	2.3	0.2
12	HAM-S1-U-4	173	4.8[b]	5.2	4.1	1.4
13	HAM-S1-U-1	317	11[b]	11	7.0	3.3
14	TOR-S1-U1-1	28	12[b]	10	10	5.4
15	TOR-S1-U1-2	238	23[b]	16	15	6.9
16	TOR-S1-U1-18	6.4	4.1[b]	5.5	4.7	1.6
17	HAM-S1-U2-16	31	3.6[b]	2.3	1.7	0.2
18	MIS-S1-U4-15	6.7	2.4[b]	3.4	3.3	0.2
19	MIS-S1-U4-19	13	1.9[b]	2.2	2.4	0.2
20	MIS-S1-U4-17	1.5	4.0[b]	2.4	1.8	0.4
21	HAM-S1-U2-4	128	2.4[b]	3.8	3.0	0.9
22	MIS-S1-U4-16	19	1.8[b]	2.5	2.0	0.1
23	HAM-S1-U2-18	25	4.4[b]	2.2	1.6	0.2
24	HAM-S1-U-5	52	8.7[b]	0.7	1.6	0.2
25	LON-S1-S1-18	35	11	9.4	9.1	6.3
26	SAR-S1-U-2	1,615	6.8[b]	4.3	6.5	2.1
27	HAM-S1-U-15	68	20[b]	5.9	9.7	1.9
28	MIS-S1-U1-3	-	11[b]	2.9	3.1	0.6

a Samples analyzed on Hewlett-Packard 5840A or 5880A GC with splitless injection and ECD detection. The packed column was 9' x 1/8" od SS,
   packed with 1% Dexsil 400 on Anachrom Q. The capillary columns were
   all 25 m x 0.2 mm ID. Concentrations are expressed as ng PCBs/m^3 air.
b A poorly resolved peak is present around RT = 26 min, which was originally
   considered as PCB. In this set of data the peak was excluded.
Source: Singer et al. (1983), reproduced with permission, copyright 1983 by
   Butterworths Publishers (Ann Arbor Science).

(Liu et al., 1984) to yield an "Aroclor" concentration. Unweathered Aroclor mixtures yielded very low deviations from the expected value, while weathered PCBs extracted from field sediment samples gave less reliable quantitations.

A single isomer for each homolog has been used to calibrate HRGC/EIMS for quantitation of PCBs in sludge (Erickson and Pellizzari, 1977, 1979) and stack gases (Haile et al., 1983a,b, 1984). Stack gas samples from the M/T Vulcanus I were analyzed by HRGC/HREIMS (Ackerman et al., 1983b). The analytical system was calibrated using a suite of three isomers for each homolog (except $C_{12}Cl_{10}$), as shown in Table 8-VI. An average response factor for the three isomers was used to quantitate the unknown isomers for that homolog. 2,3,6-Tribromobiphenyl was added to the sample before extraction or cleanup to monitor recovery and d_{12}-chrysene was coinjected with each sample as an internal standard. Instrumental detection limits were either 25 pg/µL or 100 pg/µL for each homolog.

In one of the few papers addressing analysis of noncommercial PCBs, Tindall and Wininger (1980), established homolog response ratios using an unspecified number of isomers per homolog. The highest and lowest response factors for a homolog were averaged to give the average response factor relative to tribromobiphenyl. Collard and Irwin (1982a,b, 1983) and Dow (1981) used 22 congeners to establish response factors. For homologs with more than one isomer in the standard, a summed intensity was used. A daily calibration plot at three concentrations was used for comparison of the summed peak heights for one homolog.

Martelli et al. (1981) reported the EIMS relative response factors for 45 PCB congeners (Table 7-XI). The relative standard deviation per homolog ranged from 0.7% (3 of 46 possible isomers measured) to 21% (11 of 42 isomers measured). They proposed using these average response factors on GC/EIMS quantitation of PCBs by homolog.

The relative response factors (RRF) for 77 PCB congeners (Tables 7-XII and 7-XIII and Figure 7-15), obtained by both quadrupole and magnetic sector instruments, were used to determine the average RRFs by homolog (Erickson et al., 1982, 1983b; Stanley et al., 1983). A subset of 11 congeners having average RRFs and RRTs (Table 7-XIV) were recommended for use as calibrants in a method for analysis of by-product PCBs in product and product waste samples (Erickson et al., 1982, 1983b). The approach, similar to those discussed above, utilizes the most complete set of EIMS response factors available.

Table 8-VI. PCB Congeners Used to Determine Response Factors

Homolog	PCB Stock Solution		
	1	2	3
Monochloro	2	3	4
Dichloro	2,2'	2,4	2,6
Trichloro	2',3,4	2,4,6	2,4,4'
Tetrachloro	2,2',6,6'	3,3',4,4'	2,2',4,4'
Pentachloro	2,2',4,6,6'	2,3,4,4',6	2,3,3',5,6
Hexachloro	2,2',3,3',6,6'	2,2',4,4',6,6'	2,2',3,5,5',6
Heptachloro	2,2',3,4,5,5',6	2,2',3,4,4',5,6	2,2',3,3',4,4',6
Octachloro	2,2',3,3',4,5,6,6'	2,2',3,3',4,4',5,5'	2,2',3,3',5,5',6,6'
Nonochloro	2,2'3,3',4,5,5',6,6'	2,2',3,3',4,4',5,5',6	2,2',3,3',4,4',5,6,6'
Decachloro	2,2',3,3',4,4',5,5',6,6'	-----------------	-----------------

Source: Ackerman et al. (1983b).

298

5. <u>Miscellaneous</u>: Cairns and Jacobson (1977) advocated PCB quantitation by PGC/CIMS because of the reduction in interferences by other halogenated compounds such as DDE relative to GC/ECD. They did not compare CIMS with EIMS, however.

As discussed in Chapter 7, perchlorination and dehydrochlorination, followed by PGC/ECD and PGC/FID determinations, respectively, have been proposed as PCB quantitation techniques which eliminate many of the problems arising from multiple congeners. An advantage of these techniques is that the area of a single peak is being measured, so there is less potential for error. A disadvantage is that the derivatization step introduces its own source of error. In addition qualitative information about the PCB congener distribution is lost. Safe (1976) suggested that perchlorination would be more consistently accurate than quantitation of the complex chromatogram of the original PCB mixtures because of the variability in ECD response factors (see Table 7-VI).

TLC and HPLC have also been employed as quantitative techniques. TLC spots can only be semiquantitated with visual interpretation. Probably order-of-magnitude estimations of concentration are possible. With a densitometer, TLC spots can be quantitated with more precision. HPLC quantitation is at least as precise as most GC quantitations. However, problems of quantitating multiple peaks, insufficient standards, coelution of homologs, etc., afflict HPLC in much the same way as GC. The absorption maxima and extinction coefficients for 27 congeners (Hutzinger et al., 1974a; see Chapter 2) indicate considerable variability can be expected in the of HPLC/UV response factors.

6. <u>Automated quantitation</u>: For many analyses, quantitation of PCBs is the most labor-intensive step. Even with electronic integration of all of the peaks in a chromatogram, the analyst often faces a long task of eliminating nonPCB peaks and totaling the areas. Thus, it is only logical that analysts have increasingly sought to automate the data reduction. The automated data reduction techniques which have been reported can be categorized as either simple integration routines or pattern recognition routines. Pattern recognition routines were discussed above under qualitative data reduction.

The simplest automated integration routine sums the area of all peaks within a given retention window. The total area is then compared to the corresponding area for a standard (usually an Aroclor) and the concentration reported. A more complex variation involves individual peak quantitation by comparison of the peaks to those in an Aroclor cocktail.

Bush et al. (1982; 1983) have automated such a system. Individual response factors were used for quantitation of 72
peaks in unknowns.

Zobel (1974) devised a computer fit routine for PGC
data which matched the sample chromatogram with various "co-
added" Aroclor chromatograms to obtain a best fit. "Spuri-
ously large or small peak heights, caused by interfering compounds or metabolism, are automatically sorted and rejected."
The method reports results in terms of the different Aroclors
and can be modified to generate an estimate of "premetab-
olism" PCB content.

Several authors have reported computerized quantitation techniques for PCBs in transformer oils (Newton and
Laski, 1983; Colby et al., 1983; Colby and Picker, 1983;
Gossman, 1983; Lea et al., 1983; Picker and Colby, 1983).
While automation of this time-consuming step is appealing for
economic reasons, trained analysts must both validate the
quantitation with real samples and audit the results during
routine application for QC purposes.

In an intralaboratory comparison of several matrix/
cleanup/GC column/detector/quantitation combinations, Levine
et al. (1983) found some significant differences in quantitation results. For instance, the PGC/HECD/area quantitation
results for $\sim$ 150 ppm Aroclor 1254 in waste road oil were
about twice as high as those obtained by PGC/HECD/peak
heights, PGC/ECD/area, PGC/ECD/peak height, or a similar set
of four HRGC/detector/quantitation combinations. The authors
concluded that a computerized data system did not yield more
accurate results than either a low-cost printer/plotter inte-
grator or a ruler (for peak heights).

7.   Measurement of PCB recovery with surrogates:
Recovery surrogates are added prior to any sample treatment
and are used to assess the recovery of the native PCBs
through the extraction and cleanup. Like the native PCBs,
surrogates may also be quantitated against the internal standard. Since the amount added is known, the surrogate recovery can be calculated. The criteria for selection of recovery surrogates are similar to those for internal standards
discussed above. ^{13}C-Labeled PCB congeners have been used as
recovery surrogates in by-product PCB analysis (Erickson et
al., 1982, 1983b, 1983d; Erickson, 1984a, 1984b, 1984c,
1984d). Knowledge of the percent recovery is useful in monitoring extraction/cleanup performance. The final reported
concentration may be corrected for recovery if desired, or
the value found and percent recovery reported separately. It
should be noted that if the recovery surrogates and analytes

are not, in fact, equally recovered, then the reported recovery is meaningless. This can happen if the surrogates are not fully incorporated into the matrix.

8. Discussion: The applicability of the different quantitation techniques depends on the analytical technique, the PCB concentrations, consistency of the PCB pattern within a sample set, and analytical objectives. HRGC permits identification and quantitation of individual congeners, while PGC is generally limited to either reporting an "Aroclor" concentration, or "total PCB" concentration. If MS is used as the detector, the different homologs are readily discernable, and concentration by homolog is often reported. If the PCB pattern is consistent with that of a commerical mixture (e.g., transformer askarels), quantitation of GC/ECD data against a known quantity of Aroclor may be appropriate and can yield satisfactory data. This approach must be utilized with increasing caution as the chromatographic pattern diverges from that of the standard. The objectives of the data user also affect the appropriateness of the quantitation techniques. A study of selective degradation of congeners in an Aroclor mixture would require quantitation of individual peaks, while analysis of a waste to determine disposal requirements may only require a total PCB quantitation.

The analyst employing PGC/ECD for trace environmental samples will probably obtain the best results using the Webb-McCall technique. The best technique for quantitation of environmental samples using HRGC/ECD is not as clearly defined. "Total PCB" values may be obtained by integration of all of the peaks, using response factors generated from an Aroclor cocktail (see Bush et al., 1982). The approach, used by Zell and Ballschmiter (1980), of quantitating only a selected few "diagnostic peaks" may be appropriate for some applications, provided the PCB patterns are similar and provided that the approach is thoroughly validated. For regulatory cutoff analyses, the approach used by Tuinstra et al. (1983) which uses six specific, diagnostic congeners appears to be both reasonable and expedient.

If the PCB pattern closely resembles that of the commercial mixtures (e.g., transformer oils), quantitation against an Aroclor standard, either by total area, or by the area of selected peaks may be appropriate. These analyses are often automated to reduce the labor costs. The analyst must review the data and employ appropriate QC measures to monitor the data quality.

When the PCBs are present at sufficient levels, when there are significant levels of chlorinated interferences, or when the situation demands additional qualitative confidence, EIMS should be used as the GC detector. With mass spectral data, PCBs are most often quantitated by homolog, generally with only one calibration isomer per homolog. The added information of congener-specific quantitation may be obtained the same way as with HRGC/ECD data, i.e., the response factors and retention times for each congener of interest are obtained with authentic standards.

Regardless of the quantitation technique employed, it should be described in detail or adequately referenced in the analysis report or publication. As noted repeatedly in this book, the data reduction can be a significant or even major source of analytical error. Thus, the analyst must document this step with the same detail as is customary for instrumentation and procedure.

III. DATA REPORTING

The data report must be formatted to fulfill the analytical objectives. If individual congener concentrations are needed, the report will be complex, while if "total PCB" is sufficient, the data report may consist of a single value. The report must specify the reporting units. Units such as micrograms per gram (solids), micrograms per liter (water), and micrograms per cubic meter (air) are recommended. Parts per million and parts per billion can be confusing. Not only is there international disagreement on the term "billion" (10^9 in American System; 10^{12} in British System), but also it may be unclear in some matrices whether the measure is weight/weight or weight/volume. For high density liquid samples (e.g., a halogenated solvent), the difference can be significant.

The analyst should include on the data report some measure of the qualitative confidence. This is often done in the text, or as a footnote.

The data report should include mention of any recovery correction employed and the correction factor. Recovery correction has not been customary practice in residue analysis. Often the error associated with the recovery measurement is larger than the error associated with the PCB quantitation, so a recovery correction may add to rather than reduce uncertainty of the reported value.

The analyst must treat values near the detection limit appropriately. "Zero" should never be reported; only "not detected," "trace," or other expression of the limit of detection (LOD) or the limit of quantitation (LOQ). If samples or congeners are reported as "not detected," "trace," "not quantitatable," etc., the numerical value or estimate of the LOD or LOQ should be stated in the data report. Additional guidance is available (Keith et al., 1983; Crummett, 1979; MacDougall et al., 1980; Glaser et al., 1981; Long and Winefordner, 1983).

Finally, as a QC measure, the data report should include sufficient information to trace the data. In addition to the customer's sample number, an internal sample code, data file code, notebook number, analyst identifier, etc., may be appropriate.

9

QUALITY ASSURANCE

I. GENERAL CONSIDERATIONS

Emphasis on quality assurance (QA) in chemical analysis has increased dramatically in the past few years with the realization that data of unknown quality are virtually useless. In previous chapters, QA considerations have occasionally been mentioned with regards to specific techniques. This chapter focuses on both general QA considerations and specific quality control (QC) measures applied to PCBs.

The terms "quality assurance" and "quality control" have often been inappropriately used. QA is generally defined as the program or <u>structure</u> within an organization which plans, designs, and monitors the QC procedures and affirms the data quality in reports. The elements of a QA program plan for the Office of Toxic Substances in the USEPA (EPA, 1983c) are listed in Table 9-I. The specific requirements for other QA plans can vary from this list, but the general content should be similar.

QC is the term used to describe the <u>activities</u> in the QA program which control errors and define the data quality. Some of the potential QC elements or activities are listed in Table 9-II. Few QC programs, if any, will implement all of these measures. The selection of measures and the degree to which they are applied (e.g., frequency of calibration) are dependent on the analytical objectives of the program and on the procedures, people, and equipment being used. A third term, quality assessment, describes the data <u>verification</u> process. For more details on quality assurance the reader is referred to more detailed reviews on the subject (Keith et al., 1983; MacDougall et al., 1980; EPA, 1979c,f, 1980a,b, 1983c; Cardone, 1983a,b; Cairns and Rogers, 1983; Horwitz, 1983; Kateman and Pijpers, 1981; Kirchmer, 1983; Sherma, 1981; Watts, 1980).

Table 9-I.   Suggested Table of Contents for QA Project Plan

1.0 Title page
2.0 Table of contents
3.0 Project description and objectives
4.0 Project organization and management
5.0 Personnel qualifications
6.0 Facilities, equipment, consumables, and services
    6.1 Facilities and equipment
        6.1.1 Evaluation
        6.1.2 Inspection and maintenance
        6.1.3 Calibration procedures and reference
              materials
    6.2 Consumables
    6.3 Services
7.0 Data generation
    7.1 Experimental design
    7.2 Sample collection
    7.3 Sample custody
    7.4 Laboratory analysis procedures
    7.5 Internal quality control checks
    7.6 Performance and system audits
8.0 Data processing
    8.1 Collection
    8.2 Validation
    8.3 Storage
    8.4 Transfer
    8.5 Reduction
    8.6 Analysis
9.0 Data quality assessment
    9.1 Precision
    9.2 Accuracy
    9.3 Representativeness
    9.4 Comparability
    9.5 Completeness
10.0 Corrective action
11.0 Documentation and reporting
    11.1 Documentation
    11.2 Document control
    11.3 Quality assurance reports to management
    11.4 Report design

Source: EPA, 1983c.

Table 9-II.   Quality Control Considerations in
              PCB Analysis

METHOD VALIDATION
 · Analyze blanks
 · Analyze spikes
 · Analyze standard addition samples
 · Analyze replicates (precision)
 · Assess potential interferences
 · Conduct a ruggedness test
 · Compare to other methods (accuracy)
 · Select and validate PCBs to be used for instrumental
     calibration
 · Assess transferability to other analysts
 · Establish instrumental performance criteria (e.g.,
     sensitivity, resolution)
 · Determine instrumental limit of detection
 · Determine instrumental limit of quantitation
 · Determine method limit of detection/quantitation
 · Determine range of quantitation
 · Decide on treatment of questionable identifications
 · Decide on treatment of trace data
 · Conduct a collaborative study

SAMPLING
 · Use field controls (e.g., 10%) to assess losses
 · Use field blanks (e.g., 10%) to assess contamination
 · Use a well-designed sampling scheme to fit study objectives
 · Evaluate representativeness of sampling scheme
 · Use a validated sample preservation and storage procedure
 · Use clear, unambiguous, informative, permanent labels

METHOD EXECUTION
 · Monitor instrumental performance (e.g., sensitivity,
     resolution)
 · Calibrate instrumentation
 · Calibrate apparatus (e.g., 1-mL volume marks on sample
     vials)
 · Verify reagent and standard purity
 · Verify reagent and standard identity
 · Verify reagent and standard concentration
 · Periodically check stability of standard solutions
 · Control glassware contamination
 · Monitor glassware contamination with blanks
 · Use either sample traceability (not legally defensible)
     or chain of custody (legally defensible)

Table 9-II (continued)

SAMPLE PREPARATION AND ANALYSIS
- Include blanks (e.g., 10%) with each sample set
- Include replicates (e.g., 10%) with each sample set
- Include spikes (e.g., 10%) with each sample set
- Include check samples (e.g., 10%) with each sample set
- Include blind check samples on a regular basis
- Repeat analyses on a regular basis
- Use surrogates to measure method recovery on each sample
- Use internal standards for quantitation
- Determine LOD, LOQ, MDL, or MQL for each analysis day or sample set
- Monitor retention times for PCB identification

DATA REDUCTION AND REPORTING
- Validate equations, algorithms, or programs
- Check selected identifications by a second analyst (e.g., 10%)
- Check selected quantitations by a second analyst (e.g., 10%)
- Label and annotate all chromatograms and other output
- Include sample number, date of analysis, notebook reference, or other information in analysis report so that data may be traced
- Cite method and document all deviations in the analysis report
- Report data in uniform, unambiguous units
- Report analytical uncertainty
- Report any blank on recovery corrections
- Report results of QC samples
- Footnote any questionable identifications or quantitations
- Do not report any quantitation below the LOQ
- Report the LOD, LOQ, MDL, or MQL and when it was determined
- Report results only to the appropriate number of significant figures
- Review data with another analyst
- Repeat questionable analyses

CONFIRMATION
- Analyze sample using an alternate technique (e.g., additional column cleanup)
- Use a confirmatory technique (e.g., alternate GC columns, more specific detector)
- Send to another laboratory for a repeat analysis

Table 9-II (concluded)

NETWORKS OF MULTIPLE LABORATORIES
- Designate a QA laboratory
- Use the same procedure
- Use a consistent reporting format
- Use aliquots of the same standard solution and critical reagents
- Use similar apparatus and instrumentation
- Provide assistance to the analysts from both QA lab and others in network
- Conduct periodic informal site visits for information exchange
- Conduct periodic formal systems audits
- Conduct periodic informal QC check sample analyses
- Conduct periodic formal performance audits
- Use a central sample tracking, coding, scheduling, and distribution system
- Incorporate blind duplicates, blanks, and spikes into the sample set
- Have blind duplicates analyzed by different laboratories
- Have a central data review organization
- Conduct periodic confirmatory analyses

The QA program for a given laboratory, if already in place and operational, should need little adjustment for analysis of samples for PCBs. The QC, however, must be tailored not only to the general considerations discussed in this paragraph, but also to the analytical peculiarities of PCBs discussed in the following sections and in other chapters of this book. The first step in planning a QC program is to establish the data quality needed by the end user. At this point, the analyst and user must agree (or at least compromise) on the data quality objectives; specifically the degree of qualitative confidence, limit of detection, data confidence level (i.e., precision and accuracy), validity of the method, and the amount of QC needed. Next, the analyst must design the QC program to fit these needs in the context of the analytical program. Finally, the analytical program is conducted. During this last phase, it is critical that all of the plans for QC be executed. The analyst must insert appropriate blanks and replicates. The QA staff must conduct audits. Management must insist on timely QA/QC reports so that corrective action can be taken. Last, and most importantly, the QC data and a data quality assessment should accompany the analytical report so that the user will know the data quality. The vast majority of the PCB publications omit the last step, forcing the reader to speculate on the data quality.

II. SPECIAL CONSIDERATIONS IN PCB ANALYSES

Since PCBs generally occur as complex mixtures of analytes, special QC measures must be considered. The PCBs used for calibration of the analytical instrument may be a mixture (e.g., Aroclor 1254) similar to that found in the samples or a group of individual congeners. Any realistic option is a compromise from calibration with all 209 congeners. Thus, an estimate of the error induced by the compromise should accompany the data. The selection of calibration mixtures was discussed in Chapter 8.

Because of the complexity of the data, special precautions should be taken to assure both the qualitative and quantitative aspects. Many quantitation techniques involve summing the calculated response or concentration for many individual PCB peaks to yield a total PCB value. Any systematic error replicated through several quantitations could result in a magnified error in the reported result. The complexity of the calculations also increases the chance of calculation and transcription mistakes.

A.   Reference Materials

A major component of a good QC program is the inclusion of reference materials as QC check samples. These may be routine daily accuracy checks, or may be part of a performance audit. Regardless of their use, reference materials must be validated prior to use. While in-house preparation may be appropriate in many cases, the use of reference materials certified by an external organization lends much more credence to the results. Table 9-III lists some reference materials. The availability of standards of neat PCB mixtures and individual congeners was discussed in Chapter 2.

B.   QA in Multiple Laboratory Networks

When data from more than one laboratory are to be compared, special measures must be taken to assure data comparability. In a formal multi-laboratory network, it is advisable that one organization function as a QA laboratory. The QA laboratory must ensure that all laboratories in the network:

· Use the same procedure.

· Execute these procedures without significant variation.

Table 9-III. Reference Materials for PCB Analysis

Matrix	PCB Composition	PCB Concentration	Code	Availability	Reference
Wet sediment	Aroclor 1254/1260 (1:1)	1 ppm	--	Marine Analytical Chemistry Standards Program Atlantic Research Laboratory National Research Council 1411 Oxford Street Halifax, Nova Scotia B3H 3Z1	Chau et al., 1979
Dried sediment	Aroclor 1254/1260 (1:1)	2 ppm	--		Chau and Lee, 1980
Motor oil	Aroclor 1242	100 µg/g	SRM 1581	U.S. National Bureau of Standards Washington, DC 20234	Uriano, 1982
Motor oil	Aroclor 1260	100 µg/g			
Transformer oil	Aroclor 1242	100 µg/g			
Transformer oil	Aroclor 1260	100 µg/g			
Methanol[a]	Aroclor 1242	5,000 µg/mL	E 104	QA Branch EMSL - Cincinnati U.S. EPA Cincinnati, OH 45268	EPA, 1983b
Methanol[a]	Aroclor 1254	5,000 µg/mL	E 105		
Methanol[a]	Aroclor 1232	5,000 µg/mL	E 107		
Methanol[a]	Aroclor 1248	5,000 µg/mL	E 108		
Methanol[a]	Aroclor 1260	5,000 µg/mL	E 109		
Methanol[a]	Aroclor 1016	5,000 µg/mL	E 110		
Methanol[a]	Aroclor 1221	5,000 µg/mL	E 126		
Methanol[a]	Aroclor 1262	5,000 µg/mL	E 130		
Acetone[a]	Aroclor 1268	2,500 µg/mL	E 131		
Isooctane	Aroclor 1016	1,000 µg/mL	E 125		
Isooctane	Aroclor 1242	1,000 µg/mL	E 132		
Isooctane	Aroclor 1254	1,000 µg/mL	E 135		
Isooctane	Aroclor 1260	1,000 µg/mL	E 129		
Capacitor oil	Aroclor 1016	3 levels[b]	--		
Capacitor oil	Aroclor 1242	3 levels[b]	--		

Table 9-III (continued)

Matrix	PCB Composition	PCB Concentration	Code	Availability	Reference
Capacitor oil	Aroclor 1254	3 levels[b]	-		
Capacitor oil	Aroclor 1260	3 levels[b]	-		
Hydraulic oil	Aroclor 1016	3 levels[b]	-		
Hydraulic oil	Aroclor 1242	3 levels[b]	-		
Hydraulic oil	Aroclor 1254	3 levels[b]	-		
Hydraulic oil	Aroclor 1260	3 levels[b]	-		
Transformer oil	Aroclor 1016	3 levels[b]	-		
Transformer oil	Aroclor 1242	3 levels[b]	-		
Transformer oil	Aroclor 1254	3 levels[b]	-		
Transformer oil	Aroclor 1260	3 levels[b]	-		
Fish	Aroclor 1242	2 levels[b]	-		
Fish	Aroclor 1254	2 levels[b]	-		
Fish	Aroclor 1260	2 levels[b]	-		
Sediment	Aroclor 1242	3 levels[b]	-		
Sediment	Aroclor 1254	3 levels[b]	-		

a For spiking water to prepare a water check sample for priority pollutant or other analyses.
b Levels not specified in catalog.

- Obtain similar performance (i.e., precision and accuracy).

- Report results in a consistent format.

It is advisable that all network members use aliquots of the same standard solutions, use commonly obtained reagents where critical (e.g., Florisil for column cleanup), and use similar apparatus and instrumentation. The QA measures specifically applicable to multiple laboratory analysis networks are listed in Table 9-II.

As an example of such a network, the U.S. EPA has operated a network of laboratories for pesticide analysis in a variety of sample matrices (blood, adipose, milk, urine, soil, water, air, wildlife, and others) since the late 1960s. As part of this network, an EPA laboratory (the QA Section of the Health Effects Research Laboratory, ORD, EPA, Research Triangle Park, NC, until 1982; now Environmental Monitoring and Support Laboratory, ORD, EPA, Las Vegas, NV)) functions as a central QA laboratory. Analysis of composites, development of methods, revision of the methods manual, supply of special reagents and standards, maintenance of instruments, site visits, analyst assistance, assessment of method execution, and conduct of a periodic QC check sample program are among this group's duties. The check sample program consists of issuing a standard pesticide reference material (e.g., fat spiked with pesticides and PCBs), receiving results, and evaluating laboratory performance. The results from the 10-20 participating laboratories are tabulated and each laboratory given a numerical performance score based on both qualitative and quantitative results. Results for three fat samples spiked with PCBs at 0.5-1.5 ppm levels averaged between 93% and 105% of the formulated concentration, with relative standard deviations between 12 and 34% (Personal communications, R. R. Watts, U.S. EPA, Research Triangle Park, NC, 1980-1981). However, several participants--50% in one case--did not report PCBs in these samples. It is not known whether participants "missed" the PCBs or simply chose not to report their findings. Despite the relatively good performances noted above, at least one participant was found (Lucas et al., 1980) to be short-cutting the prescribed analytical method (Watts, 1980). The participating laboratory had eliminated a liquid chromatographic fractionation and was quantitating only a single heptachlorobiphenyl peak against an Aroclor 1260 standard.

III.   PREVIOUS QC MEASURES

        The U.S. EPA has taken steps to implement strong QC
programs in various standard methods of analysis and as part
of long-term project goals (EPA, 1979c, 1980a,b, 1981a;
Bellar and Lichtenberg, 1981). Table 3-I listed the standard
procedures that acknowledge the need to follow some type of
QC program. QC measures have also been cited in several collaborative studies (DCMA, 1982; Sawyer, 1973, 1978b; Delfino
and Easty, 1979; Devenish and Harling-Bowen, 1980; Pittaway
and Horner, 1982). These and other collaborative studies are
also discussed in Chapter 10.

        The QC program for the Dry Color Manufacturers As-
sociation (DCMA, 1982) collaborative study included instrument calibration specifications, performance evaluation of
the gas chromatography column with a standard mixture of
PCBs, and measurement of sensitivity for PCBs by serial dilution of the standard, method blanks, specification of quantitation procedures and validation of sample preparation procedure. The validation of sample extraction, cleanup and
analysis included workup of blind and known spike samples.
The results of the DCMA study indicate that variance in reported PCB levels between laboratories was significantly reduced when a commercially prepared quantitation standard was
used by all participating laboratories. Data from the DCMA
report indicated relative standard deviations of 3.1 to 9.1%
within a laboratory, 2.4 to 40% between laboratories, and 7.3
to 41% for the total reproducibility for analysis of three
different pigments.

        The Chemical Manufacturers Association sponsored a
collaborative study of PCB concentrations in five different
byproduct PCB samples (Pittaway and Horner, 1982). Eight
different laboratories participated in the study. In contrast to the DCMA study, no defined protocol or QC programs
were specified for analysis of the matrices. Each laboratory
was allowed to choose the method of extraction, cleanup, instrumental determination and quantitation, and QC program it
desired. This study indicated that there are many sources of
potential error in the quantitative analysis of PCBs. The
lack of agreement of the measurements between laboratories
indicated a true need for a strong QC program to produce comparable data.

        In a study of emissions from a municipal inciner-
ator and a co-fired (refuse-derived fuel plus coal) power
plant, Haile et al. (1983a) used three laboratories to analyze the different samples. Sets of spiked fly ash were
sent periodically to the laboratories to serve as QC check

samples.   Recovery of decachlorobiphenyl spiked at the 500-
2,500 ng/g level ranged over an order of magnitude.   Duplicate analyses within a laboratory differed by as much as a
factor of 3.

Bush et al. (1983) have illustrated a good quality
control technique for single laboratory analyses.   In routine
analyses of environmental samples for PCBs by automated HRGC/
ECD, they utilized a quality control chart (Figure (9-1) to
monitor the instrumental response.   The standard was run
after every sixth sample.   The chart in Figure 9-1 also illustrates the additive effects of random errors.   While the
fluctuation of the plots for the individual congeners is
small, much larger fluctuations are seen for the "Total PCB"
plot.

IV.   RECOMMENDED QA/QC MEASURES

A good working QA program requires a set of written
standard operating procedures for instrumental operation,
routine laboratory operations, data review, reporting, and
all other aspects of data generation.   More importantly, the
QA program must have support from all levels in the organization.   The goal must be to assure that data of known quality
are being reported while minimizing interference with the
analysis process.

Once a working QA program is in place, the specific
QC aspects pertaining to PCBs are relatively simple to implement.   The QC will differ from organization to organization,
and indeed, according to the individual project.   The QC
should be discussed with the data user (i.e., the client) to
reach agreement on the desired precision and accuracy.

Summaries of the QC recommendations from three
analytical procedures are presented in this section as examples of thorough QC programs.

A.   Transformer Oil (Jung, 1981)

In a review of analytical methods for PCB analysis
in transformer oil, Jung (1981) recommended several QC measures:

1.   Analyze a quality check sample daily to assess
accuracy.

2.   Analyze 10% of all samples in duplicate, selected at random, to assess the precision.

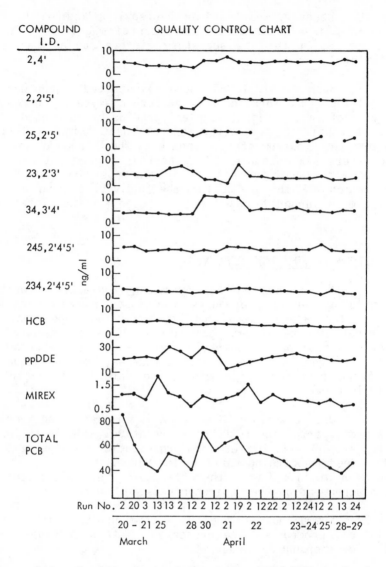

Figure 9-1.   Quality Control Chart for HRGC/ECD Analysis of
   PCBs and Other Organochlorine Compounds in Human Milk

A "quasi-milk" QC sample, containing individual PCB congeners
and insecticides at known concentrations, was analyzed after
every sixth milk sample. The results, plotted above, indicate immediately whether the previous analyses are within the
QC tolerances.

Reprinted, with permission, from Bush et al. (1983); copyright 1983 by Association of Official Analytical Chemists,
Inc.

3. Maintain a log of precision and accuracy data.

4. Maintain a record of the retention times of unknown PCBs.

5. Analyze a certified sample, if available, at
least quarterly.

B. Transformer Fluids and Waste Oils (Bellar and
Lichtenberg, 1981)

The elements of a section entitled "Precision and
Accuracy" include:

1. A formal QC program must be operational.

2. The laboratory must demonstrate its capability
with check samples on a periodic basis.

3. The analyst must demonstrate precision and accuracy by analyzing at least four replicate standard addition
samples. The recovery and standard deviation must meet EPA
performance criteria (these were to be established at a later
date).

4. Using the recovery and standard deviation from
slope, control charts are to be constructed to serve as performance criteria.

5. At least 10% of all samples or one sample per
month, whichever is greater, must be analyzed by standard addition techniques to monitor spike recoveries.

6. Each time a set of samples is analyzed or there
is a change in reagents, a laboratory reagent blank should be
processed.

7. Additional QC measures should be considered by
each laboratory. These may include field duplicates to monitor sampling precision, qualitative confirmation with a dissimilar GC column, halogen-specific detector or MS.

8. A standard sample of PCBs in a typical oil matrix must be analyzed daily before any samples are analyzed.
The results of this analysis serve as instrument status
checks, calibration curve validation, and long-term precision
measures.

9. An EPA QC sample must be analyzed on a quarterly basis. Results within 15% of the true value are acceptable. If the results are unacceptable, the analyst must
resolve the problem.

C. <u>By-product PCBs</u> (Erickson et al., 1983d)

The elements of the QA section of this document are:

1. A formal QA plan is required.

2. A formal QC program must be in operation, including recordkeeping, certification, and performance checks.

3. Procedural QC measures include:

a. GC performance criteria.

b. MS performance criteria.

c. Confirmation of at least 10% of all qualitative identifications by a second analyst.

d. Confirmation of at least 10% of all calculations by a second analyst.

4. Sample QC measures include:

a. Acceptable recoveries of ^{13}C-labeled surrogates (e.g., 50-150%).

b. Spectral data quality must be evaluated. The chlorine isotope intensities must be of the proper ratios (e.g., within ± 20% of the ratios observed for standards).

c. Internal standard areas must be within ± 20% from injection to injection.

d. For small (1-10) sample sets, 1 method blank, 1 duplicate (triplicate preferred), and 1 standard addition sample must accompany the set.

e. For intermediate (10-100) sample sets, the number of method blanks, replicates, and standard addition samples must comprise at least 10% each.

f. With large (> 100) sample sets, alternate QC measures may be proposed. For example, if contamination has never been observed in blanks, the frequency of method blanks may be reduced.

5. Additional QC, specific to each organization and analytical problem, should be considered.

10

COLLABORATIVE STUDIES

A collaborative study is the validation of an analytical method by several laboratories. Collaborative studies are generally considered the ultimate in method validation and are required by most organizations before a method is accepted as "official," "final," etc. Collaborative studies are also termed interlaboratory studies, round robins, etc.

Guidelines for a collaborative test are available (Youden and Steiner, 1975; AOAC, 1982) although many studies differ markedly in both objectives and execution. Ideally, each participating laboratory receives the same sample set, performs the analysis according to a written protocol and reports the results to a coordinator for evaluation. Two areas of fundamental disagreement are the degree of control over the participants and the data evaluation. The objective of a true collaborative study is to evaluate a given protocol, so all variables are held as constant as possible. Many studies, however, have permitted the participants to use any method they choose. These studies, then, evaluate either the "current state of the art" or the laboratories. The other point of disagreement is the data evaluation. In a true collaborative study, where the objective is to evaluate the method performance, the statistical evaluation summarizes the precision, accuracy, and any other performance measures and then attempts to evaluate potential sources of error (random, systematic, and laboratory-specific). Many studies, however, have been used to also evaluate the participant's performance. Labs are rated by how closely they meet target values.

This chapter discusses several PCB collaborative studies in some detail because they (a) demonstrate the quality of the data obtainable for many procedures, (b) emphasize those few out of the myriad methods discussed in earlier chapters which have been subjected to this level of validation, (c) illustrate the different approaches to the conduct of collaborative studies, and (d) permit direct comparison of some of the techniques for those studies which allowed the participants to select various techniques.

I. <u>WILDLIFE</u> (HOLDEN, 1973)

        This study used three test samples containing known amounts of organochlorine pesticides, PCBs, or mercury. Sixteen of the 26 participants reported values for both a hexane solution of Chlophen A-60 and a cormorant homogenate sample (Table 10-I). The average accuracy was 99% and the precision was about ± 13% for the hexane solution and ± 22% for the cormorant sample. The participants were allowed to use their customary in-house procedures, which covered the range of extraction, cleanup, GC column, and quantitation techniques. All participants apparently used PGC/ECD.

II. <u>CHICKEN FAT AND FISH</u> (SAWYER, 1973)

        Nine laboratories collaborated on the analysis of PCBs in hexane, chicken fat, and fish. Existing AOAC multipesticide methods with PGC/ECD or PGC/halogen specific detector (HECD or microcoulometric) quantitation were employed. The results shown in Table 10-I indicate excellent performance of the method for direct injection GC/ECD analysis with peak height quantitation. With the chicken fat which required laboratory preparation, the precision was poorer, but the accuracy was very near 100%. The accuracy for the fish was much lower (∿ 75%). Similar results were obtained for all three matrices using PGC/ECD or PGC/halogen specific detector with total area quantitation.

III. <u>PAPERBOARD</u> (FINSTERWALDER, 1974)

        Eleven laboratories participated in this AOAC study to validate a method for PCBs (Aroclor 1242 and 1254) in paperboard. The method involves alcoholic KOH extraction, Florisil column cleanup, and PGC/ECD determination. The results, shown in Table 10-I, indicate an average precision of about ± 20% relative standard deviation (RSD) and an average accuracy of about 85%. In addition to tabulation of the data and discussing potential outliers, the study author ranked the laboratories for each sample with a "1" for the highest reported concentration, a "2" for the next highest, etc. The sum of a laboratory's rank for each sample yielded a collaborative score. This technique is useful for identifying systematic errors which make a participant consistently either high or low. Laboratory ranking is discussed in more detail by Youden and Steiner (1975).

Table 10-I. Summary of Collaborative Studies

Matrix	Number of Participants	Method	PCB Composition	Prepared Concentration	Mean Concentration Found	Precision (% RSD)	Accuracy[b] (%)	Reference
Hexane Cormorant	16	Unspecified	Chlophen A-60 Env. residue	9.8 mg/L –	9.71 mg/L 373 mg/kg	12.9 22	99.1 –	Holden, 1973
Hexane Chicken fat Fish	9	AOAC (PGC/ECD, PH Quant.)	Aroclor 1254/1260 Aroclor 1242 Aroclor 1254	5 ppm 8.05 ppm 5.98 ppm	5.08 ppm 8.15 ppm 4.51 ppm	4.3 12.6 13.9	100.4 101.3 75.4	Sawyer, 1973
Paperboard	11	AOAC (PGC/ECD)	Aroclor 1242 Aroclor 1242 Aroclor 1254 Aroclor 1254 Aroclor 1242	12.5 ppm 8.2 ppm 12.3 ppm 8.9 ppm –	10.1 ppm 7.2 ppm[c] 10.7 ppm[c] 7.6 ppm[c] 5.6 ppm	20.2 19.8 15.3 22.8 15.8	80.8 87.8 87.0 85.4 –	Finsterwalder, 1974
Marine sediment	10	Unspecified	Env. residue	–	612 ng/g	21.9	–	Pavlou and Hom, 1976
Milk	10	AOAC (PGC/ECD)	Aroclor 1254	1.38 ppm 2.72 ppm	1.16 ppm 2.35 ppm	14.4 17.1	84 86	Sawyer, 1978b
Solvent Distilled water Paper mill effluent Paper mill effluent	8 8 6 6	Direct GC/ECD Extract/GC/ECD Extract/GC/ECD Extract/GC/ECD	Aroclor 1242 Aroclor 1242 Unknown Unknown	1.50 ng/µL – – –	1.47 ng/mL – 2.74 µg/L 5.13 µg/L	15.6 14.7 19.0 16.0	98 95.6 – 93.7	Delfino and Easty, 1979
Isooctane Wet lake sediment[d]	16 16	Unspecified Unspecified	A1254/A1260 A1254/A1260 A1254/A1260	1.00 µg/µL 1.01 ppm 1.22 ppm	1.12 ng/µL – –	19.1 18.3 19.1	112 92.8 98.5	Lee and Chau, 1981a
Isooctane Dry lake sediment	15 15	Unspecified Unspecified	A1242/A1254/A1260 Env. residue Env. residue	600 pg/µL	572 pg/µL[c] 2.054 µg/g[c] 1.244 µg/g[c]	12.0 29.8 28.2	95.4[c] 80.9 ± 38.4[e] –	Lee and Chau, 1981b
Dry pigments	10	GC/ECD	3,3'-dichlorobiphenyl Decachlorobiphenyl $C_{12}H_5Cl_5 + C_{12}H_4Cl_6$ isomers $C_{12}H_5Cl_5 + C_{12}H_4Cl_6$ isomers $C_{12}H_5Cl_5 + C_{12}H_4Cl_6$ isomers $C_{12}H_5Cl_5 + C_{12}H_4Cl_6$ isomers	– –	66.8 ppm[f] 37.2 ppm[f] 72.2 ppm[f] 73.0 ppm[g] 66.8 ppm[f] 90.1 ppm[g] 69.7 ppm[f]	10 7.3 12.9 21 17 23 41	– – –	DCMA, 1982
Air (extracts)	9	Unspecified	Env. residue	–	7.1 ng/m³ 4.4 ng/m³	26 39	– –	Bidleman, 1981

Table 10-I (continued)

Matrix	Number of Participants	Method	PCB Composition	Prepared Concentration	Mean Concentration Found[a]	Precision (% RSD)	Accuracy[b] (%)	Reference
Insulating oils	10	GC/ECD	A1242/A1254	42.8	49.0 ppm	13	105	Rouse, 1982
			A1242	5.0	4.8 ppm	0	-	
			A1242/A1260	68.1	58.4 ppm	13	86	
			A1260	50.3	49.0 ppm	18	92	
			A1254/A1260	36.7	39.2 ppm	16	107	
			A1254	31.6	30.9 ppm	14	98	
Sea water collected on XAD-2	7	Unspecified	Env. residue	-	0.3 ng/L	45	-	Palmork et al., 1982
Undecane collected on XAD-2	12	Unspecified	Aroclor 1254	25 µg/mL	205.9 mg/mL	23	104	Villeneuve, 1982
Sea water	11	Unspecified	Aroclor 1254	5 ng/L	7.7 ng/L	57	154	Villeneuve, 1982
Chlorinated benzene waste	10[h]	Unspecified	~ 80 congeners[i]	-	283 ppm	34	-	Pittaway and Horner, 1982; Hodges et al., 1983
Mixture of chlorinated benzenes	10	Unspecified	A1254	X	24 ppm	92	75	
Mixture of chlorinated benzenes	10	Unspecified	+ 23 congeners[j]	X + 64 ppm[k]	64 ppm	46	75	
Mixture of aliphatic waste	10	Unspecified	$C_{12}H_9Cl_1 + C_{12}H_8Cl_2$[l]	-	129 ppm	72	-	
Mixture of aromatic waste	10	Unspecified	$C_{12}H_9Cl + C_{12}H_5Cl_5$[m]	-	9.2 ppm	53	-	
Hexane (# 7)	4	DI GC/MS	11 congeners	5.0 µg/mL	6.6 µg/mL	31	137 ± 36	Erickson et al., 1983c
Hexane (# 8)	4	DI GC/MS	11 congeners	5.4 µg/mL	10.4 µg/mL	39	186 ± 64	
Chlorinated benzene waste (# 9)	4	DI GC/MS	~ 80 congeners[i]	-	39.7 µg/mL	20	-	
Chlorinated benzene waste (# 10)	4	DI GC/MS	~ 80 congeners	-	31.0 µg/mL	38	-	
Chlorinated benzene waste (# 11)	4	Florisil GC/MS	~ 80 congeners	-	2,960 µg/g[n]	166	-	
Chlorinated benzene waste (# 12)	4	Florisil GC/MS	~ 80 congeners	-	4,420 µg/g[o]	182	-	
Chlorinated benzene waste (# 14)	4	Interpret.	~ 80 congeners	-	23.9 µg/mL	12	-	
Herring oil	23	GC/MS	Env. residue	X	1.14 mg/kg	49	-	Musial and Uthe, 1983
Herring oil			A1254	X + 1.00 mg/kg	2.01 mg/kg	28	87 ± 23	
Bovine serum	12	GC/MS	A1254[p]	9.97 ppb[q]	23.86 ppb	37.0	239.3	Burse et al., 1983[b]
Bovine serum				49.64 ppb[q]	76.08 ppb	30.7	165.4	

322

Table 10-I (concluded)

Matrix	Number of Participants	Method	PCB Composition	Prepared Concentration	Mean Concentration Found[a]	Precision (% RSD)	Accuracy[b] (%)	Reference
Lubricating oil	19	GC/ECD	A1260	5.90 ppm	5.9	64	100	Becker, 1984
			A1242	41.0 ppm	37	38	90	
			A1260	148.3 ppm	37	57	90	
			Blank	< 1 ppm	0.55	-	-	
			A1242 and 1260	60 ppm	54	44	90	
				60 ppm	55	42	92	
			A1254	96.6 ppm	107	55	111	
			Industrial contamination	Unknown	145	43	-	
			Industrial contamination	Unknown	146	51	-	
			Interferences	< 1	10.3	252	-	

a Values termed "outlier" in the studies are included unless otherwise noted.
b Accuracy defined as mean concentration found divided by the prepared concentration.
c Outliers excluded by study authors.
d One environmental residue and two spiked samples. Values were reported as percent recovery of the spike after subtraction of the native PCBs.
e Accuracy assessed by comparison of the results reported for duplicate dry sediment samples analyzed through the full analysis scheme against an extract of this sediment which was analyzed by direct injection onto the GC.
f Preparation B: methylene chloride extraction with Florisil column cleanup.
g Preparation A: hexane/H_2SO_4 partition.
h Eight participants submitted 10 data sets (two participants reported results using two methods; e.g., GC/MS and GC/ECD).
i About 80 congeners over all 10 homologs were found.
j Twenty-three congeners (all 10 homologs) spiked into previous sample.
k Second sample ("X," mean = 24 ppm) spiked with 2-5 ppm of 22 congeners for a total spike of 64 ppm.
l Two isomers of $C_{12}H_9Cl$ and 4 isomers of $C_{12}H_8Cl_2$.
m Unspecified number of isomers of each homolog.
n One participant was much higher than all others. With the outlier omitted, the mean was 507 µg/g, RSD = 54, and range was 300-820.
o One participant was much higher than all others. With the outlier omitted, the mean was 407 µg/g, RSD = 58, and the range was 280-650.
p In vivo bound.
q Based on in-house analysis by study coordinators.

IV. MARINE SEDIMENTS (PAVLOU AND HOM, 1976)

Ten participants were asked to analyze a sediment sample to assess the reliability of chlorinated hydrocarbon measurements. All participants presented values for total PCBs, seven presented a sum of DDT metabolites, and one quantitated dieldrin, cis-chlordane, and trans-chlordane. As can be seen in Table 10-I, the RSD of the PCB values for all of the laboratories was ± 22%. The participants used a variety of techniques for all steps of the analysis. The reported concentration was slightly dependent on whether the sediment was dried and on the weight of sediment used; the authors recommended drying the sediment before extraction. The quantitation technique also affected the results. "Total PCB" and "Aroclor" quantitations both led to much less accurate results than a Webb and McCall (1973) type approach, which the authors incorrectly termed a homolog quantitation. They recommended the latter approach.

V. QUANTITATION TECHNIQUES AND MILK (SAWYER, 1978b)

Ten collaborators quantitated a synthetic mixture of one tri-, two tetra-, and one pentachlorobiphenyl; one tri- and two tetrachlorobiphenyls; and another mixture of two Aroclor 1254-fortified milk samples; one milk sample containing bioincurred PCBs; and one chicken fat sample containing bioincurred Aroclor 1242. The study was conducted by the AOAC to evaluate (a) different PGC/ECD quantitation techniques and (b) the applicability of the AOAC multiresidue pesticide method to milk.

A. Quantitation Techniques

Each collaborator was asked to analyze the two synthetic PCB mixtures and the chicken fat sample by direct injection onto a PGC/ECD system which met certain specifications. The data were to be quantitated against standard Aroclor solutions supplied by the coordinator. Three quantitation techniques were to be used: (a) summation of the height of peak matching the retention time of peaks in the Aroclor standard, (b) summation of the area of peaks matching the retention time of peaks in the Aroclor standard, and (c) the individual peak comparison of Webb and McCall (1973). The first two techniques were those recommended in Section 29.018 of the AOAC method (1980a). The Webb-McCall technique was being considered for inclusion in the method as an alternate quantitation technique.

Based on the results summarized in Table 10-II, the study author concluded that the Webb-McCall technique was generally an improvement over the other two techniques. The author also recommended that AOAC adopt the Webb-McCall technique as the technique of choice when residues do not exhibit a PCB pattern similar to that of an Aroclor standard.

B. Milk

The two milk samples were extracted, cleaned up, and determined by PGC/ECD using the AOAC method for quantitating PCB residues. The 85% average recovery and RSDs ranging from ± 14% to ± 17% (see Table 10-I) were considered adequate and consistent with previous results for PCBs in fatty foods (Sawyer, 1973). The author recommended that the AOAC method be modified to include milk and other fatty dairy products as applicable matrices.

VI. PAPER MILL EFFLUENT (DELFINO AND EASTY, 1979)

The collaborative study reported by Delfino and Easty (1979) focused on the analysis of PCBs in paper mill effluents. The study consisted of two phases. The first phase was used to determine the comparability of PCB methodologies between six different laboratories and the abilities of the participating analysts to perform the basic operations required for PCB analysis. These factors were determined by direct injection of a performance standard and also the simple extraction and analysis of a spiked aqueous solution. The second phase required analysis of both known and blind samples by a single method. A modified EPA wastewater analysis procedure (EPA, 1973) was followed by all participating laboratories, which involved liquid-liquid extraction, a Florisil column cleanup, and PGC/ECD determination. The silica gel microcolumn step for separation of PCBs from pesticides was deleted for this study, since pesticides were judged to be unlikely constituents of paper mill effluents.

The results of the first phase, extraction from distilled water, yielded an average recovery of 95.6% with a relative standard deviation of 14.7%. The relative standard deviation for direct injection of a standard solution was 15.6%. The results for paper mill effluent yielded similar results with 93.6% average recovery with a 16.0% relative

Table 10-II. Summary of Collaborative Test of PCB Quantitation Techniques

Matrix Solvent	Quantitation Technique[a]	Aroclor Standard	PCB Composition	Prepared Composition	Mean Concentration Found	Precision (% RSD)	Accuracy (%)[b]
Solvent[c]	W-M	1248	2,2',5	0.19 ng/µL	0.166 ng/µL	12.1	87.4
	W-M	1248	2,2',5,5'	0.53 ng/µL	0.474 ng/µL	10.9	89.5
	W-M	1248	2,3',4,5	0.55 ng/µL	0.572 ng/µL	10.1	104.1
	W-M	1248	2,2',4,5,5'	0.10 ng/µL	0.232 ng/µL	19.7	232.0
	PH	1248	Total (3)[d]	1.28 ng/µL	1.39 ng/µL	22.9	108.6
	A	1248	Total (3)	1.28 ng/µL	1.21 ng/µL	18.5	94.5
	W-M	1248	Total (3)	1.28 ng/µL	1.22 ng/µL	6.3	95.3
	PH	1248	Total (4)[e]	1.38 ng/µL	1.60 ng/µL	16.4	115.9
	A	1248	Total (4)	1.38 ng/µL	1.54 ng/µL	28.9	111.6
	W-M	1248	Total (4)	1.38 ng/µL	1.44 ng/µL	6.5	104.4
Chicken fat[c]	PH	1242	Aroclor 1242	-[f]	6.78 ppm	12.6	-
	PH	1248	Aroclor 1242	-	6.94 ppm	5.5	-
	A	1242	Aroclor 1242	-	7.54 ppm	16.0	-
	A	1248	Aroclor 1242	-	5.89 ppm	7.7	-
	W-M	1242	Aroclor 1242	-	5.62 ppm	8.1	-
	W-M	1248	Aroclor 1242	-	6.31 ppm	7.8	-
Milk[g]	PH	1254	Aroclor 1254	1.38 ppm	1.14 ppm	16.8	82.6
	A	1254	Aroclor 1254	1.38 ppm	1.18 ppm	11.3	85.5
	W-M	1254	Aroclor 1254	1.38 ppm	1.16 ppm	15.2	84.1
	PH	1254	Aroclor 1254	2.72 ppm	2.32 ppm	18.8	85.3
	A	1254	Aroclor 1254	2.72 ppm	2.37 ppm	14.3	87.1
	W-M	1254	Aroclor 1254	2.72 ppm	2.36 ppm	18.2	86.8
	PH	1254	Aroclor 1254	-[f]	1.34 ppm	30.4	-
	A	1254	Aroclor 1254	-	1.66 ppm	31.4	-
	W-M	1254	Aroclor 1254	-	1.15 ppm	18.4	-

a W-M = Webb and McCall (1973) individual peak quantitation; PH = total peak height versus Aroclor standard;
   A = Total area versus Aroclor standard.
b Accuracy measured as mean concentration found divided by the prepared concentration.
c These samples analyzed by direct injection into the PGC/ECD.
d All individual congeners, except 2,2',4,5,5'-pentachlorobiphenyl.
e All four individual congeners.
f Bioincurred residue; prepared concentration not determinable.
g Sample analyzed by AOAC multiresidue extraction, cleanup, and PGC/ECD method with quantitation technique as shown.
Source: Sawyer (1978b); reprinted with permission, copyright 1978 by Association of Official Analytical Chemists.

standard deviation, and indicated that the method was satisfactory for paper mill effluents. The similarity of the precision and accuracy of direct injection, a distilled water
sample, and the papermill samples indicated that the PGC/ECD
analysis (including quantitation) was the principal source of
error.

VII. <u>WET LAKE SEDIMENT</u> (LEE AND CHAU, 1981a)

Fourteen laboratories were given one isooctane solution and three sediment samples for analysis by the method
of their choice. One sediment sample contained the native
PCBs and the other two were aliquots of the first to which
1.01 and 1.22 ppm of a 1:1 mixture of Aroclor 1254 and 1260
had been added. The participants used a variety of techniques, with the only common denominator being PGC/ECD for
the instrumental determination. The results for the unspiked
sample of Lake Ontario sediment were generally low, trace or
not detected and were not summarized by the authors. The results for the spiked samples were summarized in terms of the
percent recovery of the spike. The mean percent recoveries
were 93 and 99%, with RSDs of ± 18 and ± 19%, respectively.
The fourth sample, 1.00 ng/µL of a 1:1 mixture of Aroclor
1254 and 1260, was analyzed by direct injection onto the GC.
The 112% recovery with an RSD of ± 19% was surprisingly
poorer than the results for the samples which went through
the entire method. The authors used a Youden plot (Youden
and Steiner, 1975) to compare the results for the two spiked
sediment samples (Figure 10-1). The 45° diagonal line represents the true ratio of the PCB content in the two samples.
As can be seen in Figure 10-1, the plot easily distinguishes
the systematic error (distance along the 45° line from the
design value) from random error (distance from the 45° line).
The value reported by Laboratory No. 4 for Sample No. 3 was
rejected as an outlier.

Lee and Chau presented some discussion of the relative merits of the various extraction, cleanup, and notably,
quantitation techniques employed. Eight participants used
the Webb and McCall (1973) quantitation technique and had a
mean accuracy of 103% with a RSD of ± 4.5% for the sample of
Aroclors in isooctane for direct injection. The other eight
participants used a variety of multiple-peak quantitation
techniques and had a mean accuracy of 122% with a RSD of
± 23%. Clearly, for these laboratories and this sample, the
Webb and McCall technique was both more accurate and more
precise.

The authors concluded that the RSD for these samples was ± 20%, the method detection limit was between 0.01

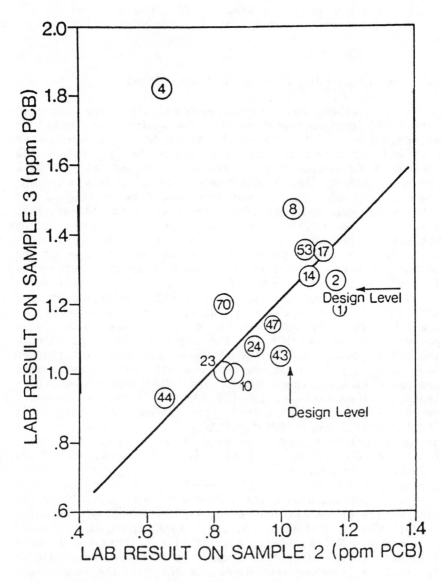

Figure 10-1.   Paired Sample (Youden) Plot for Two
               Wet Sediment Samples

Numbers in circles are the participant's identification
numbers.

Reprinted, with permission, from Lee and Chau (1981a).

and 0.02 ppm, the various extraction and cleanup methods appear to be equally efficient, and quantitation was a major source of error.

VIII.   NATURALLY CONTAMINATED DRY SEDIMENTS (LEE AND CHAU, 1981b)

        A companion to the wet lake sediment study (Lee and Chau, 1981a) discussed above, this study required 15 participants to analyze four samples (actually two duplicate aliquots) of naturally contaminated dry sediment, a cleaned up extract of one of the sediments, and a 600 pg/µL mixture of Aroclor 1242, 1254, and 1260 (1:1:1). As can be seen in Table 10-I, the results for the Aroclor mixture had accuracy and precision similar to the other studies. The precision for the sediment samples, however, was about ± 25%, even after rejection of outliers. Furthermore, the intralaboratory precision (RSD of the values reported for the blind duplicate samples) ranged from less than 1% to over 100%. Typically, the results were in fair agreement (e.g., 1.4 and 1.7 µg/g for an RSD of 14%).

        The participants used a variety of techniques for all stages of the analysis. One participant used HRGC/ECD; the rest, PGC/ECD. The authors attributed the poor performance of the participants in this study relative to that in the wet sediment study to the fact that this study utilized real samples. They recommended the use of these sediment reference materials for both internal and interlaboratory QC studies to improve the data quality.

IX.   AMBIENT AIR (BIDLEMAN, 1981)

        High-volume air samples from Boston, Massachusetts, and Columbia, South Carolina, were collected on a glass fiber filter-polyurethane foam sorbent trap. Aliquots of the organic extracts were sent to nine laboratories. The laboratories were permitted to use any procedure in the analysis. Most groups used either Florisil or silica gel column chromatography in the cleanup. Several used a chemical degradation (sulfuric acid, base, or chromium trioxide) as an additional cleanup step. Most of the participants used PGC/ECD for the sample analysis. Two laboratories used HRGC/ECD and one used GC/EIMS. The precision for the PCB measurements (± 26% to ± 39%, see Table 10-I) was comparable to that observed for most pesticides; however, the precision for the polychloroterpenes (toxaphene) was ± 116%. Bidleman (1981) recommended that the validity of sample collection also be studied in a collaborative study.

X. DRY PIGMENTS (DCMA, 1982)

        The Dry Color Manufacturers Association (DCMA) de-
veloped a method for the analysis of pigments using PGC/ECD.
The method has two sample preparation options, a hexane/
sulfuric acid partition for phthalocyanine blue pigments and
a methylene chloride extraction/Florisil column cleanup for
diarylide yellow, phthalocyanine blue, and phthalocyanine
green pigments. The 10 participants of a collaborative study
conducted by DCMA were all DCMA member companies. They were
asked to analyze five samples (one yellow, two blue, and two
green pigments). The two blue pigment samples were analyzed
by both cleanup options. Several of the participants did not
adhere to the method and their data were not included in the
summaries presented in Table 10-I. The average RSD for the
seven values in Table 10-I was about ± 19%.

        The participants reported their repeatability on four
different days, which permitted an evaluation of the within-
and between-laboratory components of the RSD. For diarylide
yellow (first sample in Table 10-I), the quantitation of the
3,3'-dichlorobiphenyl in the sample had similar within- and
between-laboratory error components. The source of error in
the quantitation of the decachlorobiphenyl in the two phthalocyanine green samples could not be deduced. The between-
laboratory error contribution accounted for almost 80% of the
total error for the four analyses of phthalocyanine blue,
which contained several penta- and hexachlorobiphenyl congeners. The higher RSDs for these samples was attributed to
the greater number of congeners and also to the large number
of interferences.

XI. INSULATING OILS (ROUSE, 1982)

        This study was conducted to test the precision of a
proposed American Society for Testing Materials (ASTM) method
(Method D 4059) for the analysis of PCBs in mineral insulating oils by GC/ECD. The study was conducted by ASTM Committee D27 - Electical Insulating Liquids and Oils. Ten participants reported results for six transformer oil samples
containing Aroclor 1242, 1254, 1260, or mixtures thereof. As
shown in Table 10-I, the average recovery was 98% and the
average RSD was 15%.

XII.   BY-PRODUCTS FROM INDUSTRIAL PROCESSES   (PITTAWAY AND
        HORNER, 1982; HODGES ET AL., 1982; WESTERBERG ET AL.,
        1984)

        This study was conducted by the Chemical Manu-
facturer's Association (CMA) to evaluate the available analytical methodologies for analysis of commercial products
and wastes. The eight participants were mostly industrial
laboratories experienced in the analysis of by-product PCBs
in industrial matrices. The study was designed to "simulate
the situation in which a company independently attempts to
determine the number and quantity of incidentally generated
chlorobiphenyls in its process and/or waste streams" (Pittaway and Horner, 1982). The participants were asked to analyze a set of five samples: a chlorinated benzene waste,
two mixtures of chlorinated benzenes, a chlorinated aliphatic
waste stream sample, and a chlorinated aromatic sample. The
samples were chosen to typify process stream matrices that
were regulated by EPA. The coordinators made no attempt at
controlling sample preparation, analysis, quantitation, reporting format, or QA. Most participants used either direct
injection or a simple dilution for sample preparation. Most
participants used GC/EIMS, although one participant used PGC/
ECD and one used PGC/FID. The latter's results were 100 to
1000 times higher than the average and were excluded from the
data analysis (Pittaway and Horner, 1982).

        As can be seen from the results in Table 10-I, the
precision ranged from ± 34% to ± 92% RSD. The accuracy for
one sample, which was a spike of another sample, was found to
be 75%. Since the data were tabulated by homolog, the error
contribution by homolog was assessed. As shown in Figure
10-2 for one of the samples, the lower homologs tended to
contribute more of the error. This may be a function of the
techniques used, but is more likely a function of the matrix
interferences, which were chlorinated benzenes and chlorinated aliphatics. In addition to the differences in techniques, the reporting units were often vague or unspecified.
Some of the overall error may have been caused by differences
in data reporting, since it is unknown whether the all of the
respondents corrected for density in their reporting of "ppm."

        Pittaway and Horner (1982) concluded that, under
uncontrolled conditions, one cannot expect to receive PCB analytical results which are sufficiently reliable for regulatory decision-making. It should be noted that the complexity
of the PCB mixtures and the matrices in this study were much
greater than those in studies involving Aroclor-derived PCBs
in environmental matrices.

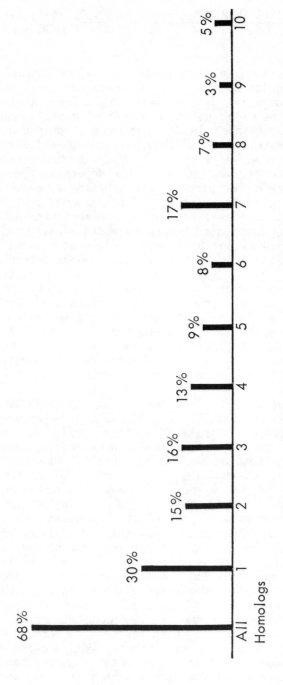

Figure 10-2. Histogram of Error Contribution by Homologs for Sample A from CMA Study

Reprinted from Hodges et al. (1983).

XIII.   BY-PRODUCTS IN A CHLORINATED AROMATIC WASTE (ERICKSON
        ET AL., 1983c)

        This study was conducted to assess a method for the
analysis of incidentally generated chlorinated biphenyls in
commercial products and product wastes (Erickson et al.,
1982). Four participants received calibration solutions at
known concentrations, instructions for analysis and data reporting, and a set of samples. The sample set included
paired samples of (a) additional ampules of the calibration
solution of 11 PCB congeners at unknown and slightly differing concentrations which required only GC/EIMS determination
(samples 7 and 8), (b) a chlorinated aromatic waste which required only GC/EIMS determination (samples 9 and 10), and (c)
the same chlorinated aromatic waste which required both laboratory preparation (Florisil column cleanup) and GC/EIMS
determination (samples 11 and 12). An additional sample,
again the chlorinated aromatic waste, was supplied in the
form of a magnetic tape (sample 14). This last sample required only data interpretation by the participants. Figure
10-3 presents a schematic of the entry points into the sample
analysis scheme.

        The results are summarized in Table 10-I. The
overall errors ranged from ± 12 to ± 182%. The two RSDs over
100% were inflated by one participant who appeared to be an
outlier. The first two samples were dilutions of the calibration solution. Since the concentrations were known, the
accuracy could be assessed as shown in Table 10-I. A comparison of the Youden pair samples (samples differing only in
concentration by about 10%; Youden and Steiner, 1975) were
compared using a Student's t-test. At the 95% confidence
level none of the participants correctly differentiated among
the samples. This indicates that the method precision is
> 10%.

        One of the samples consisted simply of a magnetic
tape containing a calibration analysis and an analysis of the
same original sample used for four of the other samples in
this study. The interpretation of this magnetic tape provided a direct assessment of the data reduction error. The
qualitative analyses identified from 55-109 peaks as PCBs although the participant reporting the highest number clearly
did not evaluate the data since they reported 14 monochlorobiphenyls. Two of the three reporting participants calculated equivalent response factors from the standard run,
while one participant reported response factors two times
higher. The ± 25% RSD for this sample was the largest individual contribution to the total error, as shown in Figure
10-4.

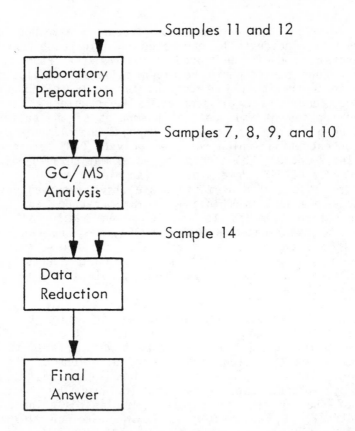

Figure 10-3. Analysis Flow Scheme for By-product
Collaborative Study, Showing
Sample Entry Points

Reprinted, with permission, from Erickson et al. (1983c).

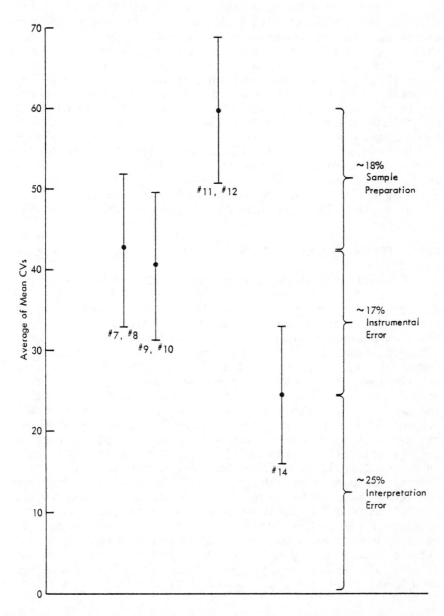

Figure 10-4.   Plot of Error in By-product Collaborative Study
by Sample Type, Showing Contributions of the Analysis Steps

Reprinted, with permission, from Erickson et al. (1983c).

The data indicate that the overall method variation appears to be ± 60% RSD. This is shown in Figure 10-4 (outliers excluded). There is about ± 25% variation associated with the data interpretation step. About ± 17% variation appears to be associated with instrumental error and ± 18% variation is associated with sample preparation. The results of this study indicate that the precision and accuracy of this method are lower than for many other methods. This collaborative study, however, was operating at the lower limit of instrumental sensitivity (selected ion monitoring mode) where precision is poor and also employed samples containing about 80 PCB congeners in a matrix containing many other chlorinated compounds. Thus, this was an extremely tough challenge to the method. A second study of the method using more collaborators, simpler PCB mixtures, and higher concentrations is currently being conducted. Preliminary results indicate that the precision, accuracy, and surrogate recovery are better at higher PCB concentrations (Bishop and Gebhart, 1984).

XIV.   HERRING (MUSIAL AND UTHE, 1983)

In this international study, 23 participants reported results for PCBs in unspiked and spiked (1.00 mg/kg Aroclor 1254 in oil) samples of herring oil. Each participant was free to choose the analytical method, although Aroclor 1254 standard solutions were provided for use as a quantitation standard. The overall precision of the higher level (spiked) sample was substantially better than the precision for the lower level sample. There was no significant difference in the quantitation based on four calculations: either the participant's usual method or the sum of three prominent Aroclor 1254 peaks compared to either the participant's own standards or a standard solution of Aroclor 1254 supplied by the coordinators. Also, no significant difference was found when the GC column efficiencies were compared. There did, however, appear to be a dependence of the results on the type of liquid phase in the GC column; the authors recommended the use of high grade silicone stationary phases. They also noted that the in-house calibration standards were as much as 6% different than that supplied by the coordinators. The authors also observed significantly higher values for participants who used Florisil cleanup as opposed to those who used alumina. A lengthy discussion of the causes was inconclusive.

XV.   BOVINE SERUM (BURSE ET AL., 1983b)

Twenty-five laboratories which are engaged in routine analysis of blood samples for PCBs and other chlorinated hydrocarbons collaborated in this study coordinated by the Centers for Disease Control (CDC). The participants were free to choose the analytical method and employed a wide variety of techniques. Only 12 participants which reported the prescribed duplicate analyses on a low- and high-level sample were included by the study authors in the statistical analyses presented in Table 10-I. The total precision of ± 37.0% and ± 30.7% for the two samples (Table 10-I) was further broken down. The intra-laboratory variance was ± 16.8% and ± 11%, while the inter-laboratory variance was ± 33.0% and ± 28.6% for the low and high level samples, respectively.

The accuracy reported in Table 10-I is highly misleading. The prepared value used for comparison with the participants' values is actually a CDC analysis of the samples which were prepared from in vivo-bound PCBs (Burse et al., 1983a). There is no data on the accuracy of the in-house analysis. Nevertheless, the two samples were dilutions of the same pool, so it may be reasonable to assume that the relative ratios are reasonably correct. Thus, the collaborative date show that there is a higher bias at lower concentrations (239% recovery for the lower concentration sample versus 165% for the higher). The authors attributed most of the accuracy error (i.e., high values by the collaborators) to two sources: high reagent blanks and failure to completely separate PCBs from DDT and its metabolites. They noted that the three participants which were within ± 3 standard deviations of the CDC mean either used a small volume of solvent to minimize the background or oxidized the DDT analogs.

XVI. LUBRICATING OILS (BECKER, 1984)

This study was part of a cooperative program between the U.S. National Bureau of Standards and the American Society for Testing and Materials to develop an accurate and relative simple method for determining PCBs in used and re-refined lubricating oils. Eleven samples were prepared, some containing known amount of Aroclors in clean oil, and some containing industrially incurred PCBs as shown in Table 10-I. Two duplicates and a blank were included in the sample set. In addition, one sample contained only an oil additive package which was suspected of causing interferences with some PCB analyses. The samples were analyzed using the participants' in-house procedures. The 19 participants all used GC/ECD, some packed and some capillary column. All laboratories used external standard calibration and quantitated the PCBs as individual Aroclors. A variety of cleanup techniques were reported, although a combination of Florisil and sulfuric acid was most widely used.

         As noted in Table 10-I, most of the results were
very close to the prepared concentrations; i.e., the accuracy
was high. However, the 40 to 60% relative standard deviation
on most of the samples indicates that the precision was not
nearly as good. An examination of the data by Becker (1984),
including Youden plots of the duplicate samples, indicated
that most of the error was systematic. The intralaboratory
precision was generally good. Becker inferred that problems
with standardization and/or quantitation caused the bias in
some of the participants' results.

BIBLIOGRAPHY

Aaronson, M. J., J. D. Tessari and S. M. Bergin. "PCBs in Transformer Oils," Bull. Environ. Contam. Toxicol. 28:584-591 (1982).

Acker, L. and F. Schulte. "Occurrence of Hexachlorobenzene and Polychlorinated Biphenylenes Besides Chlorinated Insecticides in Human Fat Tissues and Milk," Ernaehrungsforschung 16(4):559-67 (1972), Chem. Abst. 78:80552c (1973).

Ackerman, D. G., L. L. Scinto, P. S. Bakshi, R. G. Delumyea, R. J. Johnson, G. Richard and A. M. Takata. "Guidelines for the Disposal of PCBs and PCB Items by Thermal Destruction," USEPA, IERL, Research Triangle Park, NC, EPA-600/ 2-81-022, February 1981, 317 pp.

Ackerman, D. G., L. L. Scinto, P. S. Bakshi, R. G. Delumyea, R. J. Johnson, G. Richard, A. M. Takata and E. M. Sworzyn. "Destruction and Disposal of PCBs by Thermal and Non-Thermal Methods," TRW, Inc., Redondo Beach, CA, Noyes Data Corporation, Park Ridge, New Jersey, 1983a, 417 pp.

Ackerman, D. G., J. F. McGaughey and D. E. Wagoner. "At-Sea Incineration of PCB-Containing Wastes Onboard the M/T Vulcanus," TRW Inc., Redondo Beach, CA, for the U.S. Environmental Protection Agency, Office of Research and Development, Contract No. 68-02-3174, Work Assignment No. 103 (April 1983b), 273 pp.

Adams, J. D. and J. H. Caro. "Polyurethane Foam as Trapping Agent for Airborne Pesticides, Analytical Method Development," Environmental Research Laboratory, Office of Research and Development, U.S. Environmental Protection Agency, Athens, GA, EPA-600/4-80-008 (January 1980).

Adams, J., K. Menzies and P. Levins. "Selection and Evaluation of Sorbent Resins for the Collection of Organic Compounds," U.S. Environmental Protection Agency, Research Triangle Park, NC, EPA-600/7-77-044 (April 1977).

Adams, T. T., N. J. Williams, R. J. McElhaney and R. A. Viator. "Analysis for Polychlorinated Biphenyls in Environmental Samples," Union Carbide report prepared for the U.S. Department of Energy, Contract No. W 7405 eng 26 (June 1979).

Addis, G. and R. Y. Komai, Eds. "Proceedings: 1983 PCB Seminar," Electric Power Research Institute, Palo Alto, CA, EPRI-EL-3581, June 1984.

Addis, G. and J. Marks, Eds. "Proceedings: 1981 PCB Seminar," Electric Power Research Inst., Palo Alto, CA, EPRI-EL-2572, CONF-811260 (NTIS No. DE82906457), September 1982, 296 pp.

Addison, J. B. and M. E. Nearing. "An Approach to the Preparation of Standard Reference Material for the Analysis of Polychlorinated Biphenyls in Marine Sediments," Intern. J. Environ. Anal. Chem. 11:9-16 (1982).

Adlard, E. R. "A Review of Detectors for Gas Chromatography," in CRC Critical Reviews in Analytical Chemistry 5:1 (1978).

Afghan, B. K. and D. Mackay (Eds.). Hydrocarbons and Halogenated Hydrocarbons in the Aquatic Environment, Plenum Publishing Corporation, New York. Proceedings of International Symposium on the Analysis of Hydrocarbons and Halogenated Hydrocarbons in the Aquatic Environment, Ontario, Canada, 1978 (1980).

Ahling, B. and S. Jensen. "Reversed Liquid-Liquid Partition in Determination of Polychlorinated Biphenyl (PCB) and Chlorinated Pesticides in Water," Anal. Chem. 42(13):1483-1486 (1970).

Ahnoff, M., G. Eklund and B. Josefsson. "Analysis of PCB in Water from the Swedish West Coast," Acta Hydrochim. Hydrobiol. 7(2):171-178 (1979).

Ahnoff, M. and B. Josefsson. "Confirmation Studies on Polychlorinated Biphenyls (PCB) from River Waters Using Mass Fragmentography," Anal. Lett. 6(12):1083-1093 (1973).

Ahnoff, M. and B. Josefsson. "Simple Apparatus for On-Site Continuous Liquid-Liquid Extraction of Organic Compounds from Natural Waters," Anal. Chem. 46(6): 658-663 (1974).

Ahnoff, M. and B. Josefsson. "Clean Up Procedures for PCB Analysis on River Water Extracts, Bull. Environ. Contam. Toxicol. 13(2):159-166 (1975).

Ahnoff, M. and B. Josefsson. "Apparatus for in Situ Solvent Extraction of Nonpolar Organic Compounds in Sea and River Water," Anal. Chem. 48(8):1268-1270 (1976).

Aitzetmüller, K. "Adsorption Liquid Chromatography of DDT and Polychlorinated Biphenyls," J. Chromatogr. 107:411-415 (1975).

Alben, K. and E. Shpirt. "Distribution Profiles of Chloroform, Weak Organic Acids, and PCBs on Granular Activated Carbon Columns from Waterford, New York," Environ. Sci. Technol. 17(4):187-192 (1983).

Albro, P. W. "Problems in Analytic Methodology: Sample Handling, Extraction, and Cleanup," Ann. N.Y. Acad. Sci. 320: 19-27 (1979).

Albro, P. W. "Validation of Extraction and Cleanup Procedures for Environmental Analysis," Chapter 8 in Environmental Health Chemistry, The Chemistry of Environmental Agents as Potential Human Hazards, J. D. McKinney, Ed. (Ann Arbor, MI: Ann Arbor Science Publishers, Inc., 1980), pp. 163-175.

Albro, P. W. and L. Fishbein. "Quantitative and Qualitative Analysis of Polychlorinated Biphenyls by Gas-Liquid Chromatography and Flame Ionization Detection. I. One to Three Chlorine Atoms," J. Chromatogr. 69:273-283 (1972a).

Albro, P. W. and L. Fishbein. "Intestinal Absorption of Polychlorinated Biphenyls in Rats," Bull. Environ. Contam. Toxicol. 8(1):26-31 (1972b).

Albro, P. W., J. K. Haseman, T. A. Clemmer and B. J. Corbett. "Identification of the Individual Polychlorinated Biphenyls in a Mixture by Gas-Liquid Chromatography," J. Chromatogr. 136:147-153 (1977). Errata published in J. Chromatogr. 139: 404 (1977).

Albro, P. W. and B. J. Corbett. "Extraction and Clean-up of Animal Tissues for Subsequent Determination of Mixtures of Chlorinated Dibenzo-p-dioxins and Dibenzofurans," Chemosphere 7:381-385 (1977).

Albro, P. W., J. R. Hass and W. B. Crummett. "Summary of the Workshop on Recent Advances in Analytical Techniques for Halogenated Aromatic Compounds," Ann. N.Y. Acad. Sci. 320: 125-130 (1979).

Albro, P. W. and C. E. Parker. "Comparison of the Compositions of Aroclor 1242 and Aroclor 1016," J. Chromatogr. 169:
161-166 (1979).

Albro, P. W. and C. E. Parker. "General Approach to the
Fractionation and Class Determination of Complex Mixtures of
Chlorinated Aromatic Compounds," J. Chromatogr. 197:155-169
(1980).

Albro, P. W., J. T. Corbett and J. L. Schroeder. "Quantita-
tive Characterization of Polychlorinated Biphenyl Mixtures
(Aroclors® 1248, 1254 and 1260) by Gas Chromatography Using
Capillary Columns," J. Chromatogr. 205:103-111 (1981).

Albro, P. W., J. S. Schroeder, D. J. Harvan, and B. J.
Corbett. "Characteristics of an Extraction and Purification
Procedure for Chlorinated Dibenzo[p]dioxins and Dibenzofurans
in Soil and Liver," J. Chromatogr. 312:165-182 (1984).

American National Standards Institute, Inc. "American National Standard Guidelines for Handling and Disposal of
Capicator- and Transformer-Grade Askarels Containing Polychlorinated Biphenyls, ANSI C107.1-1974," New York, NY
(1974).

American Society of Mechanical Engineers. "Test Protocol:
Sampling for the Determination of Chlorinated Organic Com-
pounds in Stack Emissions" (1984). Unpublished report from
Environmental Standards Workshop.

American Society for Testing and Materials. "Standard Specifications for Chlorinated Aromatic Hydrocarbons (Askarels)
for Capacitors, ANSI/ASTM D 2233-74" in Annual Book of ASTM
Standards Part 40, Philadelphia, Pennsylvania (1978a),
p. 647-649.

American Society for Testing and Materials. "Standard Specifications for Chlorinated Aromatic Hydrocarbons (Askarels)
for Transformers, ANSI/ASTM D 2283-75," in Annual Book of
ASTM Standards, Part 40, Philadelphia, Pennsylvania (1978b),
p. 650-653.

American Society for Testing and Materials. "Standard Method
for Rapid Gas Chromatographic Estimation of High Boiling
Homologues of Chlorinated Biphenyls for Capacitor Askarels,
ANSI/ASTM D 3303-74 (Reapproved 1979)," in Annual Book of
ASTM Standards, Part 40, Philadelphia, Pennsylvania (1980a),
pp. 870-876.

American Society for Testing and Materials. "Standard Practice for Sampling Water, ASTM D 3370," in Annual Book of ASTM
Standards, Part 31, Philadelphia, Pennsylvania.

American Society for Testing and Materials. "Standard Method
for Polychlorinated Biphenyls (PCBs) in Water, ANSI/ASTM
D 3534-80," in Annual Book of ASTM Standards Part 31,
Philadelphia, Pennsylvania (1981a), pp. 816-833.

American Society for Testing and Materials. "Standard Method
for Analysis of Environmental Materials for Polychlorinated
Biphenyls, ASNI/ASTM D 3304-77," in Annual Book of ASTM
Standards Part 31, Philadelphia, Pennsylvania (1981b),
pp. 877-885.

American Society for Testing and Materials. "Standard Method
for Analysis of Polychlorinated Biphenyls in Mineral Insulating Oils by Gas Chromatography," ANSI/ASTM D 4059-83," in
Annual Book of ASTM Standards, Part 40, Philadelphia,
Pennsylvania (1983), pp. 542-550.

Anderson, R. J. and R. C. Hall. "Hall Bipolar Pulse, Differential Electrolytic Conductivity Detector for GC," Amer. Lab.
108-124 (February 1980).

Anderson, T. "The Role of Legislature in the Regulation of
Toxic Materials," in PCBs: Human and Environmental Hazards,
F. M. D'Itri and M. A. Kamrin, Eds. (Boston: Butterworth
Publishers, 1983), pp. 375-382.

Andren, A. W. "Processes Determining the Flux of PCBs Across
Air/Water Interfaces," in Physical Behavior of PCBs in the
Great Lakes, D. Mackay, S. Paterson, S. J. Eisenreich and
M. S. Simmons, Eds. (Ann Arbor, MI: Ann Arbor Science Pub-
lishers, Inc., 1983), 442 pp.

Anonymous. New Scientist, 612 (1966).

Anonymous. "Toxic Impurities in Polychlorinated Biphenyls -
Environmental Impact," in Environ. Res. 5:308-312 (1972).

Anonymous. "Extraction of PCBs from Transformer Oil for GC-
ECD Analysis with 'Baker' Disposable Extraction Column
Octyl(C_8) (7087-6)," Application Note SS-AN017 (J. T. Baker
Chemical Co., Phillipsburg, NJ), November 1981.

Anonymous. "NBS Develops Improved Technique for Measuring
PCBs in Oils," J. Assoc. Offic. Anal. Chem. 65(4):1033
(1982a).

Anonymous. "Method Improves PCB Measurements in Oil," Chem.
Eng. News 19, March 1, 1982b.

Appleby, A. "Atmospheric Freons and Halogenated Compounds,"
U.S. Environmental Protection Agency, Office of Research and
Development, EPA-600/3-76-108 (November 1976).

Araki, Y. and K. Tanaka. "Simple Screening Method for [Hepatic] Enzyme-inducing Agents of Polychlorinated Biphenyl (PCB) Type," Fukuoka-Igaku-Zasshi 65(1):47-52 (1974); Chem. Abst. 81:146433n (1974).

Armour, J. A. "Gas Chromatographic Data for Polychlorinated Biphenyl Components in Six Aroclors®," J. Chromatogr. 72:275-282 (1972).

Armour, J. A.. "Quantitative Perchlorination of Polychlorinated Biphenyls as a Method for Confirmatory Residue Measurement and Identification," J. Assoc. Offic. Anal. Chem. 56(4): 988-993 (1973).

Armour, J. A. and J. A. Burke. "Method for Separating Polychlorinated Biphenyls from DDT and Its Analogs," J. Assoc. Offic. Anal. Chem. 53(4):761-768 (1970).

Armour, J. A. and J. A. Burke. "Behavior of Chlorinated Naphthalenes in Analytical Methods for Organochlorine Pesticides and Polychlorinated Biphenyls," J. Assoc. Offic. Anal. Chem. 54:175-177 (1971).

Armstrong, D. E. and D. L. Swackhamer. "PCB Accumulation in Southern Lake Michigan Sediments: Evaluation from Core Analysis," in Physical Behavior of PCBs in the Great Lakes, D. Mackay, S. Paterson, S. J. Eisenreich, M. S. Simmons, Eds. (Ann Arbor, MI: Ann Arbor Science Publishers, Inc., 1983), 442 pp.

Armstrong, D. W. and R. Q. Terrill. "Thin Layer Chromatographic Separation of Pesticides, Decachlorobiphenyl, and Nucleosides with Micellar Solutions," Anal. Chem. 51(13): 2160-2163 (1979).

Arnoux, A., J. L. Monod, and T. Schembri. "Gas-Chromatographic and Gas Chromatographic/Mass Spectrometric Identification of PCBs, Linear Saturated Hydrocarbons, Polynuclear Aromatic Hydrocarbons and Phthalates in Deep Sediments from the Western Mediterranean Sea," Journ. Etud. Pollut. Mar. Mediterr., 6:469-474 (1983); Chem. Abstr. 101:177066f (1984).

Arpino, P. J., B. G. Dawkins and F. W. McLafferty. "A Liquid Chromatography/Mass Spectrometry System Providing Continuous Monitoring with Nanogram Sensitivity," J. Chromatogr. Sci. 12:574-578 (1974).

Association of Official Analytical Chemists. "General Method for Organochlorine and Organophosphorus Pesticides, Method 29.001," Official Methods of Analysis of the Association of Official Analytical Chemists, W. Horwitz, Ed. (13th ed., Washington, DC 1980a), pp. 466-474.

Association of Official Analytical Chemists. "PCB in Paper and Paperboard, Method 29.029," Official Methods of Analysis of the Association of Official Analytical Chemists, W. Horwitz, Ed. (13th ed., Washington, DC 1980b), p. 475-476.

Association of Official Analytical Chemists. Handbook for AOAC Members (5th Edition, 1982), 109 pp.

Atlas, E., and C. S. Giam. "Global Transport of Organic Pollutants: Ambient Concentrations in the Remote Marine Atmosphere," Science, 211:163-165 (1981).

Aue, W. A. and S. Kapila. "The Electron Capture Detector--Controversies, Comments, and Chromatograms," J. Chromatogr. Sci. 11:255-263 (1973).

Aue, W. A. and S. Kapila. "Use of Electron Capture-Induced Products for Confirmation of Identity in Pesticide Residue Analysis," Anal. Chem. 50:536-538 (1978).

Augood, D. R., D. H. Hey, and G. H. Williams. "Homolytic Aromatic Substitution. Part III. Ratio of Isomerides Formed in the Phenylation of Chlorobenzene. Competitive Experiments on the Phenylation of p-Dichlorobenzene and 1,3,5-Trichlorobenzene. Partial Rate Factors for Chlorobenzene," J. Chem. Soc. (London) pp. 44-50 (1953).

Ayer, F. A. (Ed.), "National Conference on Polychlorinated Biphenyls (November 19-21, 1975, Chicago, Illinois)," Report of proceedings prepared for the U.S. Environmental Protection Agency, Office of Toxic Substances, Report No. EPA-560/6-75-004, NTIS No. PB-253 248 (March 1976), 471 pp.

Babkina, E. I., T. P. Fanaskova and T. V. Shpotova. "Determination of Organochlorine Pesticides and Polychlorinated Biphenyls in the Ground and the Water," Gidrobiol. Zh. 18(3): 86-91 (1982); Chem. Abstr. 97:86886f (1982).

Bagley, G. E., W. L. Reichel and E. Cromartie. "Identification of Polychlorinated Biphenyls in Two Bald Eagles by Combined Gas-Liquid Chromatography-Mass Spectrometry," J. Assoc. Offic. Anal. Chem. 53(2):251-261 (1970).

Bagley, G. E. and E. Cromartie. "Elimination Pattern of Aroclor 1254 Components in the Bobwhite," J. Chromatogr. 75:219-226 (1973).

Bailey, R. E., S. J. Gonsior and W. L. Rhinehart. "Biodegradation of the Monochlorobiphenyls and Biphenyl in River Water," Environ. Sci. Technol. 17(10):617-621 (1983).

Baird, W. M. J. "Responding to Public Concern Over Environmental Pollution Hazards," in PCBs: Human and Environmental Hazards, F. M. D'Itri and M. A. Kamrin, Eds. (Boston: Butterworth Publishers, 1983), pp. 91-100.

Baker, E. L., P. J. Landrigan, C. J. Glueck, M. M. Zack, Jr., J. A. Liddle, V. W. Burse, W. J. Housworth and L. L. Needham. "Metabolic Consequences of Exposure to Polychorinated Biphenyls (PCB) in Sewage Sludge," Amer. J. Epidemiol. 112(4): 553-563 (1980).

Ballinger, D. G. "Test Procedures for Priority Organics in Municipal Wastewater and Sludges," U.S. Environmental Protection Agency, Cincinnati, Ohio, December 11, 1978.

Ballschmiter, K. "High Resolution Gas Chromatography in Environmental Analysis," in Reviews in Analytical Chem. 4:139-156 (1983a); Chem. Abstr. 99:63564b (1983).

Ballschmiter, K. "Sample Treatment Techniques for Organic Trace Analysis," Pure Appl. Chem. 55(12):1943-1956 (1983b); Chem. Abstr. 100:95791d (1984).

Ballschmiter, K. and M. Zell. "Analysis of Polychlorinated Biphenyls (PCB) by Glass Capillary Gas Chromatography. Composition of Technical Aroclor- and Clophen-PCB Mixtures," Fresenius' Z. Anal. Chem. 302:20-31 (1980).

Ballschmiter, K., Ch. Unglert and H. J. Neu. "Abbau Von Chlorierten Aromaten: Mikrobiologischer Abbau Der Polychlorierten Biphenyle (PCB). III: Chlorierte Benzoesäuren als Metabolite Der PCB," Chemosphere 6(1):51-56 (1977).

Balya, D. R. and G. H. Farrah. "Column Chromatographic Procedure for the Determination of Polychlorinated Biphenyls in Certain Industrial Oils," Anal. Lett. 13(B8):655-671 (1980).

Bartle, K. D. "Identification of Polychlorobiphenyls by High Resolution Proton Magnetic Resonance," J. Assoc. Offic. Anal. Chem. 55(5):1101-1103 (1972).

Barton, T. G. and G. P. Arsenault. "Ultimate Disposal of Polychlorinated Biphenyls," Chapter 10 in Detoxication of Hazardous Waste, J. H. Exner, Ed. (Ann Arbor, MI: Ann Arbor Science Publishers, Inc., 1982), pp. 185-199.

Bauer, U.. "Combination of Thin-layer and Gas Chromatography for Identifying Halogenated Hydrocarbons," Vom Wasser 38:49-62 (1971); Chem. Abstr. 76:136672x (1972).

Baughman, R. and M. Meselson. "An Analytical Method for Detecting TCDD (Dioxin): Levels of TCDD in Samples from Vietnam," Environ. Health Perspect. 5:27-35 (1973).

Beard, J. H., III and J. Schaum. "Sampling Methods and Analytical Procedures Manual for PCB Disposal: Interim Report, Revision 0," Office of Solid Waste, U.S. Environmental Protection Agency, Washington, DC (February 10, 1978).

Becker, D. A. "Analysis for PCBs in Oil: The NBS/ASTM Round Robin," in National Bureau of Standards Special Publication 674. Proceedings, Conference on Measurements and Standards for Recycled Oil. - IV, Gaithersburg, Maryland, pp. 33-41 (1984).

Becker, D. A. "Used Lube Oil: Hazardous Waste vs. Valuable Resource," Trace Subst. Environ. Health 16:22-27 (1982); Chem. Abstr. 99:160990v (1983).

Becker, G. and E. Schulte. "Presence of PCB in Packaging Materials," Mitteilungsbl. GDCh-Fachgruppe Lebensmittelchem. Gerichtl. Chem. 30(6):101-108 (1976); Chem. Abstr. 85:107564u (1976).

Beezhold, F. L. and V. F. Stout. "The Use and Effect of Mixed Standards on the Quantitation of Polychlorinated Biphenyls," Bull. Environ. Contam. Toxicol. 10(1):10-15 (1973).

Beggs, D. P. and D. B. Banks. "Qualitative Analysis of PCB by GC/MS," Application Note AN 176-20, Hewlett-Packard, Avondale, Pennsylvania (1976).

Bellar, T. A. and J. J. Lichtenberg. "Some Factors Affecting the Recovery of Polychlorinated Biphenyls (PCB's) from Water and Bottom Samples," in Special Technical Publication 573, American Society for Testing and Materials, Philadelphia, Pennsylvania (1975), pp. 206-219.

Bellar, T. A., J. J. Lichtenberg and S. C. Lonneman. "Recovery of Organic Compounds from Environmentally Contaminated Bottom Materials," Chapter 4 in Contaminants and Sediments, Vol. 2, R. A. Baker, Ed. (Ann Arbor, MI: Ann Arbor Science Publishers, Inc., 1980).

Bellar, T. A. and J. J. Lichtenberg. "The Determination of Polychlorinated Biphenyls in Transformer Fluid and Waste Oils," Prepared for U.S. Environmental Protection Agency, EPA-600/4-81-045 (1981).

Bellar, T. A. and B. Froning. "Application of Methods 606 and 608 for Analysis of PCBs Organochlorine Pesticides and Phthalate Esters Contained in Landfill Leachates," U.S. Environmental Protection Agency, Cincinnati, OH, EPA-600/4-82-044, NTIS No. PB82 227463 (1982), 16 pp.

Belliardo, F., E. Gionchiglia and G. M. Nano. "Analysis of Polychlorinated Biphenyl Residues in Waste Oils by High-Performance Liquid Chromatography," J. Liq. Chromatogr. 2(1): 77-83 (1979).

Benville, P. E. and R. C. Tindle. "Dry Ice Homogenization Procedure for Fish Samples in Pesticide Residue Analysis," J. Agr. Food Chem. 18(5):948-949 (1970).

Bercovici, B., M. Wassermann, S. Cucos, M. Ron, D. Wasserman and A. Pines. "Serum Levels of Polychlorinated Biphenyls and Some Organochlorine Insecticides in Women with Recent and Former Missed Abortions," Environ. Res. 30:169-174 (1983).

Berg, O. W., P. L. Diosady and G. A. V. Rees. "Column Chromatographic Separation of Polychlorinated Biphenyls from Chlorinated Hydrocarbon Pesticides, and their Subsequent Gas Chromatographic Quantitation in Terms of Derivatives," Bull. Environ. Contam. Toxicol. 7(6):338-347 (1972).

Berger, D. L. "Screening Procedure for Total Organic Halogen," Anal. Chem. 56:2271-2272 (1984).

Bergman, Å., R. Göthe and C. A. Wachtmeister. "Impregnation of Silica Gel with Tetraalkylammonium Salts in Adsorption Chromatography of Neutral Aromatic Compounds," J. Chromatogr. 123: 231-236 (1976).

Bergman, Å., B. Jansson, and I. Bamford. "Methylthio- and Methylsulfonylpolychlorobiphenyls: Synthesis and Studies of Correlations Between Structure and Fragmentation Pattern on Electron Impact," Biomedical Mass Spectrometry, 7(1):20-27 (1980).

Bergman, Å., L. Reutegardh, and M. Ahlman, "Determination of Polychlorinated Biphenyls in Commercial Silica Gel by Capillary Gas Chromatography," J. Chromatogr. 291:392-397 (1984a).

Bergman, Å., A. Hagman, S. Jacobsson, B. Jansson, and M. Ahlman. "Thermal Degradation of Polychlorinated Alkanes," Chemosphere, 13(2):237-250 (1984b).

Bernard, B. B. and B. D. Russell. "Rapid Determination of PCBs in Insulating Fluids," unpublished report, O. I. Corporation, College Station, TX (1983), 5 pp.

Bezot, P., C. Hesse-Bezot and B. Quentrec. "Transmission of Light and Local Order in Viscous Liquids. IV. Angular Dependence of Depolarized Spectra," Mol. Phys. 43(6):1407-1418 (1981); Chem. Abstr. 96:76686p (1982).

Bezot, P., C. Hesse-Bezot. "Fabry-Perot Study of Polarized and Depolarized Spectra of Liquid Pentachlorobiphenyl from -54 to 150°C," Can. J. Phys. 60(11):1709-1715 (1982).

Bickford, B., J. Bursey, L. Michael, E. Pellizzari, R. Porch, D. Rosenthal, L. Sheldon, C. Sparacino, K. Tomer, R. Wiseman, S. Yung, J. Gebhart, L. Rando, D. Perry and J. Ryan. "Preliminary Draft Report, Master Scheme for the Analysis of Organic Compounds in Water, Part III: Experimental Development and Results," EPA Contract No. 68-03-2704 (March 1980).

Bidleman, T. F. "Interlaboratory Analysis of High Molecular Weight Organochlorines in Ambient Air," Atmos. Environ. 15: 619-624 (1981).

Bidleman, T. F. "Estimation of Vapor Pressures for Nonpolar Organic Compounds by Capillary Gas Chromatography," Anal. Chem., 56:2490-2496 (1984).

Bidleman, T. F. and C. E. Olney. "High-volume Collection of Atmospheric Polychlorinated Biphenyls," Bull. Environ. Contam. Toxicol. 11(5):442-450 (1974).

Bidleman, T. F., C. P. Rice, and C. E. Olney. "High Molecular Weight Chlorinated Hydrocarbons in the Air and Sea: Rates and Mechanisms of Air/Sea Transfer," in Marine Pollutant Transfer, H. L. Windom and R. A. Duce, Eds. (Lexington, MA: Lexington Books, 1976), pp. 323-351.

Bidleman, T. F., J. R. Matthews, C. E. Olney and C. P. Rice. "Separation of Polychlorinated Biphenyls, Chlordane, and p,p'-DDT from Toxaphene by Silicic Acid Column Chromatography," J. Assoc. Offic. Anal. Chem. 61(4):820-828 (1978).

Bidleman, T. F., W. N. Billings and C. G. Simon. "Evaluation of Solid Adsorbents for Collecting Atmospheric Chlorinated Hydrocarbons," EPA 600/2-80-167 (1980).

Bidleman, T. F., E. J. Christensen and H. W. Harder. "Aerial Deposition of Organochlorines in Urban and Coastal South Carolina," Chapter 24 in Atmospheric Pollutants in Natural Waters, S. J. Eisenreich, Ed. (Ann Arbor, MI: Ann Arbor Science Publishers, Inc., 1981a), pp. 481-508.

Bidleman, T. F., E. J. Christensen, W. N. Billings and R. Leonard. "Atmospheric Transport of Organochlorines in the North Atlantic Gyre," J. Marine Res. 39(3):443-464 (1981b).

Bidleman, T. F. and R. Leonard. "Aerial Transport of Pesticides over the Northern Indian Ocean and Adjacent Seas," Atmos. Environ. 16:1099-1107 (1982).

Bidleman, T. F., N. F. Burdick, J. W. Westcott and W. N. Billings. "Influence of Volatility on the Collection of Airborne PCB and Pesticides with Filter-Solid Adsorbent Samplers," Chapter 2 in Physical Behavior of PCBs in the Great Lakes, D. Mackay, S. Paterson, S. J. Eisenreich and M. S. Simmons, Eds. (Ann Arbor, MI: Ann Arbor Science Publishers, Inc., 1983), pp. 15-48.

Bidleman, T. F., C. G. Simon, N. F. Burdick, and F. You. "Theoretical Plate Measurements and Collection Efficiencies for High-Volume Air Samplers Using Polyurethane Foam," J. Chromatogr. 301:448-453 (1984).

Billings, W. N., and T. F. Bidleman, "Field Comparison of Polyurethane Foam and Tenax-GC Resin for High-Volume Air Sampling of Chlorinated Hydrocarbons," Environ. Sci. Technol. 14(6): 679-683 (1980).

Billings, W. N. and T. F. Bidleman. "High Volume Collection of Chlorinated Hydrocarbons in Urban Air Using Three Solid Adsorbents," Atmos. Environ. 17:383-391 (1983).

Biocca, M., J. A. Moore, B. N. Gupta and J. D. McKinney. "Toxicology of Selected Symmetrical Hexachlorobiphenyl Isomers: I. Biological Responses in Chicks and Mice," Conf. Proc. - Natl. Conf. Polychlorinated Biphenyls pp. 67-72 (1976); Chem. Abstr. 85:73086x (1976).

Biocca, M., B. N. Gupta, K. Chae, J. D. McKinney and J. A. Moore. "Toxicity of Selected Symmetrical Hexachlorobiphenyl Isomers in the Mouse," Toxicol. Appl. Pharmacol. 58(3):461-474 (1981).

Biros, F. J. "An Integrated Gas Chromatograph-Flame Ionization Detector-Mass Spectrometer System for Pesticide Residue Analysis," Pestic. Chem. Proc. Int. IUPAC Congr. Pestic. Chem. 2nd 4:149-169 (1971).

Biros, F. J., A. C. Walker and A. Medbery. "Polychlorinated Biphenyls in Human Adipose Tissue," Bull. Environ. Contam. Toxicol. 5(4):317-323 (1970).

Biros, F. J., H. F. Enos, A. C. Walker and J. F. Thompson. "Analytical Aspects of Polychlorinated Biphenyl Determinations in Human and Animal Adipose Tissue," Prepr. Pap. Natl. Meet. (New York); Div. Water, Air and Waste Chem.; Amer. Chem. Soc. 12:61-66 (1972); Chem. Abstr. 81:386c (1972).

Bishop, T. A., and J. E. Gebhart. "Method Validation for Incidental Generation of Polychlorinated Biphenyls in Products and Waste Streams," Final Report, Task 68, EPA Contract No. 68-01-6721, Office of Toxic Substances, U.S. Environmental Protection Agency, Washington, DC (1984).

Boe, B. and E. Egaas. "Qualitative and Quantitative Analyses of Polychlorinated Biphenyls by Gas-Liquid Chromatography," J. Chromatogr. 180:127-132 (1979).

Bonelli, E. J.. "GC/MS Techniques for the Determination of Interferences in Pesticide Analysis," Inst. Environ. Sci. Proc. 18:251-254 (1972a).

Bonelli, E. J. "Gas Chromatograph/Mass Spectrometer Techniques for Determination of Interferences in Pesticide Analysis," Anal. Chem. 44(3):603-606 (1972b).

Boniforti, L., G. Citti and G. Laguzzi. "Identification and Quantitative Determination of Polychlorinated Biphenyls and Polynuclear Aromatic Hydrocarbons in Fly Ash from Municipal Incinerators by Gas Chromatography with Electron-Capture Detection and Gas Chromatography-Mass Spectrometry," Anal. Chem. Symp. Ser. 7:219-225 (1981); Chem. Abstr. 96:90803y (1982).

Bonner, R. F. "Environmental Analysis with a Triple Quadrupole," Int. J. Mass Spectrometry Ion Phys. 48:311-314 (1983).

Bopp, R. F., "Revised Parameters for Modeling the Transport of PCB Components Across an Air Water Interface," J. Geophysical Research, 88(C4):2521-2529 (1983).

Bostick, W. D., M. S. Denton and S. R. Dinsmore. "Development of a Portable Field Monitor for PCBs," Prepared for Electric Power Research Institute, Palo Alto, CA, EPRI CS-2828 (1983); NTIS No. DE83 007425.

Bourke, J. B. "PCB's and Pesticides," N.Y. State Assoc. Milk and Food Sanitarians, Ann. Rept. 46:41-43 (1972).

Bowes, G. W. and J. A. Lewis. "Extraction of Polychlorinated Biphenyls: Evaluation of A Column Technique Applied to Polar Bear and Seal Tissue," J. Assoc. Offic. Anal. Chem. 57(1): 138-144 (1974).

Bowes, G. W., M. J. Mulvihill, M. R. DeCamp and A. S. Kende. "Gas Chromatographic Characteristics of Authentic Chlorinated Dibenzofurans; Identification of Two Isomers in American and Japanese Polychlorinated Biphenyls," J. Agric. Food Chem. 23(6):1222-1223 (1975a).

Bowes, G. W., M. J. Mulvihill, B. R. T. Simoneit, A. L. Burlingame and R. W. Risebrough. "Identification of Chlorinated Dibenzofurans in American Polychlorinated Biphenyls," Nature 256:305-307 (1975b).

Bowes, G. W., M. J. Mulvihill, B. R. T. Simoneit, A. L. Burlingame and R. W. Risebrough. "Isolation and Identification of Chlorinated Dibenzofurans from Polychlorinated Biphenyls (PCB) and from Yusho Rice Oil Containing PCB," Chapter 8 in Dioxin--Toxicological and Chemical Aspects, F. Cattabeni, A. Cavallaro and G. Galli, Eds. (New York, NY: SP Medical and Scientific Books, 1978), pp. 79-98.

Bremer, K. E. "Dealing with Multi-Agency and Multi-State Regulation of Polychlorinated Biphenyls," in PCBs: Human and Environmental Hazards, F. M. D'Itri and M. A. Kamrin, Eds. (Boston: Butterworth Publishers, 1983), pp. 367-374.

Brinkman, U. A. Th., A. De Kok, G. De Vries and H. G. M. Reymer. "High-speed Liquid and Thin-layer Chromatography of Polychlorinated Biphenyls," J. Chromatogr. 128:101-110 (1976a).

Brinkman, U. A. Th., J. W. F. L. Seetz and H. G. M. Reymer. "High-speed Liquid Chromatography of Polychlorinated Biphenyls and Related Compounds," J. Chromatogr. 116:353-363 (1976b).

Brinkman, U. A. Th., G. De Vries, A. De Kok and A. L. De Jonge. "Discrimination Between Polychlorinated Naphthalenes and Polychlorinated Biphenyls," J. Chromatogr. 152: 97-104 (1978).

Brinkman, U. A. Th. and G. De Vries. "Relationship Between Structure and Retention of Polyhalogenated Aromatics in Two Adsorption Chromatographic Systems," J. Chromatogr. 169: 167-182 (1979).

Brinkman, U. A. Th. and A. De Kok. "Halogenated Biphenyls, Terphenyls, Naphthalenes, Dibenzodioxins and Related Products. Production, Properties and Usage," Chapter 1. R. D. Kimbrough, Ed. (New York: NY: Elsevier/North-Holland Biomedical Press, 1980), pp. 1-40.

Broto-Puig, F., M. Gassiot-Matas, R. Martinez-Fonrodona. "Application of an On-Line Potassium Hydroxide Microreactor to the Resolution of Interferences Between PCBs and DDTs in the Gas Chromatography of High-Molecular-Weight Organochlorinated Contaminants," Journ. Etud. Pollut. Mar. Mediterr. 6:449-454 (1983); Chem. Abst. 101:157348w (1984).

Brown, D. P. and M. Jones. "Mortality and Industrial Hygiene Study of Workers Exposed to Polychlorinated Biphenyls," Archives of Environmental Health 36(3):120-129 (1981).

Brown, J. F. Jr., J. T. Coe and H. D. Pocock Jr. "Human Health Effects of Electrical-Grade PCB's," Corporate Health and Safety Operation, General Electric Company, Fairfield, CT (August 1981a).

Brown, J. F. Jr., M. E. Lynch, J. C. Carnahan, and J. Singleton. "Chemical Destruction of PCBs in Transformer Oil," General Electric Company, Schenectady, NY, Technical Information Series, 81CRD257 (November 1981b).

Brown, J. F. Jr., M. E. Lynch, J. C. Carnahan and J. Singleton. "Chemical Destruction of Polychlorinated Biphenyls in Transformer Oil," Chapter 11 in Detoxication of Hazardous Waste, J. H. Exner, Ed. (Ann Arbor, MI: Ann Arbor Science Publishers, Inc., 1982), pp.201-214.

Brown J. F., Jr., and R. W. Lawton. "Polychlorinated Biphenyl (PCB) Partitioning Between Adipose Tissue and Serum," Bull. Environ. Contam. Toxicol. 33:277-280 (1984).

Brownrigg, J. T. and A. W. Hornig. "Estimation of Polychlorinated Biphenyls in the Presence of DDT-Type Compounds," Prepared for the U.S. Environmental Protection Agency, NTIS Publication No. PB-233 599 (June 1974).

Brownrigg, J. T. and A. W. Hornig. "Identification of PCB's in the Presence of DDT-Type Compounds Using Low Temperature Luminescence," Arch. Environ. Contam. Toxicol. 4:175-182 (1976).

Bruggeman, W. A., J. van der Steen and O. Hutzinger. "Reversed-Phase Thin-Layer Chromatography of Polynuclear Aromatic Hydrocarbons and Chlorinated Biphenyls. Relationship with Hydrophobicity as Measured by Aqueous Solubility and Octanol-Water Partition Coefficient," J. Chromatogr. 238(2): 335-346 (1982).

Brugger, J. E., J. J. Yezzi Jr., I. Wilder, F. J. Freestone, R. A. Miller and C. Pfrommer, Jr. "The EPA-ORD Mobile Incineration System: Present Status," Proceedings in: 1982 Hazardous Material Spills Conference Paper No. 167 (April 19-22, 1982).

Brunelle, D. J. "Reaction of Polychlorinated Biphenyls with Mercaptans in Non-polar Media: Formation of Polychlorobiphenyl Sulfides," Chemosphere 12(2):167-181 (1983).

Brunelle, D. J. and D. A. Singleton. "Destruction/Removal of Polychlorinated Biphenyls from Non-polar Media. Reaction of PCB with Poly(Ethylene Glycol)/KOH," Chemosphere 12(2):183-196 (1983).

Brunn, H. "Quantitative Gas Chromatographic Detection of Residues of Polychlorinated Biphenyls in Raw and Processed Foods of Animal Origin," Arch. Lebensmittelhyg 33(5):118-122 (1982); Chem. Abstr. 98:33135z (1983).

Burdick, N. F. and T. F. Bidleman. "Frontal Movement of Hexachlorobenzene and Polychlorinated Biphenyl Vapors through Polyurethane Foam," Anal. Chem. 53(12):1926-1929 (1981).

Burke, J. A. "Report on Chlorinated Insecticides," J. Assoc. Offic. Anal. Chem. 58(2):233-235 (1975).

Burke, J. A. "Report on Chlorinated Pesticides," J. Assoc. Offic. Anal. Chem. 59(2):338-340 (1976).

Burkhard, L. P. and D. E. Armstrong. "Labeled Perchlorination Reagent for Determination of Polychlorinated Biphenyls," Anal. Chem. 53(3):523-528 (1981).

Burns, J. E. "Pesticides in People: Organochlorine Pesticide and Polychlorinated Biphenyl Residues in Biopsied Human Adipose Tissue--Texas 1969-1972," Prepared for the U.S. Environmental Protection Agency, NTIS No. PB-280 613/1, 5 pp. (1974).

Burse, V. W., R. F. Moseman, G. W. Sovocool and E. C. Villanueva. "PCB Metabolism in Rats Following Prolonged Exposure to Aroclor 1242 and Aroclor 1016," Bull. Environ. Contam. Toxicol. 15(1): 122-128 (1976).

Burse, V. W., L. L. Needham, J. A. Liddle, D. D. Bayse and H. A. Price. "Interlaboratory Comparison for Results of Analyses for Polychlorinated Biphenyls in Human Serum," J. Anal. Toxicol. 4:22-26 (1980).

Burse, V. W., L. L. Needham, M. P. Korver, C. R. Lapeza Jr., J. A. Liddle and D. D. Bayse. Gas-Liquid Chromatographic Determination of Polychlorinated Biphenyls and a Selected Number of Chlorinated Hydrocarbons in Serum," J. Assoc. Off. Anal. Chem. 66(1):32-39 (1983a).

Burse, V. W., L. L. Needham, M. P. Korver, C. R. Lapeza Jr., J. A. Liddle and D. D. Bayse. "Assessment of Methods to Determine PCB Levels in Blood Serum: Interlaboratory Study," J. Assoc. Off. Anal. Chem. 66(1):40-45 (1983b).

Buser, H. R. "Analysis of TCDDs by Gas Chromatography-Mass Spectrometry Using Glass Capillary Columns," Chapter 4 in Dioxin--Toxicological and Chemical Aspects, F. Cattabeni, A. Cavallaro and G. Galli, Eds. (New York, NY: SP Medical and Scientific Books, 1978), pp. 27-41.

Buser, H. R., H. P. Bosshardt and C. Rappe. "Formation of Polychlorinated Dibenzofurans (PCDFs) From the Pyrolysis of PCBs," Chemosphere 7:109-119 (1978a).

Buser, H. R., H. P. Bosshardt, C. Rappe and R. Lindahl. "Identification of Polychlorinated Dibenzofuran Isomers in Fly Ash and PCB Pyrolyses," Chemosphere 7(5):419-429 (1978b).

Buser, H. R. and C. Rappe. "Formation of Polychlorinated Dibenzofurans (PCDFs) from the Pyrolysis of Individual PCB Isomers," Chemosphere 8(3):157-174 (1979).

Buser, H. R. and C. Rappe. "Isomer-Specific Separation of 2378-Substituted Polychlorinated Dibenzo-p-dioxins by High-Resolution Gas Chromatography/Mass Spectrometry," Anal. Chem. 56:442-448 (1984).

Bush, B. and F.-C. Lo. "Thin-layer Chromatography for Quantitative Polychlorinated Biphenyl Analysis," J. Chromatogr. 77: 377-388 (1973).

Bush, B., F. Baker, R. Dell'Acqua, C. L. Houck and F.-C. Lo. "Analytical Response of Polychlorinated Biphenyl Homologues and Isomers in Thin-layer and Gas Chromatography," J. Chromatogr. 109:287-295 (1975).

Bush, B. and E. L. Barnard. "Determination of Nonpolar Chlorinated Hydrocarbons and PCB in Microsamples," Anal. Lett. 15(A20):1643-1648 (1982).

Bush, B., S. Connor and J. Snow. "Glass Capillary Gas Chromatography for Sensitive, Accurate Polychlorinated Biphenyl Analysis," J. Assoc. Off. Anal. Chem. 65(3):555-566 (1982).

Bush B., J. T. Snow, and S. Connor, "High Resolution Gas Chromatographic Analysis of Nonpolar Chlorinated Hydrocarbons in Human Milk," J. Assoc. Off. Anal. Chem. 66(2):248-255 (1983).

Bush, B., J. Snow, and R. Koblintz, "Polychlorobiphenyl (PCB) Congeners, p,p-DDE, and Hexachlorobenzene in Maternal and Fetal Cord Blood from Mothers in Upstate New York," Arch. Env. Cont. Tox. 13(5):517-527 (1984).

Butler, J. "Analysis of Diverse Sample Matrices for Polychlorinated Biphenyls Using the 700A Hall Electrolytic Conductivity Detector," 1981 Pittsburgh Conference, Abstract No. 041.

Cairns, T and R. A. Jacobson. "New Approaches to FDA Analytical Problems," J. Chem. Infor. Comp. Sci. 17(2):105-109 (1977).

Cairns, T. and E. G. Siegmund. "Determination of Polychlorinated Biphenyls by Chemical Ionization Mass Spectrometry," Anal. Chem. 53(11):1599-1603 (1981a).

Cairns, T. and E. G. Siegmund. "PCBs: Regulatory History and Analytical Problems," Anal. Chem. 53(11):1183A-1193A (1981b).

Cairns, T. and W. M. Rogers. "Acceptable Analytical Data for Trace Analysis," Anal. Chem. 55(1):54A-57A (1983).

Calandra, J. C. "Summary of Toxicological Studies on Commercial PCBs," in National Conference on Polychlorinated Biphenyls, Franklin A. Ayer, Ed. U.S. Environmental Protection Agency, Office of Toxic Substances, EPA-560/6-75-004, NTIS No. PB-253 248, pp. 35-42 (1976).

Call, D. J., Y. A. Greichus and J. J. Worman. "A Gas Chromatographic-mass Spectrometric Comparison of Polychlorinated Biphenyl Residues in the Japanese Quail Brain to an Aroclor Standard," Bull. Environ. Contam. Toxicol. 11(4):333-338 (1974).

Canada, D. C. and F. E. Regnier. "Isotope Ratios as a Characteristic Selection Technique for Mass Chromatography," J. Chromatogr. Sci. 14:149-154 (1976).

Cantlon, J. E. "The PCB Problem: An Overview," in PCBs: Human and Environmental Hazards, F. M. D'Itri and M. A. Kamrin, Eds. (Boston: Butterworth Publishers, 1983), pp. 5-10.

Caragay, A. B. and P. L. Levins. "Evaluation of Protocols for Pesticides and PCB's in Raw Wastewater," Final Report, Arthur D. Little, Inc., Contract No. 68-01-3857, Office of Research and Development, Environmental Protection Agency, Report No. EPA-600/2-79-166 (November 1979).

Carcich, I. G., and T. J. Tofflemire. "Distribution and Concentration of PCB in the Hudson River and Associated Management Problems," Environmental International 7:73-85 (1982).

Cardone, M. J. "Detection and Determination of Error in Analytical Methodology. Part I. In the Method Verification Program," J. Assoc. Off. Anal. Chem. 66(5):1257-1282 (1983a).

Cardone, M. J. "Detection and Determination of Error in Analytical Methodology. Part II. Correction for Corrigible Systematic Error in the Course of Real Sample Analysis," J. Assoc. Off. Anal. Chem. 66(2):1283-1294 (1983b).

Carey, A. E. and J. A. Gowen. "PCB's in Agricultural and Urban Soil," In: Proceedings of the National Conference on PCBs, pp. 195-198, EPA 560/6-75-004 (1976).

Carson, L. J. "Interlaboratory Study of the Hall 700A Halogen Electrolytic Conductivity Gas Chromatographic Detector," J. Assoc. Off. Anal. Chem. 66(6):1335-1344 (1983).

Carson, R. Silent Spring, (Greenwich, CT: Fawcett Publications, Inc., 1962), 304 pp.

Castelli, M. G., G. P. Martelli, C. Spagone, L. Cappellini and R. Fanelli. "Quantitative Determination of Polychlorinated Biphenyls (PCB) in Marine Organisms Analyzed by High-Resolution Gas Chromatography Selected Ion Monitoring," Chemosphere 12(3): 291-298 (1983).

Chau, A. S. Y. and C. J. Sampson. "Electron Capture Gas Chromatographic Methodology for the Quantitation of Polychlorinated Biphenyls: Survey and Compromise," Environ. Lett. 8(2):89-101 (1975).

Chau, A. S. Y. and L. J. Babjak. "Column Chromatographic Determination of Mirex, Photomirex, and Polychlorinated Biphenyls in Lake Sediments," J. Assoc. Off. Anal. Chem. 62(1): 107-113 (1979).

Chau, A. S. Y., J. Carron and H.-B. Lee. "Analytical Reference Materials. II. Preparation and Sample Integrity of Homogeneous Fortified Wet Sediment for Polychlorinated Biphenyl Quality Control Studies," J. Assoc. Off. Anal. Chem. 62(6):1312-1314 (1979).

Chau, A. S. Y. and H.-B. Lee. "Analytical Reference Materials. III. Preparation and Homogeneity Test of Large Quantities of Wet and Dry Sediment Reference Materials for Long Term Polychlorinated Biphenyl Quality Control Studies," J. Assoc. Off. Anal. Chem. 63:947-951 (1980).

Chemical Manufacturers Association, "The Analysis of Chlorinated Biphenyls," submitted to the Environmental Protection Agency, August 21, 1981, in reference to OPTS-62017.

Chen, J-Y. T. and A. M. Gardner. "Multicomponent Analyses of PCBs by FTIR Spectroscopy," Amer. Lab. pp. 26-33 (1983).

Chen, K. "The Reclamation of PCB-Contaminated Transformer Oils by The Sunohio PCBX Process," Interim Report, TVA/OP/ EDT--82/45, NTIS No. DE82 906112, 49 pp. (1982).

Chen, K. "Evaluation of the Sunohio PCBX Process for Reclamation of Transformer Oils Containing PBCs," IEEE Trans. Power Appar. Syst. PAS-102(12):3893-3898 (1983); Chem. Abstr. 100:106079f (1984).

Chen, P. H., J. M. Gaw, C. K. Wong and C. J. Chen. "Levels and Gas Chromatographic Patterns of Polychlorinated Biphenyls in the Blood of Patients After PCB Poisoning in Taiwan," Bull. Environ. Contam. Toxicol. 25:325-329 (1980).

Chen, P. H., K. T. Chang and Y. D. Lu. "Polychlorinated Biphenyls and Polychlorinated Dibenzofurans in the Toxic Rice-Bran Oil that Caused PCB Poisoning in Taichung," Bull. Environ. Contam. Toxicol. 26:489-495 (1981).

Chen, P. H., M. L. Luo, C. K. Wong and C. J. Chen. "Comparative Rates of Elimination of Some Individual Polychlorinated Biphenyls from the Blood of PCB-Poisoned Patients in Taiwan," Food Chem. Toxicol. 20:417-425 (1982).

Chen, P. H. and R. A. Hites. "Polychlorinated Biphenyls and Dibenzofurans Retained in the Tissues of a Deceased Patient with Yucheng in Taiwan," Chemosphere 12(11-12):1507-1516 (1983).

Chesler, S. N., W. E. May, P. A. White, R. M. Parris and F. R. Guenther. "Determination of Polychlorinated Biphenyls in Waste and Lubricating Oils," National Bureau of Standards Special Publication 584, Proceedings of Joint Conference on Measurements and Standards for Recycled Oil/Systems Performance and Durability, Gaithersburg, MD, October 23-26, 1979, pp. 295-297, NBS, (Issued November 1980).

Chesler, S. N., F. R. Guenther, W. E. May and R. M. Parris. "SRM's for Accurate Analyses of PCBs in Oil," Abstract, Center for Analytical Chemistry, National Bureau of Standards, Washington, DC, 20234 (1981).

Chiosi, S., A. Evidente, G. Randazzo and D. Scalorbi. "Analysis of a Mixture of Polychlorinated Biphenyls, DDT and Its Analogues by High-Performance Liquid Chromatography," J. Liquid Chromatogr. 5(9):1653-1663 (1982).

Chittim, B. G., B. S. Clegg, S. H. Safe and O. Hutzinger. "Chlorinated Dibenzofurans and Dibenzo-p-dioxins: Detection and Quantitation in Electrical Equipment and Their Formation During the Incineration of PCBs," prepared under Contract No.: OSS78-00067 for Fisheries and Environment Canada (September 1979) 79 pp.

Choudhry, G. G. and O. Hutzinger, Eds. Mechanistic Aspects of the Thermal Formation of Halogenated Organic Compounds Including Polychlorinated Dibenzo-p-dioxins (New York: Gordon and Breach Science Publishers, 1983), 194 pp.

Christensen, E. J., C. E. Olney and T. F. Bidleman. "Comparison of Dry and Wet Surfaces for Collecting Organochlorine Dry Deposition," Bull. Environ. Contam. Toxicol. 23:196-202 (1979).

Claeys, R. R. "Analysis of PCBs in Pulp Mill Effluent," Special Report-NCASI (National Council of the Paper Industry for Air and Stream Improvement), No. 77-04, pp. 46-49 (1977).

Coburn, J. A., I. A. Valdmanis and A. S. Y. Chau. "Evaluation of XAD-2 for Multiresidue Extraction of Organochlorine Pesticides and Polychlorinated Biphenyls from Natural Waters," J. Assoc. Off. Anal. Chem. 60(1):224-228 (1977).

Colby, B. N. and J. E. Picker. "Automated Recognition of Aroclor GC Patterns," Abstract No. 574, 1983 Pittsburgh Conference and Exposition on Analytical Chemistry and Applied Spectroscopy (1983).

Colby, B. N., E. A. Burns and P. L. Lagus. "The S-Cubed PCBA 101, an Automated Field Analyzer for PCBs," Abstract No. 731, 1983 Pittsburgh Conference and Exposition on Analytical Chemistry and Applied Spectroscopy (1983).

Coleman, W. E. and R. G. Tardiff. "Contaminant Levels in Animal Feeds Used for Toxicity Studies," Arch. Environ. Contam. Toxicol. 8:693-702 (1979).

Colenutt, B. A. and S. Thorburn. "Optimisation of a Gas Stripping Concentration Technique for Trace Organic Water Pollutants," Intern. J. Environ. Anal. Chem. 7:231-244 (1980).

Collard, R. S. and M. M. Irwin, Jr. "GC/MS Determination of Chlorinated Biphenyls in Complex Chlorinated Hydrocarbon Process and Waste Streams," The Dow Chemical Company (1982a).

Collard, R. S. and M. M. Irwin, Jr. "Determination of Chlorinated Biphenyls (Incidental PCBs) in Chlorinated Hydrocarbon Process and Waste Streams," Abstract, 184th Annual American Chemical Society National Meeting, September 12-17, 1982b.

Collard, R. S. and M. M. Irwin. "GC/MS Determination of Incidental PCBs in Complex Chlorinated-Hydrocarbon Process and Waste Streams," Talanta 30(11):811-818 (1983).

Collins, G. B., D. C. Holmes and F. J. Jackson. "The Estimation of Polychlorobiphenyls," J. Chromatogr. 71:443-449 (1972).

Cone, M. V., M. F. Baldauf, D. M. Opresko and M. S. Uziel. "Chemicals Identified in Human Breast Milk, A Literature Search," U.S. Environmental Protection Agency, Office of Pesticides and Toxic Substances, Washington, DC, EPA 560/5-83-009; NTIS No. PB84-118538 (October 1983), 125 pp.

Connors, T. F., J. F. Rusling, and A. Owlia. "Determination of Standard Potentials and Electron-Transfer Rates for Halobiphenyls from Electrocatalytic Data," Anal. Chem. 57:170-174 (1985).

Cook, W. J. "Some Chemical Aspects of Polychlorinated Biphenyls (PCBs)," Environ. Health Perspec. 1:3-13 (1972).

Cooke, M., G. Nickless, A. M. Prescott and D. J. Roberts. "Analysis of Polychlorinated Naphthalenes, Polychlorinated Biphenyls and Polychlorinated Terphenyls via Carbon Skeleton Gas-Liquid Chromatography," J. Chromatogr. 156:293-299 (1978).

Copeland, R. A. Letter to U.S. Environmental Protection Agency, Office of Toxic Substances, Re. Manufacturing Ban Exemption Petition (TS-794), from Monochlorobiphenyl Task Force, Dow Chemical U.S.A., July 31, 1979.

Copland, G. B. and C. S. Gohmann. "Improved Method for Polychlorinated Biphenyl Determination in Complex Matrices," Environ. Sci. Technol. 16:121-124 (1982).

Cordle, F., P. Corneliussen, C. Jelinek, B. Hackley, R. Lehman, J. McLaughlin, R. Rhoden and R. Shapiro. "Human Exposure to Polychlorinated Biphenyls and Polybrominated Biphenyls," Environ. Health Perspec. 24:157-172 (1978).

Cordle, F., R. Locke and J. Springer. "Risk Assessment in a Federal Regulatory Agency: An Assessment of Risk Associated with the Human Consumption of Some Species of Fish Contaminated with Polychlorinated Biphenyls (PCBs)," Environ. Health Perspec. 45:171-182 (1982).

Corneliussen, P. E. "Report on Multiresidue Methods (Interlaboratory Studies)," J. Assoc. Off. Anal. Chem. 58(2):238-239 (1975).

Crist, H. L. and R. F. Moseman. "Simplified Micro Perchlorination Method for Polychlorinated Biphenyls in Biological Samples," J. Assoc. Off. Anal. Chem. 60(6):1277-1281 (1977).

Crummett, W. B. "The Problem of Measurements Near the Limit of Detection," Ann. N. Y. Acad. Sci. 320:43-47 (1979).

Cull, M. R., and A. J. Dobbs, "Analysis of Polychlorobiphenyls from Used Transformers for Polychlorodibenzofurans," Chemosphere 13(9):1085-1089 (1984).

Curley, A., V. W. Burse, M. E. Grim, R. W. Jennings and R. E. Linder. "Polychlorinated Biphenyls: Distribution and Storage in Body Fluids and Tissues of Sherman Rats," Environ. Res. 4:481-495 (1971).

Dale, W. E., A. Curley and C. Cueto, Jr. "Hexane Extractable Chlorinated Insecticides in Human Blood," Life Sci. 5:47-54 (1966).

Dark, W. A. and L. W. Crossman, Jr. "Applications Highlights - Polychlorinated Biphenyls," Waters Associates, Milford, Massachusetts, AH-324 (1973).

Das, K. G. and P. S. Kulkarni. "Gas-Liquid Chromatograpy," Chapter 2 in Pesticide Analysis, K. G. Das, Ed. (New York, NY: Marcel Dekker, Inc. 1981), pp 45-98.

Davenport, R. J. and B. K. Bernard (Eds.). Advances in Exposure, Health and Environmental Effects Studies of PCBs: Symposium Proceedings, Office of Toxic Substances, U.S. Environmental Protection Agency, Washington, DC, LSI-TR-507-137B, NTIS No. PB84-135771 (December 1983) 365 pp.

David, D. J. "Gas Chromatographic Detectors," Corporation (New York, NY: Wiley-Interscience Publication, 1974).

deAlencastro, L. F., V. Prélax, and J. Tarradellas. "Contamination of Silos in Switzerland by PCB Residues in Coatings," Bull. Environ. Contam. Toxicol. 33:270-276 (1984).

De Kanel, J., S.-Y. Tang and R. C. Dougherty. "Capillary GC/MS Profiling of Xenobiotic Chemicals in Biofluids in EI and NCI Modes," American Society for Mass Spectrometry, 30th Annual Conference on Mass Spectrometry and Allied Topics, Abstract, June 6-11, pp. 197 (1982).

De Kok, A., R. B. Geerdink, R. W. Frei and U. A. Th. Brinkman. "The Use of Dechlorination in the Analysis of Polychlorinated Biphenyls and Related Classes of Compounds," Intern. J. Environ. Anal. Chem. 9:301-318 (1981).

De Kok, A., R. B. Geerdink, R. W. Frei and U. A. Th. Brinkman. "Limitations in the Use of Perchlorination as a Technique for the Quantitative Analysis of Polychlorinated Biphenyls," Intern. J. Environ. Anal. Chem. 11:17-41 (1982a).

De Kok, A., R. B. Geerdink, G. De Vries and U. A. Th. Brinkman. "An Evaluation of Chromatographic Methods for the Analysis of Polychlorinated Terphenyls in Environmental Samples," Intern. J. Environ. Anal. Chem. 12:99-122 (1982b).

De Kok, A., R. B. Geerdink and U. A. Th. Brinkman. "The Determination of Polychlorinated Naphthalenes in Soil Samples by Means of Various Gas and Liquid Chromatographic Methods," Chromatogr. Biochem., Med. Environ. Res., 1, A. Frigerio, Ed. (1983), pp. 203-216.

Delfino, J. J. "Toxic Substances in the Great Lakes," Environ. Sci. Technol. 13(12):1462-1468 (1979).

Delfino, J. J. (Ed.). Methods for Analysis of Organic Compounds in the Great Lakes, Proceedings of an Invitational Workshop, April 1-2, 1980, University of Wisconsin Great Lakes Research Facility, Milwaukee, Wisconsin, WIS-SG-80-236 (1980).

Delfino, J. J. and D. B. Easty. "Interlaboratory Study of the Determination of Polychlorinated Biphenyls in a Paper Mill Effluent," Anal. Chem. 51(13):2235-2239 (1979).

Dennis, D. S. "Polychlorinated Biphenyls in the Surface Waters and Bottom Sediments of the Major Drainage Basins of the United States," Prepared for the U.S. Environmental Protection Agency, Office of Pesticide Programs, NTIS No. PB-276 313/4 (1974), 12 pp.

Denton, M. S. "Portable Field Monitor for PCBs," Abstract No. 629, 1983 Pittsburgh Conference and Exposition on Analytical Chemistry and Applied Spectroscopy, March 7-12, 1983.

Denton, M. S., S. R. Dinsmore and W. D. Bostick. "Portable Field Monitor for PCBs," in Proceedings: 1981 PCB Seminar, G. Addis and J. Marks, Eds. Report No. EPRI-EL-2572 (Palo Alto, CA: Electric Power Research Institute, 1982), pp. 3-3 to 3-21.

Denton, M. S., and M. H. Walker. "Portable Infrared Field Monitor for PCBs: Phase II." in Proceedings: 1983 PCB Seminar, G. Addis and R. Y. Komai Eds. Report No. EPRI-EL-3581 (Palo Alto, CA: Electric Power Research Institute, 1984).

Department of Health, Education and Welfare, "Final Report of the Subcommittee on the Health Effects of Polychlorinated Biphenyls and Polybrominated Biphenyls of the DHEW Committee to Coordinate Toxicology and Related Programs," Env. Health Persp. 24:129-208 (1978a).

Department of Health, Education and Welfare. "DHEW Subcommittee on Health Effects of PCBs and PBBs, General Recommendations," Env. Health Persp. 24:187-189 (1978b).

Department of Health, Education and Welfare. "DHEW Subcommittee on Health Effects of PCBs, General Summary and Conclusions," Env. Health Persp. 24:191-198 (1978c).

Department of Transportation. "Polychlorinated Biphenyls (PCBs) in Transit System Electrical Equipment," Final Report, Urban Mass Transportation Administration, Office of Technical Assistance, Washington, DC, UMTA-MA-06-0098-84-1; NTIS No. PB84-222207 (1984) 104 pp.

Dequidt, J., F. Erb, C. Van Aerde and P. Colein. "Determination of Polychlorinated Biphenyls in Biological Media," Bull. Soc. Pharm. Lille 31(2-3):149-155 (1975); Chem. Abst., 84:39391n (1976).

DeRoos, F. L., M. Cooke, J. E. Gebhart, L. E. Slivon, and P. J. Mondron. "An Update on Analytical Methods for Polychlorinated Biphenyls (PCB), Polychlorinated Dibenzofurans (PCDF) and Polychlorinated Dibenzo-p-dioxins (PCDD)," in Proceedings: 1983 PCB Seminar, G. Addis and J. Marks Eds., Report No. EPRI-EL-3581, (Palo Alto, CA, Electric Power Research Institute, 1984).

Devenish, I. W. and L. Harling-Bowen. "The Examination and Estimation of the Performance Characteristics of a Standard Method for Organo-Chlorine Insecticides and PCB," in Hydrocarbons and Halogenated Hydrocarbons in the Aquatic Environment, B. K. Afghan and D. Mackay, Eds. (New York: Plenum Press, 1980), pp. 231-253.

deVera, E. R., B. P. Simmons, R. D. Stephens and D. L. Storm. "Samplers and Sampling Procedures for Hazardous Waste Streams," Municipal Environmental Research Laboratory, U.S. Environmental Protection Agency, Cincinnati, OH, EPA-600/2-80-018 (January 1980).

De Voogt, P., J. C. Klamer and U. A. T. Brinkman. "Identification and Quantification of Polychlorinated Biphenyls in Paper Board Using Fused Silica Capillary Gas Chromatography," Bull. Environ. Contam. Toxicol. 32(1):45-52 (1984).

De Vos, R. H. "Analytical Techniques in Relation to the Contamination of the Fauna," TNO-nieuws 27:615-622 (1972).

De Vos, R. H. and E. W. Peet. "Thin-Layer Chromatography of Polychlorinated Biphenyls," Bull. Environ. Contam. Toxicol. 6(2):164-170 (1971).

Dexter, R. N. and S. P. Pavlou. "Characterization of Polychlorinated Biphenyl Distribution in the Marine Environment," Bull. Environ. Contam. Toxicol. 16(4):477-482 (1976).

D'Itri, F. M. and M. A. Kamrin, Eds. PCBs: Human and Environmental Hazards (Boston: Butterworth Publishers, 1983) 443 pp.

Dilling, W. L., G. E. Miracle and G. U. Boggs. "Organic PhotoChemistry. XVIII. Tropospheric Phototransformation Rates of 2-, 3-, and 4-Chlorobiphenyl," Preprints, Division of Environmental Chemistry, American Chemical Society National Meeting, Washington, DC, pp. 343-346 (August 1983).

DiNardi, S. R. and A. M. Desmarais. "Polychlorinated Biphenyls in the Environment," Chemistry, 49(4):14-17 (1976).

Di Toro, D. M. and L. M. Horzempa. "Reversible and Resistant Component Model of Hexachlorobiphenyl Adsorption-Desorption Resuspension and Dilution," Chapter 6 in Physical Behavior of PCBs in the Great Lakes, D. Mackay, S. Paterson, S. J. Eisenreich and M. S. Simmons, Eds. (Ann Arbor, MI: Ann Arbor Science Publishers, Inc., 1983), pp 89-113.

Di Toro, D. M., L. M Horzempa and M. C. Casey. "Adsorption and Desorption of Hexachlorobiphenyl. A. Experimental Results and Discussions. B. Analysis of Exchangeable and Non-exchangeable Components," EPA-600/3-83-088, PB83-261677 (September 1983), 322 pp.

Doguchi, M. and S. Fukano. "Residue Levels of Polychlorinated Terphenyls, Polychlorinated Biphenyls and DDT in Human Blood," Bull. Environ. Contam. Toxicol. 13:57-63 (1975).

Dolan, J. W. and R. C. Hall. "Enhancement of the Sensitivity and Selectivity of the Coulson Electrolytic Conductivity Detector to Chlorinated Hydrocarbon Pesticides," Anal. Chem. 45(13): 2198-2204 (1973).

Dolan, J. W., R. C. Hall and T. M. Todd. "Selective Detection of Chlorinated Insecticides in the Presence of Polychlorinated Biphenyls," J. Assoc. Off. Anal. Chem. 55(3): 537-538 (1972).

Dolphin, R. J. and F. W. Willmott. "Separation of Chlorinated Dibenzo-p-dioxins from Chlorinated Congeners," J. Chromatogr. 149:161-168 (1978).

Donkerbroek, J. J., N. J. R. van Eikema Hommes, C. Gooijer, N. H. Velthorst and R. W. Frei. "Sensitized Room-Temperature Phosphorescence for Detection in Continuous Flow and Chromatographic Systems," Chromatographia 15(4):218-222 (1982).

Donkerbroek, J. J., N. J. R. Van Eikema Hommes, C. Gooijer, N. H. Velthorst and R. W. Frei. "Phosphorescence Detection of Polychloronaphthalenes and Polychlorobiphenyls in Liquid Chromatography," J. Chromatogr. 255:581-590 (1983).

Donkin, P., S. V. Mann and E. I. Hamilton. "Microcoulometric Determination of Total Organochlorine Pesticide and Polychlorinated Biphenyl Residues in Grey Seal (Halichoerus grypus) Blubber," Anal. Chim. Acta 88:289-301 (1977).

Doskey, P. V. and A. W. Andren. "High-Volume Sampling of Airborne Polychlorobiphenyls with Amberlite XAD-2 Resin," Anal. Chim. Acta 110:129-137 (1979).

Dougherty, R. C. "Toxic Residues and Pollutants," Chapter 32A in Biochemical Applications of Mass Spectrometry, First Supplemental Volume, G. R. Waller and O. C. Dermer, Eds. (New York, NY: Wiley-Interscience Publication, 1980), pp. 951-968.

Dougherty, R. C. "Negative Chemical Ionization Mass Spectrometry: Applications in Environmental Analytical Chemistry," Biomed. Mass Spectrom. 8(7):283-291 (1981a).

Dougherty, R. C. "Chemical Geometrodynamics: Physical Fields can Cause Asymmetric Synthesis," Origins of Life 11:71-84 (1981b).

Dougherty, R. C., J. D. Roberts, H. P. Tannenbaum, and F. J. Biros, "Positive and Negative Chemical Ionization Mass Spectra of Polychlorinated Pesticides," in Mass Spectrometry and NMR Spectroscopy in Pesticide Chemistry, R. Haque and F. J. Biros (Eds.), New York-London (1973). pp. 33-47.

Dougherty, R. C., M. J. Whitaker, L. M. Smith, D. L. Stalling, and D. W. Kuehl, "Negative Chemical Ionization Studies of Human and Food Chain Contamination with Xenobiotic Chemicals," Environ. Health Persp., 36:103-118 (1980).

Dougherty, R. C., M. J. Whitaker, S.-Y. Tang, R. Bottcher, M. Keller, and D. W. Kuehl, "Sperm Density and Toxic Substances: A Potential Key to Environmental Health Hazards," Chapter 13 in Environmental Health Chemistry, The Chemistry of Environmental Agents as Potential Human Hazards, J. D. McKinney (Ed.), Ann Arbor Science Publishers, Inc., Ann Arbor, Michigan (1981). pp. 263-278.

Dow Chemical Company, "Determination of Chlorinated Biphenyls in the Presence of Chlorinated Benzenes," Midland MI, July 1, 1981.

Driscoll, J. N. and I. S. Krull. "Improved GC Separations with Chemically Bonded Supports," Amer. Lab. pp. 42-52 (May 1983).

Dry Color Manufacturers Association, "An Analytical Procedure for the Determination of Polychlorinated Biphenyls in Dry Phthalocyanine Blue, Phthalocyanine Green, and Diarylide Yellow Pigments," Arlington, VA (1982).

Dudenbostel, B. F. "Tentative Method of Test for Polychlorinated Biphenyls in Water," Attachment B in "Sampling Methods and Analytical Procedures Manual for PCB Disposal: Interim Report," J. H. Beard, III and J. Schaum, Office of Solid Waste, U.S. Environmental Protection Agency, Washington, DC (February 10, 1978).

Dufek, P., V. Pacáková and K. Zivný. "Gas Chromatographic Behaviour of Mono- and Dihydroxybiphenyls on Various Silicone Phases," J. Chromatogr. 211:150-154 (1981).

Duinker, J. C. and M. T. J. Hillebrand. "Characterization of PCB Components in Clophen Formulations by Capillary GC-MS and GC-ECD Techniques," Environ. Sci. Technol. 17:449-456 (1983).

Dunn, W. D., E. Johannson, D. L. Stalling, T. R. Schwartz, B. K. Marlow, J. D. Petty, and J. D. Hogan, "Application of SIMCA to the Characterization of PCB Residue Profiles in Sediment, Water, and Aquatic Biota," Abstract, 184th Annual Chemical Society National Meeting, September 12-17, 1982.

Dunn, W. J., III, D. L. Stalling, T. R. Schwartz, J. W. Hogan J. D. Petty, E. Johansson, and S. Wold. "Pattern Recognition for Classification and Determination of Polychlorinated Biphenyls in Environmental Samples," Anal. Chem. 56:1308-1313 (1984).

Durfee, R. L., G. Contos, F. C. Whitmore, J. D. Barden, E. E. Hackman, III and R. A. Westin. "PCBs in the United States - Industrial Use and Environmental Distributions," Prepared for the U.S. Environmental Protection Agency, Office of Toxic Substances, Report No. EPA 560/6-76-005 (NTIS No. PB-252 012), 488 pp. (1976).

Duvall, D. S. and W. A. Rubey. "Laboratory Evaluation of High-Temperature Destruction of Polychlorinated Biphenyls and Related Compounds," U.S. Environmental Protection Agency, EPA-600/2-77-228; NTIS No. PB 279 139 (December 1977).

Dyer, N. "PCBs - The Federal View," in Proceedings: 1981 PCB Seminar, G. Addis and J. Marks, Eds. (Palo Alto, CA: Electric Power Research Institute, 1981), pp. 1-1 to 1-10.

Dyment, P. G., L. M. Hebertson, E. D. Gomes, J. S. Wiseman and R. W. Hornabrook. "Absence of Polychlorinated Biphenyls in Human Milk and Serum from Texas and Human Milk from New Guinea," Bull. Environ. Contam. Toxicol. 6(6):532-534 (1971).

Dzidic, I., D. I. Carroll, R. N. Stillwell and E. C. Horning. "Atmospheric Pressure Ionization (API) Mass Spectrometry: Formation of Phenoxide Ions from Chlorinated Aromatic Compounds," Anal. Chem. 47(8):1308-1312 (1975).

Eadie, B. J., C. P. Rice and W. A. Frez. "The Role of the Benthic Boundary in the Cycling of PCBs in the Great Lakes," Chapter 12 in Physical Behavior of PCBs in the Great Lakes, D. Mackay, S. Paterson, S. J. Eisenreich and M. S. Simmons, Eds. (Ann Arbor, MI: Ann Arbor Science Publishers, Inc., 1983) 442 pp.

Easty, D. B. "Quantitation of Mixtures of Polychlorinated Biphenyls Isolated from Paperboard Containing Recycled Fiber," Tech. Assoc. Pulp and Paper Ind. 56(5):131-134 (1973).

Easty, D. B. and B. A. Wabers. "Determination of Polychlorinated Biphenyls in Paper Mill Effluents and Process Streams," Analytical Letters, 10(11):857-867 (1977).

Easty, D. B. and B. A. Wabers. "Determination of Polychlorinated Biphenyls in Paper Mill Effluents," Tech. Assoc. Pulp and Paper Ind. 61(10):71-74 (1978).

Ecology and Environment, Incorporated. "Summary of the Health Effects of PCBs," Report Submitted to U.S. Environmental Protection Agency and Admitted as Part of the "Official Rulemaking Record PCB Regulations for Closed and Controlled Waste Manufacturing Processes," Fed. Reg. 47:46993-5 (1982).

Eder, G. "Polychlorinated Biphenyls and Compounds of the DDT Group in Sediments of the Central North Sea and the Norwegian Depression," Chemosphere 5(2):101-106 (1976a).

Eder, G. "Evaluation of Environmental Polychlorobiphenyls and DDE in Terms of Mixtures of Commercial Preparations from Peak Heights of Packed-Column Gas Chromatograms Using a Programmable Calculator," J. Chromatogr. 121:269-277 (1976b).

Edison Electric Institute, and The National Rural Electric Cooperative Association. "Comments and Studies on the Use of Polychlorinated Biphenyls in Response to an Order of the United States Court of Appeals for the District of Columbia Circuit, Vol. III, Report of the Study of PCBs in Equipment Owned by the Electric Utility Industry," submitted to the U.S. Environmental Protection Agency, Washington, D.C. (February 12, 1982).

Edwards, R. "Some Factors in the Separation of Polychlorobiphenyls (PCBs) from Organochlorine Pesticides by Column Chromatography Combined with Gas-Liquid Chromatography," Pestic. Sci. 5:293-304 (1974).

Egestad, B., T. Curstedt and J. Sjövall. "Simple Procedures for Enrichment of Chlorinated Aromatic Pollutants from Fat, Water and Milk for Subsequent Analysis by High-Resolution Methods," Anal. Lett. 15(A3):293-307 (1982).

Eichelberger, J. W., L. E. Harris and W. L. Budde. "Application of Gas Chromatography-Mass Spectrometry with Computer Controlled Repetitive Data Acquisition from Selected Specific Ions," Anal. Chem. 46(2):227-232 (1974).

Eisenbeiss, F. and H. Sieper. "The Potential Use of High-Performance Liquid Chromatography on Residue Analysis," J. Chromatogr. 83:439-446 (1973).

Eisenreich, S. J., G. J. Hollod and T. C. Johnson. "Atmospheric Concentrations and Deposition of Polychlorinated Biphenyls to Lake Superior," Chapter 21 in Atmospheric Pollutants in Natural Waters, S. J. Eisenreich, Ed. (Ann Arbor, MI: Ann Arbor Science Publishers, Inc., 1981a) pp. 425-444.

Eisenreich, S. J., B. B. Looney and J. D. Thornton. "Airborne Organic Contaminants in the Great Lakes Ecosystem," Environmental Science and Technology 15:30-38 (1981b).

Eisenreich, S. J. and T. C. Johnson. "PCBs in the Great Lakes: Sources, Sinks, Burdens," in PCBs: Human and Environmental Hazards, F. M. D'Itri and M. A. Kamrin, Eds. (Boston: Butterworth Publishers, 1983), pp. 49-76.

Eisenreich, S. J., P. D. Capel and B. B. Looney. "PCB Dynamics in Lake Superior Water," Chapter 11 in Physical Behavior of PCBs in the Great Lakes, D. Mackay, S. Paterson, S. J. Eisenreich and M. S. Simmons, Eds. (Ann Arbor, MI: Ann Arbor Science Publishers, Inc., 1983a), 442 pp.

Eisenreich, S. J., B. B. Looney and G. J. Hollod. "PCBs in the Lake Superior Atmosphere 1978-1980," Chapter 7 in Physical Behavior of PCBs in the Great Lakes, D. Mackay, S. Paterson, S. J. Eisenreich and M. S. Simmons, Eds. (Ann Arbor, MI: Ann Arbor Science Publishers, Inc., 1983b), 442 pp.

Eisenreich, S. J. and B. B. Looney. "Evidence for the Atmospheric Flux of Polychlorinated Biphenyls to Lake Superior," Chapter 9 in Physical Behavior of PCBs in the Great Lakes, D. Mackay, S. Paterson, S. J. Eisenreich and M. S. Simmons, Eds. (Ann Arbor, MI: Ann Arbor Science Publishers, Inc., 1983), 442 pp.

Elder, D. "PCBs in N.W. Mediterranean Coastal Waters," Marine Pollution Bulletin, 7(4):63-64 (1976).

Elder, V. A., B. L. Proctor and R. A. Hites. "Organic Compounds Near Dumpsites in Niagara Falls, New York," Biomedical Mass Spectrometry 8:409-415 (1981).

Environmental Defense Fund, Natural Resources Defense Council, and Chemical Manufacturers Association. "Recommendation of the Parties for a Final EPA Rule on Inadvertent Generation of PCBs," Submitted to Don R. Clay, Acting Assistant Administrator, Environmental Protection Agency, Office of Toxic Substances, Washington, DC, April 13, 1983.

Environmental Protection Agency. "Identification of Poly-chlorinated Biphenyls in the Presence of DDT-Type Compounds," Office of Research and Monitoring, Washington, D.C., EPA-R2-72-064 (NTIS No. PB-213 900) (October 1972).

Environmental Protection Agency. "Sample Collection Manual, Ecological Monitoring Branch," Office of Pesticides Programs, Benefits and Field Studies Division, Washington, D.C. (1976).

Environmental Protection Agency, "40 CFR Part 60 - Standards of Performance for New Stationary Sources," Fed. Reg. 42: 41754-41789 (August 18, 1977).

Environmental Protection Agency. "Methods for Benzidine, Chlorinated Organic Compounds, Pentachlorophenol and Pesti-cides in Water and Wastewater," Interim Report, Environmental Monitoring and Support Laboratory, Cincinnati, OH, September 1978.

Environmental Protection Agency. "Organochlorine Pesticides and PCBs-- Method 608," Fed. Reg. 44:69501-69509 (December 3, 1979a).

Environmental Protection Agency. "Base/Neutrals, Acids, and Pesticides--Method 625," Fed. Reg. 44:69540-69552 (December 3, 1979b).

Environmental Protection Agency. "Appendix III - Example Quality Assurance and Quality Control Procedures for Organic Priority Pollutants," Fed. Reg. 44:69553-69559 (December 3, 1979c).

Environmental Protection Agency. "40 CFR 761, Polychlori-nated Biphenyls (PCBs) in Manufacturing, Processing, Dis-tribution in Commerce, and Use Prohibitions; Final Rule," Fed. Reg. 44:31514-31568 (1979d).

Environmental Protection Agency. "Analytical Protocol for Screening Publicly Owned Treatment Works (POTW) Sludges for Organic Priority Pollutants," Environmental Monitoring and Support Laboratory, Cincinnati, OH (September 1979e).

Environmental Protection Agency. "Handbook for Analytical Quality Control in Water and Wastewater Laboratories," En-vironmental Monitoring and Support Laboratory, Cincinnati, OH (March 1979f).

Environmental Protection Agency. "Interim Guidelines and Specifications for Preparing Quality Assurance Project Plans," Office of Monitoring Systems and Quality Assurance, Washington, D.C., QAMS-005/80, December 27, 1980a.

Environmental Protection Agency. "Quality Assurance Program Plan for the Office of Toxic Substances, Office of Pesticides and Toxic Substances," Washington, D.C. October 1980b.

Environmental Protection Agency. "Test Methods for Evaluating Solid Waste - Physical/Chemical Methods," Office of Water and Waste Management, Washington, D.C., SW-846 (1980c).

Environmental Protection Agency. "Ambient Water Quality Criteria for: Polychlorinated Biphenyls (PCBs)," Report for Office of Water Regulations and Standards, Criteria and Standards Division, Washington, D.C., EPA 440/5-80-068 NTIS No. PB81-117798), October 1980d.

Environmental Protection Agency. "The Analysis of Polychlorinated Biphenyls in Transformer Fluid and Waste Oils," Office of Research and Development, Environmental Monitoring and Support Laboratory, Cincinnati, OH (February 1981a).

Environmental Protection Agency. "PCB Disposal by Thermal Destruction," Report by Solid Waste Branch, Air and Hazardous Materials Division, U.S. Environmental Protection Agency, Region 6, Dallas, TX, EPA-200/9-81-001 (NTIS No. PB82 241 860), 606 pp. (1981b).

Environmental Protection Agency. "Interim Methods for the Sampling and Analysis of Priority Pollutants in Sediments and Fish Tissue," Report by Physical and Chemical Methods Branch, Environmental Monitoring and Support Laboratory, Cincinnati, OH, EPA 600/4-81-055 (1981c).

Environmental Protection Agency. "Toxic Substances Control Act Inspection Manual; Volume I, TSCA Base Manual; Volume II, PCB Inspection Manual," U.S. Environmental Protection Agency, Pesticides and Toxic Substances Enforcement Division, Washington, DC (March 1981d).

Environmental Protection Agency. "40 CFR Part 761, Polychlorinated Biphenyls (PCBs) Manufacturing, Processing, Distribution in Commerce, and Use Prohibitions; Recodification," Fed. Reg. 47:19526-19527 (May 6, 1982a).

Environmental Protection Agency. "40 CFR Part 761, Polychlorinated Biphenyls (PCBs); Manufacture, Processing, Distribution, and Use in Closed and Controlled Waste Manufacturing Processes," Fed. Reg. 47:24976-24989 (June 8, 1982b).

Environmental Protection Agency. "40 CFR Part 761, Polychlorinated Biphenyls (PCBs); Manufacturing, Processing, Distribution in Commerce, and Use Prohibitions; Use in Closed and Controlled Waste Manufacturing Processes," Fed. Reg. 47:46980-46986 (October 21, 1982c).

Environmental Protection Agency. "Analysis of Pesticides, Phthalates, and Polychlorinated Biphenyls in Soils and Bottom Sediments," HWI Sample Management Office, Alexandria, VA, unpublished method (November 4, 1982d), 12 pp.

Environmental Protection Agency. "Test Methods for Evaluating Solid Waste-Physical/Chemical Methods, SW-846, 2nd Edition," Office of Solid Waste and Emergency Response, Washington, DC (July 1982e).

Environmental Protection Agency. "40 CRF Part 761, Polychlorinated Biphenyls (PCBs) Manufacturing, Processing, Distribution in Commerce and Use Prohibitions; Use in Electrical Equipment," Fed. Reg. 47:37342-34360 (August 25, 1982f).

Environmental Protection Agency. "40 CFR Part 761, Procedural Amendment of the Approval Authority for PCB Disposal Facilities and Guidance for Obtaining Approval," Fed. Reg. 48:13181-13186 (1983a).

Environmental Protection Agency. "Quality Assurance Newsletter," Vol. 5, No. 3, Environmental Monitoring and Support Laboratory, Cincinnati, OH (April 1983b).

Environmental Protection Agency. "Quality Assurance Program Plan for the Office of Toxic Substances, Office of Pesticides and Toxic Substances," Washington, D.C. (September 30, 1983c).

Environmental Protection Agency. "40 CFR Part 761, Polychlorinated Biphenyls (PCBs); Manufacturing, Processing, Distribution in Commerce, and Use Prohibitions," in Code of Federal Regulations, Title 40, Part 425 to End (Revised as of July 1, 1983d), U.S. Government Printing Office, Washington, DC (1983d) pp. 530-566.

Environmental Protection Agency. "40 CFR Part 761, Polychlorinated Biphenyls (PCBs); Manufacture, Processing, Distribution in Commerce and Use Prohibitions; Use in Electrical Transformers, Advanced Notice of Proposed Rulemaking," Fed. Reg. 49:11070-11083 (March 23, 1984a).

Environmental Protection Agency. "40 CFR Part 761, Polychlorinated Biphenyls (PCBs); Manufacturing, Processing, Distribution in Commerce and Use Prohibitions; Response to Individual and Class Petitions for Exemptions; Exclusions, Exemptions, and Use Authorizations, Final Rule," Fed. Reg. 49:28154-28209 (July 10, 1984b).

Environmental Protection Agency. "40 CFR Part 761, Polychlorinated Biphenyls (PCBs); Manufacture, Processing, Distribution in Commerce and Use Prohibitions; Use in Electrical
Transformers," Fed. Reg. 49:39966-39989 (October 11, 1984c).

Environmental Protection Agency. "Mass Spectrometric Identi-
fication and Measurement of Polychlorinated Biphenyls as
Isomer Groups," Draft Report by Physical and Chemical Methods
Branch, Office of Research and Development, Cincinnati, OH
(October 1984d).

Environmental Protection Agency, "Organochlorine Pesticides
and PCBs--Method 608," Fed. Reg. 49(209):89-104 (October 26,
1984e).

Environmental Protection Agency. "Base/Neutrals, Acids,
and Pesticides--Method 625," Fed. Reg., 49(209):153-174
(October 26, 1984f).

Erickson, M. D. "Gas Chromatography/Fourier Transform Infrared Spectroscopy Applications," Appl. Spectrosc. Rev. 15(2):
261-325 (1979).

Erickson, M. D. "Review of the Report 'Statistical Analysis
of Data from a Round Robin Experiment on PCB Samples,'"
Letter Report, U.S. EPA Contract No. 68-01-5915, Task 06,
February 1982.

Erickson, M. D. "Analytical Method: The Analysis of By-
Product Chlorinated Biphenyls in Commercial Products and
Product Wastes, Revision 2," U.S. Environmental Protection
Agency, Office of Toxic Substances, Washington, DC, EPA 560/
5-85-010 (1984a).

Erickson, M. D. "Analytical Method: The Analysis of By-
Product Chlorinated Biphenyls in Air, Revision 2," U.S. En-
vironmental Protection Agency, Office of Toxic Substances,
Washington, DC, EPA 560/5-85-011 (1984b).

Erickson, M. D. "Analytical Method: The Analysis of By-
Product Chlorinated Biphenyls in Water, Revision 2," U.S.
Environmental Protection Agency, Office of Toxic Substances,
Washington, DC, EPA 560/5-85-012 (1984c).

Erickson, M. D. and E. D. Pellizzari. "Identification and
Analysis of Polychlorinated Biphenyls and Other Related Chem-
icals in Municipal Sewage Sludge Samples," U.S. Environmental
Protection Agency, Office of Toxic Substances, Washington,
D.C., EPA-560/6-77-021 (August 1977).

Erickson, M. D. and E. D. Estes. "Evaluation of Chlorinated Hydrocarbon Catalytic Reduction Technology" U.S. Environmental Protection Agency, Office of Research and Development, Washington, D. C., EPA-600/2-78-059 (March 1978).

Erickson, M. D., L. C. Michael, R. A. Zweidinger and E. D. Pellizzari. "Development of Methods for Sampling and Analysis of Polychlorinated Naphthalenes in Ambient Air," Environ. Sci. Technol., 12:927-931 (1978).

Erickson, M. D. and E. D. Pellizzari. "Analysis of Municipal Sewage Sludge Samples by GC/MS/Computer for Polychlorinated Biphenyls and Other Chlorinated Organics," Bull. Environ. Contam. Toxicol. 22:688-694 (1979).

Erickson, M. D., C. M. Sparacino, E. D. Pellizzari and K. B. Tomer. "Point Source Ambient Monitoring to Determine Impact of ENSCO Incinerator Located at El Dorado, Arkansas," Draft Report submitted to Phillip Schwindt, U.S. Environmental Protection Agency, Region 6, Sampling and Analysis Division, Dallas, TX, EPA Contract No. 68-01-4141, Task 29, October 1980a, 135 pp.

Erickson, M. D., B. S. H. Harris, E. D. Pellizzari, K. B. Tomer, R. D. Waddell and D. A. Whitaker, "Acquisition and Chemical Analysis of Mother's Milk for Selected Toxic Substances," Office of Toxic Substances, U.S. Environmental Protection Agency, Washington, D.C., EPA 560/13-80-029, 1980b.

Erickson, M. D. and John S. Stanley. "Methods of Analysis for By-Product PCBs--Literature Review and Preliminary Recommendations," Interim Report No. 1, Office of Toxic Substances, U.S. Environmental Protection Agency, Washington, D.C., EPA-560/5-82-005, NTIS No. PB83 126 573 (1982). 135 pp.

Erickson, M. D., J. S. Stanley, K. Turman, G. Radolovich, K. Bauer, J. Onstot, D. Rose and M. Wickham. "Analytical Methods for By-Product PCBs--Preliminary Validation and Interim Methods," Interim Report No. 4, Office of Toxic Substances, U.S. Environmental Protection Agency, Washington, D. C., EPA-560/5-82-006, NTIS No. PB83 127 696 (1982), 243 pp.

Erickson, M. D. and R. V. Shah. "Guidelines for PCB Destruction Permit Applications and Demonstration Test Plans," Draft Interim Report No. 5, Revision 1, EPA Contract No. 68-01-5915, Task 51, May 17, 1983, 80 pp.

Erickson, M. D., J. S. Stanley, J. K. Turman, G. Radolovich, J. Onstot, M. Wickham and J. Going. "Determination of Incidentally Generated PCBs in Commerical Products and Wastes by Capillary GC/EIMS," Abstract from 1983 Pittsburgh Conference and Exposition on Analytical Chemistry and Applied Spectroscopy, March 1983a.

Erickson, M. D., J. S. Stanley, J. K. Turman, J. E. Going and D. P. Redford. "Methods for Analysis of Complex Mixtures in Complex, Variable Matrices--Chlorinated Biphenyls in Commercial Products and Wastes," in Polynuclear Aromatic Hydrocarbons: Formation, Metabolism and Measurement, M. Cooke and A. J. Dennis, Eds. (Columbus, OH: Battelle Press, 1983b), pp. 483-492.

Erickson, M. D., K. M. Bauer, F. J. Bergman. "Analytical Methods for By-Product and Destruction Derived PCBs--Interlaboratory Validation A," Draft Interim Report No. 6, Task 51, EPA Contract No. 68-01-5915, August 23, 1983c.

Erickson, M. D., J. S. Stanley, G. Radolovich and R. B. Blair. "Analytical Method: The Analysis of By-Product Chlorinated Biphenyls in Commercial Products and Product Wastes," Revision 1, Prepared by Midwest Research Institute for Office of Toxic Substances, U.S. Environmental Protection Agency, Washington, DC, under Subcontract No. A-3044(8149)-271, Work Assignment No. 17 to Battelle, Washington, DC August 15, 1983d.

Erickson, M. D., J. P. Goforth, M. A. Jones, M. C. Saylor, K. B. Tomer, and E. D. Pellizzari, B. T. Cook, M. Frankenberry, J. J. Breen and F. W. Kutz. "Analysis of Blood and Adipose Tissue Samples from GSA Workers for Polychlorinated Biphenyls (PCBs) Phase I: Packed Column GC/ECD and GC/MS Analyses," Interim Report, Contract No. 68-01-3849, Task 4, U.S. Environmental Protection Agency (1983e).

Erickson, M. D., P. G. Gorman, and D. T. Heggem. "Relationship of Destruction Parameters to the Destruction/Removal Efficiency (DRE) of PCBs," Journal of the Air Pollution Control Association, in press (1984a).

Erickson, M. D., C. J. Cole, J. D. Flora, Jr., P. G. Gorman, C. L. Haile, G. D. Hinshaw, F. C. Hopkins, and S. E. Swanson. "Thermal Degradation Products from Dielectric Fluids," U.S. Environmental Protection Agency, Washington, DC, EPA 560/5-84-009; NTIS No. PB 85/38535 (1984b).

Erickson, M. D., C. J. Cole, J. D. Flora, Jr., P. G. Gorman, C. L. Haile, G. D. Hinshaw, F. C. Hopkins, S. E. Swanson, and D. T. Heggem, "PCDF Formation from PCBs Under Fire Conditions," Chemosphere (submitted) (1984c).

Erickson, M. D., J. S. Stanley, J. K. Turman, J. E. Going, D. P. Redford, and D. T. Heggem. "Determination of By-Product PCBs in Commercial Products and Wastes by High Resolution GC/EIMS," Anal. Chem. (submitted) (1984d).

Erickson, M. D., C. J. Cole, J. D. Flora, Jr., P. G. Gorman, C. L. Haile, G. D. Hinshaw, F. C. Hopkins, S. E. Swanson, and D. T. Heggem. "Formation of PCDFs Under 'Optimized' Combustion Conditions from Low-Level PCB Dielectric Fluids," Presented at EPRI PCDF Workshop, Palo Alto, California (1984e).

Erickson, M. D., C. J. Cole, J. D. Flora, Jr., P. G. Gorman, C. L. Haile, G. D. Hinshaw, F. C. Hopkins, S. E. Swanson, and D. T. Heggem. "Formation of PCDFs Under 'Optimized' Combustion Conditons from Low-Level PCB Dielectric Fluids," in Proceedings: 1984 EPRI PCDF Workshop, G. Addis and R. Komai, Eds., Electric Power Research Institute, (1985a) in press.

Erickson, C. J. Cole, J. D. FLora, P. G. Gorman, C. L. Haile, G. D. Hinshaw, F. C. Hopkins, S. E. Swanson, and D. T. Heggem. "Thermal Degradation Products from Dielectric Fluids," Presented at 189th ACS National Meeting, Miami Beach, Florida (May 1985b).

Erickson, M. D., J. S. Stanley, J. K. Turman, and G. Radolovich. "Analytical Method: The Analysis of Chlorinated Biphenyls in Liquids and Solids," U.S. Environmental Protection Agency, Office of Toxic Substances, Washington, DC, EPA-560/5-85-023 (February 1985c).

Erney, D. R. "A Feasibility Study of Miniature Silica Gel Columns for the Separation of Some Polychlorinated Biphenyls, DDT, and Analogs," Bull. Environ. Contam. Toxicol. 12(6):710-716 (1974a).

Erney, D. R. "Rapid Screening Method for Analysis of Chlorinated Pesticide and Polychlorinated Biphenyl Residues in Fish," J. Assoc. Offic. Anal. Chem. 57(3):576-579 (1974b).

Ernst, W., R. G. Schaefer, H. Goerke and G. Eder. "Aufarbeitung von Meerestieren für die Bestimmung von PCB, DDT, DDE, DDD, γ-HCH und HCB," Z. Anal. Chem. 272:358-363 (1974).

Exner, J. H. (Ed.). Detoxication of Hazardous Waste, Ann Arbor Science, Ann Arbor, MI (1982a), 362 pp.

Exner, J. H. "Summary of Polychlorinated Biphenyl Treatment Alternatives," Chapter 6 in Detoxication of Hazardous Waste, J. H. Exner, Ed. (Ann Arbor, MI: Ann Arbor Science Publishers, Inc., 1982b), pp. 119-120.

Farrington, J. W., E. D. Goldberg, R. W. Risebrough, J. H. Martin and V. T. Bowen. "U.S. 'Mussel Watch' 1976-1978: An Overview of the Trace-Metal, DDE, PCB, Hydrocarbon, and Artificial Radionuclide Data," Environ. Sci. Technol. 17:490-496 (1983).

Farwell, S. O., F. A. Beland and R. D. Geer. "Interrupted-Sweep Voltammetry for the Identification of Polychlorinated Biphenyls and Naphthalenes, Anal. Chem. 47(6):895-902 (May 1975).

Feairheller, W., P. J. Marn, D. H. Harris and D. L. Harris. "Technical Manual for Process Sampling Strategies for Organic Materials," Prepared for the U.S. Environmental Protection Agency, Office of Research and Development, Washington, D. C., Report No. EPA-600/2-76-122 (April 1976).

Fehringer, N. V. and J. E. Westfall. "Separation and Identification of DDT Analogs in the Presence of Polychlorinated Biphenyl Compounds by Two-Dimensional Thin-Layer Chromatography," J. Chromatogr. 57:397-405 (1971).

Femia, R. A., S. Scypinski, and L. J. Cline Love. "Fluorescence Characteristics of Polychlorinated Biphenyl Isomers in Cyclodextrin Media," Environ. Sci. Technol., 19(2):155-159 (1985).

Finklea, J. D., L. E. Priester, J. P. Creason, T. Hauser, T. Hinners and D. I. Hammer. "Polychlorinated Biphenyl Residues in Human Plasma Expose a Major Urban Pollution Problem," Amer. J. Publ. Health 62:645-651 (1972).

Finlay, D. J., F. H. Siff and V. J. DeCarlo. "Review of PCB Levels in the Environment," EPA-560/7-76-001; NTIS No. PB-253 735 (1976).

Finsterwalder, C. E. "Industrial Chemicals: Collaborative Study of the Determination of Polychlorinated Biphenyls in Paperboard," J. Assoc. Off. Anal. Chem. 57(3):518-521 (1974).

Fishbein, L. "Chromatographic and Biological Aspects of Polychlorinated Biphenyls," J. Chromatogr. 68:345-426 (1972).

Fishbein, L. "Toxicity of Chlorinated Biphenyls," Ann. Rev. Pharmacol. 14:139-156 (1974).

Fishbein, L. (Ed.). Potential Industrial Carcinogens and Mutagens, (Amsterdam: Elsevier, 1979).

Fisher, D. J., T. O. Rouse, and T. R. Lynn, "Field Determination of PCB in Transformer Oil 'CLOR-N-OIL Kit'," in Proceedings: 1983 PCB Seminar, G. Addis and R. Y. Komai, Eds. Report No. EPRI-EL-3581 (Palo Alto, CA: Electric Power Research Institute, 1984).

Food and Drug Administration. "Pesticide Analytical Manual," Vol. I, August 1, 1977.

Fradkin, L. and S. Barisas. "Technologies for Treatment, Reuse, and Disposal of Polychorinated Biphenyl Wastes," Argonne National Laboratory, Argonne, IL, Report No. ANL/EES-TM-168 (NTIS No. DE 82013715], 51 pp. (1982).

Frank, R., M. Holdrinet, H. E. Braun, D. P. Dodge and G. E. Sprangler. "Residues of Organochlorine Insecticides and Polychlorinated Biphenyls in Fish from Lakes Huron and Superior, Canada, 1968-76," Pestic. Monit. J. 12(2):69-80 (1978).

Frank, R., R. L. Thomas, M. Holdrinet, A. L. W. Kemp, H. E. Braun and R. Dawson. "Organochlorine Insecticides and PCB in the Sediments of Lake Huron (1969) and Georgian Bay and North Channel (1973)," Sci. Total Environ. 13:101-117 (1979).

Fries, G. F. "Polychlorinated Biphenyl Residues in Milk of Environmentally and Experimentally Contaminated Cows," Environ. Health Perspec. 1(1):55-62 (April 1972).

Friess, S. L., V. A. Drill, H. W. Hays, T. A. Loomis and C. B. Schaffer. "Potential Health Effects from Exposure to Polychlorinated Biphenyls; Laboratory Studies," in Advances in Exposure, Health and Environmental Effects Studies of PCBs: Symposium Proceedings, R. J. Davenport and B. K. Bernard (Eds.), Office of Toxic Substances, U.S. Environmental Protection Agency, Washington, D. C., Report No. LSI-TR-507-137B, NTIS No. PB84-135771 (December 1983), pp. 212-228.

Frimmel, F. "Differentiation of Polychlorinated Biphenyls from Pesticides with Combined Gas Chromatography-Mass Spectrometry," Z. Wasser Abwasser Forsch 6(4):113-116 (1973).

Fukano, S. and M. Doguchi. "PCT, PCB and Pesticide Residues in Human Fat and Blood," Bull. Environ. Contam. Toxicol. 17(5): 613-617 (1977).

Fuller, B., J. Gordon and M. Kornreich. "Environmental Assessment of PCBs in the Atmosphere," U.S. Environmental Protection Agency, Washington, D. C., EPA-450/3-77-045 (April 1976).

Furukawa, K., K. Tonomura and A. Kamibayashi. "Effect of Chlorine Substitution on the Biodegradability of Polychlorinated Biphenyls," Appl. Environ. Microbiol. 35(2):223-227 (1978).

Gaffey, W. R. "The Epidemiology of PCBs," in PCBs: Human and Environmental Hazards, F. M. D'Itri and M. A. Kamrin, Eds. (Boston: Butterworth Publishers, 1983a), pp. 279-298.

Gaffey, W. R. "Recent Epidemiologic Studies of PCBs," in Advances in Exposure, Health and Environmental Effects Studies of PCBs: Symposium Proceedings, R. J. Davenport and B. K. Bernard (Eds.), Office of Toxic Substances, U. S. Environmental Protection Agency, Washington, D. C., Report No. LSI-TR-507-137B, NTIS No. PB84-135771 (December 1983b), pp. 189-201.

Gaffney, P. E. "Chlorobiphenyls and PCBs: Formation During Chlorination," Journal Water Pollution Control Federation, 49(3):401-404 (March 1977).

Gallis, D., A. Defner-Hallowel, J. C. White and J. Waber. "Optimization of a Reversed Phase Partitioning Technique for the Analysis of Polychlorinated Biphenyls in Aqueous Samples by Gas Chromatography/Mass Spectrometry," Bull. Environ. Contam. Toxicol. 31(3):285-291; Chem. Abstr. 99:145823z (1983).

Garcia-Gutierrez, A., A. E. Mcintyre, J. N. Lester and R. Perry. "Determination of Organochlorine Compounds in Waste Water Samples by Gas Chromatography and Gas Chromatography-Mass Spectrometry Using Capillary Columns," Environ. Technol. Lett. 4:129-140; Chem. Abstr. 98:204072h (1983).

Garty, J., A. S. Perry and J. Mozel. "Accumulation of Polychlorinated Biphenyls (PCBs) in the Transplanted Lichen Ramalina Duriaei in Air Quality Biomonitoring Experiments," Nord. J. Bot. 2(6):583-586 (1983); Chem. Abstr. 98:148790b (1983).

Gassiot, M., X. Tomás, F. Broto, L. G. Sabaté and G. Codinas. "Algorithms for the Quantitative Determination of PCBs in Chromatograms of Organochlorinated Contaminants: Application to Samples of Sediments and Marine Organisms," Analytical Techniques in Environmental Chemistry 2, J. Albaiges, Ed. (New York, NY: Pergamon Press, 1982) pp. 249-258.

Gast, R. "Studies into Quantitative PCB Determination," Muench. Beitr. Abwasser, Fisch.-Flussbiol. 30:215-225 (1978); Chem. Abst. 90:115924e (1979).

General Accounting Office. "EPA Slow in Controlling PCBs," GAO/CED-82-21, 39 pages, December 30, 1981.

Gesser, H. D., A. Chow and F. C. Davis. "The Extraction and Recovery of Polychlorinated Biphenyls (PCB) Using Porous Polyurethane Foam," Anal. Letters 4(12):883-886 (1971).

Giacin, J. R. and S. G. Gilbert. "Analysis of Polychlorinated Biphenyls in Packaging Materials," in Technical Advances in Packaging with Flexible Barrier Materials, ASTM STP 548, 10-19 (1973).

Giam, C. S., A. R. Hanks, R. L. Richardson, W. M. Sackett and M. K. Wong. "DDT, DDE, and Polychlorinated Biphenyls in Biota from the Gulf of Mexico and Caribbean Sea - 1971," Pestic. Monit. J. 6(3):139-143 (1972).

Giam, C. S., H. S. Chan and G. S. Neff. "Rapid and Inexpensive Method for Detection of Polychlorinated Biphenyls and Phthalates in Air," Anal. Chem. 47(13):2319-2320 (1975).

Giam, C. S., H. S. Chan, and G. S. Neff. "Concentrations and Fluxes of Phthalates, DDTs, and PCBs to the Gulf of Mexico," in Marine Pollutant Transfer, H. L. Windom and R. A. Duce, Eds. (Lexington, MA: Lexington Books, 1976) pp. 375-386.

Giger, W., M. Reinhard, C. Schaffner and F. Zürcher. "Analyses of Organic Constituents in Water by High-Resolution Gas Chromatography in Combination With Specific Detection and Computer-Assisted Mass Spectrometry," Chapter 26 in Identification and Analysis of Organic Pollutants in Water, L. H. Keith Ed. (Ann Arbor, MI: Ann Arbor Science Publishers, Inc., 1976), pp. 433-452.

Gilman, A. P. "Monitoring for PCBs in Fish: The Human Health Perspective," in PCBs: Human and Environmental Hazards, F. M. D'Itri and M. A. Kamrin, Eds. (Boston: Butterworth Publishers, 1983), pp. 115-122.

Glaser, J. A., D. L. Foerst, G. D. McKee, S. A. Quave and W. L. Budde. "Trace Analyses for Wastewaters," Environ. Sci. Technol. 15:1426-1435 (1981).

Godefroot, M., M. Stechele, P. Sandra and M. Verzele. "A New Method for the Quantitative Analysis of Organochlorine Pesticides and Polychlorinated Biphenyls," J. High Resol. Chrom. and Chrom. Comm. 5:75-79 (1982a).

Godefroot, M. , M. Stechele, P. Sandra and M. Verzele. "A New Method for the Quantitative Analysis of Organochlorine Pesticides and Polychlorinated Biphenyls," Comm. Eur. Communities, [Rep.] EUR 1982, EUR 7623, Anal. Org. Micropollut. Water 16-23; Chem. Abstr. 97:133257p (1982b).

Goerlitz, D. F., and L. M. Law. "Note on Removal of Sulfur Interferences from Sediment Extracts for Pesticide Analysis," Bull. Environ. Contam. Toxicol. 6:9-10 (1971).

Goerlitz, D. F. and L. M. Law. "Determination of Chlorinated Insecticides in Suspended Sediment and Bottom Material," J. Assoc. Off. Anal. Chem. 57(1):176-181 (1974).

Goldstein, J. A. "Structure-Activity Relationships for the Biochemical Effects and the Relationship to Toxicity," Chapter 4 in Halogenated Biphenyls, Terphenyls, Naphthalenes, Dibenzo-dioxins and Related Products, R. D. Kimbrough, Ed. (New York, NY: Elsevier/North-Holland Biomedical Press, 1980), pp. 151-190.

Goldstein, J. A., J. D. McKinney, G. W. Lucier, P. Hickman, H. Bergman and J. A. Moore. "Toxicological Assessment of Hexachlorobiphenyl Isomers and 2,3,7,8-Tetrachlorodibenzofuran in Chicks," Toxicol. Appl. Pharmacol. 36(1):81-92 (1976).

Goodman, J. I. "Concepts in Toxicology and Carcinogenesis: A Basis for Discussing the Potential Environmental Hazard Posed by PCBs," in PCBs: Human and Environmental Hazards, F. M. D'Itri and M. A. Kamrin, Eds. (Boston: Butterworth Publishers, 1983), pp. 179-186.

Gordon, R. J., J. Szita and E. J. Faeder. "Determination of Polychlorinated Biphenyls in Transformer Oils by Capillary Gas Chromatography," Anal. Chem. 54:478-481 (1982).

Gorski, T. and T. Syrowatka. "Simplified Method for the Separation and Determination of Residues of Organochlorine Pesticides and Polychlorinated Biphenyls in Human Fatty Tissue," Chem. Abst. 91:885W (1979).

Gossman, D. G. "Data Processing as an Alternative to Extensive Sample Cleanup in the Gas Chromatographic Determination of PCBs," Abstract from the 1983 Pittsburgh Conference and Exposition on Analytical Chemistry and Applied Spectroscopy, March 7-12, 1983.

Gothe, R. "Oxidation with Tetrabutylammonium Permanganate for Quantitation of DDT Residues in GLC Determination of Chlorinated Hydrocarbons," Bull. of Environ. Contam. Toxicol. 11(5):451-455 (1974).

Grant, D. L. "Regulation of PCBs in Canada," in PCBs: Human and Environmental Hazards, F. M. D'Itri and M. A. Kamrin, Eds. (Boston: Butterworth Publishers, 1983), pp. 383-392.

Greichus, Y. A., J. J. Worman, M. A. Pearson and D. J. Call. "Analyses of Polychlorinated Biphenyls in Bird Tissues and Aroclor Standards with Gas Chromatography and Mass Spectrometry," Bull. of Environ. Contam. Toxicol. 11(2):113-120 (1974).

Griffin, D. A., A. B. Marin and M. L. Deinzer. "Optimization of Chromatographic Conditions for the Separation of p,p'-DDE from Aroclor 1254 on Silica, Using Azulene as Indicator," J. Assoc. Off. Anal. Chem. 63(5):959-964 (1980).

Griffitt, K. R. and J. C. Craun. "Gel Permeation Chromatographic System: An Evaluation," J. Assoc. Off. Anal. Chem. 57(1): 168-172 (1974).

Gross, M. L., J. O. Lay, Jr., P. A. Lyon, D. Lippstreu, N. Kangas, R. L. Harless, S. E. Taylor and A. E. Dupuy, Jr. "2,3,7,8-Tetrachlorodibenzo-p-dioxin Levels in Adipose Tissue of Vietnam Veterans," Environ. Res. 33(1):261-268 (1984); Chem. Abstr. 100:108498r (1984).

Gu, T. and M. Manes. "Adsorptive Displacement from Activated Carbon: Recovery of 4,4'-Dichlorobiphenyl," Environ. Sci. Technol. 18:55-57 (1984).

Gutierrez, A. G., A. E. McIntyre, J. N. Lester and R. Perry. "Comparison of Gas Chromatography and Gas Chromatography/Mass Spectrometry for the Analysis of Polychlorinated Biphenyls and Organochlorine Insecticides in Sewage Sludges," Environ. Technol. Lett. 4(12):521-528 (1983); Chem. Abstr. 100:56357x (1984).

Hadorn, H. and K. Zuercher. "Contamination of Food With Polychlorinated Biphenyls (PCB) by Packaging Material and Environmental Pollution," Gordian 73(12):458-462 (1973).

Haefelfinger, P. "Limits of the Internal Standard Technique in Chromatography," J. Chromatogr. 218:73-81 (1981).

Hahn, G. E. and C. A. Ward. "The Determination of PCBs in Human Blood," Presented at the FACSS 10th Annual Meeting, September 25-30, 1983.

Haile, C. L. and E. Baladi. "Methods for Determining the Total Polychlorinated Biphenyl Emissions From Incineration and Capacitor and Transformer Filling Plants," U. S. Environmental Protection Agency, EPA-600/4-77-048, NTIS No. PB-276 745/7G1 (November 1977), 90 pp.

Haile, C., J. Stanley, R. M. Lucas, D. Melroy, C. Nulton and W. Yauger, Jr. "Comprehensive Assessment of Specific Compounds Present in Combustion Processes. Vol. 1-Pilot Study of Combustion Emissions Variability," Office of Toxic Substance, U.S. Environmental Protection Agency, Washington, D.C., EPA-560/ 5-83-004 (June 1983a).

Haile, C. L., J. S. Stanley, T. Walker, G. R. Cobb and B. A. Boomer. "Comprehensive Assessment of the Specific Compounds Present in Combustion Processes, Volume 3, National Survey of Organic Emissions from Coal Fired Utility Boiler Plants," Office of Pesticides and Toxic Substances, U.S. Environmental Protection Agency, Washington, D.C., EPA-560/5-83-006 (1983b).

Haile, C. L., and V. Lopez-Avila. "Development of Analytical Test Procedures for the Measurement of Organic Priority Pollutants--Project Summary," U.S. Environmental Protection Agency, Environmental Monitoring and Support Laboratory, Cincinnati, Ohio, EPA-600/S4-84-001; (Full Report available as NTIS No. PB 84-129 048) (1984).

Haile, C. L., J. S. Stanley, A. M. Magin, R. V. Northcutt and D. P. Redford. "Emissions of Organic Pollutants from Coal-Fired Utility Boiler Plants," in Identification and Analysis of Organic Pollutants in Air, L. H. Keith, Ed. (Boston: Butterworth Publishers, 1984a), pp. 443-458.

Haile, C. L., R. B. Blair, T. Walker, and R. M. Lucas. "Assessment of Emissions of Specific Compounds from a Resource Recovery Municipal Refuse Incinerator," U.S. Environmental Protection Agency, EPA 600/5-84-002, (June 1984b).

Hall, J., F. Record, P. Wolf, G. Hunt, S. Zelenski, P. Fennelly, A. Fisher, A. Garwick, T. Hockman, W. Kilgore and D. Koenig. "Evaluation of PCB Destruction Efficiency in an Industrial Boiler," Report by GCA/Technology Division, Bedford, MA, to David C. Sanches, USEPA, Office of Research and Development, IERL, Research Triangle Park, NC, EPA-600/2-81-055a and b (NTIS Nos. PB 82-224 940 and PB 81-187 270), 172 pp. (1982).

Hammer, D. I., J. F. Finklea, L. E. Priester, J. E. Keil, S. H. Sandifer and K. Bridbord. "Polychlorinated Biphenyl Residues in the Plasma and Hair of Refuse Workers," Environ. Health Perspec. 1(1):83 (1972).

Hammond, P. B. "Biological Effects in Polychlorinated Biphenyls - Environmental Impact," Environ. Res. 5:312-338 (1972).

Hanai, T. and H. F. Walton, "Chromatography of Chlorinated Biphenyls on an Ion-Exchange Resin," Anal. Chem. 49(6):764-766 (1977).

Hanks, A. R. and B. M. Colvin. "High-Performance Liquid Chromatography," Chapter 3 in Pesticide Analysis, K. G. Das, Ed. (New York, NY: Marcel Dekker, Inc., 1981), pp 99-174.

Hannan, E. J. and D. D. Bills. "Separation of Aldrin from Aroclor 1254," Bull. Environ. Contam. Toxicol., 8(6):327-328 (1972).

Hannan, E. J., D. D. Bills and J. L. Herring. "Analysis of Polychlorinated Biphenyls by Gas Chromatography and Ultraviolet Irradiation," J. Agr. Food Chem. 21(1):87-90 (1973).

Hanneman, L. F. "The New PCB Issue - Analysis of Specific Congeners Produced by Unintentional By-Product Chemistry," Presented at Capillary Chromatography '82--An International Symposium, Tarrytown, NY, October 4-6, 1982.

Haque, R., D. W. Schmedding and V. H. Freed. "Aqueous Solubility, Adsorption, and Vapor Behavior of Polychlorinated Biphenyl Aroclor 1254," Environ. Sci. Tech. 8(2):139-142 (1974).

Haque, R. and D. Schmedding. "A Method of Measuring the Water Solubility of Hydrophobic Chemicals: Solubility of Five Polychlorinated Biphenyls," Bull. Environ. Contam. Toxicol. 14(1): 13-18 (1975).

Haque, R. and D. Schmedding. "Studies on the Adsorption of Selected Polychlorinated Biphenyl Isomers on Several Surfaces," J. Environ. Sci. Health B11(2):129-137 (1976).

Haraguchi, H., H. Kuroki, Y. Masuda, and N. Shigematsu. "Determination of Methylthio- and Methylsulfone Polychlorinated Biphenyls in Tissues of Patients with 'Yusho'," Food Chem. Toxicol. 22(4):282-288 (1984).

Harris, J. C., D. J. Larsen, C. E. Rechsteiner and K. E. Thrun. "Sampling and Analysis Methods for Hazardous Waste Incineration (First Edition)," Report to Larry D. Johnson, U.S. Environmental Protection Agency, IERL, Research Triangle Park, NC, EPA Contract No. 68-02-3111, Technical Directive No. 124, February 1982, 400 pp.

Harris, R. W., C. F. Grainger and W. J. Mitchell. "Validation of a Method for Measuring Polychlorinated Biphenyls in Natural Gas Pipelines," EPA 600/4-81-048; NTIS No. PB82-207556 (1981).

Harrison, A. G., F. I. Onuska, and C. W. Tsang. "Chemical Ionization Mass Spectrometry of Specific Polychlorinated Biphenyl Isomers," Anal. Chem., 53:1183-1186 (1981).

Harvey, G. R., H. P. Miklas, V. T. Bowen and W. G. Steinhauer. "Observations in the Distribution of Chlorinated Hydrocarbons in Atlantic Ocean Organisms," J. Marine Res. 32:103-118 (1974).

Harvey, G. R., and W. G. Steinhauer. "Transport Pathways of Polychlorinated Biphenyls in Atlantic Water," J. Marine Res. 34:561-575 (1976).

Harvey, J., Jr., G. Zweig, R. Cannizzaro, H. Dishburger and J. Sherma (Ed.), "Pesticide Analytical Methodology," ACS Symposium Series 136 (Washington, D. C.: Amer. Chem. Soc., 1980).

Harz, A., and U. Muelder. "Gas Chromatographic Determination of Mirex and Polychlorinated Biphenyls," Lebensmittelchem. Gerichtl. Chem. 37(6):146-174 (1983); Chem. Abst. 101:5594k (1984).

Hass, J. R. and M. D. Friesen. "Qualitative and Quantitative Methods for Dioxin Analysis," Ann. N.Y. Acad. Sci. 320:28-42 (1979).

Hass, J. R., M. D. Friesen and M. K. Hoffman. "Recent Mass Spectrometric Techniques for the Analysis of Environmental Contaminants," Chapter 11 in Environmental Health Chemistry, The Chemistry of Environmental Agents as Potential Human Hazards, J. D. McKinney, Ed. (Ann Arbor, MI: Ann Arbor Science Publishers, Inc., 1981), pp. 219-243.

Hattori, Y., Y. Kuge and M. Nakamoto. "The Correlation Between the Electron-Capture Detector Response and the Chemical Structure for Polychlorinated Biphenyls," Bull. Chem. Soc. Jpn. 54(9):2807-2810; Chem. Abstr. 96:34427s (1981).

Hattula, M. L. "Some Aspects of the Recovery of Chlorinated Residues (DDT-Type Compounds and PCB) From Fish Tissue by Using Different Extraction Methods," Bull. Environ. Contam. Toxicol. 12(3):301-307 (1974a).

Hattula, M. L. "Simultaneous Clean Up of Fish Fat Containing Low Levels of Residues and Separation of PCB From Chlorinated Pesticides by Thin-Layer Chromatography," Bull. Environ. Contam. Toxicol. 12(3):331-337 (1974b).

Hattula, M. L. and O. Karlog. "Adsorption of Polychlorinated Biphenyls (PCB) on Glass Surfaces," Dan. Tidsskr. Farm. 45(7): 259-261 (1971).

Heeg, F. J., R. Zinburg, H. J. Neu and K. Ballschmiter. "Re-
tention Index Calculation Based on a Non-Linear Relationship
Between Net Retention Time and Carbon Number of n-Alkanes,"
Chroma-tographia 12(7):451-458 (1979).

Heesen, T. C., and D. R. Young. "Precision of Chlorinated
Hydrocarbon Measurements," in Southern California Coastal
Water Research Project Annual Report for the Year Ended
June 30, 1977, p. 69-74 (1977) (NTIS No. PB274 463/9G1).

Heesen, T. C., D. R. Young, and D. McDermott-Ehrlich. "Evaluation of a Technique for Measuring Dry Atmospheric Deposition Rates of DDT and PCB Residues," Atmospheric Environment
13:1677-1680 (1979).

Heller, S. R., J. M. McGuire and W. L. Budde. "Trace Organics by GC/MS," Environ. Sci. Technol. 9(3):210-213 (March
1975).

Heller, S. R. and G. W. A. Milne. "1978 Indices to EPA/NIH
Mass Spectral Data Base," U.S. G.P.O., Washington, D.C.
(1978). p. 25409.

Henderson, J. E. and W. H. Glaze. "GC/MS Analysis of XAD-2
Extracts of Superchlorinated Septage," Water Res. 16:211-218
(1982).

Hernandez, A. and H. F. Walton. "Liquid Chromatography of
Chlorinated Biphenylols," J. Chromatogr. 242:346-348 (1982).

Herzel, F. "Polychlorinated Biphenyls and Their Discrimination from Organochlorine Insecticides," Vom Wasser 38:71-80
(1971).

Hesselberg, R. J. and J. L. Johnson. "Column Extraction of
Pesticides from Fish, Fish Food and Mud," Bull. Environ. Contam. Toxicol. 7:115-120 (1972).

Higuchi, K. (Ed.). PCB Poisoning and Pollution, (New York,
NY: Academic Press, 1976).

Hilker, D. R., K. M. Aldous, R. M. Smith, P. W. O'Keefe and
J. Jurusik. "Comparison of Methods for the Determination of
PCDDs and PCDFs in Transformer Oil and Transformer Oil Soot,"
Presented at the American Society for Mass Spectrometry,
Thirty-First Annual Conference on Mass Spectrometry and
Allied Topics, Boston, MA, May 8-13, 1983.

Hingorani, N. G., "PCB Technical Report from EPRI, No. 9,"
EPRI Technical Newsletter, Electrical Power Reserch Institute, Palo Alto, California (November 28, 1984).

Hirota, K., Y. Takata, Y. Arikawa, T. Yoshihara, H. Akimori
and S. Ganno. "Preparation and Application of Glass Capillary Columns," Bunseki Kagaku 23(10):1194-1201 (1974).

Hirwe, S. N., R. E. Borchard, L. G. Hansen and R. L. Metcalf.
"Gas-Liquid Chromatography - Mass Spectrometric Characteriza-
tion of Aroclor 1242 and 1254 Components," Bull. Environ.
Contam. Toxicol. 12(2):138-144 (1974).

Hodges, K. L., T. A. Robinson, C. J. Hensler, R. S. Kaley,
H. Caspers, F. Ewald and A. R. Pittaway. "Exposure Studies
Relating to Industrial Processes Containing Incidental PCB,"
in   Advances in Exposure, Health and Environmental Effects
Studies of PCBs: Symposium Proceedings, R. J. Davenport and
B. K. Bernard (Eds.), Office of Toxic Substances, U.S. En-
vironmental Protection Agency, Washington, D.C., Report No.
LSI-TR-507-137B,   NTIS   No. PB84-135771   (December 1983),
pp. 137-181.

Hoeting, A. L. "FDA Regulation of PCB in Food," in PCBs:
Human and Environmental Hazards, F. M. D'Itri and M. A.
Kamrin, Eds. (Boston: Butterworth Publishers, 1983),
pp. 393-408.

Hofstader, R. A., C. A. Bache and D. J. Lisk. "Interference
in the Electron-Capture Technique for Determination of Polychlorinated Biphenyls by Sulfur-Containing Compounds in Petroleum Products," Bull. Environ. Contam. Toxicol. 11(2):136-
138 (1974).

Holden, A. V. "The Analysis of Fish for Organochlorine Residues," International Symposium on Identification and Measurement of Environmental Pollutants, Ottawa, Ontario, Canada
(June 1971).

Holden, A. V. "International Cooperative Study of Organochlorine and Mercury Residues in Wildlife, 1969-71," Pestic.
Monit. J. 7(1): 37-52 (1973).

Holden, A. V. "Report on the Fourth ICES Organochlorine Intercalibration Exercise," International Council for the Exploration of the Sea, Copenhagen, Denmark, CM 1980/E:40
(1980).

Holden, A. V. and K. Marsden. "Single-Stage Clean-Up of Animal Tissue Extracts for Organochlorine Residue Analysis,"
Journal of Chromatography, 44:481-492 (1969).

Holdrinet, M. V. H. "Preliminary Results of an Interlaboratory PCB Check Sample Program," Environ. Qual. Safety Suppl.
3 (Pesticides):51-56 (1975).

Holdrinet, M. V. H. "Confirmation of Mirex and cis- and trans-Chlordane in the Presence of Other Organochlorine Insecticides and Polychlorinated Biphenyls," Bull. Environ. Contam. Toxicol. 21:46-52 (1979).

Hollod, G. J. and S. J. Eisenreich. "Collection of Atmospheric Polychlorinated Biphenyls on Amberlite XAD-2 Resins," Anal. Chim. Acta 124:31-38 (1981).

Holmes, D. C. and M. Wallen. "A Simple Differentiation of Polychlorobiphenyls from Chlorinated Naphthalenes," J. Chromatogr. 71:562-563 (1972).

Hopper, M. L. and D. D. Hughes. "An Improved GPC System for Pesticides in Fats," Laboratory Information Bulletin No. 1958, FSB/EDRO, U.S. Food and Drug Administration, Kansas City, MO, p. 50-55 (July 1976).

Horn, E. G., L. J. Hetling and T. J. Tofflemire. "The Problem of PCBs in the Hudson River System," Ann. N. Y. Acad. Sci. 320:591-609 (1979).

Hornig, A., and H. Masters. "Destruction of PCB-Contaminated Soils with a High-Temperature Fluid-Wall (HTFW) Reactor," Municipal Environmental Research Laboratory--Cincinnati, OH, Office of Research and Development, EPA-600/D-84-072 (1984).

Horwitz, W. "Evaluation of Analytical Methods Used for Regulation of Foods and Drugs," Anal. Chem. 54(1):67A-76A (1982).

Horwitz, W. "Today's Chemical Realities," J. Assoc. Off. Anal. Chem. 66(5):1295-1301 (1983).

Horzempa, L. M. and D. M. Di Torse. "Extent of Reversibility of Polychlorinated Biphenyl Adsorption," Water Research 17: 851-859 (1983).

Hubbard, H. L. "Chlorinated Biphenyl and Related Compounds," in Encyclopedia of Chemical Technology, 2nd Ed. (New York, NY: Kirk-Othmer, Publishers - Wiley and Sons Interscience, 1964), Vol. 5 pp. 289-297.

Huckins, J. N., J. E. Swanson and D. L. Stalling. "Perchlorination of Polychlorinated Biphenyls," J. Assoc. Off. Anal. Chem. 57(2):416-417 (1974).

Huckins, J. N., D. L. Stalling and J. L. Johnson. "Silicic Acid Chromatographic Separation of Polychlorinated Biphenyls and Pesticides: Some Contaminants and Limitations," J. Assoc. Off. Anal. Chem. 59(5):975-981 (1976).

Huckins, J. N., D. L. Stalling and W. A. Smith. "Foam-Charcoal Chromatography for Analysis of Polychlorinated Dibenzodioxins in Herbicide Orange," J. Assoc. Off. Anal. Chem. 61:32-38 (1978).

Huckins, J. N., D. L. Stalling and J. D. Petty. "Carbon-Foam Chromatographic Separation of Non-o,o'-Chlorine Substituted PCBs from Aroclor Mixtures," J. Assoc. Off. Anal. Chem. 63(4): 750-755 (1980).

Humphrey, H. E. B. "Population Studies of PCBs in Michigan Residents," in PCBs: Human and Environmental Hazards, F. M. D'Itri and M. A. Kamrin, Eds. (Boston: Butterworth Publishers, 1983), pp. 299-310.

Hunt, D. F., J. Schabanowitz, T. M. Harvey, and M. Coates. "Scheme for the Direct Analysis of Organics in the Environment by Tandem Mass Spectrometry," Anal. Chem., 57:525-537 (1985).

Hunt, G. T., P. Wolf and P. F. Fennelly. "Incineration of Polychlorinated Biphenyls in High-Efficiency Boilers: A Viable Disposal Option," Environ. Sci. Technol. 18:171-179 (1984).

Hunter, R. G. "Environmental Effects of Polychlorinated Biphenyls: Important Ecological Aspects," in Advances in Exposure, Health and Environmental Effects Studies of PCBs: Symposium Proceedings, R. J. Davenport and B. K. Bernard (Eds.), Office of Toxic Substances, U.S. Environmental Protection Agency, Washington, D.C., Report No. LSI-TR-507-137B, NTIS No. PB84-135771 (December 1983), pp. 265-291.

Hutzinger, O. "PCB Symposium," Chemosphere 12(7/8):N39-N43 (1983a).

Hutzinger, O. "Summary of Recent Advances in Exposure, Health and Environmental Effects Studies of PCBs," in Advances in Exposure, Health and Environmental Effects Studies of PCBs: Symposium Proceedings," R. J. Davenport and B. K. Bernard (Eds.), Office to Toxic Substances, U.S. Environmental Protection Agency, Washington, D.C., Report No. LSI-TR-507-137B, NTIS No. PB84-135771 (December 1983b), pp. 340-345.

Hutzinger, O., S. Safe, and V. Zitko, "Analysis of Chlorinated Aromatic Hydrocarbons by Exhaustive Chlorination: Qualitative and Structural Aspects of the Perchloro-Derivatives of Biphenyl, Naphthalene, Terphenyl, Dibenzofuran, Dibenzodioxin and DDE," Intern. J. Environ. Anal. Chem., 2, 95-106 (1972a).

Hutzinger, O., S. Safe and V. Zitko. "Photochemical Degradation of Chlorobiphenyls (PCBs)," Environ. Health Perspec.
1(1): 15-20 (1972b).

Hutzinger, O., W. D. Jamieson, S. Safe and V. Zitko. "Exhaustive Chlorination as a Technique in the Analysis of Aromatic Hydrocarbons," J. Assoc. Off. Anal. Chem. 56(4):982-986
(1973).

Hutzinger, O., S. Safe, and V. Zitko, The Chemistry of PCB's,
(CRC Press: Cleveland, Ohio, 1974a) 269 pp.

Hutzinger, O., S. Safe and V. Zitko. "Preparation, Gas Chromatographic Behavior, and Spectroscopic Properties of Hydroxylated Chlorobiphenyls," J. Assoc. Off. Anal. Chem.
57(5):1061-1067 (1974b).

Hutzinger, O., R. A. Heacock and S. Safe. "Thin-Layer Chromatography and Colour Reactions of Some Hydroxylated Chlorobiphenyls," J. Chromatogr. 97:233-247 (1974c).

Hutzinger, O. and A. A. M. Roof. "Polychlorinated Biphenyls
and Related Halogenated Compounds," in Analytical Techniques
in Environmental Chemistry, J. Albaiges, Ed. (New York, NY:
Pergamon Press, 1980a), pp. 167-184.

Hutzinger, O. and A. A. M. Roof. "Hydrocarbons and Halo-
genated Hydrocarbons in the Aquatic Environment: The
Thoughts on the Philosophy and Practice of Environmental
Analytical Chemistry," Environ. Sci. Res. 16:9-20 (1980b).

Iida, Y. and T. Kashiwagi. "Analysis of Polychlorinated Biphenyls by Gas Chromatography-Chemical Ionization Mass Spectrometry," Seikei Daigaku Kogakubu Kogaku Hokoku 19:1461-1462
(1975).

Iida, Y., S. Daishima and T. Kashiwagi. "Determination of
Polychlorobiphenyls by Chemical Ionization Mass Spectrometry," Bunseki Kagaku 32(2):80-86; Chem. Abstr. 98:154737f
(1983).

International Agency for Research on Cancer. "IARC Monographs on the Evaluation of the Carcinogenic Risk of Chemicals to Humans--Polychlorinated Biphenyls and Polybrominated
Biphenyls," Volume 18 (Lyon, France, 1978), pp. 43-103.

International Joint Commission. "Great Lakes Water Quality -
Appendix E. Status Report on the Persistent Toxic Pollutants
in the Lake Ontario Basin," IJC (1977).

Ishii, D. and T. Takeuchi. "High-Performance Liquid Chromatography Using Flexible Fused-Silica Micro-Packed Columns," J. Chromatogr. 255:349-358 (1983).

Ismail, R. J. and F. L. Bonner. "New, Improved Thin Layer Chromatography for Polychlorinated Biphenyls, Toxaphene, and Chlordane Components," J. Assoc. Off. Anal. Chem. 57(5):1026-1032 (1974).

Issaq, H. J., J. Klose, and G. M. Muschik. "Separation of Polychlorinated Biphenyls (Aroclor 1254) by High Performance Liquid Chromatography," J. Chromatogr. 302:159-166 (1984).

IT Corporation. "Initial Report for Destruction of Polychlorinated Biphenyls in a Mobile Incineration System at EPA Region II Facility, Edison, NJ, Volume I," U.S. Environmental Protection Agency, Municipal Environmental Research Laboratory-Ci, Oil and Hazardous Material Spills Branch, Edison, NJ, September 18, 1981, 16 pp.

IT Corporation. "Trial Burn Plan for the U.S. Environmental Protection Agency Mobile Incineration System at EPA Region II Facility, Edison, NJ," Prepared for: U.S. Environmental Protection Agency, Municipal Environmental Research Laboratory-Ci, Oil and Hazardous Material Spills Branch, Edison, NJ, February 26, 1982a, 148 pp.

IT Corporation. "USEPA Mobile Incineration System SPCC Plan," Prepared for U.S. Environmental Protection Agency, Municipal Environmental Research Laboratory, Solid and Hazardous Waste Research Division, Oil and Hazardous Material Spills Branch, Edison, NJ, July 16, 1982b.

IT Corporation. "USEPA Mobile Incineration System, Phase II Interim Trial Burn Results," Prepared for: U.S. Environmental Protection Agency, Municipal Environmental Research Laboratory, Solid and Hazardous Waste Research Division, Oil and Hazardous Materials Spills Branch, Edison, NJ, December 10, 1982c, 32 pp.

IT Corporation. "Mobile Incineration System Trial Burn Quality Assurance Project Plan EERU/QA-2," Prepared for: U.S. Environmental Protection Agency, Municipal Environmental Research Laboratory, Solid and Hazardous Waste Research Division, Oil and Hazardous Spills Branch, Edison, NJ, December 30, 1982d.

Jacobson, S. W., J. L. Jacobson, P. M. Schwartz and G. G. Fein. "Intrauterine Exposure of Human Newborns to PCBs: Measures of Exposure," in PCBs: Human and Environmental Hazards, F. M. D'Itri and M. A. Kamrin, Eds. (Boston: Butterworth Publishers, 1983), pp. 311-344.

James, R. C. and R. D. Harbison. "Assessment of the Human Risks to PCBs Associated with the Expected Environmental Exposures," in Advances in Exposure, Health and Environmental Effects Studies of PCBs: Symposium Proceedings, R. J. Davenport and B. K. Bernard (Eds.), Office of Toxic Substances, U.S. Environmental Protection Agency, Washington, D.C., Report No. LSI-TR-507-137B, NTIS No. PB84-135771 (December 1983), pp. 300-336.

Jennings, W. "Gas Chromatography with Glass Capillary Columns," 2nd Edition (New York, NY: Academic Press, 1980).

Jensen, S. Ambio 1:123 (1972).

Jensen, S., A. G. Johnels, M. Olsson, and G. Olterlind. "DDT and PCB in Marine Animals from Swedish Waters," Nature 224: 247-250 (1969).

Jensen, S., L. Renberg and R. Vaz. "Problems in the Quantification of PCB in Biological Material," Committee Proceeding PCB 2nd Conference, Wenner-Gren Center, 1972, 7-14 (1973).

Jensen, S. and G. Sundström. "Structures and Levels of Most Chlorobiphenyls in Two Technical PCB Products and in Human Adipose Tissue," Ambio 3(2):70-76 (1974).

Jensen, S., L. Renberg and R. Vaz. "Methods for Analysis of DDT and PCB in Environmental Samples Using Chromatographic Methods," FAD Fisheries Technical Paper, Rome, FIRI/T137 (1975). pp. 229-236.

Jensen, S., L. Renberg and L. Reutergardh. "Residue Analysis of Sediment and Sewage Sludge for Organochlorines in the Presence of Elemental Sulfur," Anal. Chem. 49(2):316-318 (1977).

Jiang, K., Z. Kang and Y. Bian. "Quantitative Analysis of Polychlorinated Biphenyl Residues in Environmental Samples by GC-MS," Huanjing Kexue Xuebao 2(1):85-89; Chem. Abstr. 96: 194988d (1982a).

Jiang, K., R. Chen, J. Wang, Z, Kang and Y. Bian. "Environmental Analysis of Polychlorinated Biphenyls by Gas Chromatography and Mass Spectroscopy - Use of Chinese Commercial Products as References," Fenxi Huaxue 10(12):711-715 (1982b); Chem. Abstr. 98:185022y (1983).

Jiang, K., Z. Kang and Y. Bian. "Determination of Polychlorinated Biphenyl Residues in the Environment by GC-MS with Multiion Detection," Huanjing Hauxue 1(4): 274-280 (1982c); Chem. Abst. 98:29072j (1983).

Jiang, K., Z. Kang, and Y. Bian. "Determination of Poly-chlorinated Biphenyl Residues in the Environment by Quantitative GC/MS Analysis--o,p'-DDE Internal Standard Method," Huanjing Huaxue 3(3):71-75 (1984); Chem. Abst. 101:150579p (1984).

Johnson, L. D. and R. G. Merrill. "Stack Sampling for Organic Emissions, Toxicol. Environ. Chem. 6:109-126 (1983).

Jones, J. W. and H. S. Alden. "An Acneform Dermatergosis," Arch. Dermatol. Syphilol. 33:1022-1034 (1936).

Jung, J. D. "A Review of Methods for PCB Analysis of Trans-former Oil," Proc. Electr./Electron. Insul. Conf. 15th, 231-236 (1981); Chem. Abst. 97:16335b (1982).

Junk, G. A. and J. J. Richard. "Vapor-Phase Sampling of Organic Compounds," in Identification and Analysis of Organic Pollutants in Air, L. H. Keith, Ed. (Boston: Butterworth Publishers, 1984), pp. 61-78.

Kafadar, K. and K. R. Eberhardt. "Statistical Analysis of Some Gas Chromatography Measurements," J. Res. Nat. Bur. Stand. 88(1):37-46 (1983).

Kalmaz, E. V., R. B. Craig and G. W. Zimmerman. "Kinetics Model and Simulation of Concentration Variations of Species of Polychlorinated Biphenyls Involved in Photochemical Trans-formation," Chapter 14 in Detoxication of Hazardous Waste, J. H. Exner, Ed. (Ann Arbor, MI: Ann Arbor Science Pub-lishers, Inc., 1982), pp. 233-240.

Kaminsky, L. S. and M. J. Fasco. "High-Performance Liquid Chromatography of Polychlorinated Biphenyls," J. Chromatogr. 155:363-370 (1978).

Kaminsky, R. and R. A. Hites. "Analysis of Compounds from Niagara Falls Dump Sites Using NCI GC/MS," Abstract from 30th Annual Conference on Mass Spectrometry and Allied Topics, American Society for Mass Spectrometry, June 6-11, 1982.

Kamps, L. R., W. J. Trotter, S. J. Young, L. J. Carson, J. A. G. Roach, J. A. Sphon, J. T. Tanner and B. McMahon. "Poly-chlorinated Quaterphenyls Identified in Rice Oil Associated with Japanese 'Yusho' Poisoning," Bull. Environ. Contam. Toxicol. 20:589-591 (1978).

Kamps, L. R., W. J. Trotter, S. J. Young, A. C. Smith, J. A. G. Roach and S. W. Page. "Separation and Quantitation of 3,3',4,4'-Tetrachlorobiphenyl and 3,3',4,4',5,5'-Hexachlo-robiphenyl in Aroclors Using Florisil Column Chromatography and Gas-Liquid Chromatography," Bull. Environ. Contam. Toxicol. 23: 51-56 (1979).

Kan, T., K. Kamata, T. Ueta, R. Yamazoe and T. Totani. "Fluorescence Reactions of Organohalogen Compounds. I. Fluorometry of Polychlorinated Biphenyls (PCB) with Diphenyl-amine on Thin-Layer Chromatograms," Tokyo Toritsu Eisei Kenkyusho Kenky Nempo 24:137-145 (1973); Chem. Abst. 80:115771w (1974).

Kapila, S. and W. A. Aue. "Chemical Degradation of Single, Gas Chromatographic Peaks for Confirmation of Pesticide Residue Identity," J. Chromatogr. Sci. 15:569-572 (1977).

Karasek, F. W. "Plasma Chromatography of the Polychlorinated Biphenyls," Anal. Chem. 43(14):1982-1986 (1971).

Karppanen, E. and L. Kolho. "The Concentration of PCB in Human Blood and Adipose Tissue in Three Different Research Groups," PCB Conference II, 1972, Stockholm, Natl. Swedish Environ. Protection Board, Publication No. 1973:4E, 124-8 (1973).

Kashimoto, T., H. Miyata, S. Kunita, T.-C. Tung, S.-T. Hsu, K.-J. Chang, S.-Y Tang, G. Ohi, J. Nakagawa and S.-I. Yamamoto. "Role of Polychlorinated Dibenzofuran in Yusho (PCB Poisoning)," Archives of Environmental Health 36(6): 321-326 (1981a).

Kashimoto, T., H. Miyata and N. Kunita. "The Presence of Polychlorinated Quaterphenyls in the Tissues of Yusho Victims," Food Cosmet. Toxicol. 19:335-340 (1981b).

Kashimoto, T., H. Miyata, S. Fukushima, N. Kunita, T. C. Tung, S. T. Hsu, C. J. Chang, S. Y. Tang, G. Ohi and S. Yamamoto. "Chlorinated Compounds in Taiwanese 'Yusho' Patients' Blood," Abstract from 30th Annual Conference on Mass Spectrometry and Allied Topics, American Society for Mass Spectrometry, June 6-11, 1982, pp. 198-199.

Kateman, G. and F. W. Pijpers (Eds.). Quality Control in Analytical Chemistry (John Wiley and Sons: Wiley-Interscience Publishers, 1981).

Kauss, P. B., K. Suna and A. F. Johnson. Montiroing of PCBs in Water, Sediments and Biota of the Great Lakes - Some Recent Examples," Chapter 20 in Physical Behavior of PCBs in The Great Lakes, D. Mackay, S. Paterson, S. J. Eisenreich and M. S. Simmons, Ed. (Ann Arbor, MI: Ann Arbor Science Publishers, Inc., 1983), pp. 385-409.

Kawabata, J. "Simple Method for the Determination of PCBs [Polychlorinated Biphenyls] by a Combination of Thin-Layer Chromatography and UV Absorption," Kogai To Taisaku 10(10): 1112-1116 (1974); Chem. Abst. 83:201652b (1975).

Kawaguchi, T., S. Hiratsuka, T. Yoneshima and Y. Nagao. "A Method of Analysis for Polychlorobiphenyl Gas Chromatograms," Tokyo-Toritsu Kogyo Gijutsu Senta Kenkyu Hokoku 5:57-60 (1975); Chem. Abst. 86:83287y (1977).

Keith, L. H., W. Crummett, J. Deegan Jr., R. A. Libby, J. K. Taylor and G. Wentler. "Principles of Environmental Analysis," Anal. Chem. 55:2210-2218 (1983).

Kelso, G. L., M. D. Erickson, B. A. Boomer, S. E. Swanson, D. C. Cox, and B. D. Schultz. "Cleanup of PCB Spills from Capacitors and Transformers," Draft Interim Report No. 1, Work Assignment Task 37, EPA Contract No. 68-02-3938, U.S. Environmental Protection Agency, Office of Toxic Substances, Washington, DC (January 1985).

Kennedy, P. A., D. J. Roberts and M. Cooke. "Determination of Polychlorinated Naphthalenes in the Presence of Polychlorinated Biphenyls by Capillary Gas Chromatography," J. Chromatogr. 249:257-265 (1982).

Kerkhoff, M. A. T, A. De Vries, R. C. C. Wegman and A. W. M. Hofstee. "Analysis of PCBs in Sediments by Glass Capillary Gas Chromatography," Chemosphere 11(2):165-174 (1982).

Khan, M. A., A. F. Novak and R. M. Rao. "Comparative Evaluation of Polychlorinated Biphenyl Solutions," Bull. Environ. Contam. Toxicol. 16(3):360-367 (1976).

Kilikidis, S. D., J. E. Psomas, A. P. Kamarianos and A. G. Panetsos. "Monitoring of DDT, PCBs, and Other Organochlorine Compounds in Marine Organisms from the North Aegean Sea," Bull. Environ. Contam. Toxicol. 26:496-501 (1981).

Kimbrough, R. D. "The Toxicity of Polychlorinated Polycyclic Compounds and Related Chemicals," CRC Crit. Rev. Toxicol. 2: 445-498 (1974).

Kimbrough, R. D., (Ed.) Halogenated Biphenyls, Terphenyls, Naphthalenes, Dibenzodioxins and Related Products (New York: Elsevier/North-Holland Biomedical Press, 1980a), 406 pp.

Kimbrough, R. D. "Environmental Pollution of Air, Water and Soil," Chapter 3 in Halogenated Biphenyls, Terphenyls, Naphthalenes, Dibenzodioxins and Related Products,   R. D. Kimbrough, Ed. (New York, NY: Elsevier/North-Holland Biomedical Press, 1980b), pp. 77-80.

Kimbrough, R. D. "Occupational Exposure," Chapter 9 in Halogenated Biphenyls, Terphenyls, Napththalenes, Dibenzodioxins and Related Compounds, R. D. Kimbrough, Ed. (New York, NY: Elsevier/North-Holland Biomedical Press, 1980c), pp. 333-398.

Kimbrough, R., J. Buckley, L. Fishbein, G. Flamm, L. Kasza, W. Marcus, S. Shibko and R. Teske. "Animal Toxicology," Environ. Health Persp. 24: 173-184 (1978).

Kirchmer, C. J. "Quality Control in Water Analyses," Environ. Sci. Technol. 17(4):174A-181A (1983).

Kirshen, N. A. "PCBs in Transformer Fluids," Varian Instrum. Appl. 15(2): 1-10; Chem. Abst. 94(26):219095j (1981a).

Kirshen, N. A. "PCBs in Transformer Fluids," Amer. Lab. 65-69 (December 1981b).

Kitchens, J. F., W. E. Jones, III, G. L. Anspach and D. C. Schubert. "Light-Activated Reduction of Chemicals for Destruction of Polychlorinated Biphenyls in Oil and Soil," Detoxication of Hazardous Waste, J. H. Exner, Ed. (Ann Arbor, MI: Ann Arbor Science Publishers, Inc., 1982), pp. 215-226.

Klimisch, H. M. and D. N. Ingebrigtson. "Determination of Polychlorinated Biphenyls in Silicone Fluids," Anal. Chem. 52:1675-1678 (1980).

Kloepfer, R. D. "Preparation of Fish Tissue for Extractable Organics Analysis," Method No. EE015TR, U.S. Environmental Protection Agency, Region VII, Kansas City, MO (October 19, 1983), 3 pp.

Koch, R. "Circular Thin-Layer Chromatography as a Rapid Method for a Qualitative Detection of Organochlorine Compounds," Acta Hydrochim. Hydrobiol. 7(3):355-356 (1979); Chem. Abst. 91:101574z (1979).

Kodama, H., N. Kawamura and H. Ota. "A Simple Method for the Determination of PCB in Human Milk and Blood Using an Improved Essential Oil Distillator," Nippon Eiseigaku Zasshi 31(6):644-651 (1977); Chem. Abst. 87:96853a (1977).

Kodama, H. and O. Hideo. "Transfer of Polychlorinated Biphenyls to Infants From Their Mothers," Arch. Environ. Health 35(2):95-100 (1980).

Koeniger, M., P. Wallnoeer and G. Engelhardt. "Residue Determination of Polychlorinated Biphenysl (PCBs) in the Presence of Chlorinated Hydrocarbon Pesticides in Eggs of Wild Birds," Nachrichtenbl. Dtsch. Pflanzenschutzdienstes 27(9): 131-135 (1975); Chem. Abst. 84:85033v (1976).

Kohli, K. K., P. W. Albro and J. D. McKinney. "Radioisotope Dilution Assay (RIDA) for the Estimation of Polychlorinated Biphenyls (PCBs)," J. Anal. Toxicol. 3:125-128 (1979a).

Kohli, P., W. Albro and J. D. McKinney. "Radioisotope Dilution Assay (RIDA) for the Estimation of Polychlorinated Biphenyls (PCBs)," Environ. Health Persp. 33:347 (1979b).

Kolbye, A. C., Jr. "Regulatory Considerations Regarding Limiting Human Exposures to PCBs," in PCBs: Human and Environmental Hazards, F. M. D'Itri and M. A. Kamrin, Eds. (Boston: Butterworth Publishers, 1983), pp. 77-90.

Kondrat, R. W. and R. G. Cooks. "Direct Analysis of Mixtures by Mass Spectrometry," Anal. Chem. 50(1):81A-92A (1978).

Kováts, von E. "Gas-Chromatographische Charakterisierung Organischer Verbindungen. Teil 1: Retentionsindices Aliphatischer Halogenide, Alkohole, Aldehyde und Ketone," Helv. Chim. Acta 41:1915-1932 (1958).

Kratochvil, B., D. Wallace and J. K. Taylor. "Sampling for Chemical Analysis," Anal. Chem. 56:113R-129R (1984).

Kraul, I. and O. Karlog. "Persistent Organochlorinated Compounds in Human Organs Collected in Denmark 1972-73," Acta Pharmacol. et Toxicol. 38:38-48 (1976).

Kreiss, K., M. M. Zack, R. D. Kimbrough, L. L. Needham, A. L. Smrek and B. T. Jones. "Association of Blood Pressure and Polychlorinated Biphenyl Levels," J. Amer. Med. Assoc. 245(24):2505-2509 (1981).

Krull, I. S. "Recent Advances in PCB Analysis," in Residue Reviews, F. A. Gunther and J. D. Gunther (Eds.), 66, New York (1977).

Krupcik, J., P. A. Leclercq, A. Simova, P. Suchanek, M. Collak and J. Hrivnak. "Possibilities and Limitations of Capillary Gas Chromatography and Mass Spectrometry in the Analysis of Polychlorinated Biphenyls," J. Chromatogr. 119:217-283 (1976).

Krupcik, J., J. Kriz, D. Prusova, P. Suchanek and Z. Cervenka. "Analysis of Polychlorinated Biphenyls by High-Performance Liquid Chromatography and Capillary Gas-Liquid Chromatography," J. Chromatogr. 142:797-807 (1977).

Krupcik, J., P. A. Leclercq, J. Garaj and A. Simova. "Analysis of Alkylated Mixtures of Polychlorinated Biphenyls by Capillary Gas Chromatography-Mass Spectrometry," J. Chromatogr. 191:207-220 (1980).

Krupcik, J., J. Mocak, A. Simova, J. Garaj and G. Guiochon. "Optimization of Experimental Conditions for the Analysis of Complex Mixtures by Gas Chromatography," J. Chromatogr. 238: 1-12 (1982).

Kuehl, D. W. and E. N. Leonard. "Isolation of Xenobiotic Chemicals from Tissue Samples by Gel Permeation Chromatography," Anal. Chem. 50(1):182-185 (1978).

Kuehl, D. W., E. N. Leonard, K. J. Welch and G. D. Veith. "Identification of Hazardous Organic Chemicals in Fish from the Ashtabula River, Ohio, and Wabash River, Indiana," J. Assoc. Off. Anal. Chem. 63(6):1238-1244 (1980a).

Kuehl, D. W., M. J. Whitaker and R. C. Dougherty. "Micromethods for Toxic Residue Screening by Negative Chemical Ionization Mass Spectrometry," Anal. Chem. 52:935-940 (1980b).

Kuge, Y. "Pollution Analysis and Examples of Measurement," Kankyo Gijutsu 12(10):659-665 (1983); Chem. Abstr. 100: 79161t (1984).

Kuratsune, M. "An Abstract Results of Laboratory Examinations of Patients with Yusho and of Animal Experiments," Environ. Health Perspec. 1:129-136 (1972).

Kuratsune, M. "Yusho," Chapter 9B1 in Halogenated Biphenyls, Terphenyls, Naphthalenes, Dibenzodioxins and Related Products, R. D. Kimbrough, Ed. (New York, NY: Elsevier/North-Holland Biomedical Press, 1980), pp. 287-302.

Kuratsune, M. and Y. Masuda. "Polychlorinated Biphenyls in Non-Carbon Copy Paper," Env. Health Persp., 1:61-62 (1972).

Kuratsune, M., T. Yoshimura, J. Matsuzaka and A. Yamaguchi. "Epidemiologic Study on Yusho, A Poisoning Caused by Ingestion of Rice Oil Contaminated with a Commerical Brand of Polychlorinated Biphenyls," Environ. Health Perspec. 1:119-128 (1972).

Kuroki, H. and Y. Masuda. "Determination of Polychlorinated Dibenzofuran Isomers Retained in Patients with Yusho," Chemosphere 7(10):771-777 (1978)

Kutz, F. W. and S. C. Strassman. "Residues of Polychlorinated Biphenyls in the General Population of the United States," in Proceedings of the National Conference on Polychlorinated Biphenyls, (Chicago, IL: November 19-21, 1975), F. A. Ayer, Ed. Office of Toxic Substances, U.S. Environmental Protection Agency, Washington, D.C., EPA-560/6-75-004, NTIS No. PB 253 248 (March 1976), pp. 139-143.

Kutz, F. W., S. C. Strassman and J. F. Sperling. "Survey of Selected Organochlorine Pesticides in the General Population of the United States: Fiscal Years 1970-1975," Ann. N. Y. Acad. Sci. 320:60-68 (1979).

Kveseth, N. J. and E. M. Brevik. "Column Chromatographic Method for Cleaning Up Extracts from Biological Material and Simultaneous Separation of PCBs and DDE," Bull. Environ. Contam. Toxicol. 21:213-218 (1979).

LaBrosse, J. and R. J. Anderegg. "Using the Mass Spectrometer as a Chlorine-Selective Detector," Abstract from 30th Annual Conference on Mass Spectrometry and Allied Topics, American Society for Mass Spectrometry, June 6-11, 1982.

Laitem, L. and P. Gaspar. "A T.L.C. Procedure for Identification of DDT and Its Metabolites in Presence of PCB," Bull. Environ. Contam. Toxicol. 19:264-265 (1978).

Lam, N. K., and M. Kopanica. "Determination of Trichlorobiphenyl by Adsorptive Stripping Voltammetry," Anal. Chim. Acta 161:315-324 (1984).

Lamparski, L. L., T. J. Nestrick, and R. H. Stehl. "Determination of Part-per-Trillion Concentrations of 2,3,7,8-Tetrachlorodibenzo-p-dioxin in Fish," Analytical Chemistry, 51(9):1453-1458 (1979).

Lamparski, L. L., and T. J. Nestrick, "Micro Chlorination Procedure for Synthesis of Higher Chlorinated Dibenzo-p-dioxins from [^{13}C]-2,3,7,8-Tetrachlorodibenzo-p-dioxin," Anal. Chem., 54:402-406 (1982).

Landrigan, P. J. "General Population Exposure to Environmental Concentrations of Halogenated Biphenyls," Chapter 9A in Halogenated Biphenyls, Terphenyls, Naphthalenes, Dibenzodioxins and Related Products, R. D. Kimbrough, Ed. (New York, NY: Elsevier/North-Holland Biomedical Press, 1980), pp. 267-286.

Lao, R. C., R. S. Thomas, and J. L. Monkman, "Application of Computerized Gas Chromatography-Mass Spectrometry to the Analysis of Polychlorinated Biphenyls," Dynamic Mass Spectrom., 4: 107-131 (1976).

Lawrence, J. F. "Confirmatory Tests," Chapter 10 in Pesticide Analysis, K. G. Das, Ed. (New York, NY: Marcel Dekker, Inc., 1981), pp 425-460.

Lawrence, J., and H. M. Tosine, "Adsorption of Polychlorinated Biphenyls from Aqueous Solutions and Sewage," Environ. Sci. Technol., 10(4):381-383 (1976).

Lawrence, J. F. and D. Turton, "High-Performance Liquid Chromatographic Data for 166 Pesticides," J. Chromatogr., 159: 207-266 (1978).

Lea, Robert E., R. Bramston-Cook and J. Tschida. "Pattern Recognition for Identification and Quantitation of Complex Mixtures in Chromatography," Anal. Chem. 55:626-629 (1983).

Lech, J. J. and R. E. Peterson. "Biotransformation and Persistence of Polychlorinated Biphenyls (PCBs) in Fish," in PCBs: Human and Environmental Hazards, F. M. D'Itri and M. A. Kamrin, Eds. (Boston: Butterworth Publishers, 1983), pp. 187-202.

Lederman, T. C. and G-Y. Rhee. "Bioconcentration of a Hexachlorobiphenyl in Great Lakes Planktonic Algae," Canadian J. of Fisheries and Aquatic Sci. 39:380-387 (1982).

Lee, H. B. and A. S. Y. Chau. "National Interlaboratory Quality Control Study No. 25. PCBs in Wet Sediments," Rep. Ser. - Inland Waters Dir. (Can.) Report Series No. 71:12 pp. (1981a); Chem. Abst. 97: 222636d (1982).

Lee, H. B. and A. S. Y. Chau. "National Interlaboratory Quality Control Study No. 27. PCBs in Naturally Contaminated Dry Sediments," Rep. Ser. - Inland Waters Dir. (Can.) Report Series No. 72, 15 pp. (1981b); Chem. Abst. 97:22263 (1982).

Leib, A. J., and D. D. Bills, "Influence of Storage Temperature of Florisil on Analysis of Polychlorinated Biphenyls," Bull. Environ. Contam. Toxicol., 12(3):328-330 (1974).

Leifer, A., R. H. Brink, G. C. Thom, and K. G. Partymiller. "Environmental Transport and Transformation of Polychlorinated Biphenyls," U.S. Environmental Protection Agency, Office of Pesticides and Toxic Substances, Washington, D.C., EPA-560/5-83-025, NTIS No. PB84-142579 (1983).

Lentzen, D. E., D. E. Wagoner, E. D. Estes and W. F. Gutknecht. "IERL-RTP Procedures Manual: Level 1 Environmental Assessment (Second Edition)," Prepared for U.S. Environmental Protection Agency, Office of Research and Development, EPA-600/7-78-201, October 1978.

Leoni, V., "The Separation of Fifty Pesticides and Related Compounds and Polychlorobiphenyls into Four Groups by Silica Gel Microcolumn Chromatography," J. Chromatogr., 62:63-71 (1971).

Leoni, V., E. d'Allessandro de Luca and A. M. Simeone. "Techniques of Qualitative and Quantitative Analysis of Polychlorinated Biphenyls in Food Products and Packing Materials," Rass. Chim. 25(2):99-111 (1973); Chem. Abst. 79:77061j (1973).

Leoni, V., M. Biocca and E. d'Allessandro de Luca. "I Policlorodifenili Nei Tessuti Adiposi Umani: Accertamento Sperimentale E Possible Significato Igienico," Il Farmaco 31(2): 57-79 (1976a).

Leoni, V., G. Puccetti, R. J. Colombo and A. M. d'Ovidio. "The Use of Tenax for the Extraction of Pesticides and Polychlorinated Biphenyls from Water. II. Tests with Artificially Polluted and Natural Waters," J. Chromatogr. 125: 399-407 (1976b).

Leoni, V. and C. Vannucchi. "Analytical Methods for Water. 6. Determination of Polychlorinated Biphenyls and Polychlorinated Terphenyls in Wastewater," Quad. - Ist. Ric. Acque 11: 41 pp. (1981); Chem. Abst. 97:115204f (1982).

Lerman, S. I. and J. P. Hendricks. "Determination of Polychlorinated Biphenyls in Transformer Oil," Chromatogr. Newsl. 9(1):5-6 (1981); Chem. Abst. 95(7):55674r (1981).

Lerman, S. I., H. Gordon and J. P. Hendricks. "A Study in Laboratory Automation - Analysis of PCBs in Transformer Oils," Amer. Lab. 14(2):176-181 (February 1982).

Levine, S. P., M. T. Homsher and J. A. Sullivan. "Comparison of Methods of Analysis of Polychlorinated Biphenyls in Oils," J. Chromatogr. 257:255-266 (1983).

Levins, P. L., C. E. Rechsteiner and J. L. Stauffer. "Measurement of PCB Emissions from Combustion Sources," U.S. Environmental Protection Agency, Report No. EPA-600/7-79-047 (February 1979).

Levins, P. L., C. E. Rechsteiner, Jr. and J. L. Stauffer. "A New Procedure for the Measurement of Polychlorinated Biphenyls (PCBs) in Combustion Sources," AIChE Sym. Series 76(196):330-337 (1980).

Levy, G. C. and J. M. Hewitt. "Analysis of Polychlorinated Biphenyls by Carbon-13 Nuclear Magnetic Resonance Spectroscopy," J. Assoc. Offic. Anal. Chem. 60(1):241-242 (1977).

Lewis, E. and W. D. Jamieson. "Use of Negative Chemical Ionization GC/MS to Study Polychlorinated Biphenyls in Marine Sediments," Int. J. Mass Spectrom. Ion Physics 48:303-306 (1983).

Lewis, R. G. "Procedures for Sampling and Analysis of Polychlorinated Biphenyls in the Vicinities of Hazardous Waste Disposal Sites," U.S. Environmental Protection Agency, Research Triangle Park, North Carolina, March 16, 1982, 14 pp.

Lewis, R. G., A. R. Brown and M. D. Jackson. "Evaluation of Polyurethane Foam for Sampling of Pesticides, Polychlorinated Biphenyls and Polychlorinated Naphthalenes in Ambient Air," Anal. Chem. 49(12):1668-1672 (1977a).

Lewis, R. G., A. R. Brown and M. D. Jackson. "Sampling for Low Levels of Airborne Pesticides, Polychlorinated Biphenyls, and Polychlorinated Naphthalenes," Paper No. 78, 173rd National Meeting, American Chemical Society, New Orleans, Louisiana (1977b).

Lewis, R. G. and M. D. Jackson. "Modification and Evaluation of a High-Volume Air Sampler for Pesticides and Semivolatile Industrial Organic Chemicals," Anal. Chem. 54:592-594 (1982).

Lewis, R. G. and K. E. MacLeod. "Portable Sampler for Pesticides and Semivolatile Industrial Organic Chemicals in Air," Anal. Chem. 54:310-315 (1982).

Liberti, A., D. Brocco, V. Di Palo and M. Possanzini. "Evaluation of Organochlorine Compounds in the Emissions of Urban Incinerators," in Analytical Techniques in Environmental Chemistry, J. Albaiges, Ed. (New York, NY: Pergamon Press, 1980), pp. 157-166.

Liddle, J. A. "Method Standardization and Interlaboratory Compatibility of Serum Polychlorinated Biphenyl Analysis," Abstract, 184th Annual Chemical Society National Meeting, September 12-17, 1982.

Lincer, J. L. "Polychlorinated Biphenyls: Their Potential Interference with Pesticide Residue Analysis and Present Analytical Status," Progr. Anal. Chem. 5:109-131 (1973).

Liu, R. H., S. Ramesh and J. Y. Liu. "Qualitative and Quantitative Determinations of Aroclor Formulations," Abstract from the Thirty-First Annual Conference on Mass Spectrometry and Allied Topics, American Society for Mass Spectrometry, May 8-13, pp. 213 (1983).

Liu, R. H., S. Ramesh, J. Y. Liu, and S. Kim. "Qualitative and Quantitative Analyses of Commercial Polychlorinated Biphenyl Formulation Mixtures by Single Ion Monitoring Gas-Liquid Chromatography/Mass Spectrometry and Multiple Regression," Anal. Chem. 56:1808-1812 (1984).

Long, G. L. and J. D. Winefordner. "Limit of Detection - A Closer Look at the IUPAC Definition," Anal. Chem. 55(7): 712A-724A (1983).

Longanbach, J. R. and W. H. Mink. "Development of a Process for PCB Removal from Triaryl Phosphate Hydraulic Fluids by Vacuum Distillation," Environ. Sci. Technol. 17(5):305-307 (1983).

Longbottom, J. E. and J. J. Lichtenberg, Eds. "Methods for Organic Chemical Analysis of Municipal and Industrial Wastewater," U. S. Environmental Protection Agency, Report No. EPA-600/4-82-057 (July 1982).

Lovell, R. J., R. A. Miller, C. Pfommer, Jr., J. E. Brugger, and J. J. Yezzi, Jr. "Trial Burn Testing of the EPA-ORD Mobile Incineration System," Enviroscience, Inc., Knoxville, TN, EPA-600/D-84-054, NTIS No. PB84-175520 (1984.

Lovett, A. M., S. Nacson, N. H. Hijazi, and R. Chan. "Real Time Ambient Air Measurements for Toxic Chemical," in Proceedings: A Specialty Conference on: Measurement and Monitoring of Non-Criteria (Toxic) Contaminants in Air, E. R. Frederick, Ed., The Air Pollution Control Association, Pittsburgh, PA (1983), pp. 113-125.

Lucas, R. M., M. D. Erickson, P. V. Piserchia and S. R. Williams. "PCB Residue Levels in Human Adipose Tissue, A Statistical Evaluation by Racial Grouping," Office of Toxic Substances, U.S. Environmental Protection Agency, Washington, D.C., EPA-650/13-79-015 (November 1980).

Lucas, R. M., V. G. Iannacchione and K. D. Melroy. "Poly-chlorinated Biphenyls in Human Adipose Tissue and Mother's Milk," Office of Toxic Substances, U.S. Environmental Pro-tection Agency, Washington, D.C., EPA-560/5-83-011, NTIS No. PB83-253179 (1982).

Luckas, B., H. Pscheidl and D. Haberland. "Determination of Chlorinated Pesticides and Polychlorinated Biphenyls by De-rivatization Gas Chromatography," J. Chromatogr. 147:41-46 (1978).

Lunde, G. and E. B. Ofstad. "Determination of Fat-Soluble Chlorinated Compounds in Fish," Z. Anal. Chem. 282:395-399 (1976).

Luster, M. I., P. W. Albro, G. Clark, K. Chae, S. K. Chaudhary, L. D. Lawson, J. T. Corbett and J. D. McKinney. "Production and Characterization of Antisera Specific for Chlorinated Biphenyl Species: Initiation of a Radioimmuno-assay for Aroclors," Toxicol. Appl. Pharmacol. 50:147-155 (1979).

Luster, M. I., P. W. Albro, K. Chae, S. K. Chaudhary and J. D. McKinney "Development of Radioimmunoassays for Chlori-nated Aromatic Hydrocarbons," Chapter 14 in Environmental Health Chemistry, The Chemistry of Environmental Agents as Potential Human Hazards, J. D. McKinney Ed. (Ann Arbor, MI: Ann Arbor Science Publishers, Inc., 1981), pp. 279-297.

MacDougall, D. et al. "Guidelines for Data Acquisition and Data Quality Evaluation in Environmental Chemistry," Anal. Chem. 52:2242-2249 (1980).

Mackay, D. "Environmental Pathways of Polychlorinated Bi-phenyls," in Comments and Studies on the Use of Polychori-nated Biphenyls in Response to an Order of the United States Court of Appeals for the District of Columbia Circuit, Vol. IV, Submitted by The Utility Solid Waste Activities Group, The Edison Electric Institute and The National Rural Electric Cooperative Association to The U. S. Environmental Protection Agency, February 12, 1982a, 61 pp.

Mackay, D. "Correlation of Bioconcentration Factors," Environ. Sci. Technol. 16(5):274-278 (1982b).

Mackay, D., R. Mascarenhas, W. Y. Shiu, S. C. Valvani, and S. H. Yalkowsky. "Aqueous Solubility of Polychlorinated Bi-phenyls," Chemosphere 9:257-264 (1980).

Mackay, D., A. Bobra, D. W. Chan, and W. Y. Shiu. "Vapor Pressure Correlations for Low-Volatility Environmental Chem-icals," Environ. Sci. Technol. 16:645-649 (1982).

Mackay, D. and S. Paterson. "Fugacity Models of Indoor Exposure to Volatile Chemicals," Chemosphere 12(2):143-154 (1983).

Mackay, D., S. Paterson, S. J. Eisenreich, and M. S. Simmons. Physical Behavior of PCBs in the Great Lakes, Ann Arbor Science, Ann Arbor, MI, (1983a), 442 pp.

Mackay, D., W. Y. Shiu, J. Billington and G. L. Huang. "Physical Chemical Properties of Polychlorinated Biphenyls," Chapter 4 in Physical Behavior of PCBs in the Great Lakes, D. Mackay, S. Paterson, S. J. Eisenreich and M. S. Simmons, Eds. (Ann Arbor, MI: Ann Arbor Science Publishers, Inc., 1983b), pp 59-69.

Mackay, D., and A. I. Hughes. "Three-Parameter Equation Describing the Uptake of Organic Compounds by Fish," Environ. Sci. Technol. 18(6):439-444 (1984).

MacLeod, K. E. "Sources of Emissions of Polychlorinated Biphenyls into the Ambient Atmosphere and Indoor Air," U.S. Environmental Protection Agency, Report No. EPA-600/4-79-022 (March 1979).

MacNeil, J. D., S. Safe and O. Hutzinger. "The Ultraviolet Absorption Spectra of Some Chorinated Biphenyls," Bull. Environ. Contam. Toxicol. 15(1):66-77 (1976).

Manri, T., Y. Shinbori, S. Murakawa and Y. Mochizuki. "Determination of Chlorobiphenyl in Rat Adipose Tissues by Neutron Activation Analysis," Radioisotopes 20(8):371-375 (1971); Chem. Abst. 76:11738s (1972).

Marchand, M., D. Vas, and E. K. Duursma. "Levels of PCBs and DDTs in Mussels from the N.W. Mediterranean," Marine Pollut. Bull. 7(4):65-69 (1976).

Margeson, J. H. "Methodology for Measurement of Polychlorinated Biphenyls in Ambient Air and Stationary Sources - A Review," U.S. Environmental Protection Agency, Report No. EPA-600/4-77-021 (April 1977).

Markovec, L. M., and R. J. Magee. "Identification of Major Perchloroaromatic Compounds in Waste Products from the Production of Carbon Tetrachloride and Tetrachloroethylene," Analyst, 109(4):497-501 (1984).

Martelli, G. P., M. G. Castelli and R. Fanelli. "Analytical Response of Single Polychlorinated Biphenyls Analysed by Selected Ion Monitoring," Biomed. Mass Spectrom. 8(8):347-350 (1981).

Mason, B. J. "Preparation of Soil Sampling Protocol: Techniques and Strategies," ETHURA, McLean, Virginia, under subcontract to Environmental Research Center, University of Nevada, Cooperative Agreement No. CR808529-01-2, for U.S. Environmental Protection Agency, Las Vegas (October 1982).

Mass Spectrometry Data Centre, in collaboration with ICI Ltd. Eight Peak Index of Mass Spectra, 2nd ed., Vol. 1-3, AWRE, Aldermaston, Reading RG 7/4PR, United Kingdom (1970).

Masuda, Y. and H. Shiokawa. "Experimental File. 42. Chromatography. Three Experiments," Kagaku No Jikken 23(7):669-671 (1972); Chem. Abst. 77:87143k (1972).

Masuda, Y., H. Kuroki, T. Yamaryo, K. Haraguchi, M. Kuratsune and S. T. Hsu. "Comparison of Causal Agents in Taiwan and Fukuoka PCB Poisonings," Chemosphere 11(2):199-206 (1982).

Masuda, Y., KH. Kuroki, and J. Nagayama. "Polychlorinated Dibenzofurans in the Tissues of Patients with Yusho and Their Enzyme-Inducing Activities on Aryl Hydrocarbon Hydroxylase," Chlorinated Dioxins Dibenzofurans Total Environ. 375-384 (1983); Chem. Abst. 100:152051p (1984).

Masui, T., M. Yamamoto and S. Kimura. "Problems in Polychlorinated Biphenyl Analysis," Shizuoka-ken Eisei Kenkyusho Hokoku 19:59-64 (1976); Chem. Abst. 90:109442e (1979).

Masumoto, H. T. "Study of the Silicic Acid Procedure of Armour and Burke for the Separation of Polychlorinated Biphenyls from DDT and Its Analogs," J. Assoc. Offic. Anal. Chem. 55(5):1092-1100 (1972).

Masumoto, H. T. "Total Polychlorinated Biphenyl Quantitation by Reduction," EDRO SARAP Res. Tech. Rep. 1:Paper 20-73, 30 pp. (1976); Chem. Abst. 88:73094k (1978).

Mathar, W., and H. Beck. "Simple Use of Fat-Containing Foods for the Determination of PCB Residues by Distillation with Steam," Lebensmittelchem. Gerichtl. Chem., 37(6):147-148 (1983); Chem. Abst. 100:173236t (1984).

Matthews, H. B. "Metabolism of PCBs in Mammals: Routes of Entry, Storage, and Excretion," in PCBs: Human and Environmental Hazards, F. M. D'Itri and M. A. Kamrin, Eds. (Boston: Butterworth Publishers, 1983), pp. 203-214.

Matthews, H., G. Fries, A. Gardner, L. Garthoff, J. Goldstein, Y. Ku and J. Moore "Metabolism and Biochemical Toxicity of PCBs and PBBs," Env. Health Persp. 24:147-155 (1978).

Matthews, H. B. and S. Kato. "The Metabolism and Disposition of Halogenated Aromatics," Ann. N. Y. Acad. Sci. 320:131-137 (1979).

Mattsson, P. E. and S. Nygren. "Gas Chromatographic Determination of Polychlorinated Biphenyls and Some Chlorinated Pesticides in Sewage Sludge Using a Glass Capillary Column," J. Chromatogr. 124:265-275 (1976).

McCallum, R. L. "Order Dismissing Interlocutory Appeal," Before the Administrator U.S. Environmental Protection Agency, Washington, DC. In the Matter of: The Dow Chemical Company, Appellant. Docket No. TSCA (16(a))-1, July 28, 1982.

McClure, V. E. "Transport of Heavy Chlorinated Hydrocarbons in the Atmosphere," Environ. Sci. Technol. 10(13):1223-1229 (1976).

McConnell, E. E. "Acute and Chronic Toxicity, Carcinogenesis, Reproduction, Teratogenesis and Mutagenesis in Animals," Chapter 5 in Halogenated Biphenyls, Terphenyls, Naphthalenes, Dibenzodioxins and Related Products, R. D. Kimbrough, Ed. (New York, NY: Elsevier/North-Holland Biomedical Press, 1980), pp. 109-150.

McConnell, E. E., J. R. Hass, N. Altman, J. A. Moore. "A spontaneous Outbreak of Polychlorinated Biphenyl (PCB) Toxicity in Rhesus Monkeys (Macaca Mulatta): Toxicopathology," Lab. Anim. Sci. 29(5):666-673 (1979).

McCracken, W. E. "Edible Tissue Sampling for Fish Contaminant Analysis," in PCBs: Human and Environmental Hazards, F. M. D'Itri and M. A. Kamrin, Eds. (Boston: Butterworth Publishers, 1983), pp. 123-140.

McInnes, R. G. "Technical Assistance in Support of Permitting Activities for the Thermal Destruction of PCBs," USEPA, Office of Research and Development, IERL, Research Triangle Park, NC, EPA 600/2-81-240 (NTIS No. PB82 231 325), 70 pp. (1982).

McInnes, R. G. and R. J. Johnson. "Provision of Technical Assistance to Support Regional Office Implementation of the PCB Regulations--East and West," Draft Project Summary Report by GCA Corporation, New Bedford, MA, and TRW, Inc., Redondo Beach, CA, on EPA Contract No. 68-02-3168, Work Assignment No. 45, and Contract No. 68-02-3174, Work Assignment No. 68, for David C. Sanchez, USEPA, Office of Research and Development, IERL, Research Triangle Park, NC, 186 pp. (1982).

McKinney, J. D., K. Chae, B. N. Gupta, J. A. Moore, and J. A. Goldstein. "Toxicological Assessment of Hexachlorobiphenyl Isomers and 2,3,7,8-Tetrachlorodibenzofuran in Chicks. I. Relationship of Chemical Parameters," Tox. and Appl. Pharma., 36:65-80 (1976).

McKinney, J. D. "Environmental Health Chemistry--Definitions and Interrelationships: A Case in Point," Chapter 1 in Environmental Health Chemistry, The Chemistry of Environmental Agents as Potential Human Health Hazards, J. D. McKinney, Ed. (Ann Arbor, MI: Ann Arbor Science Publishers, Inc., 1981), pp. 3-15.

McKinney, J. D., L. Moore, A. Prokopetz and D. B. Walters. "Validated Extraction and Cleanup Procedures for Polychlorinated Biphenyls and DDE in Human Body Fluids and Infant Formula," J. Assoc. Off. Anal. Chem. 67(1):122-129 (1984).

McKone, H. T. and A. Daub. "A Rapid and Efficient Cleanup Technique for the Quantitative Determination of Polychlorinated Biphenyls in Fish," Chromatogr. Mass Spectrom. Biomed. Sci. 2:497-503 (1983).

McLafferty, F. W. Interpretation of Mass Spectra, 3rd Edition, (Mill Valley, CA: University Science Books, 1980).

McLafferty, F. W., R. Knutti, R. Venkataraghavan, P. J. Arpino and B. G. Dawkins. "Continuous Mass Spectrometric Monitoring of a Liquid Chromatograph with Subnanogram Sensitivity Using an On-Line Computer," Anal. Chem. 47(9):1503-1505 (1975).

McLeod, H. A. and P. J. Wales. "A Low Temperature Cleanup Procedure for Pesticides and Their Metabolites in Biological Samples," J. Agr. Food Chem. 20(3):624-627 (1972).

McMahon B. and J. A. Burke. "Analytical Behavior Data for Chemicals Determined Using AOAC Multiresidue Methodology for Pesticide Residues in Foods," J. Assoc. Off. Anal. Chem., 81(3):640-652 (1978).

McMurtrey, K. D., N. J. Wildman and H. Tai. "Pyrolysis Gas Chromatography-Mass Spectrometry of Polychlorinated Biphenyls on Sediment," Bull. Environ. Contam. Toxicol. 31(6):734-737 (1983).

McNair, H. M. and E. J. Bonelli. Basic Gas Chromatography, 5th Edition. (Walnut Creek, CA, Varian Aerograph, March 1969.)

McQuade, J. M. "PCB Analysis by X-Ray Fluorescence," in Proceedings: 1981 PCB Seminar, G. Addis and J. Marks, Eds., Report No. EPRI-EL-2572, (Palo Alto, CA: Electric Power Research Institute, 1982), pp. 2-9.

Menzie, C. "Metabolism of Pesticides - Update II," U. S. Department of Interior, Fish and Wildlife Service, Washington, D.C. Special Scientific Report - Wildlife No. 212 (1978).

Menzie, C. M. "Metabolism of Pesticides Update III," U.S. Department of the Interior, Fish and Wildlife Service, Washington, D.C., Special Scientific Report--Wildlife 232, NTIS No. PB83-175349 (1980).

Mes, J. and D. S. Campbell. "Extraction Efficiency of Polychlorinated Biphenyl, Organochlorine Pesticides, and Phthalate Esters from Human Adipose Tissue," Bull. Environ. Contam. Toxicol. 16(1):53-60 (1976).

Mes, J., D. S. Campbell, R. N. Robinson and D. J. A. Davies. "Polychlorinated Biphenyl and Organochlorine Pesticide Residues in Adipose Tissue of Canadians," Bull. Environ. Contam. Toxicol. 17(2):196-203 (1977).

Mes, J. and D. J. Davies. "Variation in the Polychlorinated Biphenyl and Organochlorine Pesticide Residues During Human Breastfeeding and Its Diurnal Pattern," Chemosphere 7(9): 699-706 (1978).

Mes, J. and D. J. Davies. "Presence of Polychlorinated Biphenyl and Organochlorine Pesticide Residues and the Absence of Polychlorinated Terphenyls in Canadian Human Milk Samples," Bull. Environ. Contam. Toxicol. 21:381-387 (1979).

Mes, J., D. Davies and J. Truelove. "The Determination of Polychlorinated Biphenyl in Small Samples of Monkey Milk and Tissues. I.," Intern. J. Environ. Anal. Chem. 8:89-98 (1980).

Mes, J. and P. Y. Lau. "Distribution of Polychlorinated Biphenyl Congeners in Human Milk and Blood During Lactation," Bull. Environ. Contam. Toxicol. 31(6):639-643 (1983).

Mes, J., J. A. Doyle, B. R. Adams, D. J. Davies, and D. Turton. "Polychlorinated Biphenyls and Organochlorine Pesticides in Milk and Blood of Canadian Women During Lactation," Arch. Environ. Contam. Toxicol. 13(2):217-223 (1984); Chem. Abst. 100:152123r (1984).

Messier, F. M-F. Lévesque and R. Massé. "Metabolism of
4-Chlorobiphenyl by the Achromobacter Strain B-218 and
Bacillus Brevis Strain B-257," Abstract from The Thirty-First
Annual Conference on Mass Spectrometry and Allied Topics,
American Society for Mass Spectrometry, May 8-13, 1983,
p. 225.

Mestres, R., C. Chevallier and M. Pagnon. "Mass Spectrometric Confirmation of the Identity and Content of Pesticide
and Chlorinated Biphenyl Residues in the Sediments of the
Mediterranean Sea," Trav. Soc. Pharm. Montpellier 36(2):151-
160 (1976); Chem. Abst. 85:73422d (1976).

Mestres, R. and C. Chevallier. "XXXII. Method of Research
and Determination of PCB and Phthalate Pesticide Residues in
Water," Ann. Falsif. Expert. Chim. 70(750):101-111 (1977);
Chem. Abst. 87:79446c (1977).

Mestres, R., C. Chevallier, C. Espinoza and R. Cornet. "Application of Coupled Gas Chromatography-Mass Spectrometry in
Methods for the Study and Determination of Pesticide Residues
and Organic Micropollutants in Environmental and Food Materials," Ann. Falsif. Expert. Chim. 70(751):177-188 (1977);
Chem. Abst. 87:63535v (1977).

Metcalf, R. L. "Screening Compounds for Early Warnings About
Environmental Pollution," in Trace Substances in Environmental Health - VIII, D. D. Hemphill (Ed.), Proceedings of
University of Missouri's 8th Annual Conference on Trace Substances in Environmental Health," Columbia, Missouri, June
11-13, 1974. pp. 213-217.

Meuser, J. M. and W. C. Weimer. "Amine-Enhanced Photodegra-
dation of Polychlorinated Biphenyls," Battelle Pacific North-
west Labs, Richland, WA, Report No. EPRI-CS-2513 (NTIS No.
DE82 021378), 57 pp. (July 1982).

Middleditch, B. S., S. R. Missler and H. B. Hines. Mass
Spectrometry of Priority Pollutants, Plenum Press, New York
(1981).

Mieure, J. P., O. Hicks, R. G. Kaley and V. W. Saeger.
"Characterization of Polychlorinated Biphenyls," in National
Conference on Polychlorinated Biphenyls (November 19-21,
1975, Chicago, Illinois), F. A. Ayer (Ed.), prepared for U.S.
Environmental Protection Agency, Report No. EPA-560/6-75-004;
NTIS No. PB253 248 (March 1976).

Miki, T. "PCBs [Polychlorinated Biphenyls] and Organochlorine Pesticide Residues in Sugars," Seito Gijutsu Kenky-
ukaishi 25: 32-38 (1975); Chem. Abst. 83:149456z (1975).

Millar, J. D., R. E. Thomas and H. J. Schattenberg, III. "Determination of Organochlorine Pesticides and Polychlorinated Biphenyls in Water by Gas Chromatography," Anal. Chem. 53:214-219 (1981).

Millar, J. D., R. E. Thomas and D. E. Johnson. "Determination of Pesticides and PCBs in Industrial and Municipal Wastewaters," U.S. Environmental Protection Agency, Contract No. 68-03-2606, Report No. EPA-600/4-82-023 (NTIS No. PB82-214222) (March 1982).

Millar, J. D., R. E. Thomas, and H. J. Schattenberg. "EPA Method Study 18, Method 608--Organochlorine Pesticides and PCB's," Environmental Protection Agency, Environmental Monitoring and Support Laboratory, Cincinnati, Ohio, EPA-600/4-84-061; NTIS No. PB84 211358 (1984) 197 pp.

Miller, R. A. and R. D. Fox. "Catalyzed Wet Oxidation of Hazardous Wastes," Chapter 13 in Detoxication of Hazardous Waste, J. H. Exner, Ed. (Ann Arbor, MI: Ann Arbor Science Publishers, Inc., 1982), pp. 227-232.

Miller, S. "The Persistent PCB Problem," Environ. Sci. Technol. 16(2):98A-99A (1982).

Mills, P. A., J. H. Onley and R. A. Gaither. "Rapid Method for Chlorinated Pesticide Residues in Nonfatty Foods," J. Ass. Offic. Anal. Chem. 46(2):186-191 (1963).

Mills, P. A. "Variation of Florisil Activity: Simple Method for Measuring Adsorbent Capacity and Its Use in Standardizing Florisil Columns," J. Assoc. Offic. Anal. Chem. 51(1):29-32 (1968).

Mitchum, R. K., W. A. Korfmacher and G. F. Moler. "Capillary Gas Chromatography/ Atmospheric Pressure Negative Chemical Ionization Mass Spectrometry of the 22 Isomeric Tetrachlorodibenzo-p-dioxins," Anal. Chem. 54:719-722 (1982).

Miyata, H. and T. Kashimoto. "The Finding of Polychlorodibenzofurans in Commercial PCBs (Aroclor, Phenoclor and Clophen)," Shokuhin Eiseigaku Zasshi 17(6):434-437 (1976).

Miyata, H., T. Kashimoto and N. Kunita. "Detection and Determination of Polychlorodibenzofurnas in Normal Human Tissues and Kanemi Rice Oils Caused 'Kanemi Yusho'," J. Food Hyg. Soc. 18(3):260-265 (1977).

Mizushima, Y. and H. Mukai. "Study of Cleanup Operations in PCB Analysis," Niigata-ken Kogai Kenkyusho Kenkyu Hokoku 6:110-114 (1982); Chem. Abst. 98:10864x (1983).

Mizutani, T. and M. Matsumoto. "Determination of Polychlorinated Biphenyls by an Exhaustive Chlorination Method,"
Shokuhin Eiseigaku Zasshi 13(5):398-404 (1972); Chem. Abst.
78:66686v (1973).

Mizutani, T. and M. Matsumoto. "Separation and Determination
of Polychlorinated Biphenyls and DDE by Oxidation in a Solid
Support," Eisei Kagaku 19(5): 287-292 (1973); Chem. Abst. 80:
116981b (1974).

Modi, G., M. Piccinini and S. Bonciani. "Study of Pesticide
Contamination in Some Tuscany Wines," Boll. Chim. Unione
Ital. Lab. Prov. 2(3):133-147 (1976); Chem. Abst. 85:141275k
(1976).

Moein, G. J. "Study of the Distribution and Fate of Polychlorinated Biphenyls and Benzenes After Spill of Transformer
Fluid," Report No. EPA 904/9-76-014, NTIS No. PB288484
(1976).

Moolenaar, R. J. "Distribution and Fate of Chlorobiphenyls
in the Environment," in Advances in Exposure, Health and En-
vironmental Effects Studies of PCBs: Symposium Proceedings,
R. J. Davenport and B. K. Bernard (Eds.), Office of Toxic
Substances, U.S. Environmental Protection Agency, Washington,
D.C., Report No. LSI-TR-507-137B, NTIS No. PB84-135771
(December 1983), pp. 67-96.

Morita, M., J. Nakagawa, K. Akiyama, S. Mimura and N. Isono.
"Detailed Examination of Polychlorinated Dibenzofurans in PCB
Preparations and Kanemi Yusho Oil," Bull. Environ. Contam.
Toxicol. 18(1):67-73 (1977).

Morita, M., J. Nakagawa, and C. Rappe. "Polychlorinated Dibenzofuran (PCDF) Formation From PCB Mixture by Heat and Oxygen," Bull. Environ. Contam. Toxicol. 19:665-670 (1978).

Moseley, M. A. and E. D. Pellizzari. "Development and Eval-
uation of Wall Coated Open-Tubular Columns for GC Analysis of
Individual Polychlorinated Biphenyl Isomers," J. High Res.
Chromatogr. and Chromatogr. Commun. 5:404-412 (1982).

Moser, J. H. and K. R. Huibregtse. "Handbook for Sampling
and Sample Preservation of Water and Wastewater," EPA-600/
4-76-049 (NTIS No. PB-259 946) (1976).

Moye, H. A. "High Speed Liquid Chromatography of Pesticides," J. Chromatogr. Sci. 13:268-278 (1975).

Muldrew, D. H., B. L. Worobey and G. R. B. Webster. "Sorption of [^{14}C] 2,4,5,2',4',5'-Hexachlorobiphenyl to Glass and Plastic Surfaces," Proc. - Annu. Workshop Pestic. Residue Anal. (West. Can.), 16th, D. C. G. Muir, Ed., pp. 98-100 (1981); Chem. Abstr. 96:1520p (1982).

Mulhern, B. M. "An Improved Method for the Separation and Removal of Organochlorine Insecticides from Thin-layer Plates," J. Chromatogr. 34:556-558 (1968).

Mulhern, B. M., E. Cromartie, W. L. Reichel and A. Belisle. "Semiquantitative Determination of Polychlorinated Biphenyls in Tissue Samples by Thin Layer Chromatography," J. Assoc. Offic. Anal. Chem. 54(3):548-550 (1971).

Mullin, M. D. and J. C. Filkins. "Analysis of Polychlorinated Biphenyls by Glass Capillary and Packed-Column Chromatography," Chapter 11 in Advances in the Identification and Analysis of Organic Pollutants in Water, L. H. Keith Ed., Vol. 1 (Ann Arbor, MI: Ann Arbor Science Publishers, Inc., 1981), pp. 187-196.

Mullin, M., G. Sawka, L. Safe, S. McCrindle and S. Safe. "Synthesis of the Octa- and Nonachlorobiphenyl Isomers and Congeners and Their Quantitation in Commercial Polychlorinated Biphenyls and Identification in Human Breast Milk," J. Anal. Toxicol. 5:138-142 (1981).

Mullin, M. D., C. M. Pochini, S. H. Safe and L. M. Safe. "Analysis of PCBs Using Specific Isomer High-Resolution Capillary Gas Chromatography," Chapter 12 in PCBs: Human and Environmental Hazards, F. M. D'Itri and M. A. Kamrin, Eds. (Boston: Butterworth Publishers, 1983), pp. 165-176; Chem. Abstr. 100:79164w (1984).

Mullin, M. D., C. M. Pochini, S. McCrindle, M. Romkes, S. H. Safe and L. M. Safe. "High-Resolution PCB Analysis: Synthesis and Chromatographic Properties of All 209 PCB Congeners," Environ. Sci. Technol. 18:468-476 (1984).

Murphy, P. G. "Sulfuric Acid for the Cleanup of Animal Tissues for Analysis of Acid-Stable Chlorinated Hydrocarbon Residues," J. Assoc. Offic. Anal. Chem. 55(6):1360-1362 (1972).

Murphy, T. J., A. Schinsky, G. Paolucci and C. P. Rzeszutko. "Inputs of Polychlorinated Biphenyls from the Atmosphere to Lakes Huron and Michigan," Chapter 22 in Atmospheric Pollutants in Natural Waters, S. J. Eisenreich, Ed. (Ann Arbor, MI: Ann Arbor Science Publishers, Inc., 1981a), pp. 445-458.

Murphy, T. J., T. C. Heesen, and D. R. Young. "Exchange of Comments: Evaluation of a Technique for Measuring Dry Aerial Deposition Rates of DDT and PCB Residues," Atmos. Environ. 15:206-208 (1981b).

Murphy, T. J., and A. W. Schinsky. "Net Atmospheric Inputs of PCBs to the Ice Cover on Lake Huron," J. Great Lakes Res. 9(1):92-96 (1983).

Murphy, T. J., J. C. Pokojowczyk and M. D. Mullin. "Vapor Exhange of PCBs with Lake Michigan: The Atmosphere as a Sink for PCBs," Chapter 3 in Physical Behavior of PCBs in the Great Lakes, D. Mackay, S. Paterson, S. J. Eisenreich and M. S. Simmons, Eds. (Ann Arbor, MI: Ann Arbor Science Publishers, Inc., 1983), pp 49-58.

Musial, C. J., O. Hutzinger, V. Zitka and J. Crocker. "Presence of PCB, DDE and DDT in Human Milk in the Provinces of New Brunswick and Nova Scotia, Canada," Bull. Environ. Contam. Toxicol. 12(3):258-267 (1974).

Musial, C. J. and J. F. Uthe, "Interlaboratory Calibration Results of Polychlorinated Biphenyl Analyses in Herring," J. Assoc. Off. Anal. Chem. 66(1):22-31 (1983).

Musty, P. R. and G. Nickless. "Use of Amberlite XAD-4 for Extraction and Recovery of Chlorinated Insecticides and Polychlorinated Biphenyls from Water," J. Chromatogr. 89:185-190 (1974a).

Musty, P. R. and G. Nickless. "The Extraction and Recovery of Chlorinated Insecticides and Polychlorinated Biphenyls from Water Using Porous Polyurethane Foams," J. Chromatogr. 100(1): 83-94 (1974b).

Musty, P. R. and G. Nickless. "Extractants for Organochlorine Insecticides and Polychlorinated Biphenyls from Water," J. Chromatogr. 120:369-378 (1976).

Myers, D. S., S. D. Myers and J. J. Kelly. "PCB White Paper, Part II," Natl. Eng. 86(9):26-32; Chem. Abstr. 94:194024g (1982).

Nagayama, J., Y. Masuda and M. Kuratsune. "Chlorinated Dibenzofurans in Kanechlors and Rice Oils Used by Patients with Yusho," Fukuoka Igaku Zasshi 66(10):593-599 (1975).

Nagayama, J., M. Kuratsune and Y. Masuda. "Determination of Chlorinated Dibenzofurans in Kanechlors and 'Yusho Oil'," Bull. Environ. Contam. Toxicol. 15(1):9-13 (1976).

Nakagawa, H., M. Kayama and E. Ariyoshi. "Measurements of Polychlorinated Biphenyl (PCB) in Water, Sediments, and Organisms of Two Rivers in Hiroshima Prefecture," J. Fac. Fish Anim. Husb. Hiroshima Univ. 14(2):253-259 (1975); Public Health Abst. 62(6):34268 (1976).

Nakagawa, J., M. Morita and Y. Higuchi. "Analysis of Polychlorinated Dibenzofurans by Gas Chromatography Using Glass Capillary Columns," Tokyo-toritsu Eisei Kenkyusho Kenkyu Nempo 30-1:260-264 (1979); Chem. Abst. 93:160694c (1980).

Nakamura, A. and T. Kashimoto. "Studies on a Calculation Method for Polychlorinated Biphenyl (PCB) Isomers. Analysis Using an Apiezon L. Column," Shokuhin Eiseigaku Zasshi 18(1): 1-12 (1977); Chem. Abst. 87:63524r (1977).

Nakatsu, K., J. F. Brien, H. Taub, W. J. Racz and G. S. Marks. "Gram Quantity Synthesis and Chromatographic Assessment of 3,3',4,4'-Tetrachlorobiphenyl," J. Chromatogr. 239: 97-106 (1982).

Namovicz, R. M. (Ed.). Environ. Health Perspec., Experimental Issue Number One, National Institute of Environmental Health Sciences, Research Triangle Park, NC, 181 pp. (April 1972).

Napier, J. M., M. A. Travaglini, E. G. Laggis and M. A. Makerewicz. "Evaluation and Development of Polychlorinated Biphenyl Removal Processes," Oak Ridge Y-12 Plant, Oak Ridge, TN, Report No. Y/DZ-1, February 5, 1982.

National Bureau of Standards. "Standard Reference Material 1581. Polychlorinated Biphenyls in Oil," U.S. Department of Commerce, Washington, D.C., Summer 1982, 1 pp.

National Institute for Occupational Safety and Health. NIOSH Manual of Analytical Methods, Second Edition, Part I, NIOSH Monitoring Methods, Vol. 1, "Polychlorinated Biphenyls (PCB) in Air, Analytical Method P&CAM 244," U.S. Department of Health, Education, and Welfare, Cincinnati, Ohio, April 1977a.

National Institute for Occupational Safety and Health. NIOSH Manual of Analytical Methods, Second Edition, Part I, NIOSH Monitoring Methods, Vol. 1, "Polychlorinated Biphenyls (PCB) in Air, Analytical Method P&CAM 253," U.S. Department of Health, Education, and Welfare, Cincinnati, Ohio, April 1977b.

National Institute for Occupational Safety and Health. "Criteria for a Recommended Standard....Occupational Exposure to Polychlorinated Biphenyls (PCBs)," U.S. Department of Health, Education, and Welfare, (Public Health Service, Center for Disease Control, and National Institute for Occupational Safety and Health), DHEW (NIOSH) Publication No. 77-225, 224 pp. (September 1977c).

National Research Council. Polychlorinated Biphenyls, National Academy of Sciences, Washington, D.C., 182 pp. (1979).

National Technical Information Service. "Polychlorinated Biphenyls in the Environment, 1980-September, 1981," PB82-803867, 70 pp. (1982).

National Technical Information Service. "Polychlorinated Biphenyls in the Environment. 1977-January, 1983," PB83-859322, 199 pp. (1983a).

National Technical Information Service. "Polychlorinated Biphenyls in the Environment. September 1980-February 1983," PB83-804716, 154 pp. (1983b).

National Technical Information Service. "Polychlorinated Biphenyls: Occurrence in Sediments and Soils. 1977-January 1984 (Citations from the Selected Water Resource Abstracts Data Base)," PB84-860790, 124 pp. (1984a).

National Technical Information Service. "Polychlorinated Biphenyls: Occurrence and Treatemnt in Municipal and Industrial Wastes, 1977-1983, (Citations from the Selected Water Resource Abstracts Data Base)," PB84-860949 (1984b).

National Technical Information Service. "Polychlorinated Biphenyls in the Freshwater Environment, 1977-January 1984 (Citations from the Selected Water Resources Abstracts Data Base)," PB84-857358, 118 pp. (1984c).

National Technical Information Service. "Polychlorinated Biphenyls in the Environment, September 1980-April 1984 (Citations from the NTIS Data Base)," PB84-865724, 188 pp. (1984d).

Needham, L. L., A. L. Smrek, S. L. Head, V. W. Burse and J. A. Liddle. "Column Chromatography Separation of Polychlorinated Biphenyls from Dichlorodiphenyltrichloroethane and Metabolites," Anal. Chem. 52:2227-2229 (1980).

Needham, L. L., V. W. Burse and H. A. Price. "Temperature-Programmed Gas Chromatographic Determination of Polychlorinated And Polybrominated Biphenyls in Serum," J. Assoc. Off. Anal. Chem. 64(5):1131-1137 (1981).

Neely, W. B. "Reactivity and Environmental Persistence of PCB Isomers," Chapter 5 in Physical Behavior of PCBs in the Great Lakes, D. Mackay, S. Paterson, S. J. Eisenreich and M. S. Simmons, Eds. (Ann Arbor, MI: Ann Arbor Science Publishers, Inc., 1983) pp 71-88.

Neidert, E., and P. W. Saschenbrecker. "Improved Storherr Tube for Assisted and Sweep Co-Distillation Cleanup of Pesticides, Polychlorinated Biphenyls, and Pentachlorophenol from Animal Fats," J. Assoc. Off. Anal. Chem., 67(4):773-775 (1984).

Nelson, N. "Comments on Research Needs," Environ. Health Perspec. 1:181-185 (1972).

Nero, V. P., and R. D. Hudson. "Liquid Chromatographic Cleanup Prior to Determination of Polychlorinated Biphenyls in Oil by Gas Chromatography/Mass Spectrometry," Anal. Chem. 56:1041-1043 (1984).

Neu, H. J., M. Zell and K. Ballschmiter. "Identifizierung von Einzelkomponenten in komplexen Gemischen durch Retentions-Index-Vergleich nach Capillar-Gas-Chromatographie mit Elektroneneinfangdetektor (ECD)," Fresenius' Z. Anal. Chem. 293: 193-200 (1978).

Neu, H. J. and R. Zinburg. "Are We Using the Full Resolving Power of Capillary GC?" J. High Resol. Chromatogr. & Chromatogr. Commun., 2:395-399 (1979).

Neulicht, R. M., M. D. Erickson, and R. V. Shah. "Guidelines for PCB Destruction Permit Applications and Demonstration Test Plans," Work Assignment No. 6, Draft Interim Report No. 1, Revision No. 2, EPA Contract No. 68-02-3938, U.S. Environmental Protection Agency, Office of Toxic Substances, Washington, DC (March 1985).

Newsome, W. H. and J. B. Shields. "Radioimmunoassay of PCBs in Milk and Blood," Intern. J. Environ. Anal. Chem. 10:295-304 (1981).

Newton, D. A. and R. R. Laski. "A Computer Routine for the Rapid Quantitation of Combinations of Aroclors 1242, 1254, and 1260," J. Chromatogr. Sci. 21:161-165 (1983).

Nicholson, W. J. and J. A. Moore (Eds.). "Health Effects of Halogenated Aromatic Hydrocarbons," Ann. N. Y. Acad. Sci. Vol. 320 (1979).

Nickerson G. B. and S. T. Likens. "Quantitative Analysis of Organochlorine Pesticides and PCB's," J. Chromatogr. 21:1-5 (1966).

Nisbet, I. C. T. "Environmental Occurrence and Human Exposure in Polychlorinated Biphenyls - Environmental Impact," Environ. Res. 5:287-308 (1972a).

Nisbet, I. C. T. "Transport Models and Monitoring Schemes for PCBs in Polychlorinated Biphenyls - Environmental Impact," Environ. Res. 5:348-352 (1972b).

Nisbet, C. T. and A. F. Sarofim. "Rates and Routes of Transport of PCBs in the Environment," Environ. Health Perspec. 1:21-38 (1972a).

Nisbet, I. C. T. and A. F. Sarofim. "Transport and Transformation in the Environment in Polychlorinated Biphenyls - Environmental Impact," Environ. Res. 5:213-287 (1972b).

Nordstrom, R. J. "Detection of PCBs by Infrared Spectroscopy," in Proceedings: 1983 Seminar, G. Addis and R. Y. Komai, Eds., Report No. EPRI-EL-3581 (Palo Alto, CA: Electric Power Research Institute), 1984.

Nordstrom, R. J. and B. McIntosh. "Infrared Spectroscopy for Field Measurements of PCBs," in Proceedings: 1981 PCB Seminar, G. Addis and J. Marks, Eds., Report No. EPRI-EL-2573 (Palo Alto, CA: Electric Power Research Institute), 1982.

Norstrom, R. J., R. W. Risebrough and D. J. Cartwright. "Elimination of Chlorinated Dibenzofurans Associated with Polychlorinated Biphenyls Fed to Mallards (Anas platyrhynchos)," Toxicol. Appl. Pharmacol. 37:217-228 (1976).

Nose, K. "Decachlorination of Polychlorinated Biphenyls and Its Application to Soil and Rice Analyses," Nippon Nogei Kagaku Kaishi 46(12):679-681 (1972); Chem. Abst. 78:146633r (1973).

Nose, K. "Assay of Residual PCB [Polychlorinated Biphenyl] in Water, Soil, and Agricultural Products," Noyaku Seisan Gijutsu 30:29-36 (1973); Chem. Abst. 79:101513f (1973).

Nose, K. "Determination of PCB (Polychlorinated Biphenyls)," Yukagaku 25(10):638-644 (1976); Chem. Abst., 86:26565p (1977).

Nowicki, H. G. "Application of Azulene as Visual Aid to Monitor Column Chromatographic Fractionation of Samples for Pesticide and Polychlorinated Biphenyl Determination," J. Assoc. Offic. Anal. Chem. 64(1):16-18 (1981).

Nulton, C. P., C. L. Haile, and D. P. Redford. "Determination of Total Organic Halogen in Environmental Extracts by Gas Chromatography with Hall Detection," Anal. Chem. 56:598-599 (1984).

Nygren, S. and P. E. Mattsson. "Flow Programming in Glass Capillary Column-Electron Capture Gas Chromatograpy by Using the Valve in the Splitter Line," J. Chromatogr. 123:101-108 (1976).

Nyquist, R. A., C. L. Putzig and D. P. Peterson. "Identification of Pentachlorobiphenyl Isomers by Application of Diffuse Reflectance Fourier Transform Infrared Spectroscopy," Appl. Spectrosc. 37(2):140-153 (1983).

Oehme, M., and H. Stray, "Quantitative Determination of Ultra-Traces of Chlorinated Compounds in High-Volume Air Samples from the Arctic Using Polyurethane Foam as Collection Medium," Fresenius' Z. Anal. Chem., 311:665-673 (1982).

Oehme, M. and B. Ottar. "Toxic Organic Air Pollutants in the Arctic," in Proceedings: A Speciality Conference On: Measurement and Monitoring of Non-Criteria (Toxic) Contaminants in Air, E. R. Frederick (Ed.), The Air Pollution Control Association, Pittsburgh, PA, pp. 60-67 (1983).

Ofstad, E. B., G. Lunde, and K. Martinsen, "Chlorinated Aromatic Hydrocarbons in Fish from an Area Polluted by Industrial Effluents," Sci. Total Environ., 10:219-230 (1978).

Ogata, J. N., J. D. Okun, J. W. Hylin, and A. Bevenue, "Gas Chromatographic Method for the Analysis of Polychlorinated Biphenyls in Transformer Oil," J. Chromatogr., 189:425-427 (1980).

O'Keefe, P. W., R. M. Smith, D. R. Hilker, K. M. Aldous, and W. Gilday. "A Semiautomated Cleanup Method for Polychlorinated Dibenzo-p-dioxins and Polychlorinated Dibenzofurans in Environmental Samples," in Chlorinated Dioxins and Dibenzofurans in the Total Environment, II, L. H. Keith, C. Rappe, and G. Choudhary, Eds. (Boston: Butterworth Publishers, 1985) pp. 111-124.

Okumura, T., T. Kadono, and M. Nakatani, "Thin-layer Chromatography on Precoated Adsorbents Fixed with Fused Glass. V. Thin-layer Chromatography on Kieselguhr Sintered Plate," Yakugaku Zasshi 93(1):79-86 (1973); Chem. Abst. 78:105744j (1973).

O'Mara, T. and B. Magel. "Sample Analysis for Neal's Landfill Case," unpublished memorandum, U.S. Environmental Protection Agency Region V, Chicago, IL, October 27, 1982.

Onuska, F. I. and M. Comba, "Identification and Quantitative Analysis of Polychlorinated Biphenyls on WCOT Glass Capillary Columns," in Hydrocarbons and Halogenated Hydrocarbons in the Aquatic Environment, B. K. Afgham and D. Mackay, Eds. (New York: Plenum Press, 1980) pp. 285-302.

Onuska, F. I., R. J. Kominar and K. A. Terry. "Identification and Determination of Polychlorinated Biphenyls by High-Resolution Gas Chromatography," J. Chromatogr. 279:111-118 (1983).

Onuska, F. I. "Narrow-Bore Wall-Coated Open-Tubular Columns for Fast High-Resolution Gas Chromatographic Separations of Toxicants of Environmental Concern," Journal of Chromatography, 289:207-221 (1984).

Organization for Economic Cooperation and Development. Polychlorinated Biphenyls, Their Use and Control, Environmental Directorate, Paris (1973).

Organization for Economic Cooperation and Development. OECD Report on Protection of the Environment by Control of Polychlorinated Biphenyls, Paris (1979).

Osterroht, C., "Development of a Method for the Extraction and Determination of Non-polar, Dissolved Organic Substances in Sea Water," J. Chromatogr. 101:289-298 (1974).

Osterroht, C., "Dissolved PCB's and Chlorinated Hydrocarbon Pesticides in the Baltic, Determined by Two Different Sampling Procedures," Marine Chem. 5:113-121 (1977).

Oswald, E. O., L. Levy, B. J. Corbett, and M. P. Walker, "Differentiation and Characterization of Isomeric Polychlorinated Biphenyls by Gas-Liquid Chromatography Coupled with Electron Impact and Chemical Ionization Mass Spectrometry," J. Chromatogr. 93:63-90 (1974a).

Oswald, E. O., P. W. Albro, and J. D. McKinney, "Utilization of Gas-Liquid Chromatography Coupled with Chemical Ionization and Electron Impact Mass Spectrometry for the Investigation of Potentially Hazardous Environmental Agents and Their Metabolites," J. Chromatogr. 98:363-448 (1974b).

Ouw, H. K., G. R. Simpson, and D. S. Siyali, "Use and Health Effects of Aroclor 1242, a Polychlorinated Biphenyl, in an Electrical Industry," Arch. Environ. Health, 31:189-194 (1976).

Paasivirta, J. and M. Pitkänen. "Structure Analysis of the Main Components in PCB Mixture Clophen A 60," Finn. Chem. Lett. 89-93 (1975).

Pacco, J. M. and A. K. Mukherji. "Determination of Polychlorinated Biphenyls in a Polymer Matrix by Gel Permeation Chromatography Using Micro-Styragel® Columns," J. Chromatogr. 144: 113-117 (1977).

Palmork, K. H., J. C. Duinker, A. H. Knap, and J. P. Villeneuve. "Organochlorines," in Scientific Report of the Intercalibration Exercise, Intergovernmental Oceanographic Commission Technical Series, Report No. 22, UNESCO, Paris (ISBN 92-3-102077-3) (1982) pp. 60-83.

Pankow, J. F., L. M. Isabelle, and W. E. Asher. "Trace Organic Compounds in Rain. 1. Sampler Design and Analysis by Adsorption/Thermal Desorption (ATD)," Environ. Sci. Technol. 18:310-318 (1984); Errata published in Environ. Sci. Technol. 18:987 (1984).

Parker, C. E., P. W. Albro, M. J. Bobenrieth, T. W. Cochran and J. D. Robinson. "Quantitation of Halogenated Aromatic Compounds by Gas Chromatography-Mass Spectrometry," J. Chromatogr. 278(1):1-11 (1983).

Parkinson, A., R. Cockerline, and S. Safe, "Polychlorinated Biphenyl Isomers and Congeners as Inducers of Both 3-Methylcholanthrene- and Phenobarbitone-Type Microsomal Enzyme Activity," Chem.-Biol. Interactions, 29:277-289 (1980a).

Parkinson, A., L. Robertson, L. Safe, and S. Safe. "Polychlorinated Biphenyls as Inducers of Hepatic Microsomal Enzymes: Structure-Activity Rules," Chem.-Biol. Interactions, 30:271-285 (1980b).

Parlar, H. and M. Mansour. "Gaschromatographic Determination of Several Cyclodiene Insecticides in the Presence of Polychlorinated Biphenyls by Photoisomerisation Reactions," in Analytical Techniques in Environmental Chemistry 2, J. Albaiges, Ed. (New York: Pergamon Press, 1982), pp. 241-247.

Parris, R. M., F. R. Guenther, W. E. May, and S. N. Chesler. "Analysis of PCBs in Oil: Technique and SRM Development," in National Bureau of Standards Special Publication 674; Proceedings, Conference on Measurements and Standards for Recycled Oil - IV, held at NBS, Gaithersburg, Maryland (July 1984) pp. 27-32.

Pastel, M., B. Bush and J. S. Kim. "Accumulaton of Polychlorinated Biphenyls in American Shad During Their Migration in the Hudson River, Spring 1977," Pestic. Monit. J. 14(1): 11-22 (1980).

Pavlou, S. P. "Environmental Dynamics of Trace Organics Contaminants in Estuarine and Coastal Zone Ecosystems," in Analytical Techniques in Environmental Chemistry, J. Albaiges, Ed. (New York: Pergamon Press, 1980), pp. 387-399.

Pavlou, S. P. and W. Hom. "Interlaboratory Calibration Results from Chlorinated Hydrocarbon Analyses in Marine Sediments," Marine Chem. 4:155-163 (1976).

Pavlou, S. P., R. N. Dexter and W. Hom. "Characterization of Chlorinated Hydrocarbons in the Marine Environment: Sampling and Analytical Aspects," in Analytical Techniques in Environmental Chemistry, J. Albaiges, Ed. (New York: Pergamon Press, 1980), pp. 185-196.

Pearson, C. R. "Halogenated Aromatics," in The Handbook of Environmental Chemistry, O. Hutzinger, Ed. (New York, NY: Springer-Verlag, 1982), pp. 89-116.

PEDCo Environmental, Inc. "Substitutes for PCB's for Use in Indoor Electrical Transformers," Contract No. 68-01-3935, Work Assignment 1-16, PN 3607-6, Office of Pesticides and Toxic Substances, U.S. Environmental Protection Agency, Washington, D.C. (January 6, 1984).

Pellizzari, E. D. "Electron Capture Detection in Gas Chromatography," J. Chromatogr. 98:323-361 (1974).

Pellizzari, E. D. "State-of-the-Art Instrumental Organic Analysis in Environmental Chemistry," Chapter 10 in Environmental Health Chemistry, J. D. McKinney, Ed. (Ann Arbor, MI: Ann Arbor Science Publishers, Inc., 1981), pp. 195-218.

Pellizzari, E. D. "Analysis of Adipose and Blood Sera Samples for Individual PCB Isomers," MRI Subcontract No. 82-4900-21, EPA Contract No. 68-01-5915, Monthly Tech. Prog. Report No. 2, March 1, 1982.

Pellizzari, E. D., K. B. Tomer and M. A. Moseley. "High-Resolution Gas Chromatography and Negative Ion Chemical Ionization Mass Spectrometry of Polychlorinated Biphenyls," Chapter 12 in Advances in the Identification and Analysis of Organic Pollutants in Water, L. H. Keith, Ed., Vol. 1 (Ann Arbor, MI: Ann Arbor Science Publishers, Inc., 1981), pp. 197-218.

Pellizzari, E. D., S. D. Cooper, T. D. Hartwell and D. A. Whitehurst. "Analysis of Adipose and Blood Sera Samples for Individual PCB Isomers," Final Report, Midwest Research Institute, Kansas City, MO, Prepared for Office of Pesticides and Toxic Substances, U.S. Environmental Protection Agency, Contract No. 68-01-5915, Task 46 (1983a).

Pellizzari, E. D., M. A. Moseley, S. D. Cooper, J. V. Harry B. A. Demian and M. D. Mullin. "Recent Advances in the Analysis of Polychorinated Biphenyls in Environmental and Biological Media," in Advances in Exposure, Health and Environmental Effects Studies of PCBs: Symposium Proceedings, R. J. Davenport and B. K. Bernard (Eds.), Office of Toxic Substances, U.S. Environmental Protection Agency, Washington, D.C., Report No. LSI-TR-507-137B, NTIS No. PB84-135771 (December 1983b), pp. 4-60.

Pepe, M. G. and J. J. Byrne. "Adhesion-Binding of 2,2',4,4',5,5'-Hexachlorobiphenyl to Glass and Plastic: A Posible Source of Error for PCB Analysis," Bull. Environ. Contam. Toxicol. 25:936-940 (1980).

Perlman, H. L. "Accelerated Decision," U.S. Environmental Protection Agency, Before the Administrator, in re: Dow Chemical Company, Respondent. Docket No. TSCA (16(a))-1, September 22, 1980.

Perry, T. W., R. J. Everson, K. S. Hendrix, R. C. Peterson and F. R. Robinson. "Placental Transfer of Ingested Aroclor 1254 in the Bovine," in Trace Substances in Environmental Health 16:326-330 (1982).

Peterman, P. H., J. J. Delfino, D. J. Dube, T. A. Gibson and F. J. Priznar. "Chloro-organic Compounds in the Lower Fox River, Wisconsin," in Hydrocarbons and Halogenated Hydrocarbons in the Aquatic Environment, B. K. Afghan and D. Mackay, Eds. (New York: Plenum Publishing Corporation, 1980), pp. 145-160.

Peyton, T. O. "Biological Disposal of Hazardous Waste," Enzyme Microb. Technol. 6(4):146-154 (1984).

Picer, M. and M. Ahel. "Separation of Polychlorinated Biphenyls from DDT and Its Analogues on a Miniature Silica Gel Column," J. Chromatogr. 150:119-127 (1978).

Picer, N. and M. Picer. "Evaluation of Macroreticular Resins for the Determination of Low Concentratons of Chlorinated Hydrocarbons in Sea Water and Tap Water," J. Chromatogr. 193: 357-369 (1980).

Picker, J. E., and B. N. Colby, "Field Determination of Aroclors Using an Automated Electron Capture Detector Gas Chromatograph," in Proceedings: 1983 PCB Seminar, G. Addis and R. Y. Komai, Eds., Report No. EPRI-EL-3581 (Palo Alto, CA: Electric Power Research Institute), 1984.

Piechalak, B. "The Semiquantitative Detection of Polychlorinated Biphenyls (PCBs) in Contaminated Soils by Thin-Layer Chromatography," in Proceedings: 1983 PCB Seminar, G. Addis and R. Y. Komai, Eds., Report No. EPRI-EL-3581 (Palo Alto, CA: Electric Power Research Institute), 1984.

Pittaway, A. R., R. S. O'Connor and E. J. Heiden. "A Report of a Survey on the Incidental Manufacture, Processing, Distribution, and Use of Polychlorinated Biphenyl at Concentrations Below 50 ppm," Report prepared for Chemical Manufacturers Association by Regulatory Research Service (November 1981).

Pittaway, A. R. and T. W. Horner. "Statistical Analysis of Data from a Round Robin Experiment on PCB Samples," Report prepared for Chemical Manufacturers Association, Washington, D.C. (March 18, 1982).

Plumb, R. H., Jr. "Procedures for Handling and Chemical Analysis of Sediment and Water Samples," Prepared for U.S. Environmental Protection Agency/Corps of Engineers Technical Committee on Criteria for Dredged and Fill Material, Contract No. EPA-4805572010, NTIS No. AD A103788 (May 1981).

Polcyn, A. J., S. A. Whitlock and T. E. Siedhoff. "PCB Waste Destruction Study: High Efficiency Boiler," in Proceedings: A Specialty Conference on: Measurement and Monitoring of Non-Criteria (Toxic) Contaminants in Air, E. R. Frederick, Ed., (Pittsburgh, PA: The Air Pollution Control Association, 1983), pp. 361-373.

Polishuk, Z. W., M. Ron, M. Wassermann, S. Cucos, D. Wassermann and C. Lemesch. "Pesticides in People. Organochlorine Compounds in Human Blood Plasma and Milk," Pestic. Monit. J. 10(4):121-129 (1977).

Pomerantz, I., J. Burke, D. Firestone, J. McKinney, J. Roach and W. Trotter. "Chemistry of PCBs and PBBs," Environ. Health Perspec. 24:133-146 (1978).

Poole, C. F. and S. A. Schuette. "Isolation and Concentration Techniques for Capillary Column Gas Chromatographic Analysis," J. Chromatogr. pp. 526-549 (1983).

Porter, M. L., and J. A. Burke. "An Isolation and Cleanup Procedure for Low Levels of Organochlorine Pesticide Residues in Fats and Oils," J. Assoc. Offic. Anal. Chem. 56:733-738 (1973).

Pressley, T. A. and J. E. Longbottom. "The Determination of Organohalide Pesticides and PCBs in Industrial and Municipal Wastewater: Method 617," U.S. Environmental Protection Agency, Report No. EPA-600/4-82-006, 35 pp.; NTIS PB82-156001 (1982).

Price, H. A., and R. L. Welch. "Occurrence of Polychlorinated Biphenyls in Humans," Environmental Health Perspectives, I:73-78 (1972).

Pyysalo, H., K. Wickström, and R. Litmanen. "A Baseline Study on the Concentrations of Chlordane-, PCB- and DDT-Compounds in Finnish Fish Samples in the Year 1982," Chemosphere, 12(6):837-842 (1983).

Que Hee, S. S., J. A. Ward, M. W. Tabor and R. R. Suskind. "Screening Method for Aroclor 1254 in Whole Blood," Anal. Chem. 55:157-160 (1983).

Rapaport, R. A. and S. J. Eisenreich. "Chromatographic Determination of Octanol-Water Partition Coefficients (K_{ow}'S) for 58 Polychlorinated Biphenyl Congeners," Environ. Sci. Technol. 18:163-170 (1984).

Rappe, C. "Analysis of Polychlorinated Dioxins and Furans," Environ. Sci. Technol. 18(3):78A-90A (1984).

Rappe, C., H. R. Buser, H. Kuroki, and Y. Masuda. "Identification of Polychlorinated Dibenzofurans (PCDFs) Retained in Patients with Yusho," Chemosphere 8(4):259-266 (1979).

Rappe, C. and H. R. Buser. "Chemical Properties and Analytical Methods," Chapter 2 in Halogenated Biphenyls, Terphenyls, Naphthalenes, Dibenzodioxins and Related Products, R. D. Kimbrough, Ed. (New York, NY: Elsevier/North-Holland Biomedical Press, 1980), pp. 41-76.

Rappe, C., S. Marklund, P.-A. Bergqvist and M. Hansson. "Polychlorinated Dibenzo-p-dioxins, Dibenzofurans and Other Polynuclear Aromatics Formed During Incineration and Polychlorinated Biphenyl Fires," in Chlorinated Dixoins and Dibenzofurans in the Total Environment, G. Choudhary, L. H. Keith, C. Rappe (Eds.) (Ann Arbor Science Book: Butterworth Publishers, 1983), pp. 99-124.

Reggiani, G. "Toxicology of TCDD and Related Compounds: Observations in Man," in Chlorinated Dioxins and Related Compounds, O. Hutzinger, R. W. Frei, E. Merian and F. Pocchiari, Eds. (New York, NY: Pergamon Press, 1982), pp. 463-493.

Reynolds, L. M. "Polychlorobiphenyls (PCB's) and Their Interference with Pesticide Residue Analysis," Bull. Environ. Contam. Toxicol. 4(3):128-143 (1969).

Reynolds, L. M., and T. Cooper. "Analysis of Organochlorine Residues in Fish," Water Quality Parameters, ASTM STP 573, American Society for Testing and Materials, pp. 196-205 (1975).

Ribick, M. A., G. R. Dubay, J. D. Petty, D. L. Stalling, and C. J. Schmitt. "Toxaphene Residues in Fish: Identification, Quantification, and Confirmation at Part per Billion Levels," Environ. Sci. Technol. 16:310-318 (1982).

Rice, C. P. and W. A. Frez. "Application of Capillary Chromatography to the Study of the Cycling of PCBs on Suspended Particles," Final Report Prepared for the Great Lakes Environmental Research Laboratory - The National Oceanographic and Atmospheric Administration, Department of Commerce, Grant NA79RAD00006, NTIS No. PB82-245903 (1981).

Rice, C. P., P. A. Meyers and G. S. Brown. "Role of Surface Microlayers in the Air-Water Exhange of PCBs," Chapter 10 in Physical Behavior of PCBs in the Great Lakes, D. Mackay, S. Paterson, S. J. Eisenreich and M. S. Simmons, Eds. (Ann Arbor, MI: Ann Arbor Science Publishers, Inc., 1983), pp. 157-179.

Rice, C. P., B. J. Eadie, and K. M. Erstfeld. "Enrichment of PCBs in Lake Michigan Surface Films," J. of Great Lakes Research, 8(2):265-270 (1982).

Richardson, W. L., V. E. Smith and R. Wethington. "Dynamic Mass Balance of PCB and Suspended Solids in Saginaw Bay--A Case Study," Chapter 18 in Physical Behavior of PCBs in The Great Lakes, D. Mackay, S. Paterson, S. J. Eisenreich and M. S. Simmons, Eds. (Ann Arbor, MI: Ann Arbor Science Publishers, Inc., 1983), pp. 329-366.

Ringer, R. K. "Toxicology of PCBs in Mink and Ferrets," in PCBs: Human and Environmental Hazards, F. M. D'Itri and M. A. Kamrin, Eds. (Boston: Butterworth Publishers, 1983), pp. 227-240.

Risebrough, R. W. "Determination of Polychlorinated Biphenyls in Environmental Samples," Presented at the International Symposium on Identification and Measurement of Environmental Pollutants, Ottawa, Ontario, Canada, June 14-17, 1971.

Risebrough, R. W., B. W. de Lappe, and W. Walker II. "Transfer of Higher Molecular Weight Chlorinated Hydrocarbons to the Marine Environment," in Marine Pollutant Transfer, H. L. Windom, R. A. Duce, Eds. (Lexington, MA: Lexington Books, 1976). pp. 261-321.

Riva, M., A. Carisano and A. Gaghetta. "Rapid GLC-ECD [Gas-Liquid Chromatography-Electron Capture Detector] Determination of Chloroorganic Pesticide and Polychlorobiphenyl (PCB's) Residues in Animal Foods. General Considerations about Ecological Contamination," Riv. Ital. Sostanze Grasse 50(12):434-442 (1973); Chem. Abst. 81:11924c (1974).

Robbins, A. L. and C. R. Willhite. "A Rapid Method for the Analysis of Polychlorinated Biphenyls in Milk," Bull. Environ. Contam. Toxicol. 21:428-431 (1979).

Roberts, J. R., D. W. Rodgers, J. R. Bailey and M. A. Rorke. "Polychorinated Biphenyls: Biological Criteria for an Assessment of Their Effects on Environmental Quality," Associate Committee on Scientific Criteria for Environmental Quality. Ottawa, Canada: National Research Council of Canada (1978).

Rodgers, P. W. "Model Simulation of PCB Dynamics in Lake Michigan," Chapter 17 in Physical Behavior of PCBs in the Great Lakes, D. Mackay, S. Paterson, S. J. Eisenreich and M. S. Simmons, Eds. (Ann Arbor, MI: Ann Arbor Science Publishers, Inc., 1983), pp. 311-327.

Rodriguez, C. F., W. A. McMahon and R. E. Thomas. "Method Development for Determination of Polychlorinated Hydrocarbons in Municipal Sludge," Final Report, Contract No. 68-03-2606, Environmental Protection Agency, EPA-600/2-80-029; NTIS No. PB 82-234 071 (March 1980).

Rogan, W. J., B. C. Gladen, J. D. McKinney, and P. W. Albro. "Chromatographic Evidence of Polychlorinated Biphenyl Exposure From a Spill," J. Amer. Med. Assoc. 249(8):1057-1058 (1983).

Rohleder, H., H. Staudacher and W. Suemmermann. "High-pressure Liquid Chromatography for the Separation of Lipophilic Organochlorine Xenobiotics from Triglycerides in Trace Analysis," Fresenius' Z. Anal. Chem. 279(2):152-153 (1976); Chem. Abst. 84:160197g (1976).

Ross, P. F., D. L. Osheim and H. A. Nelson. "PCB Residues in Feedlot Steers," Bull. Environ. Contam. Toxicol. 26:485-488 (1981).

Rouse, T. O., "PCB Round Robin Analysis," in Proceedings: 1981 PCB Seminar, G. Addis and J. Marks, Eds., Report No. EPRI-EL-2572 (Palo Alto, CA: Electric Power Research Institute), 1982.

Rote, J. W. and W. J. Morris. "Use of Isotopic Abundance Ratios in Identification of Polychlorinated Biphenyls by Mass Spectrometry," J. Assoc. Offic. Anal. Chem. 56(1):188-199 (1973).

Roth, R. W., J. R. Heys, D. H. T. Chien, G. A. Rotert, J. H. Saugier and M. D. Erickson. "Methods of Analysis for Incidentally Generated PCBs--Synthesis of ^{13}C-PCB Surrogates," Draft Interim Report No. 3, Revision No. 1, EPA Contract No. 68-01-5915, Task 51, prepared by Midwest Research Institute, Kansas City, MO, for Office of Toxic Substances, U.S. Environmental Protection Agency, Washington, D.C., November 22, 1982, 91 pp.

Rubenstein, H. M. "Polychlorinated Biphenyls: Single Isomer Formation from 2,4-Dichlorobenzoyl Peroxide," Abstract No. 614, 1983 Pittsburgh Conference and Exposition on Analytical Chemistry and Applied Spectroscopy, March 7-12, 1983.

Russell, D. J. and B. McDuffie. "Analysis for Phthalate Esters in Environmental Samples: Separation from PCB's and Pesticides Using Dual Column Liquid Chromatography," Int. J. Environ. Anal. Chem. 15(3):165-183; Chem. Abstr. 99:151456y (1983).

Rust, S. W. "Study of Errors Generated in the Chemical Analysis of Environmental Samples," Final Report, Task 67, Contract No. 68-01-6721, U.S. Environmental Protection Agency, Office of Toxic Substances, Washington, DC (1984).

Ruzo, L. O., M. J. Zabik and R. D. Schuetz. "Polychlorinated Biphenyls: Photolysis of 3,4,3',4'-Tetrachlorobiphenyl and 4,4'-Dichlorobiphenyl in Solution," Bull. Environ. Contam. Toxicol. 8(4):217-218 (1972).

Ryan, J. J., P-Y Lau, J. C. Pilon, D. Lewis, H. A. McLeod, and A. Gervals. "Incidence and Levels of 2,3,7,8-Tetrachlorodibenzo-p-dioxin in Lake Ontario Commercial Fish," Environ. Sci. Technol., 18:719-721 (1984).

Ryan, R. M., D. R. Pendleton and J. M. Jenks. "Coastal Impacts of PCB Incineration Operations in the Gulf of Mexico," in Proceedings: A Specialty Conference on: Measurement and Monitoring of Non-criteria (Toxic) Contaminants in Air, E. R. Frederick, Ed. (Pittsburgh: The Air Pollution Control Association, 1983), pp. 351-360.

Sabate, L. G., X. Tomas, M. A. Colom and A. Garcia-Carrillo. "Quantitation of PCB - Chesbyshev's Method," Comput. Appl. Lab. 1(2):146; Chem. Abstr. 99:224441b (1983).

Saeki, S., A. Tsutsui, K. Oguri, H. Yoshimura and M. Hamana. "Isolation and Structure Elucidation of the Amino Component of KC-400 (Chlorobiphenyls)," Fukuoka-Igaku-Zasshi 62(1): 21-24 (1971); Chem. Abst. 74:146294y (1971).

Safe, S. "Overview of Analytical Identification and Spectroscopic Properties," in National Conference on Polychlorinated Biphenyls (November 19-21, 1975, Chicago, Illinois), F. A. Ayer, Ed., EPA-560/6-75-004; NTIS No. PB 253-248, March 1976.

Safe, S. "Metabolism, Uptake, Storage and Bioaccumulation," Chapter 4 in Halogenated Biphenyls, Terphenyls, Naphthalenes, Dibenzodioxins and Related Products, R. D. Kimbrough, Ed. (New York, NY: Elsevier/North-Holland Biomedical Press, 1980), pp. 81-107.

Safe, S. "Polychlorinated Biphenyls (PCBs) and Polybrominated Biphenyls (PBBs): Biochemistry, Toxicology, and Mechanism of Action," CRC Crit. Rev. Toxicol. 13:319-395 (1984).

Safe, S., N. Platonow, O. Hutzinger and W. D. Jamieson. "Analysis of Organochlorine Metabolites in Crude Extracts by High Resolution Photoplate Mass Spectrometry," Biomed. Mass Spectrom. 2:201-203 (1975).

Safe, S., C. Wyndham, A. Parkinson, R. Purdy and A. Crawford. "Halogenated Biphenyl Metabolism," in Hydrocarbons and Halogenated Hydrocarbons in the Aquatic Environment, B. K. Afghan and D. Mackay, Eds. (New York, NY: Plenum Press, 1980), pp. 537-544.

Safe, S. and R. K. Boyd. "Pesticide Analysis by Mass Spectrometry," in Pesticide Analysis Conf. Proc., K. G. Das, Ed. (New York: Dekker, 1981), pp. 329-368; Chem. Abst. 95: 110007b (1981).

Safe, S., A. Parkinson, L. Robertson, R. Cockerline, L. Safe, S. Bandiera and A. Okey. "PCBs as AHH Inducers," in Chlorinated Dioxins and Related Compounds, O. Hutzinger, R. W. Frei, E. Merian and F. Pocchiari, Eds. (New York: Pergamon Press, 1981), pp. 383-392.

Safe, S., L. W. Robertson, L. Safe, A. Parkinson, S. Bandiera, T. Sawyer, and M. A. Campbell. "Halogenated Biphenyls: Molecular Toxicology," Can J. Physiol. Pharmacol., 60:1057-1064 (1982).

Safe, S., M. Mullin, L. Safe, C. Pochini, S. McCrindle and M. Romkes. "High Resolution PCB Analysis," Chapter 1 in <u>Physical Behavior of PCBs in The Great Lakes</u>, D. Mackay, S. Paterson, S. J. Eisenreich and M. S. Simmons, Eds. (Ann Arbor, MI: Ann Arbor Science Publishers, Inc., 1983a), pp. 1-13

Safe, S., L. Robertson, T. Sawyer, A. Parkinson, S. Bandiera, L. Safe and M. Campbell. "PCDDs and Related Compounds: Metabolism and Biochemistry," in <u>Human and Environmental Risks of Chlorinated Dioxins and Related Compounds</u>, R. E. Tucker, A. L. Young and A. P. Gray, Eds. (New York, NY: Plenum Press, 1983b), pp. 393-403.

Safe, S., M. Mullin, L. Safe, C. Pochini and S. McCrindle. "High Resolution PCB (Polychlorinated Biphenyls) Analysis," Environmental Research Laboratory, U.S. Environmental Protection Agency, Duluth, MN, EPA-600/D-83-095; NTIS No. PB83-246124; <u>Chem. Abstr.</u> 100:61153g (1983c).

Safe, S., A. Parkinson, L. Robertson, T. Sawyer and S. Bandiera. "PCBs (Polychlorinated Biphenyls): Structure-Activity Relationships," Environmental Research Laboratory, U.S. Environmental Protection Agency, Washington, D.C., EPA-600/D83-096, NTIS No. PB83-247486 (1983d).

Safe, S., A. Parkinson, L. Robertson, T. Sawyer, S. Bandiera, L. Safe, M. A. Campbell and M. Mullin. "PCBs: Structure-Activity Relationships," in <u>Advances in Exposure, Health and Environmental Effects of PCBs: Symposium Proceedings</u>, R. J. Davenport and B. K. Bernard (Eds.), Office of Toxic Substances, U.S. Environmental Protection Agency, Washington, D.C., Report No. LSI-TR-507-137B; NTIS No. PB-84-135771 (December 1983e), pp. 229-248.

Sans, W. W. "Multiple Insecticide Residue Determination Using Column Chromatography, Chemical Conversion, and Gas-Liquid Chromatography," <u>J. Agr. Food Chem.</u> 15:192-198 (1967).

Saperstein, M. D., R. J. Gordon and E. J. Faeder. "PCB Contamination in Distribution Transformers," <u>J. Environ. Sci. Health</u> A17(2):241-251 (1982).

Sarofim, A. F. "Properties, Production, and Uses in Polychlorinated Biphenyls - Environmental Impact," <u>Environ. Res.</u> 5:258-273 (1972a).

Sarofim, A. F. "Analytical Methods in Polychlorinated Biphenyls - Environmental Impact," <u>Environ. Res.</u> 5:338-348 (1972b).

Sarro, T. L., D. R. Moore and D. G. Ackerman. "Emissions Testing During Incineration of PCBs at Energy Systems Company, El Dorado, Arkansas," Draft Report by TRW, Inc., Redondo Beach, CA, to Philip C. Schwindt, U.S. Environmental Protection Agency, Region VI, Dallas, TX, EPA Contract No. 68-02-2174, Work Assignment 56 (September 1981a), 171 pp.

Sarro, T. L., D. R. Moore and D. G. Ackerman. "Emissions Testing During Incineration of PCBs at Rollins Environmental Services, Inc., Deer Park, TX," Draft Report by TRW, Inc., Redondo Beach, CA, to Philip C. Schwindt, U.S. Environmental Protection Agency, Region VI, Dallas, TX, EPA Contract No. 68-02-3174, Work Assignment 56 (September 1981b), 128 pp.

Sauter, A. D., P. E. Mills, W. L. Fitch and R. Dyer. "Inter-laboratory GC/MS Response Factor Precision," J. High Resol. Chromatogr. & Chromatogr. Commun. 5:27-30 (1982).

Savage, E. P., J. D. Tessari, J. W. Malberg, H. W. Wheeler and J. R. Bagby. "A Search for Polychlorinated Biphenyls in Human Milk in Rural Colorado," Bull. Environ. Contam. Toxicol. 9(4):222-226 (1973a).

Savage, E. P., J. D. Tessari, J. W. Malberg, H. W. Wheeler and J. R. Bagby. "Organochlorine Pesticide Residues and Polychlorinated Biphenyls in Human Milk, Colorado--1971-72," Pestic. Monit. J. 7(1):1-3 (1973b).

Sawyer, L. D. "Collaborative Study of the Recovery and Gas Chromatographic Quantitation of Polychlorinated Biphenyls in Chicken Fat and Polychlorinated Biphenyl-DDT Combinations in Fish," J. Assoc. Offic. Anal. Chem. 56(4):1015-1023 (1973).

Sawyer, L. D. "Quantitation of Polychlorinated Biphenyl Residues by Electron Capture Gas-Liquid Chromatography: Reference Material Characterization and Preliminary Study," J. Assoc. Offic. Anal. Chem. 61(2):272-281 (1978a).

Sawyer, L. D. "Quantitation of Polychlorinated Biphenyl Residues by Electron Capture Gas-Liquid Chromatography: Collaborative Study," J. Assoc. Offic. Anal. Chem. 61(2):282-291 (1978b).

Schneider, J. F., S. Bourne, and A. S. Boparai, "Parallel Capillary Column Gas Chromatography in the Determination of Chlorinated Pesticides and PCBs," Journal of Chromatographic Science, 22 (1984).

Schulte, E. and L. Acker. "Identifizierung und Metabolisierbarkeit von polychlorierten Biphenylen," Naturwissenschaften 61:79-80 (1974a).

Schulte, E. and L. Acker. "Gas-Chromatographie mit Glas-capillaren bei Temperaturen bis zu 320°C und ihre Anwendung zur Trennung von Polychlorbiphenylen," Fresenius' Z. Anal. Chem. 268(4):260-267; Chem. Abst. 81:115377t (1974b).

Schulte, E., H. P. Thier and L. Acker. "Residual Analysis of Polychlorinated Biphenyls in Foods of Animal Origin: Experiences and Proposals for Standardization," Dtsch. Lebensm.-Rundsch. 72(7):229-232 (1976); Chem. Abst. 85:121894h (1976).

Schulte, E. and R. Malisch. "Berechnung der Wahren PCB-Gehalte in Umweltproben I. Ermittlung der Zusammensetzung Zweier Technischer PCB-Gemische," Fresenius' Z. Anal. Chem. 314:545-551 (1983).

Schulte, E., and R. Malisch. "Calculation of the Real PCB Content in Environmental Samples II. Gas Chromatographic Determination of the PCB Concentration in Human Milk and Butter," Fresenius' Z. Anal. Chem. 319:54-59 (1984).

Schutjes, C. P. M., E. A. Vermeer, G. J. Scherpenzeel, R. W. Bally, and C. A. Cramers. "Practical Aspects of Fast Gas Chromatography on 50 µm I.D. Capillary Columns: Combination with Electron-Capture Detection," Journal of Chromatography, 289:157-162 (1984).

Schwalb, A. L. and A. Marquez. "Salt River Project's Experience with the Horiba Sulfur/Chlorine-in-Oil Analyzer," in Proceedings: 1981 PCB Seminar, G. Addis and J. Marks, Eds. Report No. EPRI-EL-2572 (Palo Alto, CA: Electric Power Research Institute, 1982), pp. 2-23.

Schwartz, P. M., S. W. Jacobson, G. Fein, J. L. Jacobson and H. A. Price. "Lake Michigan Fish Consumption as a Source of Polychlorinated Biphenyls in Human Cord Serum, Maternal Serum, and Milk," Am. J. Public Health 73(3):293-296 (1983).

Schwartz, T. R. and R. G. Lehmann. "Determination of Poly-chlorinated Biphenyls in Plant Tissue," Bull. Environ. Contam. Toxicol. 28:723-727 (1982).

Schwartz, T. R., J. D. Petty, D. L. Stalling, J. W. Hogan, M. K. Marlow, R. D. Campbell and R. L. Little. "A MUMPs (DSM-11) Derived Data Base for Congener Specific PCB Analysis Leading to Pattern Recognition Studies," Abstract, 184th Annual Chemical Society National Meeting, September 12-17, 1982.

Schwartz, T. R., J. D. Petty and E. M. Kaiser. "Preparation of n-Alkyl Trichloroacetates and Their Use as Retention Index Standards in Gas Chromatography," Anal. Chem. 55:1839-1840 (1983).

Schwartz. T. R., R. D. Campbell, D. L. Stalling, R. L. Little, J. D. Petty, J. W. Hogan and E. M. Kaiser. "Laboratory Data Base for Isomer-Specific Determination of Polychlorinated Biphenyls," Anal. Chem. 56:1303-1308 (1984).

Scinto, L. L., P. A. Painter, A. M. Takata and T. J. Hennings. "Preliminary Operations Plan and Guidelines for the At-sea Incineration of Liquid PCB Wastes," Office of Research and Development, U.S. Environmental Protection Agency, Research Triangle Park, NC, EPA-600/2-82-068, NTIS No. PB83-181834 (1982).

Seiber, J. N. "Reversed-Phase Liquid Chromatography of Some Pesticides and Related Compounds. Solubility-Retention Relationships," J. Chromatogr. 94:151-157 (1974).

Seidl, G. and K. Ballschmiter. "Isolation of PCB's from Soil. Recovery Rates Using Different Solvent Systems," Chemosphere 5:373-376 (1976a).

Seidl, G. and K. Ballschmiter. "Isolation of PCB's from Vegetable Oils: Recovery and Efficiency of 'Clean Up' Methods," Chemosphere 5:363-366 (1976b).

Seidl, G. and K. Ballschmiter. "Quantitation of Polychlorinated Biphenyl (PCB)-Residues after Hydrodechlorination to Biphenyl Using Liquid Chromatography with UV-Detection," Fresenius' Z. Anal. Chem. 296:281-284 (1979).

Serum, J. W., S. C. Tong, L. E. St. John Jr., C. A. Bache, D. R. Mertens and D. J. Lisk. "Electron-Capturing Compounds and Selected Elements in Paper," Bull. Environ. Contam. Toxicol. 10(2):88-96 (1973).

Sevcík, J. "Detectors in Gas Chromatography," J. Chromatogr. Library Vol. 4 (New York, NY: Elsevier Scientific Publishers, 1976).

Sexton, F. W. and D. E. Lentzen. "Audit of the Vulcanus Incineration Ship Prior to the August 1982 PCB Burn, Mobile, Alabama," U.S. Environmental Protection Agency, Office of Research and Development, Industrial Environmental Research Laboratory, Research Triangle Park, NC, Report No. EPA-600/7-83-023; NTIS No. PB83-193698 (April 1983).

Shahied, S. I., R. P. Stanovick, D. E. McInturff and E. Missaghi. "Determination of Polychlorinated Biphenyl (PCB's) Residues in Grades of Pulp, Paper and Paperboard," Bull. Environ. Contam. Toxicol. 10(2):80-87 (1973).

Shaw, D. G. "Discrimination Between PCB and DDT Residues by a Gas Chromatographic-Mass Spectrometric Technique," Bull. Environ. Contam. Toxicol. 8(4):208-211 (1972).

Shaw, G. R., H. C. Chapman and G. W. Roache. "Determination of Organochlorine Pesticides and Polychlorinated Biphenyls in Sediment Samples Containing Oil Residues," Residue (Melbourne) 3(2):2-8 (1976); Chem. Abst. 88:1362y (1978).

Shaw, G. R. and D. W. Connell. "Physiochemical Properties Controlling Polychlorinated Biphenyl (PCB) Concentrations in Aquatic Organisms," Environ. Sci. Technol. 18:18-23 (1984).

Sherma, J. "Gas-Chromatography Analysis of Polychlorinated Biphenyls and Other Nonpesticide Organic Pollutants," Chapter 5 in Advances in Chromatography, J. C. Giddings, E. Grushka, R. A. Keller and J. Cazes, Eds. (New York, NY: Marcel Dekker, Inc., 1975), pp. 141-176.

Sherma, J. Manual of Analytical Quality Control for Pesticides and Related Compounds in Human and Environmental Samples, EPA-600/2-81-059; NTIS No. PB81-222721 (April 1981).

Shirai, F. "Detection of Polychlorinated Terphenyls on Food Wrappers by Reversed-Phase Partition Thin-Layer Chromatography," Eisei Kagaku 20(5): 282-286 (1974); Chem. Abst. 82: 84559t (1975).

Skrentny, R. F., R. W. Hemken and H. W. Dorough. "Silo Sealants as a Source of Polychlorobiphenyl (PCB) Contamination of Animal Feed," Bull. Environ. Contam. Toxicol. 6(5):409-416 (1971).

Simon, C. G. and T. F. Bidleman. "Sampling Airborne Polychlorinated Biphenyls with Polyurethane Foam--Chromatographic Approach to Determining Retention Efficiencies," Anal. Chem. 51(8):1110-1113 (1979).

Singer, E., T. Jarv and M. Sage. "Survey of Polychlorinated Biphenyls in Ambient Air Across the Province of Ontario," Chapter 19 in Physical Behavior of PCBs in the Great Lakes, D. Mackay, S. Paterson, S. J. Eisenreich and M. S. Simmons, Eds. (Ann Arbor, MI: Ann Arbor Science Publishers, Inc., 1983), pp 367-383.

Sissons, D. and D. Welti. "Structural Identification of Polychlorinated Biphenyls in Commercial Mixtures by Gas-Liquid Chromatography, Nuclear Magnetic Resonance and Mass Spectrometry," J. Chromatogr. 60:15-32 (1971).

Siyali, D. S. "Polychlorinated Biphenyls, Hexachlorobenzene and Other Organochlorine Pesticides in Human Milk," Med. J. Aust. 2:815-818 (1973).

Sleight, S. D. "Pathologic Effects of PCBs in Mammals," in PCBs: Human and Environmental Hazards, F. M. D'Itri and M. A. Kamrin, Eds. (Boston: Butterworth Publishers, 1983), pp. 215-226.

Smith, A. B., J. Schloemer, L. K. Lowry, A. W. Smallwood, R. N. Ligo, S. Tanaka, W. Stringer, M. Jones, R. Hervin and C. J. Glueck. "Metabolic and Health Consequences of Occupational Exposure to Polychlorinated Biphenyls," Br. J. Ind. Med. 39:361-369 (1982).

Smith, G. C., G. A. Gauger and R. M. Frey. "Using Capillary Gas Chromatography to Determine Polychlorinated Biphenyls (PCBs) in Electrical Insulating Liquids," IEEE Trans. Power Appar. Syst. PAS-101(7):2260-2267 (1982); Chem. Abstr. 97: 229462c (1982).

Smith, J. "Quality Assurance Plan for Measurment of Incidentally Generated Chlorinated Biphenyls (PCBs)," Unpublished Memorandum, U.S. Environmental Protection Agency, Office of Toxic Substances, Washington, DC, April 6, 1982.

Smith, L. M., D. L. Stalling, and J. L. Johnson. "Determination of Part-per-Trillion Levels of Polychlorinated Dibenzofurans and Dioxins in Environmental Samples," Anal. Chem. 56: 1830-1842 (1984).

Smodlaka, N. "Unidentified Compounds in Seawater Chromatographically Similar to PCBs," Marine Pollut. Bull. 5:84-86 (1974); Chem. Abstr. 83:12063d (1975).

Smrek, A. L. and L. L. Needham. "Simplified Cleanup Procedures for Adipose Tissue Containing Polychlorinated Biphenyls, DDT, and DDT Metabolites," Bull. Environ. Contam. Toxicol. 28:718-722 (1982).

Snyder, D. and R. Reinert. "Rapid Separation of Polychlorinated Biphenyls from DDT and Its Analogues on Silica Gel," Bull. Environ. Contam. Toxicol. 6(5):385-390 (1971).

Snyder, L. R. and J. J. Kirkland. Introduction to Modern Liquid Chromatography, 2nd Ed. (New York, NY: Wiley-Interscience, 1979), 863 pp.

Sonchik, S., D. Madeleine, P. Macek and J. Longbottom. "Evaluation of Sample Preparation Techniques for the Analysis of PCBs in Oil," J. Chromatogr. Sci. 22:265-271 (1984).

Spaw, S. N., D. R. Pendleton and J. M. Jenks. "Environmental Sampling and Analysis of Airborne Contaminants Identified as Skin Irritants: Deer Park, Texas," in Proceedings: A Specialty Conference on: Measurement and Monitoring of Non-criteria (Toxic) Contaminants in Air, E. R. Frederick, Ed. (Pittsburgh: The Air Pollution Control Association, 1983), pp. 156-167.

Spearman, R. I. C. "Biochemistry of Adipose Tissue and its Regulation," in The Physiology and Pathophysiology of the Skin (London, New York: Academic Press, 1982), pp. 2283-2325; Chem. Abstr. 98:14654b (1982).

Spies, D. N. "Rapid Field Extraction Technique for Determining Extent of PCB Contaminated Sediments," in Hazardous Materials Spills, Conference Proceedings, J. Ludwigson (Ed.), pp. 435-437 (1982); Chem. Abst. 97:60688t (1982).

Spittler, T. M. "Field Measurement of PCB's in Soil and Sediment Using a Portable Gas Chromatograph," Natl. Conf. Manage. Uncontrolled Hazard. Waste Sites, pp. 105-107 (1983); Chem. Abst. 100:220890p (1984).

Spittler, T. M. "Field Measurement of Polychlorinated Biphenyls in Soil and Sediment Using a Portable Gas Chromatograph," in Environmental Sampling for Hazardous Wastes, G. E. Schweitzer and J. A. Santolucito, Eds., ACS Symposium Series 267 (Washington, DC, American Chemical Society, 1984) pp. 37-42.

Stahl, E., Ed. Thin-Layer Chromatography: A Laboratory Handbook (New York: Springer-Verlag, 1969).

Stahr, H. M. "Analysis of PCBs by Thin-Layer Chromatography," J. Liq. Chromtogr. 7(7):1393-1402 (1984).

Stalling, D. L. "Analysis of Organochlorine Residues in Fish: Current Research at the Fish-Pesticide Research Laboratory," in Pestic. Chem., Proc. Intl. IUPAC Congr. Pest. Chem., 2nd 4:413-438 (1971).

Stalling, D. L. "Application of Analytical Methods Research to Monitoring Organic Residues in Fish," The Institute of Electrical and Electronics Engineers, Inc., Annals No. 75CH1004-I 7-5 (1976).

Stalling, D. L. and J. N. Huckins. "Gas-Liquid Chromatography--Mass Spectrometry Characterization of Polychlorinated Biphenyls (Aroclors) and ^{36}Cl-Labeling of Aroclors 1248 and 1254," J. Assoc. Offic. Anal. Chem. 54(4):801-807 (1971).

Stalling, D. L., R. C. Tindle and J. L. Johnson. "Cleanup of Pesticide and Polychlorinated Biphenyl Residues in Fish Extracts by Gel Permeation Chromatography," J. Assoc. Offic. Anal. Chem. 55(1):32-38 (1972).

Stalling, D. L. and J. N. Huckins. "Reverse Phase Thin Layer Chromatography of Some Aroclors, Halowaxes, and Pesticides," J. Assoc. Offic. Anal. Chem. 56(2):367-372 (1973).

Stalling, D. L., J. Johnson and J. N. Huckins. "Automated Gel Permeation--Carbon Chromatographic Cleanup of Dioxins, PCBs, Pesticides, and Industrial Chemicals," in Environmental Quality and Safety, Supplement Vol. III, Pesticides Lectures of the IUPAC, Third International Congress of Pesticide Chemistry, Helsinki, July 1974, F. Coulson and F. Korte, Eds. (Stuttgart, Germany: G. Thieme Publishing, 1975), pp. 12-18.

Stalling, D. L., J. N. Huckins, J. D. Petty, J. L. Johnson and H. O. Sanders. "An Expanded Approach to the Study and Measurement of PCBs and Selected Planar Halogenated Aromatic Environmental Pollutants," Ann. N.Y. Acad. Sci. 320:48-59 (1979a).

Stalling, D. L., L. M. Smith and J. D. Petty. "Approaches to Comprehensive Analyses of Persistent Halogenated Environmental Contaminants," in Measurement of Organic Pollutants in Water and Wastewater, ASTM STP 686, C. E. Van Hall, Ed. (American Society for Testing and Materials, 1979b), pp. 302-323.

Stalling, D. L., J. N. Huckins and J. D. Petty. "Presence and Potential Significance of o-o'-Unsubstituted PCB Isomers and Trace Aroclor® 1248 and 1254 Impurities," in Hydrocarbons and Halogenated Hydrocarbons in the Aquatic Environment, B. K. Afghan and D. Mackay, Eds. (New York: Plenum Press 1980a), pp. 131-139.

Stalling, D. L., J. D. Petty, G. R. Dubay and R. A. Smith. "Application of LC/MS to Chromatographic Separation of Aromatics Using Carbon as the Stationary Phase," J. Chromatogr. Sci. 18:107-108 (1980b).

Stalling, D. L., J. D. Petty, L. M. Smith and G. R. Dubay. "Contaminant Enrichment Modules and Approaches to Automation of Sample Extract Cleanup," Chapter 9 in Environmental Health Chemistry, The Chemistry of Environmental Agents as Potential Human Hazards, J. D. McKinney, Ed. (Ann Arbor, MI: Ann Arbor Science Publishers, Inc., 1981), pp. 177-193.

Stalling, D. L., J. D. Petty, L. M. Smith, C. Rappe, and H. R. Buser. "Isolation and Analysis or Polychlorinated Furans in Aquatic Samples," in Chlorinated Dioxins and Related Compounds: Impact on the Environment, O. Hutzinger, R. W. Frei, E. Merian, F. Peschari, Eds. (Pergamon Press, 1982).

Stan, H.-J. "Combined Gas Chromatography-Mass Spectrometry," Chapter 9 in Pesticide Analysis, K. G. Das, Ed. (New York: Marcel Dekker, Inc., 1981), pp. 369-423.

Stanley, J., C. Haile, A. Small and E. Olson. "Sampling and Analysis Procedures for Assessing Organic Emissions from Stationary Combustion Sources for Exposure Evaluation Division Studies. Methods Manual," U.S. Environmental Protection Agency, EPA-560/5-82-014 (1982).

Stanley, J. S., M. D. Erickson, J. K. Turman, G. Radolovich, J. Onstot, K. Bauer and J. E. Going. "Relative Response Factors and Relative Retention Times of PCBs Obtained by Capillary GC/EIMS," Abstract No. 801 presented at the 1983 Pittsburgh Conference and Exposition on Analytical Chemistry and Applied Spectroscopy, March 7-12, 1983.

Stanley, J. S., C. L. Haile, A. M. Magin, R. V. Northcutt and D. P. Redford. "Quality Assurance Program for Combustion Source Studies," in Identification and Analysis of Organic Pollutants in Air, L. H. Keith, Ed. (Boston: Butterworth Publishers, 1984), pp. 459-473.

Stanovick, R. P., S. Shahied and E. Missaghi. "Determination of Polychlorinated Biphenyl (Aroclor 1242) Migration Into Food Types," Bull. Environ. Contam. Toxicol. 10(2):101-107 (1973).

Steichen, R. J., R. G. Tucker and E. Mechon. "Standardization of Aroclor Lots for Individual-Peak Gas Chromatographic Calibration," J. Chromatogr. 236:113-126 (1982).

Steinwandter, H. "Contributions to Silica Gel Application in Pesticide Residue Analysis," Fresenius' Z. Anal. Chem. 312: 342-345 (1982a).

Steinwandter, H. "Contributions to the Application of Gel Chromatography in Residue Analysis," Fresenius' Z. Anal. Chem. 313:536-538 (1982b).

Steinwandter, H. "Contributions to Silica Gel Application in Residue Analysis. V. Simple Micro Method for Liquid Chromatographic Separation of Chlorinated Hydrocarbon Pesticides and Polychlorinated Biphenyls (PCB's), Fresenius' Z. Anal. Chem. 316(5):493-494 (1983).

Steinwandter, H.   "Chlorination of Organic Compounds. II.
Kinetics of PCB Perchlorination," Fresenius' Z. Anal. Chem.
317:869-871 (1984).

Steinwandter, H. and H. Bruene. "Chlorination of Organic
Compounds. I. A Simple 10 Min Perchlorination Technique for
the Quantitative Determination of Polychlorinated Biphenyls
(PCB's)," Fresenius' Z. Anal. Chem. 314(2):160 (1983).

Stenhagen, E., S. Abrahamsson and F. W. McLafferty. Registry
of Mass Spectral Data Vol. 1-4, Wiley, New York (1974).

Stijve, T. and E. Cardinale. "Rapid Determination of Chlorinated Pesticides, Polychlorinated Biphenyls, and a Number of
Phosphated Insecticides in Fatty Foods," Mitt. Geb. Leben-
smittelunters. Hyg. 65(1):131-150 (1974); Chem. Abst. 82:
137862v (1975).

Stolzenburg, T. R. and A. W. Andren. "Determination of the
Aqueous Solubility of 4-chlorobiphenyl," Anal. Chim. Acta
151(1):271-274 (1983).

Strachan, W. M. J., H. Huneault, W. M. Schertzer, and F. C.
Elder. "Organochlorines in Precipitation in the Great Lakes
Region," in Hydrocarbons and Halogenated Hydrocarbons in the
Aquatic Environment, B. K. Afghan and D. Mackay, Eds. (New
York: Plenum Press, 1980), pp. 387-396.

Strachan, W. M. J., and H. Huneault. "Automated Rain Sampler
for Trace Organic Substances," Environ. Sci. Technol. 18:
127-130 (1984).

Stratton, C. L. and P. C. Geiszler. "Analysis of Polychlorinated Biphenyl (PCB) in Human Blood Serum Samples," Report
prepared for U.S. Environmental Protection Agency, EPA-560/6-
78-007, NTIS No. PB-291 458/8 (October 1977).

Stratton, C. L., K. L. Tuttle and J. M. Allan. "Environ-
mental Assessment of Polychlorinated Biphenyls (PCBs) near
New Bedford, MA Municipal Landfill," Report prepared for U.S.
Environmental Protection Agency, Report No. EPA 560/6-78-006
(May 1978a).

Stratton, C. L., S. A. Whitlock and J. M. Allan. "A Method
for the Sampling and Analysis of Polychlorinated Biphenyl
(PCB) in Air," Report prepared for U.S. Environmental Protection Agency, Report No. EPA-600/4-78-048, NTIS No. PB
288 410/4 (August 1978b).

Stratton, C. L., J. M. Allan and S. A. Whitlock. "Advances in the Application of the Perchlorination Technique for the Quantitation and Confirmation of Polychlorinated Biphenyls (PCBs)," Bull. Environ. Contam. Toxicol. 21:230-237 (1979).

Straub, C. P. and J. M. Sprafka. "Environmental Levels of PCB in Great Lakes Fish," Environmental Research Laboratory, U.S. Environmental Protection Agency, Duluth, MN, EPA-600/8-83-094, NTIS No. PB83-264481 (1983).

Strik, J. J. T. W. A., F. M. H. Debets and G. Koss. "Chemical Porphyria," Chapter 7 in Halogenated Biphenyls, Terphenyls, Naphthalenes, Dibenzodioxins and Related Products, R. D. Kimbrough, Ed. (New York: Elsevier/North-Holland Biomedical Press, 1980), pp. 191-240.

Su, G. C. C. and H. A. Price. "Element Specific Gas Chromatographic Analyses of Organochlorine Pesticides in the Presence of PCB's by Selective Cancellation of Interfering Peaks," J. Agr. Food Chem. 21:1099-1102 (1973).

Sundaram, K. M. S and P. G. Davis. "Analysis of DDT Residues in Animal Tissues and Soils Collected from Different Regions of Canada," File Rep. - Chem. Control Res. Inst., Ottawa 3: 63 pp. (1974); Chem. Abst. 82:93952t (1975).

Sundström, G. and C. A. Wachtmeister. "Synthesis of ^{14}C-Labelled and Unlabelled PCB Compounds," in PCB Conference II, National Swedish Environment Protection Board, Stockholm, Publications 1973:4E (1972), pp. 73-86.

Sundström, G., O. Hutzinger, F. W. Karasek and J. Michnowicz. "Environmental Chemistry of Substitutes for Polychlorinated Biphenyls. I. Composition and Properties of an Alkylchlorobiphenyl Product," J. Assoc. Offic. Anal. Chem. 59(5):982-988 (1976).

Supelco, Chromatography Supplies Catalog 20, p. 26.

Sutcliffe, C. R. and S. D. Nielson. "Adsorption of Polychlorinated Biphenyls on Glass Surfaces," Presented at FACSS 10th Annual Meeting, September 25-30, 1983.

Swain, W. R. "An Overview of the Scientific Basis for Concern with Polychlorinated Biphenyls in the Great Lakes," in PCBs: Human and Environmental Hazards, F. M. D'Itri and M. A. Kamrin, Eds. (Boston: Butterworth Publishers, 1983), pp. 11-48.

Swanson, S. E., M. D. Erickson, and L. Moody. "Products of Thermal Degradation of Dielectric Fluids," U.S. Environmental Protection Agency, Office of Toxic Substances, Report No. EPA-560/5-85-022 (1985) 23 pp.

Swift, R. and H. Settle. "A Procedure for the Determination of Polychlorinated Biphenyls in Fat Samples," Residue (Melbourne) 3(2):9-12 (1976); Chem. Abst. 87:199289a (1977).

Sworzyn, E. M. and D. G. Ackerman. "Interim Guidelines for the Disposal/Destruction of PCBs and PCB Items by Non-thermal Methods," Environmental Protection Agency, Contract No. 68-02-3174, Task 41, Report No. EPA-600/2-82-069 (1981).

Sworzyn, E. M. and D. G. Ackerman, "Interim Guidelines for the Disposal/Destruction of PCBs and PCB Items by Non-thermal Methods," Office of Research and Development, U.S. Environmental Protection Agency, Research Triangle Park, NC, EPA-600/2-82-069; NTIS No. PB82-217 498, 177 pp. (1982).

Szelewski, M. J., D. R. Hill, S. J. Spiegel and E. C. Tifft, Jr. "Loss of Polychlorinated Biphenyl Homologues during Chromium Trioxide Extraction of Fish Tissue," Anal. Chem. 51(14):2405-2407 (1979).

Tahiliani, V. H., "CLOR-N-OIL Field Test Program," in Proceedings: 1983 PCB Seminar, G. Addis and R. Y. Komai, Eds. Report No. EPRI-EL-3581 (Palo Alto, CA: Electric Power Research Institute), 1984.

Tai, H., M. T. Williams and K. D. McMurtrey. "Separation of Polychlorinated Biphenyls from Toxaphene by Silicic Acid Column Chromatography," Bull. Environ. Contam. Toxicol. 29:64-67 (1982).

Takamiya, K. "Perchlorination Reaction Applied to the Rapid Determination of PCBs," Bull. Environ. Contam. Toxicol. 30: 600-605 (1983).

Takei, G. H., S. M. Kauahikaua and G. H. Leong. "Analysis of Human Milk Samples Collected in Hawaii for Residues of Organochlorine Pesticides and Polychlorobiphenyls," Bull. Environ. Contam. Toxicol. 30:606-613 (1983).

Takeshita, R. and T. Yamashita. "Reversed-Phase Partition Thin-Layer Chromatography of Chlorinated Pesticides and Polychlorinated Biphenyls," Eisei Kagaku 18(6):388-392 (1972); Chem. Abst. 78:144191w (1973).

Talhelm, D. R. "Economic Impacts of PCB Regulations in Food and Fish," in PCBs: Human and Environmental Hazards, F. M. D'Itri and M. A. Kamrin, Eds. (Boston: Butterworth Publishers, 1983), pp. 409-422.

Tanabe, H. "Methods of Analysis of PCB [Polychlorinated Biphenyls] in Edible Oil and Fat," Yukagaku 22(1):35-40 (1973); Chem. Abst. 78:119783h (1973).

Tanabe, H. "PCB Microanalysis," in PCB Poisoning and Pollution, K. Higuchi, Ed. (Tokyo: Kodansha, Ltd; New York: Academic Press 1976), pp. 127-145.

Tanabe, S., and R. Tatsukawa. "Chlorinated Hydrocarbons in the North Pacific and Indian Oceans," Journal of the Oceanographical Society of Japan 36:217-226 (1980).

Tanabe, S., M. Kawano, and R. Tatsukawa. "Chlorinated Hydrocarbons in the Antarctic, Western Pacific, and Eastern Indian Oceans," Transactions of the Tokyo University of Fisheries 5:97-109 (1982).

Tanabe, S., and R. Tatsukawa. "Vertical Transport and Residence Time of Chlorinated Hydrocarbons in the Open Ocean Water Column," Journal of the Oceanographical Society of Japan 39:53-62 (1983).

Tanabe, S., H. Hidaka and R. Tatsukawa. "PCBs and Chlorinated Hydrocarbon Pesticides in Antarctic Atmosphere and Hydrosphere,' Chemosphere 12(2):277-288 (1983).

Tanner, H. A. "Regulation of PCBs in Michigan," in PCBs: Human and Environmental Hazards, F. M. D'Itri and M. A. Kamrin, Eds. (Boston: Butterworth Publishers, 1983), pp. 347-352.

Tarradellas, J., P. Diercxsens and M. B. Bouche. "Methods of Extraction and Analysis of PCBs from Earthworms," Intern. J. Environ. Anal. Chem. 13:55-67 (1982).

Tas, A. C. and R. H. de Vos. "Characterization of Four Major Components in a Technical Polychlorinated Biphenyl Mixture," Environ. Sci. Technol. 5(12):1216-1218 (1971).

Tas, A. C. and R. J. C. Kleipool. "Characterization of the Components of Technically Polychlorinated Biphenyl Mixtures--II," Bull. Environ. Contam. Toxicol. 8(1):32-36 (1972).

Tatsukawa, R. and T. Wakimoto. "Pollution Analysis. Determination of Polychlorinated Biphenyl in Soil," Kogai Bunseki Shishin 6:45-56 (1972), Chem. Abst. 82:11793e (1975).

Tausch, H., G. Stehlik and H. Wihlidal. "Analyse von Organo-chlorpestizid-und PCB-Rückständen in Fischen mittels Kapil-largaschromatographie/Massenspecktrometrie," Chromatographia 14(7):403-410 (1981).

Taylor, J. K. "Validation of Analytical Methods," Anal. Chem. 55(6): 600A-608A (1983).

Teichman, J., A. Bevenue and J. W. Hylin. "Separation of Polychlorobiphenyls from Chlorinated Pesticides in Sediment and Oyster Samples for Analysis by Gas Chromatography," J. Chromatogr. 151:155-161 (1978).

Telling, G. M. and D. J. Sissons. "Determination of Organo-chlorine Insecticide Residues in Fatty Foodstuffs Using a Clean-up Technique Based on a Single Column of Activated Alumina," Journal of Chromatography, 137:405-423 (1977).

Tenzner, R. B. Ford, Jr., W. Mattox, and J. E. Brugger, "Mobile System for the Detoxification/Incineration of Cleanup Residuals from Hazardous Material Spills," in Disposal of Oil and Debris Resulting from a Spill Cleanup Operation, ASTM STP 703, J. S. Farlow and C. Swanson, Eds., American Society for Testing and Materials (1980) pp. 118-136.

Tessari, J. D. "Analytical Methods for PCBs in Human Milk," Env. Chem: Human & Animal Health 5:227-229 (1977).

Tessari, J. D. and E. P. Savage. "Gas-Liquid Chromatographic Determination of Organochlorine Pesticides and Polychlori-nated Biphenyls in Human Milk," J. Assoc. Offic. Anal. Chem. 63(4): 736-741 (1980).

Tessari, J. D., L. Griffin and M. J. Aaronson. "Comparison of Two Cleanup Procedures (Mills, Onley, Gaither vs Automated Gel Permeation) for Residues of Organochlorine Pesticides and Polychlorinated Biphenyls in Human Adipose Tissue," Bull. Environ. Contam. Toxicol. 25:59-64 (1980).

Thielemann, H. "Dünnschicht-chromatographische Auftrennung und Identifizierung eines Gemisches von polychlorierten Bi-phenylen (PCB) und p,p'-DDE an parraffinimprägnierten Kieselgur G-Schichten," Fresenius' Z. Anal. Chem. 282:144 (1976).

Thielemann, H. "Dünnschichtchromatographische Nachweisgrenzen (semiquantitative Bestimmung) von polychloriertem Biphenyl (Chlophen A_{50}®) sowie Identifizierung des Insektizids Thiodan (Endosulfan)," Z. Chem. 18:147-148 (1978).

Thielemann, H. "Separation and Identification of Polychlor-inated Biphenyls and p,p'-DDE in Paraffin-Impregnated Com-mercial Sheets by Repeated Thin-Layer Chromatography," Z. Gesamte Hyg. Ihre Grenzgeb. 26(6):463-464 (1980); Chem. Abst. 94:202208a (1981).

Thomann, R. V. and J. P. Connolly. "Age Dependent Model of PCB in a Lake Michigan Food Chain," U.S. Environmental Pro-tection Agency, Report No. EPA-600/3-84-026; NTIS PB84-155993 (1984). 122 pp.

Thomann, R. V. and J. A. Mueller. "Steady State Modeling of Toxic Chemical-Theory and Application to PCBs in the Great Lakes and Saginaw Bay," Chapter 16 in Physical Behavior of PCBs in the Great Lakes, D. Mackay, S. Paterson, S. J. Eisen-reich and M. S. Simmons, Eds. (Ann Arbor, MI: Ann Arbor Sci-ence Publishers, Inc., 1983), pp 283-309.

Thomas, R. L. and R. Frank. "PCBs in Sediment and Fluvial Suspended Solids in the Great Lakes," Chapter 14 in Physical Behavior of PCBs in the Great Lakes, D. Mackay, S. Paterson, S. J. Eisenreich and M. S. Simmons, Eds. (Ann Arbor, MI: Ann Arbor Science Publishers, Inc., 1983), pp 245-267.

Thomson, B. A. and J. R. Roberts. "The Development of an Analytical Technique for the Rapid in situ Detection of PCBs and Trichlorobenzene in Clay," in A Case Study of A Spill of Industrial Chemicals--Polychlorinated Biphenyls and Chlori-nated Benzenes, National Research Council of Canada, Associ-ate Committee on Scientific Criteria for Environmental Qual-ity (NRCC No. 17586), Section VII (Appendix 3) (1980). 22 pp.

Thomson, B. A., T. Sakuma, J. Fulford, D. A. Lane, N. M. Reid, and J. B. French. "Fast In Situ Measurement of PCB Levels in Ambient Air to ng m ^{3} Levels Using a Mobil Atmo-spheric Pressure Chemical Ionization Mass Spectrometer Sys-tem," in Advances in Mass Spectrometry, Vol. 8B, A. Quayle, Ed., (Heyden and Son Ltd., London, 1980) pp. 1422-1428.

Thomson, B. A. and J. R. Roberts. "A New Technique for the Rapid Analysis of Soil for the Presence of Polychlorinated Biphenyls," Intern. J. Environ. Anal. Chem. 11:139-151 (1982).

Tiernan, T. O., M. L. Taylor, J. G. Solch, G. F. Vanness, J. H. Garrett and M. D. Porter. "Incineration of Chemical Wastes Containing Polychlorinated Biphenyls: Assessment of Tests Conducted at Rollins Environmental Services, Deer Park, Texas, and Energy Systems Company, El Dorado, Arkansas," Chapter 9 in Detoxication of Hazardous Waste, J. H. Exner, Ed. (Ann Arbor, MI: Ann Arbor Science Publishers, Inc., 1982), pp. 143-183.

Tindall, G. W. and P. E. Wininger. "Gas Chromatography-Mass Spectrometry Method for Identifying and Determining Polychlorinated Biphenyls," J. Chromatogr. 196:109-119 (1980).

Tindle, R. C. and D. L. Stalling. "Apparatus for Automated Gel Permeation Cleanup for Pesticide Residue Analysis. Applications to Fish Lipids," Anal. Chem. 44(11):1768-1773 (1972).

Tofflemire, T. J., T. T. Shen and E. H. Buckley. "Volatilization of PCB from Sediment and Water: Experimental and Field Data," Chapter 21 in Physical Behavior of PCBs in the Great Lakes, D. Mackay, S. Paterson, S. J. Eisenreich and M. S. Simmons, Eds. (Ann Arbor, MI: Ann Arbor Science Publishers, Inc., 1983), pp 411-422.

Tong, H. Y., D. L. Shore, and F. W. Karasek. "Identification of Organic Compounds Obtained from Incineration of Municipal Waste by High-Performance Liquid Chromatographic Fractionation and Gas Chromatography-Mass Spectrometry," Journal of Chromatography, 285:423-441 (1984).

Trench, W. C. "New PCB Rulemaking - A Repeat of History or Final Conclusions?" in Proceedings: 1981 PCB Seminar, G. Addis and J. Marks, Eds., Report No. EPRI-EL-2572 (Palo Alto, CA: Electric Power Research Institute, 1981), Section 1, pp. 11-34.

Tressl, G. and K. Wessely. "Analysis of Chloropesticides and PCB's in Cheese by Glass Capillary GC/MS Using the Selected Ion Monitoring Technique," Application Note AN 176-22, Hewlett-Packard Company, Avondale, Pennsylvania (1976).

Trevisani, G. R. "Simultaneous Studies on Chlorinated Pesticides, Polychlorinated Biphenyls, Polychlorinated Triphenyls, and Polychlorinated Naphthalenes in Fatty Foods of Various Types," Boll. Chim. Unione Ital. Lab. Prov., Parte Sci. 6(2): 117-142 (1980); Chem. Abst. 93:202765j (1980).

Trotter, W. J. "Removing the Interference of DDT and Its Analogs in the Analysis for Residues of Polychlorinated Biphenyls," J. Assoc. Offic. Anal. Chem. 58(3):461-465 (1975).

Trotter, W. J. and S. J. V. Young. "Limitation on the Use of Antimony Pentachloride for Perchlorination of Polychlorinated Biphenyls," J. Assoc. Offic. Anal. Chem. 58(3):466-468 (1975).

Trotter, W. J., S. J. V. Young, J. L. Casterline, Jr., J. A. Bradlaw and L. R. Kamps. "Industrial Chemcals: Induction of Aryl Hydrocarbon Hydroxylase Activity in Cell Cultures by Aroclors, Residues from Yusho Oil Samples, and Polychlorinated Biphenyl Residues from Fish Samples," J. Assoc. Off. Anal. Chem. 65(4):838-841 (1982).

Tsushimoto, G., S. Asano, J. E. Trosko and C-C. Chang. "Inhibition of Intercellular Communications by Various Congeners of Polybrominated Biphenyl and Polychlorinated Biphenyl," in PCBs: Human and Environmental Hazards, F. M. D'Itri and M. A. Kamrin, Eds. (Boston: Butterworth Publishers, 1983), pp. 241-252.

Tuinstra, L. G. M. Th. and W. A. Traag. "Automated Glass Capillary Gas Chromatograpic Analysis of PCB and Organochlorine Pesticide Residues in Agricultural Products," J. High Resol. Chromatogr. & Chromatogr. Commun. 2:723-728 (1979a).

Tuinstra, L. G. M. Th. and W. A. Traag. "Automated $(GC)^2$ Analysis of PCB and Organochlorine Pesticide Residues in Agricultural Products," Med. Fac. Landbouww. Rijksuniv. Gent 44(2): 885-893 (1979b).

Tuinstra, L. G. M. Th., W. A. Traag and H. J. Keukens. "Quantitative Determination of Individual Chlorinated Biphenyls in Milkfat by Splitless Glass Capillary Gas Chromatography," J. Assoc. Offic. Anal. Chem. 63(5):952-958 (1980).

Tuinstra, L. G. M. Th., W. A. Traag and A. J. Van Munsteren. "Determination of Individual Chlorinated Biphenyls in Agricultural Products by Automated Capillary Gas Chromatography. Determination in Cattle Feed and Its Relation to Milk Residues," J. Chromatogr. 204:413-419 (1981).

Tuinstra, L. G. M. Th. and W. A. Traag. "Capillary Gas Chromatographic-Mass Spectrometric Determination of Individual Chlorobiphenyls in Technical Aroclors," J. Assoc. Off. Anal. Chem. 66(3):708-717 (1983).

Tuinstra, L. G. M. Th., J. J. M. Driessen, H. J. Keukens, T. J. Van Munsteren, A. H. Roos and W. A. Traag. "Quantitative Determination of Specified Chlorobiphenyls in Fish with Capillary Gas Chromatography and Its Use for Monitoring and Tolerance Purposes," Intern. J. Environ. Anal. Chem. 14:147-157 (1983).

Ueta, T., K. Kamata, T. Kan, M. Kazama and T. Totani. "Fluorescence Reactions for Organic Halogen Compounds. II. In Situ Fluorometry of Polychlorinated Biphenyls and Their Isomers on Thin-Layer Chromatograms Using Diphenylamine," Tokyo Toritsu Eisei Kenkyusho Kenkyu Nempo 25:111-118 (1974); Chem. Abst. 83:21991c (1975).

Ugawa, M., A. Nakamura and T. Kashimoto. "Calculation Method for Polychlorinated Biphenyl (PCB) Isomers in Gas Chromatographic Determination," Shokuhin Eiseigaku Zasshi 14(5):415-424 (1973); Chem. Abst. 80:90955u (1974).

Ugawa, M., A. Nakamura and T. Kashimoto. "Studies on a Calculation Method for Polychlorinated Biphenyl Isomers (PCBs)," in New Methods in Environmental Chemistry and Toxicology, Collection of Papers Presented at the Research Conference on New Methodology in Ecological Chemistry, Susono, Japan, November 23-25, 1973, F. Coulston, F. Korte, and M. Goto (Eds.), International Academic Printing Co., Ltd., Tokyo (1973). pp. 253-267.

Uk, S., C. M. Himel and T. Dirks. "Mass Spectrometric Identification of Mirex Residues in Crude Extracts and in the Presence of Polychlorinated Biphenyls," Bull. Environ. Contam. Toxicol. 8(2):97-104 (1972).

United Kingdom Department of the Environment. "Organochlorine Insecticides and Polychlorinated Biphenyls in Waters 1978; Tentative Method. Methods for the Examination of Waters and Associated Materials," Organochlorine Insectic. Polychlorinated Biphenyls Waters 28 pp. (1979).

United States Congress, Toxic Substances Control Act, Public Law 94-469, October 11, 1976.

Underwood, J. C. "Separation of Polychlorinated Biphenyls from DDT and Its Analogs Using Chromic Acid and Silica Gel," Bull. Environ. Contam. Toxicol. 21:787-790 (1979).

Urabe, H., H. Koda and M. Asahi. "Present State of Yusho Patients," Ann. N. Y. Acad. Sci. 320:273-283 (1979).

Uriano, G. A. "National Bureau of Standards Certificate of Analysis, Standard Reference Material 1581 - Polychlorinated Biphenyls in Oils," Washington, DC, June 25, 1982.

Uthe, J. F., J. Reinke and H. O'Brodovich. "Field Studies on the Use of Coated Porous Polyurethane Plugs as Indwelling Monitors of Organochlorine Pesticides and Polychlorinated Biphenyl Contents of Streams," Environ. Lett. 6(2):103-115 (1974).

Uthe, J. F. and C. J. Musial. "Report of the Fifth ICES Intercalibration Study of PCBs in Biological Material," International Council for the Exploration of the Sea, Copenhagen, Denmark, ICES C.M. 1980/E:8, Marine Environmental Quality Committee (1980).

Utility Solid Waste Activities Group, Edison Electric Institute, and National Rural Electric Cooperative Association. "Comments and Studies on the Use of Polychorinated Biphenyls in Response to an Order of the United States Court of Appeals for the District of Columbia Circuit," U.S. Environmental Protection Agency, February 12, 1982, Volumes I-IV.

Uyeta, M., S. Taue, K. Chikasawa and M. Mazaki. "Photoformation of Polychlorinated Biphenyls from Chlorinated Benzenes," Nature 264:583-584 (1976).

Vannucchi, C., R. Salvadori, R. Nottoli, G. Ghimenti and G. Taponeco. "Identification and Quantification of Aromatic Polychlorinated Hydrocarbon Residues in the Environment," Riv. Sci. Tecnol. Alimenti Nutr. Um. 6(2):101-114 (1976); Chem. Abst. 85:175663a (1976).

Vannucchi, C. and M. Berlincioni. "Sampling and Analytical Method to Determine PCB Concentrations in the Air of the Working Areas of an Electrical Industry," Am. Ind. Hyg. Assoc. J. 41:352-360 (1980).

Van Ravenswaay, E. O. "The Science-Policy Interface in Regulatory Decision-Making," in PCBs: Human and Environmental Hazards, F. M. D'Itri and M. A. Kamrin, Eds. (Boston: Butterworth Publishers, 1983), pp. 353-366.

Van Vliet, H. P. M., Th. C. Bootsman, R. W. Frei and U. A. Th. Brinkman. "On-Line Trace Enrichment in High-Performance Liquid Chromatography Using a Pre-Column," J. Chromatogr. 185:483-495 (1979).

Veierov, D. and N. Aharonson. "Economic Method for Analysis of Fluid Milk for Organochlorine Residues at the 10 ppb Level," J. Assoc. Offic. Anal. Chem. 63(3):532-535 (1980).

Veierov, D. and N. Aharonson. "Improved Cleanup of Large Lipid Samples for Electron Capture Gas Chromatographic Quantitation and Gas Chromatographic-Mass Spectrometric Confirmation of Organochlorine Residues," J. Assoc. Offic. Anal. Chem. 63(2): 202-207 (1980).

Veith, G. D. "Baseline Concentrations of Polychlorinated Biphenyls and DDT in Lake Michigan Fish, 1971," Pestic. Monit. J. 9(1):21-29 (1975).

Veith, G. D. and N. M. Austin. "Detection and Isolation of Bioaccumuable Chemicals in Complex Effluents," Chapter 20 in Identification and Analysis of Organic Pollutants in Water, L. H. Keith, Ed. (Ann Arbor, MI: Ann Arbor Science Publishers, Inc., 1976), pp. 297-302.

Veith, G. D. and L. M. Kiwus. "An Exhaustive Steam-Distillation and Solvent-Extraction Unit for Pesticides and Industrial Chemicals," Bull. Environ. Contam. Toxicol. 17: 631-636 (1977).

Veith, G. D., D. W. Kuehl, E. N. Leonard, K. Welch and G. Pratt. "Polychlorinated Biphenyls and Other Organic Chemical Residues in Fish from Major United States Watersheds Near the Great Lakes, 1978," Pestic. Monit. J. 15:1-8 (1981).

Veith, G. D. and P. Kosian. "Estimating Bioconcentration Potential from Octanol/Water Partition Coefficients," Chapter 15 in Physical Behavior of PCBs in the Great Lakes, D. Mackay, S. Paterson, S. J. Eisenreich and M. S. Simmons, Eds. (Ann Arbor, MI: Ann Arbor Science Publishers, Inc., 1983), pp 269-282.

Velie, M. and G. Kuntz. "Federal Polychlorinated Biphenyl Regulations," Chapter 7 in Detoxication of Hazardous Waste, J. H. Exner, Ed. (Ann Arbor, MI: Ann Arbor Science Publishers, Inc., 1982), pp. 121-130.

Ver Duin, C. "The Commerical Fishermen's View of the PCBs Problem in the Great Lakes," in PCBs: Human and Environmental Hazards, F. M. D'Itri and M. A. Kamrin, Eds. (Boston: Butterworth Publishers, 1983), pp. 109-112.

Versar, Inc. "Revised Materials Balance for Inadvertently Produced PCBs," Report to U.S. Environmental Protection Agency, Washington, DC (April 22, 1982).

Villeneuve, J. P. "Intercalibration of Organochlorine Standard Solutions," in Scientific Report of the Intercalibration Exercise, Intergovernmental Oceanographic Commission Technical Series Report No. 22, UNESCO, Paris (ISBN 92-3-102077-3), (1982) pp. 84-91.

Vodicnik, M. J. "Factors Affecting the Bioaccumulation and Persistence of Polychlorinated Biphenyls," in Advances in Exposure, Health and Environmental Effects Studies of PCBs: Symposium Proceedings, R. J. Davenport and B. K. Bernard (Eds.), Office of Toxic Substances, U.S. Environmental Protection Agency, Washington, D.C., Report No. LSI-TR-507-137B; NTIS No. PB84-135771 (December 1983), pp. 97-127.

Vogel, G., K. Brooks, I. Frankel, S. Haus and W. Jacobsen. "Guidance Manual for Evaluating Permit Applications for the Operation of Incinerator Units," Report by The Mitre Corporation, McLean, VA, to U.S. Environmental Protection Agency, Contract No. 68-01-6092, December 31, 1980, 221 pp.

Voice, T. C., C. P. Rice and W. J. Weber, Jr. "Effect of Solids Concentration on the Sorptive Partitioning of Hydrophobic Pollutants in Aquatic Systems," Environ. Sci. Technol. 17(9):513-518 (1983).

Vos, J. G., J. H. Koeman, H. L. van der Maas, M. C. ten Noever de Brauw and R. H. de Vos. "Identification and Toxicological Evaluation of Chlorinated Dibenzofuran and Chlorinated Naphthalene in Two Commerical Polychlorinated Biphenyls," Food Cosmet. Toxicol. 8:625-633 (1970).

Vos, J. G., R. E. Faith and M. I. Luster. "Immune Alterations," Chapter 8 in Halogenated Biphenyls, Terphenyls, Naphthalenes, Dibenzodioxins and Related Products, R. D. Kimbrough, Ed. (New York, NY: Elsevier/North-Holland Biomedical Press, 1980), p. 241-266.

Voyksner, R. D., J. R. Hass, G. W. Sovocool and M. M. Bursey. "Comparison of Gas Chromatography/High-Resolution Mass Spectrometry and Mass Spectrometry/Mass Spectrometry Detection of Polychlorinated Biphenyls and Tetrachlorodibenzofuran," Anal. Chem. 55:744-749 (1983).

Vuceta, J., J. R. Marsh, S. Kennedy, L. Hildemann and S. Wiley. "State-of the-Art Review: PCDDs and PCDFs in Utility PCB Fluid," CS-3308, Research Project 1263-11, Final Report, Electric Power Research Institute, Palo Alto, CA (November 1983).

Wakimoto, T., R. Tatsukawa and T. Ogawa. Kogai to Taisaku 7:517 (1971); Fish Res. Bd. Can. Translation No. 2185.

Wakimoto, T., M. Fukushima, R. Tatsukawa and T. Ogawa. "Separation of PCBs [Polychlorinated Biphenyls] from p,p'-DDE and Other Organochlorine Pesticides by a Newly Developed Silica Gel," Nippon Nogei Kagaku Kaishi 49(10):499-503 (1975); Chem. Abst. 84:116448r (1976).

Walsh, E. J. "Interpretation of PCB Field Testing Kits," in Proceedings: 1983 PCB Seminar, G. Addis and R. Y. Komai, Eds. Report No. EPRI-EL-3581 (Palo Alto, CA: Electric Power Research Institute), 1984.

Ward, R. S. and A. Pelter. "The Analysis of Mixtures of Closely Related Naturally-occurring Organic Compounds Using High Performance Liquid Chromatography," J. Chromatogr. Sci. 12:570-574 (1974).

Wardall, G. L. "Method for the Extraction of Organochlorine Compounds from Quail Eggs," Analyst 102:54-55 (1977).

Warshaw, R., A. Fischbein, J. Thornton, A. Miller and I. J. Selikoff. "Decrease in Vital Capacity in PCB-Exposed Workers in a Capacitor Manufacturing Facility," Ann. N. Y. Acad. Sci. 320:277-283 (1979).

Washington, T. L. "The Environmentalist's View of the PCBs Problem in the Great Lakes," in PCBs: Human and Environmental Hazards, F. M. D'Itri and M. A. Kamrin, Eds. (Boston: Butterworth Publishers, 1983), pp. 101-108.

Wassermann, M., D. Wassermann, S. Cucos and H. J. Miller. "World PCBs Map: Storage and Effects in Man and His Biologic Environment in the 1970s," Ann. N.Y. Acad. Sci. 320:69-124 (1979).

Wassermann, M., M. Ron, B. Bercovici, D. Wassermann, S. Cucos and A. Pines. "Premature Delivery and Organochlorine Compounds: Polychlorinated Biphenyls and Some Organochlorine Insecticides," Environ. Res. 28:106-112 (1982).

Watanabe, I., T. Yakushiji, K. Kuwabara, S. Yoshida, K. Koyama, I. Hara and N. Kunita. "Studies on Polychlorinated Biphenyl (PCB) Isomers in Blood of Ordinary Persons, Oil Sickness Patients, and Occupationally Exposed Workers. 2. Apiezon L Column Analysis," Osaka-furitsu Koshu Eisei Kenkyusho Kenkyu Hokoku, Shokuhin Eisei Hen 8:51-58 (1977); Chem. Abst. 88: 183989p (1978).

Watanabe, I., T. Yakushiji and N. Kunita. "Distribution Differences Between Polychlorinated Terphenyls and Polychlorinated Biphenyls in Human Tissues," Bull. Environ. Contam. Toxicol. 25:810-815 (1980).

Watts, R. R. (Ed.), Analysis of Pesticide Residues in Human and Environmental Samples, A Compilation of Methods Selected for Use in Pesticide Monitoring Programs, U.S. Environmental Protection Agency, Research Triangle Park, NC, EPA-600/8-80-038 (June 1980).

Weast, R. C. and S. M. Selby (Eds.). CRC Handbook of Chemistry and Physics 48th Ed. (Cleveland, OH: The Chemical Rubber Co., 1967).

Weaver, G. "PCB Contamination in and Around New Bedford, Mass," Environ. Sci. Technol. 18(1):22A-27A (1984).

Webb, R. G. and A. C. McCall. "Identities of Polychlorinated Biphenyl Isomers in Aroclors," J. Assoc. Offic. Anal. Chem. 55(4):746-752 (1972).

Webb, R. G., and A. C. McCall. "Quantitative PCB Standards for Electron Capture Gas Chromatography," J. Chromatogr. Sci. 11:366-373 (1973).

Weinberger, R., P. Yarmchuk and L. J. Cline Love. "Micelle-Stabilized Room Temperature Phosphorescence and Fluorescence of Polychlorinated and Polybrominated Biphenyls," Abstract No. 295 from the 1983 Pittsburgh Conference and Exposition on Analytical Chemistry and Applied Spectroscopy, March 7-12, 1983.

Weininger, D., D. E. Armstrong and D. L. Swackhamer. "Application of a Sediment Dynamics Model for Estimation of Vertical Burial Rates of PCBs in Southern Lake Michigan," Chapter 22 in Physical Behavior of PCBs in the Great Lakes, D. Mackay, S. Paterson, S. J. Eisenreich and M. S. Simmons, Eds. (Ann Arbor, MI: Ann Arbor Science Publishers, Inc., 1983), pp. 423-439.

Weitzman, L. "Treatment and Destruction of Polychlorinated Biphenyls and Polychlorinated Biphenyl-Contaminated Materials," Chapter 8 in Detoxication of Hazardous Waste, J. H. Exner, Ed. (Ann Arbor, MI: Ann Arbor Science Publishers, Inc., 1982), pp. 131-142.

Welborn, M. E., R. E. Borchard, L. G. Hansen and R. L. Metcalf. "Extraction and Analysis of Aroclor 1254 Components in Blood," J. Assoc. Offic. Anal. Chem. 57(6):1248-1252 (1974).

Wells, D. E. and A. A. Cowan. "Use of Gas Chromatography - Mass Spectrometry in the Environmental Analysis of Industrial Pollutants," in Recent Advances in Chromatography-Mass Spectrometry (Anal. Proc.) pp. 242-246 (1982).

Welsch, F. "Effects of Polychlorinated Biphenyls on the Expression of Embryotoxicity Caused by Model Teratogens," in PCBs: Human and Environmental Hazards, F. M. D'Itri and M. A. Kamrin, Eds. (Boston: Butterworth Publishers, 1983), pp. 253-276.

Welti, D. and D. Sissons. "The Proton Chemical Shifts of Polychlorinated Biphenyls," Organic Magnetic Resonance 4: 309-319 (1972).

West, P. R., S. K. Chaudhary and R. H. Mitchell. "Photode-chlorination of Polychlorinated Biphenyls Induced by Hydro-quinone in Basic Media," Extended Abstracts, Division of En-vironmental Chemistry, American Chemical Society, Washington, D.C., pp. 384-187 (September 1983).

Westcott, J. W., and T. F. Bidleman. "Determination of Poly-chlorinated Biphenyl Vapor Pressures by Capillary Gas Chro-matography," J.Chromatogr. 210:331-336 (1981).

Westerberg, R. B., S. L. Alibrando and F. J. van Lenten. "Determination of Polychlorinated Biphenyls Using Limited Mass Scan Gas Chromatography Mass Spectrometry," J. Chro-matogr. 284(2):447-456 (1984).

Westin, R. A. "Polychlorinated Biphenyls 1929-1979," Office of Toxic Substances, U.S. Environmental Protection Agency, Washington, D.C., EPA-560/6-79/004; NTIS No. PB-2965591/8 (1979).

Westöö, G. and K. Norén. "Determination of Organochlorine Pesticides and Polychlorinated Biphenyls in Animal Foods," Acta Chem. Scand. 24(5):1639-1644 (1970).

Whitmore, F. C. "Destruction of Polychlorinated Biphenyls in Sewage Sludge During Incineration," Report by Versar, Inc., Springfield,VA, to U.S. Environmental Protection Agency, Washington, DC, EPA Contract No. 68-01-1587 (NTIS No. PB-258 162) 73 pp. (1976).

Whitmore, F. C. and J. D. Barden. "A Study of PCB Destruc-tion Efficiency and Performance for a Coal-Fired Utility Boiler; Volume 1. Test and Evaluation," U.S. Environmental Protection Agency, Office of Research and Development, Research Triangle Park, NC, EPA-600/2-82-101a (NTIS No. PB84-110147) 79 pp. (October 1983a).

Whitmore, F. C. and J. D. Barden. "A Study of PCB Destruc-tion Efficiency and Performance for a Coal-Fired Utility Boiler; Volume 2. Test Protocol," U.S. Environmental Pro-tection Agency, Office of Research and Development, Research Triangle Park, NC, EPA-600/2-83-101b (NTIS No. PB84-110154) 89 pp. (1983b).

Williams, C. H., C. L. Prescott, P. B. Stewart and G. Choudhary. "Formation of Polychlorinated Dibenzofurans and Other Potentially Toxic Chlorinated Pyrolysis Products in PCB Fires," Extended Abstract, Division of Environmental Chemistry, American Chemical Society, Washington, D.C., pp. 265-266 (September 1983).

Williams, C. H. Jr., C. L. Prescott, and L. D. Garretson, "Detection of Polychlorinated Dibenzofurans and Other Chlorinated Pyrolysis Products in the Soot Formed in PCB Fires," Proceedings: 1983 PCB Seminar, G. Addis and R. Y. Komai, Eds. Report No. EPRI-EL-3581 (Palo Alto, CA: Electric Power Research Institute, 1984).

Williams, C. H., Jr., C. L. Prescott, P. B. Stewart, and G. Choudhary. "Formation of Polychlorinated Dibenzofurans and Other Potentially Toxic Chlorinated Pyrolysis Products in PCB Fires," in Chlorinated Dioxins and Dibenzofurans in the Total Environment II, L. H. Keith, C. Rappe, and G. Choudhary, Eds., (Boston: Butterworth Publishers, 1985). pp. 457-468.

Williams, D. T. and B. J. Blanchfield. "Thin Layer Chromatographic Separation of Two Chlorodibenzo-p-dioxins from Some Polychlorinated Biphenyl and Organochlorine Pesticides," J. Assoc. Offic. Anal. Chem. 54(6):1429-1431 (1971).

Williams, D. T. and B. J. Blanchfield. "Screening Method for the Detection of Chlorodibenzo-p-dioxins in the Presence of Chlorobiphenyls, Chloronaphthalenes, and Chlorodibenzofurans," J. Assoc. Offic. Anal. Chem. 55(1):93-95 (1972).

Williams, D. T. and F. M. Benoit. "The Determination of Polychlorinated Biphenyls in Selected Household Products," Bull. Environ. Contam. Toxicol. 21:179-184 (1979).

Williams, D. T., G. L. LeBel and T. Furmanczyk. "Polychlorinated Biphenyl Contamination of Laboratory Air," Chemosphere 9:45-50 (1980).

Willis, D. E. and R. F. Addison. "Identification and Estimation of the Major Components of a Commercial Polychlorinated Biphenyl Mixture, Aroclor 1221," J. Fish. Res. Board Can. 29(5):592-595 (1972).

Willmott, F. W. and R. J. Dolphin. "A Novel Combination of Liquid Chromatography and Electron Capture Detecton in the Analysis of Pesticides," J. Chromatogr. Sci. 12:695-700 (1974).

Wilson, N. K. and M. Anderson. "Carbon-13 and Proton Magnetic Resonance Studies of Chlorinated Biphenyls," in Mass Spectrometry and NMR Spectroscopy in Pesticide Chemistry, R. Haque and F. J. Biros, Eds. (New York, NY: Plenum Press, 1973), pp. 197-218.

Wingender, R. J. and R. M. Williams. "Evidence for the Long-Distance Atmospheric Transport of Polychlorinated Terphenyl," Environ. Sci. Technol., 18:625-628 (1984).

Winslow, S. G. and H. B. Gerstner (Eds.), Polychlorinated Bi-phenyls, Polybrominated Biphenyls, and Their Contaminants: A Literature Compilation 1965-1977, Oak Ridge National Laboratory, Oak Ridge, Tennessee (1978).

Wolbach, C. D., W. F. Fitch, N. Flynn and B. Markoja. "An-alytical Results of a PCB Test Incineration," in Second Sym-posium on Process Measurements for Environmental Assessment (February 1980, Atlanta), J. C. Harris (Ed.), Environmental Protection Agency, Report No. EPA-600/9-81-018 (1981).

Wolff, M. S., J. Thornton, A. Fischbein, R. Lilis and I. J. Selikoff. "Disposition of Polychlorinated Biphenyl Congeners in Occupationally Exposed Persons," Toxicol. Appl. Pharmacol. 62:294-306 (1982a).

Wolff, M. S., A. Fischbein, J. Thornton, C. Rice, R. Lahs and I. J. Selikoff. "Body Burden of Polychlorinated Biphenyls Among Persons Employed in Capacitor Manufacturing," Int. Arch. Occup. Environ. Health 49:199-203 (1982b).

Wolff, M. S., H. A. Anderson, I. J. Selikoff. "Human Tissue Burdens of Halogenated Aromatic Chemicals in Michigan," J. Am. Med. Assoc. 247(15):2112-2116 (1982c).

Wong, P. T. S. and K. L. E. Kaiser. "Bacterial Degradation of Polychlorinated Biphenyls II. Rate Studies," Bull. En-viron. Contam. Toxicol. 13(2):249-255 (1975).

World Health Organization. "Polychlorinated Biphenyls and Terphenyls. Environmental Health Criteria 2," Geneva: World Health Organization (1976) 85 pp.

Yakushiji, T., I. Watanabe, K. Kuwabara and S. Yoshida. "Identification of Low Chlorinated Biphenyls in Human Milk by Gas Chromatography-Mass Spectrometry," J. Chromatogr. 154: 203-210 (1978).

Yakushiji, T., I. Watanabe, S. Yoshida, R. Tanaka, T. Kashi-moto and N. Kunita. "Analytical Methods for Organochlorine Compounds in Human Milk," Osaka-furitsu Koshu Eisei Kenkyusho Kenkyu Hokoku, Shokuhin Eisei Hen 11:87-91 (1980); Chem. Abstr. 96: 137221z (1982).

Yakushiji, T., I. Watanabe, K. Kuwabara, R. Tanaka, T. Kashimoto, N. Kunita, and I. Hara. "Rate of Decrease and Half-Life of Polychlorinated Biphenyls (PCBs) in the Blood of Mothers and Their Children Occupationally Exposed to PCBs," Arch. Environ. Contam. Toxicol. 13(3):341-345 (1984); Chem. Abst. 101:42857u (1984).

Yalkowsky, S. H., S. C. Valvani, and D. Mackay. "Estimation of the Aqueous Solubility of Some Aromatic Compounds," Residue Reviews 85:43-55 (1983).

Yarbrough, J. D. and M. R. Wells. "Vertebrate Insecticide Resistance: The in vitro Endrin Effect on Succinic Dehydrogenase Activity on Endrin-Resistant and Susceptible Mosquitofish," Bull. Environ. Contam. Toxicol. 6(2):171-176 (1971).

Yezzi, J., J. Brugger, I. Wilder, F. Freestone, R. Miller, C. Pfrommer, and R. Lovell. "Results of the Initial Trial Burn of the EPA-ORD Mobile Incineration System," Environmental Protection Agency, Municipal Environmental Research Laboratory--Cincinnati, OH, EPA-600/D-84-088 (1984).

Yobs, A. R. "Levels of Polychlorinated Biphenyls in Adipose Tissue of the General Population of the Nation," Environ. Health Perspec. 1:79-81 (1972).

Yoshimura, H., N. Ozawa, and S. Saeki. "Inductive Effect of Polychlorinated Biphenyls Mixture and Individual Isomers on the Hepatic Microsomal Enzymes," Chem. Pharm. Bull., 26:1215-1221 (1978).

Yoshimura, H., S. Yoshihara, N. Ozawa and M. Miki. "Possible Correlation Between Induction Modes of Hepatic Enzymes by PCBs and Their Toxicity in Rats," Ann. N. Y. Acad. Sci. 320:179-192 (1979).

Yost, R. A. and C. G. Enke. "Triple Quadrupole Mass Spectrometry for Direct Mixture Analysis and Structure Elucidation," Anal.Chem. 51(12):1251A-1264A (1979).

Yost, R. W., L. S. Ettre and R. D. Conlon (Eds). Practical Liquid Chromatography - An Introduction (Norwalk, CT: Perkin-Elmer, 1980).

Youden, W. J. and E. H. Steiner. Statistical Manual of the Association of Official Analytical Chemists (Arlington, VA: Association of Official Analytical Chemists, 1975), 88 pp.

Young, S. J. V. and J. A. Burke. "Micro Scale Alkali Treatment for Use in Pesticide Residue Confirmation and Sample Cleanup," Bull. Environ. Contam. Toxicol. 7(2/3):160-167 (1972).

Young, S. J., C. Finsterwalder and J. A. Burke. "Extraction and Cleanup for Determination of Polychlorinated Biphenyls in Paper and Paperboard," J. Assoc. Off. Anal. Chem. 56:957-961 (1973).

Young, S. J. V. and L. R. Kamps. "Gas-Liquid Chromatographic Determination of Nonpolar Organochlorine Pesticide Residues in a Crude Vegetable Oil and Its Refinery By-Products," J. Assoc. Off. Anal. Chem. 65(4):916-920 (1982).

Young, S., M. Clower, Jr., J. A. G. Roach. "Method for Determinination of Organohalogen Pesticide Residues in Vegetable Oil Refinery By-Products," J. Assoc. Off. Anal. Chem. 67(1): 95-106 (1984).

Zabik, M. J. "The Photochemistry of PCBs," in PCBs: Human and Environmental Hazards, F. M. D'Itri and M. A. Kamrin, Eds. (Boston: Butterworth Publishers, 1983), pp. 141-164.

Zelenski, S. G., J. Tashiro and L. R. Worthen. "A Gas Chromatographic Method of Quantitating DDT in the Presence of Interferring Polychlorinated Biphenyl," J. Chromatogr. 84: 67-73 (1973).

Zelenski, S. G., J. Hall and S. E. Haupt. "Applying for a Permit to Destroy PCB Waste Oil; Vol. I. Summary," U.S. Environmental Protection Agency, Office of Research and Development, Research Triangle Park, NC, EPA-600/2-81-033a; NTIS No. PB81-173 346, 85 pp. (March 1981a).

Zelenski, S. G., J. Hall and S. E. Haupt. "Applying for a Permit to Destroy PCB Waste Oil; Vol. II. Documentation," U.S. Environmental Protection Agency, Office of Research and Development, Research Triangle Park, NC, EPA-600/2-81-033b; NTIS No. PB81-234874, 220 pp. (March 1981b).

Zell, M., H. J. Neu and K. Ballschmiter. "Identifizierung der PCB-Komponenten durch Retentionsindexvergleich nach Kapillar-Gaschromatographie," Chemosphere 6:69-76 (1977).

Zell, M., H. J. Neu and K. Ballschmiter. "Single Component Analysis of Polychlorinated Biphenyl (PCB)- and Chlorinated Pesticide Residues in Marine Fish Samples," Fresenius' Z. Anal. Chem. 292:97-107 (1978).

Zell, M. and K. Ballschmiter. "Baseline Study of the Global Pollution. III. Trace Analysis of Polychlorinated Biphenyls (PCB) by ECD Glass Capillary Gas Chromatography in Environmental Samples of Different Trophic Levels," Fresenius' Z. Anal. Chem. 304:337-349 (1980).

Zhang, T., T. Gu, and X. Xu. "Determination of Polychlorinated Biphenyls in Seawater," Haiyang Yu Huzhao 14(4):353-356 (1983); Chem. Abst. 101:11919m (1984).

Zimmerli, B.   "Beitrag zur Bestimmung von Umweltkontaminan-
tien Mittels der Hydrierenden Reaktionsgaschromatographie,"
J. Chromatogr. 88:65-75 (1974).

Zimmerli, B., B. Marek and H. Sulser.   "Determination of
Chlorinated Biphenyls and Chloride Pesticides," Mitt. Geb.
Lebensmittclunters. Hyg. 64(1):70-79 (1973); Chem. Abst. 79:
124762a (1973).

Zitko, V.   "Polychlorinated Biphenyls and Organochlorine
Pesticides in Some Freshwater and Marine Fishes," Bull. Environ. Contam. Toxicol. 6(5):464-470 (1971a).

Zitko, V.   "Effects of Pesticide-grade Hexanes on the Silicic
Acid Chromatography of Polychlorinated Biphenyls and Organochlorine Pesticides," J. Chromatogr. 59:444-445 (1971b).

Zitko, V.   "Problems in the Determination of Polychlorinated
Biphenyls," Intern. J. Environ. Anal. Chem. 1:221-231 (1972).

Zitko, V.   "Chromatography of Chlorinated Paraffins on Alumina and Silica Columns," J. Chromatogr. 81:152-155 (1973).

Zitko, V.   "The Detection of Aromatic and Chlorinated Hydrocarbons in Marine Lipids," J. Am. Oil Chemists' Soc. 52:131A
(1975).

Zitko, V.   "Levels of Chlorinated Hydrocarbons in Eggs of
Double-Crested Cormorants from 1971 to 1975," Bull. Environ.
Contam. Toxicol. 16(4):399-405 (1976).

Zitko, V. "The Interference of Aromatic Hydrocarbons in the
Determination of PCB's," in Proceedings of the Joint Conference on Sensing of Environmental Pollutants, 4th, New Orleans
(1977). pp. 757-760.

Zitko, V.   "'Shorthand' Numbering of Chlorobiphenyls," Chemosphere 12(6):835-836 (1983).

Zitko, V. and P. M. K. Choi.   "PCB and Other Industrial Halogenated Hydrocarbons in the Environment." Technical Report
No. 272.   St. Andrews, New Brunswick, Canada: Fisheries Research Board of Canada (1971).

Zitko, V., O. Hutzinger and S. Safe.   "Retention Times and
Electron-Capture Detector Responses of Some Individual Chlorobiphenyls," Bull. Environ. Contam. Toxicol. 6(2):160-163
(1971).

Zitko, V. and P. M. K. Choi.   "PCB and p,p'-DDE in Eggs of
Cormorants, Gulls, and Ducks from the Bay of Fundy, Canada,"
Bull. Environ. Contam. Toxicol. 7(1):63-64 (1972).

Zitko, V., O. Hutzinger, and P. M. K. Choi, "Determination of Pentachlorophenol and Chlorobiphenylols in Biological Samples," Bull. Environ. Contam. Toxicol. 12(6):649-653 (1974a).

Zitko, V. P. M. K. Choi, D. J. Wildish, C. F. Monaghan and N. A. Lister. "Distribution of PCB and p,p'-DDE Residues in Atlantic Herring (Clupea harengus harengus) and Yellow Perch (Perca flavescens) in Eastern Canada-1972," Pestic. Mon. J., 8(2): 105-109 (1974b).

Zobel, M. G. R. "Quantitative Determination of Polychlorinated Biphenyls--A Computer Approach," J. Assoc. Offic. Anal. Chem. 57(4):791-795 (1974).

Zoll, D. F., G. V. Cox, R. J. Fensterheim and E. W. Warren. "Comments in Response to Proposed Rule on Manufacture, Processing, Distribution and Use of Polychlorinated Biphenyls in Closed and Controlled Waste Manufacturing Processes," Submitted to the U.S. Environmental Protection Agency by the Chemical Manufacturers Association Special Program Panel on PCBs, EPA Docket No. OPTS-62017A, July 8, 1982, 80 pp.

Zweig, G. and J. Sherma. CRC Handbook of Chromatography, (Cleveland, OH: CRC Press, 1972).

APPENDIX A

NOMENCLATURE AND PHYSICAL CONSTANTS OF POLYCHLORINATED BIPHENYLS

Table A-I. Nomenclature and Physical Constants
of Polychlorinated Biphenyls

IUPAC No.[a]	Compound	CAS No.	Melting Point (°C)[b]	Solubility in H_2O (ppm)[b]
	Biphenyl	92-52-4	71[c]	7.2[d]
	Monochlorobiphenyl	27323-18-8		
1	2	2051-60-7	34	5.9
2	3	2051-61-8	16.5	3.5
3	4	2051-62-9	77.7	1.19
	Dichlorobiphenyl	25512-42-9		
4	2,2'	13029-08-8	60.5	1.50
5	2,3	16605-91-7	27.7-28.2	
6	2,3'	25569-80-6	oil	
7	2,4	33284-50-3	24.1-24.4	1.40
8	2,4'	34883-43-7	46	1.88
9	2,5	34883-39-1	22-23?	0.59[d]
10	2,6	33146-45-1	35-36	
11	3,3'	2050-67-1	29	
12	3,4	2974-92-7	49-50	
13	3,4'	2974-90-5	oil	
14	3,5	34883-41-5	31-32	
15	4,4'	2050-68-2	148-149	0.08
	Trichlorobiphenyl	25323-68-6		
16	2,2',3	38444-78-9	28.1-28.8	
17	2,2',4	37680-66-3		
18	2,2',5	37680-65-2	43-44	0.14[d]
19	2,2',6	38444-73-4		
20	2,3,3'	38444-84-7		
21	2,3,4	55702-46-0	101-102	
22	2,3,4'	38444-85-8	73-73.2	
23	2,3,5	55720-44-0	41	
24	2,3,6	58702-45-9		
25	2,3',4	55712-37-3		
26	2,3',5	38444-81-4	40-40.5	
27	2,3',6	38444-76-7		
28	2,4,4'	7012-37-5	57-58	0.085
29	2,4,5	15862-07-4	78-79	0.092[d]
30	2,4,6	35693-92-6	62.5	
31	2,4',5	16606-02-3	67	

Table A-I (Continued)

IUPAC No.[a]	Compound	CAS No.	Melting Point (°C)[b]	Solubility in H_2O[b] (ppm)[b]
32	2,4',6	38444-77-8		
33	2',3,4	38444-86-9	60	0.078
34	2',3,5	37680-68-5	58	
35	3,3',4	37680-69-6		
36	3,3',5	38444-87-0		
37	3,4,4'	38444-90-5	86.8-87.8	0.015[d]
38	3,4,5	53555-66-1		
39	3,4',5	38444-88-1	88	
	Tetrachlorobiphenyl	26914-33-0		
40	2,2',3,3'	38444-93-8	119.5-121.5	0.034
41	2,2',3,4	52663-59-9		
42	2,2',3,4'	36559-22-5	68-70	
43	2,2',3,5	70362-46-8		
44	2,2',3,5'	41464-39-5	46.5-47	0.170
45	2,2',3,6	70362-45-7		
46	2,2',3,6'	41464-47-5	125.5-127	
47	2,2',4,4'	2437-79-8	41, 83	0.068
48	2,2',4,5	70362-47-9		
49	2,2',4,5'	41464-40-8	64-66	
50	2,2',4,6	62796-65-8		
51	2,2',4,6'	65194-04-7		
52	2,2',5,5'	35693-99-3	87-89	0.046
53	2,2',5,6'	41464-41-9	103-104.5	
54	2,2',6,6'	15968-05-5	198	
55	2,3,3',4	74338-24-2		
56	2,3,3',4'	41464-43-1	96-97	
57	2,3,3',5	70424-67-8		
58	2,3,3',5'	41464-49-7	127.5-129	
59	2,3,3',6	74472-33-6		
60	2,3,4,4'	33025-41-1	142	0.058
61	2,3,4,5	33284-53-6	92-92.5	0.019[d]
62	2,3,4,6	54230-23-7		
63	2,3,4',5	74472-35-8	104	
64	2,3,4',6	52663-58-8		
65	2,3,5,6	33284-54-7	79	
66	2,3',4,4'	32598-10-0	124	0.058
67	2,3',4,5	73575-53-8		
68	2,3',4,5'	73575-52-7		
69	2,3',4,6	60233-24-1		
70	2,3',4',5	32598-11-1	104	0.041
71	2,3',4',6	41464-46-4		

Table A-I (Continued)

IUPAC No.[a]	Compound	CAS No.	Melting Point (°C)[b]	Solubility in H_2O[b] (ppm)[b]
72	2,3',5,5'	41464-42-0	105.5-106.5	
73	2,3',5',6	74338-23-1		
74	2,4,4',5	32690-93-0	125	
75	2,4,4',6	32598-12-2		
76	2',3,4,5	70362-48-0		
77	3,3',4,4'	32598-13-3	173	0.175
78	3,3',4,5	70362-49-1		
79	3,3',4,5'	41464-48-6	119-120	
80	3,3',5,5'	33284-52-5	164	
81	3,4,4',5	70362-50-4		
	Pentachlorobiphenyl	25429-29-2		
82	2,2',3,3',4	52663-62-4	119-120.5	
83	2,2',3,3',5	60145-20-2		
84	2,2',3,3',6	52663-60-2		
85	2,2',3,4,4'	65510-45-4		
86	2,2',3,4,5	55312-69-1		0.0098[e]
87	2,2',3,4,5'	38380-02-8	111.5-113	0.022
88	2,2',3,4,6	55215-17-3		0.012[d]
89	2,2',3,4,6'	73575-57-2		
90	2,2',3,4',5	68194-07-0		
91	2,2',3,4',6	58194-05-8		
92	2,2',3,5,5'	52663-61-3		
93	2,2',3,5,6	73575-56-1		
94	2,2',3,5,6'	73575-55-0		
95	2,2',3,5',6	38379-99-6	98.5-100	
96	2,2',3,6,6'	73575-54-9		
97	2,2',3',4,5	41464-51-1	81-82	
98	2,2',3',4,6	60233-25-2		
99	2,2',4,4',5	38380-01-7		
100	2,2',4,4',6	39485-83-1		
101	2,2',4,5,5'	37680-73-2	76.5-77.5	0.031
102	2,2',4,5,6'	68194-06-9		
103	2,2',4,5',6	60145-21-3		
104	2,2',4,6,6'	56558-16-8		
105	2,3,3',4,4'	32598-14-4	101-105	
106	2,3,3',4,5	70424-69-0		
107	2,3,3',4',5	70424-68-9		
108	2,3,3',4,5'	70362-41-3		
109	2,3,3',4,6	74472-35-8		
110	2,3,3',4',6	38380-03-9		
111	2,3,3',5,5'	39635-32-0		

Table A-I (Continued)

IUPAC No.[a]	Compound	CAS No.	Melting Point (°C)[b]	Solubility in H_2O[b] (ppm)
112	2,3,3',5,6	74472-36-9		
113	2,3,3',5',6	68194-10-5		
114	2,3,4,4',5	74472-37-0	98-99	
115	2,3,4,4',6	74472-38-1		
116	2,3,4,5,6	18259-05-7	123	0.0068[d]
117	2,3,4',5,6	68194-11-6		
118	2,3',4,4',5	31508-00-6	105-107	
119	2,3',4,4',6	56558-17-9		
120	2,3',4,5,5'	68194-12-7		
121	2,3',4,5',6	56558-18-0		
122	2',3,3',4,5	76842-07-4		
123	2',3,4,4',5	65510-44-3		
124	2',3,4,5,5'	70424-70-3		
125	2',3,4,5,6'	74472-39-2		
126	3,3',4,4',5	57465-28-8		
127	3,3',4,5,5'	39635-33-1		
	Hexachlorobiphenyl	26601-64-9		
128	2,2',3,3',4,4'	38380-07-3	145.5-146.6	0.00044[d]
129	2,2',3,3',4,5	55215-18-4		0.00085[d]
130	2,2',3,3',4,5'	52663-66-8		
131	2,2',3,3',4,6	61798-70-7		
132	2,2',3,3',4,6'	38380-05-1		
133	2,2',3,3',5,5'	35694-04-3	128-129	
134	2,2',3,3',5,6	52704-70-8		0.00091[d]
135	2,2',3,3',5,6'	52744-13-5		
136	2,2',3,3',6,6'	38411-22-2	114-114.5	
137	2,2',3,4,4',5	35694-06-5	77-78	
138	2,2',3,4,4',5'	35065-28-2	78.5-80	
139	2,2',3,4,4',6	56030-56-9		
140	2,2',3,4,4',6'	59291-64-4	69.5-71	
141	2,2',3,4,5,5'	52712-04-6		
142	2,2',3,4,5,6	41411-61-4	134-137	
143	2,2',3,4,5,6'	68194-15-0		
144	2,2',3,4,5',6	68194-14-9		
145	2,2',3,4,6,6'	74472-40-5		
146	2,2',3,4',5,5'	51908-16-8		
147	2,2',3,4',5,6	68194-13-8		
148	2,2',3,4',5,6'	74472-42-7		
149	2,2',3,4',5',6	38380-04-0	oil	
150	2,2',3,4',6,6'	68194-08-1		
151	2,2',3,5,5',6	52663-63-5	100-101	

Table A-I (Continued)

IUPAC No.[a]	Compound	CAS No.	Melting Point (°C)[b]	Solubility in H_2O[b] (ppm)
152	2,2',3,5,6,6'	68194-09-2		
153	2,2',4,4',5,5'	35065-27-1	103-104	0.0013[d]
154	2,2',4,4',5,6'	60145-22-4	oil	
155	2,2',4,4',6,6'	33979-03-2	112.5	0.00091[d]
156	2,3,3',4,4',5	38380-08-4		
157	2,3,3',4,4',5'	69782-90-7		
158	2,3,3',4,4',6	74472-42-7		
159	2,3,3',4,5,5'	39635-35-3		
160	2,3,3',4,5,6	41411-62-5	97-100	
161	2,3,3',4,5',6	74472-43-8		
162	2,3,3',4',5,5'	39635-34-2		
163	2,3,3',4',5,6	74472-44-9		
164	2,3,3',4',5',6	74472-45-0		
165	2,3,3',5,5',6	74472-46-1		
166	2,3,4,4',5,6	41411-63-6	160-165	
167	2,3',4,4',5,5'	52663-72-6		
168	2,3',4,4',5',6	59291-65-5	110-111	
169	3,3',4,4',5,5'	32774-16-6	201-202	
	Heptachlorobiphenyl	28655-71-2		
170	2,2',3,3',4,4',5	35065-30-6	134.5-135.5	
171	2,2',3,3',4,4',6	52663-71-5		
172	2,2',3,3',4,5,5'	52663-74-8		
173	2,2',3,3',4,5,6	68194-16-1		
174	2,2',3,3',4,5,6'	38411-25-5	130.5-130.7	
175	2,2',3,3',4,5',6	40186-70-7		
176	2,2',3,3',4,6,6'	52663-65-7		
177	2,2',3,3',4',5,6	52663-70-4		
178	2,2',3,3',5,5',6	52663-67-9		
179	2,2',3,3',5,6,6'	52663-64-6		
180	2,2',3,4,4',5,5'	35065-29-3	109-110	
181	2,2',3,4,4',5,6	74472-47-2		
182	2,2',3,4,4',5,6'	60145-23-5	152-153	
183	2,2',3,4,4',5',6	52663-69-1		
184	2,2',3,4,4',6,6'	74472-48-3		
185	2,2',3,4,5,5',6	52712-05-7	147-150	0.00048[d]
186	2,2',3,4,5,6,6'	74472-49-4		
187	2,2',3,4',5,5',6	52663-68-0		
188	2,2',3,4',5,6,6'	74487-85-7		
189	2,3,3',4,4',5,5'	39635-31-9	162-163	
190	2,3,3',4,4',5,6	41411-64-7	116-118	
191	2,3,3',4,4',5',6	74472-50-7		

Table A-I (Continued)

IUPAC No.[a]	Compound	CAS No.	Melting Point (°C)[b]	Solubility in H_2O (ppm)[b]
192	2,3,3',4,5,5',6	74472-51-8		
193	2,3,3',4',5,5',6	69782-91-8		
	Octachlorobiphenyl	31472-83-0[f]		
194	2,2',3,3',4,4',5,5'	35694-08-7	156-157	0.0014[d]
195	2,2',3,3',4,4',5,6	52663-78-2		
196	2,2',3,3',4,4',5,6'	42740-50-1		
197	2,2',3,3',4,4',6,6'	33091-17-7	132	
198	2,2',3,3',4,5,5',6	68194-17-2		
199	2,2',3,3',4,5,5',6'[g]	52663-75-9		
200	2,2',3,3',4,5,6,6'[g]	52663-73-7		
201	2,2',3,3',4,5',6,6'[g]	40186-71-8		
202	2,2',3,3',5,5',6,6'	2136-99-4	161	0.00018[d]
203	2,2',3,4,4',5,5',6	52663-76-0		
204	2,2',3,4,4',5,6,6'	74472-52-9		
205	2,3,3',4,4',5,5',6	74472-53-0		
	Nonachlorobiphenyl	53742-07-7		
206	2,2',3,3',4,4',5,5',6	40186-72-9	204.5-206.5	0.00011[d]
207	2,2',3,3',4,4',5,6,6'	52663-79-3		
208	2,2',3,3',4,5,5',6,6'	52663-77-1		
	Decachlorobiphenyl	2051-24-3		
209	2,2',3,3',4,4',5,5',6,6'	2051-24-3	305-306	0.00049[d]

a　Ballschmiter, K., and M. Zell (1980).
b　All melting point and water solubility data from Hutzinger, et al. (1974a) unless otherwise noted. Other experimental values were often reported; where major discrepancies exist, extreme values are separated by a comma. The other references report conflicting values for many of the congeners. Do not compare values from different citations without consulting primary reference.
c　CRC Handbook of Chemistry and Physics (57th ed.).
d　Yalkowsky et al. (1983).
e　Mackay et al. (1980).
f　Four chlorines on each ring at unspecified locations.
g　Revised numbering sequence as noted by Schulte and Malisch (1983).

COMPOSITION OF SOME COMMERCIAL PCB MIXTURES

Table B-I. Qualitative and Percent Chlorobiphenyl and Biphenyl Compositions of Commercial PCB Preparations

CL-Substituted Positions	1221	1221	1221	1221	1232	1016	1242	1242	1242	1248	1248	1254	1254	A50	1260	1260	A60	A60	DP6
0	13	16	e	16	e	0.5	e		e	e		e		e	e	e			
2	28	32	e	35	e	1	e	0.8	e	e		e		e	e	e			
3	3	3	e	3															
4	19	19	e	20	e	2	e		e	e		e		e	e	e			
2.3						0.4													
2.4	4	3		2		1	e	<0.7	e	e	<0.1	e		e	e	e			
2.5		0.2		tr				e	m										
2.6		0.3		0.4		tr													
2.2'	9	5	e	5	e	7	e	<10	M	e		e		e	e	e			
2.3'	3	3	e	2	e	1	e	<5	M	e		e		e	e	e			
2.4'	14	10	e	11	e	11	e	e	M	e	0.5	e		e	e	e			
3.4		1		e				e											
3.5						tr													
3.3'																			
3.4'				1			e	1	M	e	<3	e		e	e	e			
4.4'	6	4	e	4	e	2	e	1	M	e	<3	e		e	e	e			
2.3.4																			
2.3.5																			
2.3.6																			
2.2'.3		0.1			e	5	e		M?	e									
2.3.3'					e	tr	e		M?	e									
2.3.4'						tr													
2.4.5																			
2.4.6																			
2.2'.4		0.3	e	e	e	4	e	11	M	e	8	e		e	e	e			
2.3'.4			e	e	e	4	e	<15	M	e	<13	e		e	e	e			
2.4.4'		0.2	e	e	e	4	e	7	M?	e	3	e		e	e	e			
2.2'.5		0.6		0.6	e	12	e	2	M	e	0.1	e		e	e	e			
2.3'.5		0.2		9		9	e	e	M	e	<13	e		e	e	e			
2.4'.5		0.2				10	e		M			e		e	e	e			
2.2'.6				1	e	1	e	e	e	e		e							
2.3'.6				0.3		0.3		e	M?										
2.4'.6				2		2			M										
3.4.5																			
2'.3.4		0.1	e		e	tr	e	16	M	e	21	e	0.3	e	e	e			
3.3'.4									M										

Table B-I (Continued)

	1221	1221	1221	1221	1232	1016	1242	1242	1242	1248	1248	1254	1254	1254	A50	1260	1260	1260	A60	A60	DPs
2',3.5						tr															
3,3'.5																					
3,4'.5						tr															
2,3,4.5																					
2,3,4.6																					
2,3,5.6																					
2,2',3.4						3	M			7					1				0.7		
2,3,3'.4						0.4		m			E		E								
2,3,4.4'									M?				E								
2,2',3.5						0.2															
2,3,3'.5																					
2,3,4'.5						<2															
2,2',3.6							6			E					2				1		
2,3,3'.6								M?													
2,3,4'.6						tr															
2,2',4.5																					
2,3',4.5																					
2,4,4'.5																					
2,2',4.6						<2	4			E		E	M		2	<0.4			1		
2,3',4.6						tr		M?													
2,4,4'.6																					
2',3,4.5																					
3,3',4.5																					
3,4,4'.5				E																	
2,2',3.3'																					
2,2',3.4'						1	12	E		E			E								
2,2',3.5'						tr		E			E										
2,2',3.6'						1				16											
2,3,3'.4'						1	E			E	E										
2,3,3'.5'																					
2,2',4.4'						1			e		E		4								
2,2',4.5'						3	tr				E		8								
2,2',4.6'						0.1			M?		E										
2,3',4.4'						tr		M?						E	1						
2,3',4.5'									M?												
2,3',5.5'						2		M?										E			
2,2',5.5'	0.14					2	M?	M?			E		M		5			E			

471

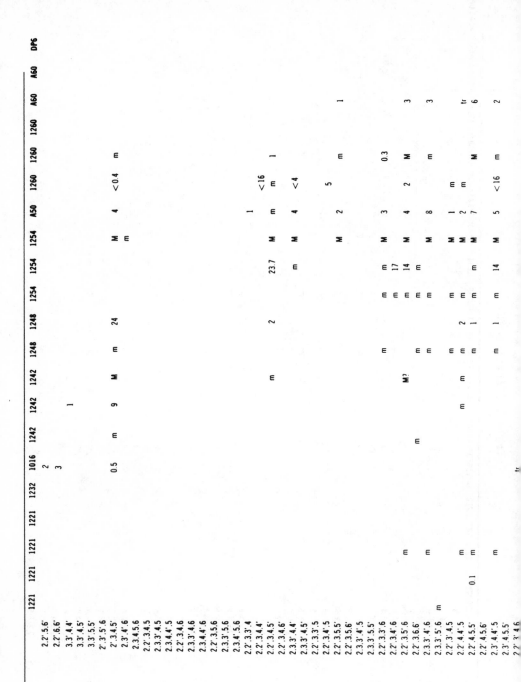

Table B-I (Continued)

	1221	1221	1221	1232	1016	1242	1242	1248	1248	1254	1254	1254	A50	1260	1260	1260	1260	A60	A60	DP6
2,2',4,5',6																				
2,2',4,6,6'																				
2,3',4,4',6																				
2,3',4,5',6																				
2,3,3',4',5'																				
2,3',4,4',5'																				
2,3',4',5,5'																				
2,3',4',5',6																				
3,3',4,4',5																				
3,3',4,5,5'																				
2,2',3,4,5,6																				
2,3,3',4,5,6																				
2,3,4,4',5,6		E																		
2,2',3,3',4,5																				
2,2',3,4,4',5	E																			
2,2',3,4,5,6																				
2,2',3,4,5,6'		E					E													
2,3,3',4,4',6											E		0.8		<9		E	2		
2,3,3',4,5,6																E				
2,2',3,3',5,6													1			E		3		
2,2',3,4',5,6		E					E				2	m	1		M			2		
2,2',3,5,5',6													<1					2		
2,2',3,5,6,6'											12	M	5		M	E		11	E	
2,3,3',4',5,6												M	2		M			3		E
2,2',3,4,4',6'	m																			

Table B-I (Continued)

	1221	1221	1221	1221	1232	1242	1016	1242	1242	1248	1248	1254	1254	1254	1254	A50	1260	1260	1260	1260	A60	A60	DP6
2.2',3.3',5.5'		m									<0.1					0.9	<16				3		
2.3,4',5.5'																					2		
2.3.3',4',5.5'		m														1	<15				4		
2.2',3,3',5.6	m																						
2.2',4,4',5.6		m											4	M		4	<4	M		m	13	m	m
2.2',4.4',5.5'													0.4	m		0.5				m	1	m	
2.3,4,4',5.5'														e									
3.3',4.4',5.5'																0.5	4	M		m	1	m	m
2.3',4,4',5',6																2		M			7	m	m
2.2',4',5.6.6'																							
2.2',4.4',6.6'																							
2.3.3',4',5',6															m								
2.2',3.3',6.6'		m										e											
2.2',3',4.5.6'		m																					
2.2',3.3',4.5.6		m										e				1	<4	M		m	4	m	m
2.2',3.4,4',5.6		m														0.2	<9	e			0.9	m	m
2.2',3.4.5.5'.6														M		0.3	12	M			4	m	m
2.2',3.4.5.6.6'														e		1	<20	m			8	m	
2.3.3',4.4',5.6													2			tr		M			tr		
2.3.3',4.5.5',6														e		0.1					0.4		
2.2',3.3',4.4',5														e		0.1	<20	M			0.4		
2.2',3.3',4.5.5'																0.2					2		
2.2',3.3',4.5.6'																							
2.2',3.4,4',5.5'																							
2.3.3',4.4',5.5'			m																				
2.2',3.3',4.4',6		m															e						
2.2',3.3',4.5',6		m																					
2.2',3.4,4',6.6'																							
2.3.3',4,6,6'	m																						
2.3.3',4.4',5',6																							
2.2',3.3',4',5.6																							
2.2',3.3',5.5'.6																							
2.2',3.3',5.6.6'																							
2.2',3.4',5.5'.6																0.3					2		
2.2',3.4',5.6.6'																tr					0.5		
2.3.3',4',5.5'.6		m														1					1		
2.2',3.3',4',5.6																0.4					3		
2.2',3.4.4',5.5'.6																			M				
2.2',3.4.4',5.5'.6																			m				
2.2',3.3',4.5.6																			e	e			

474

Table B-I (Concluded)

	1221	1221	1221	1221	1232	1016	1242	1242	1248	1248	1254	1254	1254	A50	1260	1260	1260	A60	A60	DP6
2,3,3',4,4',5,5',6														0.4	2	m		0.7		
2,2',3,3',4,4',5,5'															5	m		0.7		
2,2',3,3',4,4',5,6'	m													0.1	m	M				
2,2',3,3',4,4',6,6'														tr		m				
2,2',3,3',4,5,6,6'														tr		m				
2,2',3,3',4,5',6,6'															0.4			tr		
2,2',3,3',5,5',6,6'	m															m				
2,2',3,3',4,4',5,6,6'																m				
2,2',3,3',4,5,5',6,6'																m				
2,2',3,3',4,4',5,5',6,6'																				
Reference	a	b	c	c	b	c	b	c	d	c	b	c	d	e	b	d	e	f	c	f

Note: Qualitatively major peaks = M, minor peaks = m, ambiguous identities = ?, quantitatively, percentages rounded.

a Nagayama et al. (1976).
b Albro, P.W., NIEHS, Research Triangle Park, North Carolina, written communication (November 1976).
c Willis and Addison (1972).
d Sissons and Welti (1971).
e Jensen and Sundström (1974).
f Tas and deVos (1971).
Source: NIOSH (1977c).

MASS SPECTRAL CHARACTERISTICS OF PCBs

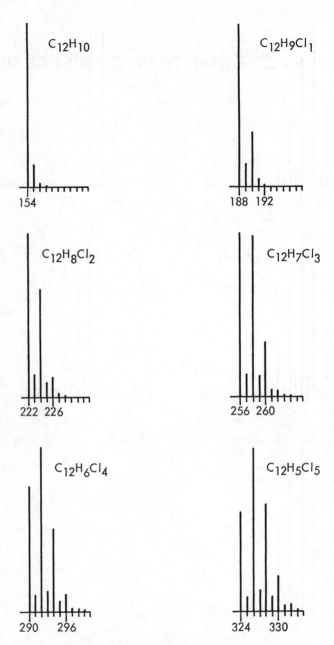

Figure C-1. Mass Spectral Patterns of PCBs
a Mono- Through Pentachlorobiphenyls

The molecular ion clusters were calculated using natural
abundance ratios of carbon, hydrogen, and chlorine.

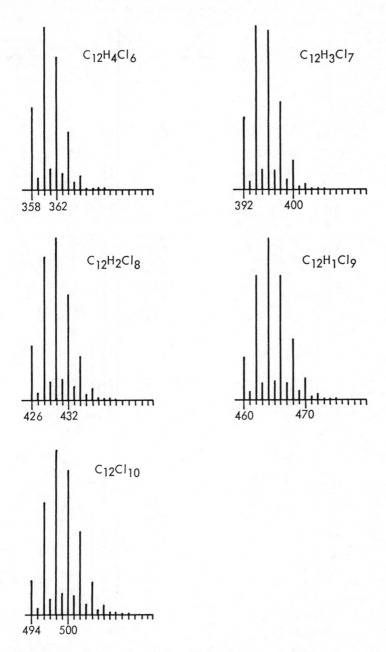

Figure C-1 (concluded).   Mass Spectral Patterns of
PCBs Hexa- Through Decachlorobiphenyl

The molecular ion clusters were calculated using natural
abundance ratios of carbon, hydrogen, and chlorine.

Table C-1. Major Molecular Cluster Ions for Common Clorinated Aromatics[a]

No. of Chlorines (n)	PCBs $C_{12}H_{10-n}Cl_n$		PCNs $C_{10}H_{8-n}Cl_n$		PCDDs $C_{12}H_{8-n}Cl_nO_2$		PCDFs $Cl_{12}H_{8-n}Cl_nO$	
	Exact Mass	Relative Abundance	Exact Mass	Relative Abundance	Exact Mass	Relative Abundance	Exact Mass	Relative Abundance
0	154.0783	-	128.0626	-	184.0525	-	168.0576	-
1	188.0393	100.00	162.0237	100.00	218.0135	100.00	202.0186	100.00
	190.0363	33.42	164.0207	33.16	220.0105	33.82	204.0156	33.62
2	222.0003	100.00	195.9847	100.00	251.9745	100.00	235.9796	100.00
	223.9974	66.04	197.9817	65.79	253.9716	66.45	237.9766	66.24
	225.9944	11.16	199.9788	10.99	255.9686	11.43	239.9737	11.29
3	255.9614	100.00	229.9457	100.00	285.9355	100.00	269.9406	100.00
	257.9584	98.66	231.9428	98.41	287.9326	99.07	271.9377	98.87
	259.9555	32.70	233.9398	32.46	289.9296	33.10	273.9347	32.90
	261.9525	3.72	235.9369	3.64	291.9267	3.86	275.9318	3.79
4	289.9224	76.17	263.9067	76.31	319.8965	75.93	303.9016	76.05
	291.9194	100.00	265.9038	100.00	321.8936	100.00	305.8987	100.00
	293.9165	49.43	267.9008	49.27	323.8906	49.68	307.8957	49.55
	295.9135	10.96	269.8979	10.86	325.8877	11.13	309.8928	11.05
	297.9106	0.94	271.8949	0.92	327.8847	0.99	311.8898	0.97
5	323.8834	61.01	297.8677	61.10	353.8576	60.86	337.8627	60.93
	325.8805	100.00	299.8648	100.00	355.8546	100.00	339.8597	100.00
	327.8775	65.72	301.8618	65.57	357.8517	65.96	341.8568	65.84
	329.8746	21.69	303.8590	21.57	359.8487	21.91	343.8538	21.80
	331.8716	3.62	305.8559	3.57	361.8458	3.70	345.8509	3.66
6	357.8444	50.88	331.8288	50.95	387.8186	50.78	371.8237	50.83
	359.8415	100.00	333.8258	100.00	389.8156	100.00	373.8207	100.00
	361.8385	82.02	335.8229	81.87	391.8127	82.25	375.8178	82.14
	363.8356	35.97	337.8199	35.82	393.8097	36.23	377.8148	36.10
	365.8326	8.92	339.8170	8.85	395.8068	9.05	379.8119	8.99
7	391.8054	43.64	365.7898	43.69	421.7796	43.56	405.7847	43.60
	393.8025	100.00	367.7868	100.00	423.7767	100.00	407.7817	100.00
	395.7995	98.32	369.7839	98.18	425.7737	98.55	409.7788	98.44
	397.7966	53.80	371.7809	53.61	427.7708	54.10	411.7758	53.95
	399.7936	17.72	373.7780	17.60	429.7678	17.90	413.7729	17.81
8	425.7665	33.33	399.7508	33.40	455.7406	33.21	439.7457	33.27
	427.7635	87.24	401.7479	87.35	457.7377	87.07	441.7428	87.15
	429.7606	100.00	403.7449	100.00	459.7347	100.00	443.7398	100.00
	431.7576	65.58	405.7420	65.48	461.7318	65.76	445.7369	65.67
	433.7547	26.93	407.7390	26.83	463.7288	27.10	447.7339	27.02
9	459.7275	25.94						
	461.7245	76.38						
	463.7216	100.00						
	465.7186	76.45						
	467.7157	37.62						
10	493.6885	20.77						
	495.6856	67.92						
	497.6826	100.00						
	499.6797	87.31						
	501.6767	50.08						

Table C-1 (Concluded)

No. of Chlorines (n)	PCBPs $C_{12}H_{8-n}Cl_n$		PCHBs $C_{12}H_{9-n}Cl_nOH$		Cl-Benzene $C_6H_{6-n}Cl_n$		Cl-Phenol $C_{12}H_{5-n}Cl_nOH$	
	Exact Mass	Relative Abundance	Exact Mass	Relative Abundance	Exact Mass	Relative Abundance	Exact Mass	Relative Abundance
0	152.0626	-	170.0732	-	78.0470	-	94.0419	-
1	186.0237	100.00	204.0342	100.00	112.0080	100.00	128.0029	100.00
	188.0207	33.41	206.0313	33.62	114.0051	32.81	130.0000	33.01
2	219.9847	100.00	237.9953	100.00	145.9690	100.00	161.9639	100.00
	221.9817	66.04	239.9923	66.24	147.9661	65.43	163.9610	65.63
	223.9788	11.16	241.9894	11.29	149.9631	10.76	165.9580	10.89
3	253.9457	100.00	271.9563	100.00	179.9300	100.00	195.9250	100.00
	255.9428	98.66	273.9533	98.87	181.9271	98.06	197.9220	98.26
	257.9398	32.70	275.9504	32.90	183.9241	32.11	199.9191	32.31
	259.9369	3.72	277.9474	3.79	185.9212	3.53	201.9161	3.59
4	287.9067	76.17	305.9173	76.05	213.8911	76.52	229.8860	76.40
	289.9038	100.00	307.9143	100.00	215.8881	100.00	231.8830	100.00
	291.9008	49.43	309.9114	49.55	217.8852	49.05	233.8801	49.18
	293.8979	10.96	311.9084	11.05	219.8822	10.72	235.8771	10.80
	295.8949	0.95	313.9055	0.97	221.8793	0.89	237.8742	0.91
5	321.8677	61.01	339.8783	60.93	247.8521	61.23	263.8470	61.16
	323.8648	100.00	341.8754	100.00	249.8491	100.00	265.8440	100.00
	325.8618	65.72	343.8724	65.84	251.8462	65.36	267.8411	65.48
	327.8589	21.69	345.8695	21.80	253.8432	21.38	269.8381	21.49
	329.8559	3.62	347.8665	3.66	255.8403	3.51	271.8352	3.55
6	355.8288	50.88	373.8393	50.83	281.8131	51.04		
	357.8258	100.00	375.8364	100.00	283.8102	100.00		
	359.8229	82.02	377.8334	82.14	285.8072	81.67		
	361.8199	35.97	379.8305	36.10	287.8043	35.59		
	363.8170	8.92	381.8275	8.99	289.8013	8.74		
7	389.7898	43.64	407.8004	43.60				
	391.7868	100.00	409.7974	100.00				
	393.7839	98.32	411.7945	98.44				
	395.7809	53.80	413.7915	53.95				
	397.7780	17.72	415.7886	17.81				
8	423.7508	33.33	441.7614	33.27				
	425.7479	87.24	443.7584	87.15				
	427.7449	100.00	445.7555	100.00				
	429.7420	65.58	447.7525	65.67				
	431.7390	26.93	449.7496	27.02				
9			475.7224	25.90				
			477.7194	76.31				
			479.7165	100.00				
			481.7135	76.53				
			483.7106	37.72				
10								

a PCBs = polychlorinated biphenyls; PCNs = polychlorinated naphthalenes; PCDDs = polychlorinated dibenzo-p-dioxins; PCDFs = polychlorinated dibenzofurans; PCBPs = polychlorinated biphenylenes; and PCHBs = polychlorinated hydroxybiphenyls.

PGC/ECD CHROMATOGRAMS OF AROCLOR MIXTURES

Hexane solutions were chromatographed on a 180 x 0.2 cm ID glass column, packed with 1.5% SP 2250/1.95% SP 2401 on 100/120 mesh Supelcoport. The nitrogen carrier gas flow rate was 30 mL/min. The injector and detector temperatures were 250°C and 300°C, respectively. The column temperatures are noted on each figure.

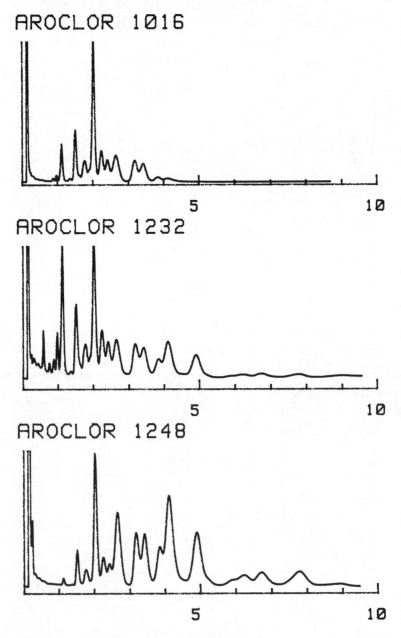

Figure D-1.   Isothermal Chromatograms of Aroclors 1016,
              1232, and 1248

The column temperature was 180°C.

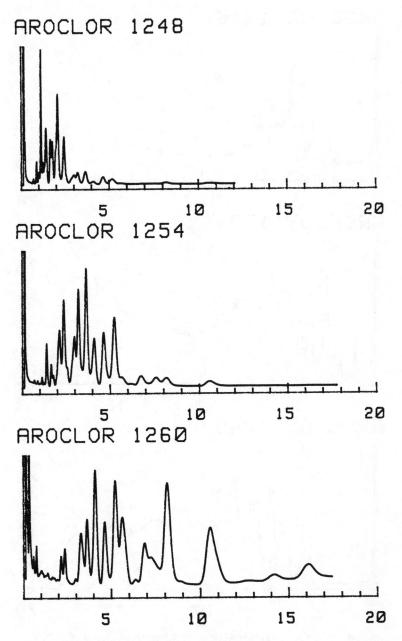

Figure D-2.   Isothermal Chromatograms of Aroclors 1248, 1254, and 1260

The column temperature was 200°C.

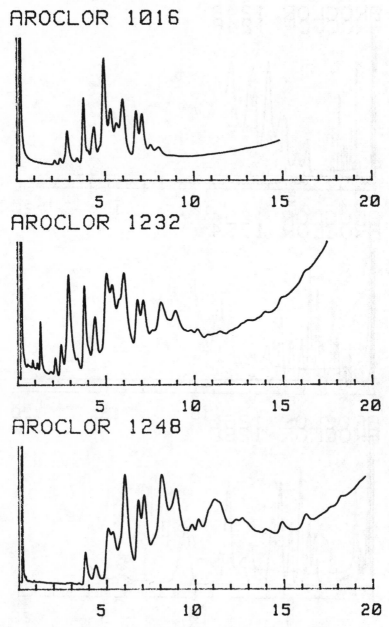

Figure D-3.   Temperature-Programmed Chromatogram
of Aroclors 1016, 1232, and 1248

The column temperature was programmed from 150°C to 250°C at
10°C/min.

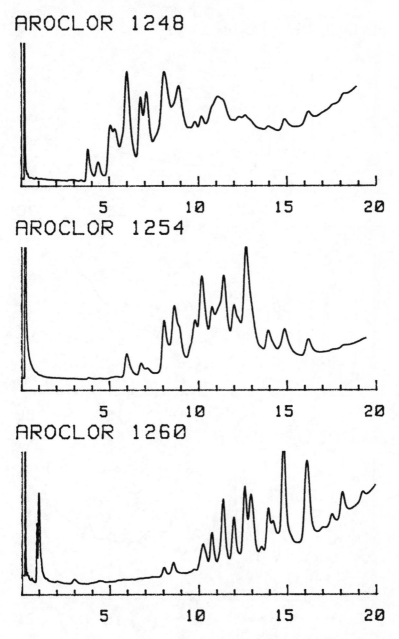

Figure D-4.   Temperature-Programmed Chromatogram
of Aroclors 1248, 1254, and 1260

The column temperature was programmed from 150°C to 250°C at
10°C/min.

APPENDIX E

TERMS AND ABBREVIATIONS

Table E-1. Glossary of Terms

Accuracy: Closeness of the analytical result to the "true" value.

Analysis: The ascertainment of the identity and/or the concentration of the constituents or components of a sample. Analysis is often used incorrectly in place of determination. Only samples can be analyzed; constituents or components are determined (see below). Examples of correct usage are: Analysis of fish for PCBs; determination of PCBs in fish.]

Analyte: Chemical compound or element which is the subject of an analysis.

Aroclor: Trade name (Monsanto) for a series of commercial PCB and polychlorinated terphenyl mixtures marketed in the United States.

Askarel: A general term for a group of nonflammable synthetic chlorinated aromatic hydrocarbons used as electrical insulating media. See ASTM 1978a, b.

Brockmann Activity: Amount of water added to alumina to control its adsorbent activity (Activity I = 0% water; Activity V = 15% water).

By-product PCBs: PCBs unintentionally generated as impurities in synthesis of other products (as opposed to commercial PCBs).

CAS Registry Number: Unique number assigned by Chemical Abstracts Service to each chemical compound (see Appendix A).

Chlophen: Trade name (Bayer, GFR) for a series of PCB mixtures.

Congener: One of 209 PCBs or other group of compounds, not necessarily the same homolog.

Destruction and removal efficiency (DRE): A measure of an incinerator's (or alternative method of destruction) performance in removing or destroying PCBs (or another compound). DRE is expressed as percent efficiency:

$$\frac{mass_{in} - mass_{out}}{mass_{in}} \times 100$$

Table E-1 (Continued)

Determination: The ascertainment of the quantity or concentration of a specific substance in a sample. See analysis.

Electron impact mass spectrometry (EIMS): Low resolution mass spectrometry operated in the electron impact ionization mode.

Equivalent method: Any method, certified against the primary method, which can be used for routine analysis of samples.

External standard: Standards for calibration which are <u>not</u> added to the sample extract.

Florisil: Trade name (Floridin Company) for a synthetic magnesium silicate used for liquid chromatographic cleanup and also for air sampling.

High resolution gas-liquid chromatography: Gas chromatography with a capillary column including WCOT, SCOT, fused silica, glass, and metal.

Homolog: One of the 10 degrees of chlorination of PCBs ($C_{12}H_9Cl$ through $C_{12}Cl_{10}$) or other group of compounds varying by systematic addition of a substituent.

Internal standard: Standards used expressly for quantitation added to sample extract immediately prior to the analytical determination.

Isomer: Any PCB or other cmpound which has the same molecular formula, but different positional substitutions. 2,2'-Dichlorobiphenyl and 2,3-dichlorobiphenyl are isomeric; 4-chlorobiphenyl and 2,3,4-trichlorobiphenyl are not.

Limit of detection (also MDL): Lowest concentration at which an analyte can be identified as present in the sample at a stated statistical confidence level.

Lower limit of quantitation: Lowest concentration to which a value can be assigned at a stated statistical confidence level.

Table E-1 (Continued)

Mean: Arithmetic mean.

Method: A series of techniques which form a specific, well-defined sampling or chemical analysis for a specified compound(s)/matrix(ces) combination. A distinct adaptation of a technique for a selected measurement purpose (e.g., a specific GC/ECD operating mode for analysis of PCBs, including column specifications and sample preparation.

Method detection limit: See limit of detection.

Mineral oil: Liquid mixture of hydrocarbons obtained from petroleum.

Packed column gas chromatography (PGC): Gas-liquid chromatography performed using a column, typically 180 cm long x 2 mm ID, packed with a liquid phase on a granular solid support material.

Part per million (ppm): One part in 10^6. For gaseous mixtures, a volume/volume (v/v) basis is typically used and:

$$1 \text{ ppm} = \text{mg/m}^3 \times \frac{RT}{MW}$$

where RT = 22.4 L/g-mole at 0°C and 1 atm
          = 24.5 L/g-mole at 25°C and 1 atm
   and MW = molecular weight of compound, i.e., g/g-mole

For low concentration aqueous samples, a weight/volume (w/v) basis is most commonly used and 1 ppm = 1 mg/L ($\sim$ 1 mg/kg for liquids with density $\sim$ 1). For nonaqueous liquids and solid materials, a weight/weight (w/w) basis is most commonly used and 1 ppm = 1 mg/kg.

Polychlorinated biphenyl (PCB): One of 209 individual compounds having the molecular formula $C_{12}H_nCl_{10_n}$, where n = 0-9. 4-Chlorobiphenyl and 3,4,3',4'-tetrachlorobiphenyl are examples. This definition includes mono-chlorobiphenyls, but not biphenyl.

Polychlorinated dibenzo-p-dioxin (PCDD): One of 75 individual compounds having the molecular formula $C_{12}H_nCl_{8-n}O_2$, where n = 0-7. This definition includes monochlorodibenzo-p-dioxins.

Table E-1 (Continued)

Polychlorinated dibenzofuran (PCDF): One of 135 individual
    compounds having the molecular formula $C_{12}H_nCl_{8-n}O$,
    where n = 0-7. This definition includes monochlorodi-
    benzofurans.

Procedure: The written directions necessary to use a method
    or series of methods and techniques.

Protocol: A sampling or analysis procedure which is highly
    specific and from which few or no deviations are al-
    lowed.

Qualitative: Having to do with establishing the presence or
    identity of a compound.

Quantitative: Having to do with measuring the amount or
    concentration of a compound in a sample.

Relative retention time: Retention time of a compound on a
    chromatographic system, relative to an internal stan-
    dard; unitless number.

Response factor: Instrumental response of an analyte mea-
    sured against an internal standard.

Retention index: Systematic, unitless measure of a com-
    pound's chromatographic retention as compared to an
    homologous series of standards, usually the n-alkanes.

Retention time: Time between injection and detection of a
    compound on a chromatographic system under specified
    conditions, expressed in seconds or minutes.

Saponification: Chemical reaction of a fat with strong base
    to form a glycerol and an acid salt.

Sensitivity: The slope of instrument response with respect
    to the amount of analyte. Also used colloquially in
    reference to lowest detectable amount of analyte.

Silica gel: Granular form of silicic acid (H_2SiO_3).

Standard operating procedure: A written QA document which
    describes the way an organization typically conducts a
    routine activity. May address instrumental operation,
    instrumental maintenance, application of a laboratory
    technique, data review, or management oversight.

Table E-1 (Continued)

Surrogate: Nonanalyte compounds added to the sample prior to any analytical manipulations for the express purpose of measuring recovery through extraction, cleanup, etc.

Technique: Scientific principle or specific operation (e.g., GC/ECD, Florisil column cleanup, or Webb and McCall quantitation).

Yusho: A mass food poisoning incident caused by ingestion of a commercial rice oil contaminated with PCBs and other haloaromatics.

Table E-2. List of Abbreviations

ASME   American Society of Mechanical Engineers

ANSI   American National Standards Institute

AOAC   Association of Official Analytical Chemists

ASTM   American Society for Testing and Materials

BHC   Benzene hexachloride (hexachlorocyclohexane);
              several possible isomers

CI   Chemical ionization (mass spectrometry)

CIMS   Positive chemical ionization mass spectrometry

CLE   Continuous liquid-liquid extraction

DCMA   Dry Color Manufacturer's Association

DDE   1,1-Dichloro-2,2-bis($\underline{p}$-chlorophenyl)ethylene

DDT   1,1,1-Trichloro-2,2-bis($\underline{p}$-chlorophenyl)ethane

ECD   Electron capture detector

EI   Electron impact ionization (mass spectrometry)

EICP   Extracted ion current plot

EIMS   Electron impact ionization mass spectrometry

EPA   (U.S.) Environmental Protection Agency

EPRI   Electric Power Research Institute

FDA   (U.S.) Food and Drug Administration

FFAP   Free fatty acid phase

FID   Flame ionization detector

FTIR   Fourier transform infrared spectrometry

GC   Gas-liquid chromatography (column type
              unspecified)

GC/MS   Gas-liquid chromatography/mass spectrometry
              (ionization mode unspecified)

Table E-2 (Continued)

GPC	Gel permeation chromatography
HECD	Hall electrolytic conductivity detector (other similar detectors such as the Coulson are included)
HPLC	High performance liquid chromatography
HREIMS	High resolution electron impact mass spectrometry
HRGC	High resolution gas-liquid chromatography
ID	Inside diameter
IR	Infrared spectrometry
IUPAC	International Union of Pure and Applied Chemistry
K	Partition coefficient
K_{ow}	Octanol-water partition coefficient
KD	Kuderna-Danish evaporator
KOH	Potassium hydroxide
LMS	Limited mass scanning (mass spectrometry)
LOD	Limit of detection. Lowest concentration at which an analyte can be identified as present in the sample at a stated statistical confidence level
LOQ	Limit of quantitation.
M	Parent m/z ion in a mass spectrum (equivalent to molecular weight)
MDL	Method detection limit
MOG	Mills-Onley-Gaither procedure for analysis of fatty foods and related matrices (Mills et al., 1963)
MS/MS	Mass spectrometry/mass spectrometry

Table E-2 (Continued)

m/z	Mass-to-charge ratio in mass spectrometry; m/e, amu, and dalton also describe the mass units in mass spectrometry
NAA	Neutron activation analysis
NBS	(U.S.) National Bureau of Standards
NCI	Negative chemical ionization (mass spectrometry)
NCIMS	Negative chemical ionization mass spectrometry
NIOSH	(U.S.) National Institute for Occupational Safety and Health
NMR	Nuclear magnetic resonance spectrometry
NRC	National Research Council
NTIS	(U.S.) National Technical Information Service
OECD	Organization for Economic Cooperation and Development
PAM	Pesticide Analytical Manual (FDA)
PBB	Polybrominated biphenyl
PCB	Polychlorinated biphenyl
PCBP	Polychlorinated biphenylene
PCCY	Polychlorinated chrysene
PCDD	Polychlorinated dibenzo-p-dioxin
PCDF	Polychlorinated dibenzofuran
PCN	Polychlorinated naphthalene
PCPY	Polychlorinated pyrenes
PCQ	Polychlorinated quaterphenyl
PCQE	Polychlorinated quaterphenyl ether
PCT	Polychlorinated terphenyl
PGC	Packed column gas-liquid chromatography

Table E-2 (Continued)

PID	Photoionization detector
ppb	Parts per billion (10^{-9}; American system)
ppm	Parts per million (10^{-6})
Precision	Reproducibility of an analysis, measured by SD of replicates
PUF	Polyurethane foam
QA	Quality assurance. An organization's program for assuring the integrity of data it produces or uses
QC	Quality control. The specific activities and procedures designed and implemented to measure and control the quality of data being produced
R_f	Movement of a TLC spot, measured as a fraction of the solvent front. Also used with column chromatography to measure the fraction of the total column length a band moves.
RF	Response factor
RI	Retention index
RIA	Radioimmunoassay or radioisotope dilution assay
RIC	Reconstructed ion chromatogram (in GC/MS)
RMR	Relative molar response
RP	Reverse phase (liquid chromatography)
RRF	Relative response factor
RRT	Relative retention time
RSD	Percent relative standard deviation (SD/mean x 100)
RT	Retention time
SASS	Source Assessment Sampling System
SCOT	Support coated open tubular (HRGC column)

Table E-2 (Continued)

SIM	Selected ion monitoring (also multiple ion detection, MID, or mass fragmentography; in GC/MS)
SIMCA	SIMple Classification by Analogy (principal components modeling technique)
TCD	Thermal conductivity detector
TCDD	Tetrachlorodibenzo-p-dioxin
TCDF	Tetrachlorodibenzofuran
TIC	Total ion current chromatogram (in GC/MS)
TLC	Thin-layer chromatography
TOCl	Total organic chlorine
TOX	Total organic halogen
TSCA	Toxic Substances Control Act, PL 94-469 (1976)
USWAG	Utilities Solid Waste Activities Group of the Edison Electric Institute
UV	Ultraviolet (spectroscopy)
WHO	World Health Organization
XAD-2	Polystyrene-divinylbenzene copolymer; also marketed with different numerical suffices. Trade mark, Rohm and Haas
XRF	X-ray fluorescence

Mammals (occurrence in), 24-26 (also see animals, humans)
Mass spectra, 215-216, 275-277, 478-481
Mass spectrometry, 212-238, 295-299 (also see high
  resolution gas chromatography, mass spectra, and packed
  column chromatography)
Mass, exact, 10, 480-481 (also see molecular weight)
Melting point, 10, 461-467
Mercury, 164
Method detection limit, 55-60, 72, 77, 80, 85, 94, 102,
  138, 198, 200, 201, 231, 236, 244, 247, 254, 327, 492 (also
  see detection limit and limit of detection)
Microcoulometry, 260
Milk
  Analysis of, 56, 59, 102, 106, 107, 119, 121, 122, 127, 256,
    313, 315-316, 321, 324-326 (also see food, analysis of)
  Occurrence in, 1, 24, 25, 32
Mills-Onley-Gaither (see Florisil)
Mineral oil (see oil, mineral)
Mobile mass spectrometer, 75, 85, 231 (also see portable
  instrument)
Modified Method 5 sampling train, 61, 78-84 (also see
  source sampling)
Molecular weight, 7, 9, 10 (also see mass, exact)
Monochlorobiphenyl, 5, 22, 39, 462
MS/MS, 94, 236-238, 254, 259, 265, 496
Natural gas, 56, 59, 84
NCIMS, 231-236, 258, 259, 265, 497 (also see high
  resolution gas chromatography)
Neutron activation analysis, 257
Nuclear magnetic resonance spectrometry, 14, 255
Octanol-water partition coefficient, 10-13, 244
Oil, 85, 122, 133, 153, 154, 157, 253 (also see capacitor
  fluids, hydraulic fluids)
  Cooking (see Yusho)
  Insulating, 322, 330
  Lubricating, 323, 337-338
  Mineral, 60, 77, 111-112, 145, 148, 155, 202, 209-211, 256,
    330, 492 (also see transformer oil)
  Motor, 292, 311
  Rice, 32-33 (also see Yusho)
  Silicone, 75, 111, 113, 155, 253
  Transformer, 60, 61, 85, 111-113, 117, 122, 127, 133,
    145-148, 154, 155, 158, 162, 163, 186, 202, 209-211,
    247, 253, 255-256, 259, 263, 264, 270, 273, 274, 281,
    287, 292, 293, 300, 301, 311-312, 315, 317, 330
  Vegetable, 113-114, 155, 157
  Waste, 60, 61, 85, 112, 157, 163, 186, 211, 281, 287, 300,
    317